Data Science and Machine Learning using **Python**

Second Edition

About the Author

Reema Thareja teaches at the School of Open Learning, University of Delhi. She has an experience of over 20 years. During her career, she has taught various courses to both undergraduate and postgraduate students. She has authored a plethora of books based on Computer Fundamentals, Artificial Intelligence, Data Science, Machine Learning, and programming languages including C, C++, and Python.

Dr Thareja has published 30 research papers in prestigious international journals and filed four patents. Her h-index is 16, and her i10-index is 12. To make learning engaging and fun, she launched a Computer Science Learning and Quizzing mobile app, Jruma, available for both Android and iOS devices.

She is recognized as a best-selling author of books in Computer Science. Her books are widely acclaimed both in India and internationally. For her contributions, she has received several awards, including:

- The Nobel Laureate Maria Goeppert-Mayer Inspiring Woman of the Year 2021 Award in Computer Science by the International Multi-Disciplinary Research Foundation (IMRF).
- "India's Top 50 Women Leaders in the Education Industry" for 2020 by uLektz Wall of Fame.
- The Knowledge Mobilization Award at the 7th Annual Research Awards by Shri Paramhans Education & Research Foundation Trust on July 4, 2021.

Dr Thareja serves as a Board Member of Studies in Computer Science for P.B. Siddhartha College of Arts & Science, Vijayawada, and Sri Durga Malleswara Siddhartha Mahila Kalasala. She is also a member of the Technical Advisory Board of Refactor Academy. She has been an invited speaker at numerous Faculty Development Programs (FDPs), conferences, student workshops, and webinars in India, the UAE, and the USA. Notable speaking engagements include the Global Virtual Summit held in New York in 2021, the International Dialogue on Empowered Future – Women's Role on International Women's Day 2021, and an upcoming international conference in France in October 2023.

To provide her students with exposure to international projects, Dr Thareja mentored three initiatives led by NRIs for California-based startups. She has also recorded MOOCs courses for MBA and BA programs offered by the School of Open Learning, University of Delhi. Additionally, she is a member of the committee formed by the University of Delhi to design and implement AI Literacy courses.

Data Science and Machine Learning using **Python**

Second Edition

Reema Thareja
School of Open Learning
University of Delhi

McGraw Hill Education (India) Private Limited

Published by McGraw Hill Education (India) Private Limited
Registered Office: Anjana Complex No: 5/90 A, Butt Road, St. Thomas Mount, Chennai – 600016

Data Science and Machine Learning using Python, 2e

Print Edition:
ISBN (13): 978-93-6444-877-2
ISBN (10): 93-6444-877-4

E-Book Edition:
ISBN (13): 978-93-6444-246-6
ISBN (10): 93-6444-246-6

1 2 3 4 5 6 7 8 9 7101558 29 28 27 26 25

Printed and bound in India.

Typeset at Transcend Content Solution, 163F Jaigirghat Road, Panchanantala, Kolkata – 700 063, and printed at Magic International Pvt. Ltd., Plot No. 26E, Sector-31, (Industrial), Site-IV, Greater Noida 201306

Cover Designer: Vipin Kumar Raghav
Cover Image Source: Shutterstock

Visit us at: www.mheducation.co.in
Write to us at: support.india@mheducation.com
CIN: U80302TN2010PTC111532
Toll Free Number: 18001035875

Dedicated to

my family
and my uncle Mr. B.L. Thareja, who is
a well-known author by himself.

Preface

This new edition of the book builds upon the foundation established in the first edition, incorporating significant updates and enhancements to reflect advancements in data visualization and analytics. This edition features 13 chapters, compared to 12 in the previous edition, with each chapter enriched by real-world business scenarios and examples to illustrate the practical application of concepts. While retaining the core structure and content of the previous edition, this version introduces new topics and expands existing chapters to provide a more comprehensive and practical guide for readers.

New to this addition

Chapter 6 has been enriched with an extensive range of 3D visualization techniques, including scatter plots, surface plots, bar charts, line charts, pie charts, wireframe models, volume rendering, heatmaps, bubble charts, icon-based visualization, and hierarchical data representation using Sankey diagrams. These additions aim to equip readers with the tools to effectively visualize complex datasets in three dimensions.

A new Chapter 8 delves into advanced data analytics techniques, offering detailed coverage of contingency tables and the Chi-Square test for categorical data analysis. It introduces time series forecasting methods such as ARIMA and SARIMA models, alongside longitudinal data analysis for repeated measurements over time. The chapter also explores hypothesis testing in Python, featuring T-tests, Z-tests, and the interpretation of p-values. Furthermore, it introduces Content-Based Recommender Systems, a critical component of personalized recommendation engines.

Chapter 11 has been expanded to include techniques for time series analysis using Python, covering both univariate and multivariate approaches.

This edition strives to provide readers with the latest tools and methodologies in data visualization and analytics, ensuring they are well-equipped to tackle contemporary challenges in the field. We hope this updated version continues to serve as a valuable resource for learners and professionals alike.

Online Resources

The online resources provided for both instructors and students are designed to enhance the effectiveness of teaching and learning.

Instructor Resources (Available on https://connect.mheducation.com/)

- ❑ PowerPoint Presentations

Student Resources (Available on https://www.mheducation.co.in/)

- ❑ Datasets
- ❑ Appendices
- ❑ Solutions to Programming Exercises
- ❑ Answers to 'Give the Output' Questions
- ❑ Answers to Spot the Error Problems
- ❑ Image Library
- ❑ Video Library
- ❑ Application Based Problems
- ❑ Multiple Choice Questions
- ❑ Answers to Chapter End Exercises

Reema Thareja

Preface to the First Edition

Python is an interpreted, object-oriented, high-level programming language that supports dynamic binding to make it very attractive for Rapid Application Development. Python's simple, easy-to-learn syntax emphasizes readability, program modularity and code reuse. The Python interpreter and the extensive standard library are available free for use on all major platforms.

Python is a powerful language and has helped to enhance productivity of users. Debugging Python programs is easy. A big advantage of using this language is that a bug or bad input will never cause a segmentation fault. An appropriate exception is raised as soon as an error is encountered.

Python is widely used to analyze both structured as well as unstructured data. It can be used for analyzing Facebook as well as Twitter data for semantic analysis. Python can easily help users to import data from Microsoft Excel, Microsoft Access, MySQL, SQLite, Oracle, and so on. For analyzing large datasets, Python uses distributed computing techniques to split tasks between multiple processing nodes to reduce execution time.

Python has become a staple in data science, allowing data analysts and other professionals to use the language to conduct complex statistical calculations, create data visualizations, build machine learning algorithms, manipulate and analyze data, and complete other data-related tasks.

Python can build a wide range of different data visualizations, like line and bar graphs, pie charts, histograms, and 3D plots, to name a few. Python also has a number of libraries that enable coders to write programs for data analysis and machine learning more quickly and efficiently. These libraries include Pandas, NumPy, SciPy, TensorFlow and Keras. For data visualization, there are very helpful packages including matplotlib, seaborn, datashader, etc. Classical machine learning algorithms for supervised or unsupervised learning can be implemented using scikit-learn and StatsModels. Apart from these packages, tasks like natural language processing and image processing can be accomplished using nltk, OpenCV2, scikit-image libraries.

As companies are increasingly collecting data for analysis, the demand for data scientists is also on the rise. A data scientist or data analyst with good knowledge of Python can easily get a salary starting from 50K. All these factors, give us a sound reason to thoroughly study this subject and make a career in it.

About the Book

The book has been specifically written to serve as a textbook for students pursuing their undergraduate or postgraduate degree. It can also be used by professionals who either wish to work in the area of Data Science and Machine Learning using Python or are already working in it. The objective of this book is to introduce the concepts of Python programming language in a lucid way so that the reader can easily use these concepts to perform data science and machine learning applications for solving real world problems.

Every chapter in this book contains multiple programming examples to impart practically sound knowledge of the concept. To further enhance the understanding of the subject, there are numerous objective-type, subjective-type and programming exercises at the end of each chapter.

The book aims to impart sound understanding of concepts to acquaint the reader with the techniques and applications in the area. Salient features of the book include:

- Easy to understand
- Glossary of important terms at the end of each chapter
- Comprehensive exercises at the end of each chapter
- Lots of programs that have been executed
- Appendices which give additional information
- Case studies which include programs that apply concepts learnt in chapters

Organization of the Book

The book is organized into 12 chapters, 9 appendices and 5 case studies.

Chapter 1 recapitulates the basics of Python programming language.

Chapter 2 gives a briefing on different vital data structures in Python that will be frequently used in writing our data science and machine learning codes.

Chapter 3 illustrates working with functions, built-in modules and user-defined modules in Python.

Chapter 4 is the first chapter that demonstrates functions defined in the NumPy module to analyze data in a variety of ways. Creating, indexing, sub-setting, normalizing, sorting, transposing, appending, reshaping, resizing, slicing arrays, retrieving, inserting, deleting elements, broadcasting, performing operations on arrays are discussed in the chapter.

Chapter 5 gives a detailed coverage on Pandas. Creating, pivoting, sorting, combining, summarizing, transforming, reindexing, joining, concatenating data frames, working with missing values, using descriptive statistics, row or column wise application of functions, pipe(), apply(), applymap(), aggregation, data wrangling, working with time series data structures are covered in the chapter.

Chapter 6 unleashes the concept of data visualization. Different graphs like bar chart, histograms, frequency polygons, box plots, scatter plots, correlation matrix plot are illustrated in the chapter. A very powerful data visualization library –Seaborn is also discussed in detail in the chapter. Under the Seaborn library topics like analysis of time series data, point plots, sparse matrix visualization, bubble charts, heatmaps, pair grid, facet grid, violin plots, hexbin plot are illustrated.

Chapter 7 talks about file handling. Topics like opening, closing, reading, writing, appending and repositioning files have been discussed. Working with text, binary, CSV, JSON files and pickle module have also been captured in detail.

Chapter 8 demonstrates interfacing MySQL. Creating tables, working with primary keys, inserting and manipulating data, using aggregate functions and other SQL functions and clauses are discussed. The main highlight of the chapter is working with NoSQL database. For this, creating database, collection, running queries filtering and limiting results have been demonstrated in MongoDB.

Chapter 9 introduces machine learning concepts, challenges, applications and techniques. Important topics like pre-processing data, feature selection, dealing with outliers are also illustrated in the chapter.

Chapter 10 covers regression analysis. Linear, multiple, polynomial, regularized, lasso, Elasticnet and Logistic regression techniques are captured in detail.

Chapter 11 is all about classification and clustering. Algorithms like KNN, decision trees, random forests, k-means, DBSCAN, Naïve Bayes, Neural Networks, Support Vector Machine are analyzed and implemented in the chapter.

Chapter 12 introduces Deep learning, Natural Language Processing and Reinforcement Learning concepts. Implementation of these concepts using libraries like Keras, Tensorflow and nltk are illustrated in the chapter. Other highlights of the chapter include topics like the Bellman Equation and Dynamic Programming, Monte-Carlo Learning, Monte-Carlo Evaluation and Temporal-Difference Learning.

The book also provides appendices and application based problems related to various chapters. These are parts of Online Resource Material. To access these, please scan the QR codes provided in the TOC.

Appendix A is about Candidate Elimination Algorithm

Appendix B discusses Gradient Descent in Machine Learning

Appendix C unleashes the concepts of Outlier Detection

Appendix D talks about Principal Component Analysis

Appendix E presents information about Web Scrapping and making Word Cloud

Appendix F assembles functions that helps us in Working with Date and Time

Appendix G summarizes Market Basket Analysis

Appendix H illustrates Plotting Geographical Data

Appendix I organizes concepts related to Sentiment Analysis

Application-based Problem 1 creates a Neural Network with a User-Defined Sigmoid Function.

Application-based Problem 2 applies Logistic Regression on Titanic Data Set.

Application-based Problem 3 constructs Spam Detection Technique Using Naïve Bayes Algorithm.

Application-based Problem 4 performs Data Analysis Using Pandas.

Application-based Problem 5 is based on Support Vector Machine Algorithm (SVM).

Acknowledgements

The writing of this text book was a mammoth task for which a lot of help was required from many people. Fortunately, I have had the finest support of my family, friends and fellow teaching staff at the Shyama Prasad Mukherji College.

My special thanks would always go to my father Late Sh. Janak Raj Thareja, my mother Smt. Usha Thareja, my brother Pallav and sisters Kimi and Rashi who were a source of abiding inspiration and divine blessings for me. I am especially thankful to my son Goransh who has been very patient and cooperative in letting me realize my dreams. My sincere thanks will go to my uncle Mr. B.L. Thareja for his inspiration and guidance in writing this book.

I would like to acknowledge the technical assistance provided by Mr. Vedant Behel, who spared his precious time to help design and test the programs.

Last but not the least, my acknowledgements will always be incomplete if I do not thank the entire team of McGraw Hill, India for giving their valuable feedback to improve my technical writing skills.

Reema Thareja

Publisher's Note

McGraw Hill Education (India) invites suggestions and comments from you, all of which can be sent to *support.india@mheducation.com* (kindly mention the title and author name in the subject line).

Piracy-related issues may also be reported.

Contents in Brief

Contents

CHAPTER

1 Basics of Python Programming

1.1 Introduction to Python

Python is a powerful computer programming language that has a perfect combination of performance and features that makes it suitable for a variety of applications varying from simple programs to complex deep learning and artificial intelligence (AI)–based projects. Python is a high-level, interpreted, interactive, object-oriented, reliable, platform-independent, scripted and open-source language with complete access to operating system APIs. The best part of this language is that it is very simple and uses English-like words. Python has a vast library of modules to support the integration of complex solutions from pre-built components. In short, it is a complete programming language with the following features–

Simple and Easy to Learn: Python is easy to learn as it has English-like words. Simple syntax allows programmers to concentrate on the solution to the problem rather than the language itself. Even for the readers, a Python program is clearly defined and easily readable. Structure and syntax of a Python program are so simple that anyone with or without Computer Science background can easily understand it.

> **Programming Tip**
>
> Python interpreter allows interaction with programmer during development as well as during the testing phase.

Versatile: Python supports development of a wide range of applications ranging from simple text processing to WWW browsers to games.

Free and Open Source: Python is an example of an open-source software that allows anyone all over the world to read the source code, edit it, freely distribute it and even use the code to write new programs.

High-level Language: When writing programs in Python, the programmers do not have to worry about the low-level details like managing memory used by the program, etc. They just need to concentrate on writing solutions of the current problem at hand.

Interactive: Programs in Python work in interactive mode thereby allowing programmers to easily interact with the interpreter directly at the Python prompt to write their programs.

Portable: Python is a portable language. This means that Python programs behave the same on a wide variety of hardware and operating systems. The same interface can be used on any operating system and any underlying hardware without making any changes in the code.

Object-Oriented: Python supports object-oriented as well as procedure-oriented style of programming. So, it supports encapsulating data and functionalities within objects, as well as building the program around procedures or functions.

Interpreted: We know that an interpreted language has a simpler execution cycle and it works faster. Python is processed at run-time by the interpreter. Python converts the source code into an intermediate form called ***bytecode***, which is then translated into the native language of your computer so that it can be executed. Bytecodes also help to make the Python code portable.

Dynamic: Python is a dynamic language; this means in case of any run-time error, Python allows interactive program development.

Extensible: Since Python is an open-source software, anyone can add any additional functionality to the Python interpreter.

Embeddable: Programmers can embed Python within their C, C++, COM, ActiveX, CORBA and Java programs to give 'scripting' capabilities for users.

Extensive Libraries: Python has an extensive library that is easily portable across different platforms and used to perform a wide range of applications varying from text processing, maintaining databases, to GUI programming.

Secure: Python language is a secured language that provides an environment for protecting against tampering of data. Modules can be distributed to prevent altering the source code. Apart from this, additional security checks can be easily added to implement additional security features.

Robust: Python programs do not allow programmers to manipulate memory directly. Moreover, errors are raised as exceptions. These exceptions are then caught and handled by the program code. For every syntactical mistake, a simple and easy-to-interpret message is displayed, thereby making the language robust.

Multi-threaded: Python supports multi-threading features that help programmers to execute more than one process of a program simultaneously or to perform some vital process management tasks.

> **Programming Tip**
>
> BitTorrent, YouTube, Dropbox, Deluge, Cinema 4D, and Bazaar are a few globally-used applications based on Python

Garbage Collection: Python run-time environment handles garbage collection of all Python objects. For this, a reference counter is maintained to assure that no object that is currently in use is deleted. An object that is no longer used or has gone out of scope is collected for garbage collection. This feature of Python frees the programmers from the worry of memory leak (failure to delete) and dangling reference (deleting too early) problems. Even the programmers can themselves perform memory management functions by explicitly deleting an unused object.

1.1.1 Applications of Python

Since being introduced in the year 1989, Python is widely used for a plethora of web-based, desktop-based, graphic design, scientific, and computational applications. The popularity of this programming language is constantly rising. Because of its simplicity, Python is being taught to school students as the first programming language they learn to develop coding skills.

- Python is being used for applications including ***image processing, text processing***, web and enterprise level applications using scientific and numeric data from network.
- Python is used as an ***embedded scripting*** language for various testing/building/deployment/monitoring frameworks, scientific apps and quick scripts.
- ***3D software*** like Maya uses Python for automating small user tasks or for doing more complex integration such as talking to databases and asset management systems.
- Python provides good integration with database and other web standards. Therefore, it is a popular language for ***web development***. For example, website *Quora* has a lot of code written in Python. Besides this, *Odoo, a* consolidated suite of business applications, and *Google App engine* are other popular web applications based on Python.
- For web development, Python has frameworks such as Django and Pyramid, micro-frameworks such as Flask and Bottle and advanced content management systems such as Plone and Django CMS. These frameworks provide libraries and modules, which simplify content management, interaction with database and interfacing with different internet protocols such as HTTP, SMTP, XML-RPC, FTP and POP.
- Python is a preferred choice for developing ***desktop-based applications***. For this, Python has various GUI toolkits like wxPython, PyQt or PyGtk, which allow programmers to create highly functional graphical user interface (GUI) including,
- *Image processing and graphic design applications:* Python is used to make 2D imaging software such as Inkscape, GIMP, Paint Shop Pro and Scribus. It is also used to make 3D animation packages, like Blender, 3ds Max, Cinema 4D, Houdini, Lightwave and Maya.
- *Scientific and computational applications:* Features like high speed, productivity and availability of tools, such as Scientific Python and Numeric Python, have made Python a preferred language to perform computation and processing of scientific data. 3D modelling software, such as FreeCAD and finite element method software, like Abaqus, are coded in Python. In addition to this, IPython supports visualisations and parallel computing.
- Python has various modules that support ***development of games***. While PySoy is a 3D game engine, PyGame, on the other hand, provides functionality and a library for game development. Games like Civilization-IV, Disney's Toontown Online, Vega Strike, etc. are coded using Python.
- Python is a suitable coding language for ***customising large applications***. For example, Reddit, which was originally written in Common Lips, was rewritten in Python in 2005. A large part of Youtube code is also written in Python.
- Programmers can use Python to write codes for developing an ***operating system***. For example, Python forms an integral part of Linux distributions. Ubuntu's Ubiquity Installer and Fedora's and Red Hat Enterprise Linux's Anaconda Installer are all written in Python. Even Gentoo Linux uses Python for Portage, its package management system.
- Python is used to develop ***other languages***. For example, Boo language uses an object model, syntax and indentation, similar to Python. Apple's Swift, CoffeeScript, Cobra and OCaml all have syntax similar to Python.
- Python is often used for prototype development. Moreover, agility, extensibility and scalability of code written in Python support faster development from initial prototype.
- Python is used for ***network programming*** as it has an easy-to-use socket interface, functions for email processing and support for FTP, IMAP and other Internet protocols.

1.2 Python tokens

Tokens are the small units of the programming language (Figure 1.1). Python supports following types of tokens. In this chapter, we will read about literals in detail.

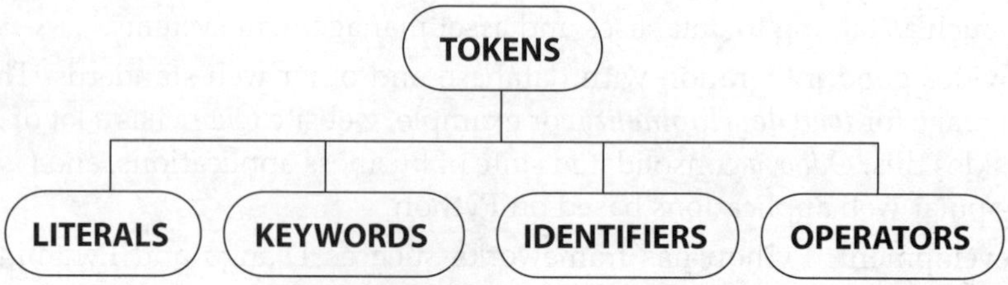

Figure 1.1 Tokens in Python

1.3 Literal constants

The word 'literal' has been derived from literally. The value of a literal constant can be used directly in programmes. For example, 7, 3.9, 'A' and "Hello" are examples of literal constants. The number 7 always represents itself and nothing else. Moreover, it is a constant because its value cannot be changed. Hence, it is known as *literal constant*. In this section, we will read about number and string constants in Python.

1.3.1 Numbers

> **Programming Tip**
> You can specify integers in octal as well as hexadecimal number system

Number, as the name suggests, refers to a numeric value. You can use four types of numbers in Python programs. These include integers, long integers, floating-point and complex numbers.

- Numbers like 5 or other whole numbers are referred to as *integers*. Integers can be positive or negative or even equal to zero. They do not have any decimal point.
- Bigger whole numbers are called *long integers*. For example, 535633629843L is a long integer. Note that a long integer must have 'l' or 'L' as the suffix.
- Numbers like are 3.23 and 91.5E-2 are termed as *floating-point numbers*. They are real numbers with a decimal point dividing the integer and fractional parts. The real part of the number can be either negative or positive or even equal to zero.
- Numbers of a + bi form (like −3 + 7i) are *complex numbers*, where a is the real part and b is the imaginary part of the number. Both a and b are floating-point numbers, and j represents square root of −1.

> The 'E' notation indicates powers of 10. In this case, 91.5E–2 means 91.5 * 10–2

Remember that commas are never used in numeric literals or numeric values. Therefore, numbers like 3,567 1,23.89 -8,904 are not allowed in Python.

1.3.1.1 Types of integer literals

There are three types of integer literals – decimal, octal and hexadecimal integer literal.

Decimal Integer Literal: Any integer literal that does not start with a zero (0) is a decimal integer literal. Example, +17,-26, 1234, -89072.

Octal Integer Literal: Any integer literal that starts with digit zero followed by letter o is treated as an octal integer literal in Python. Example, 0o12, 0o7654. Type the following statements in IDLE and see the output.

```
>>> 0o12          >>> -0o12        >>> 0o7654       >>> 0o1789
10                -10              4012             SyntaxError: invalid syntax
Note that decimal equivalent of                     Digits 8 and 9 are not there
  the octal value is displayed                        in octal number system
```

Hexadecimal Integer Literal: Any integer literal that starts with digit zero followed by letter x is treated as an octal integer literal in Python. Example, 0x1234, 0xA7B6F. Type the following statements in IDLE and see the output.

```
>>> 0x1234     >>> 0xABCD       >>> 0x7B9CF1   >>> 0xTG1F
4660           43981            8101105        SyntaxError: invalid token
Note that decimal equivalent of the            Digits T and G are not
  hexadecimal value is displayed                 there in hexadecimal
                                                 number system
```

1.3.1.2 Large floating-point numbers

Large floating-point numbers are efficiently represented in scientific notation. For example, $5.0012304*10^6$ (6 digits of precision) can be written as 5.0012304e+6 in scientific notation.

Do you remember that in a scientific notation, we have two parts – exponent and the mantissa. The mantissa appears before e and the exponent part follows e. While mantissa can be an integer or a floating-point number, the exponent is always an integer. Both mantissa and exponent can be either negative or positive.

1.3.1.3 Built-in format() function

Any floating-point value may contain an arbitrary number of decimal places, so it is always recommended to use the built-in format() function to produce a string version of a number with specific number of decimal places. Observe the difference between the following outputs.

```
# Without using format()          # Using format()
>>> float(16/(float(3)))          >>> format(float(16/(float(3))), '.2f')
5.333333333333333                 '5.33'
```

Here, .2f in the format() function rounds the result to two decimal places of accuracy in the string produced. For very large (or very small) values, 'e' can be used as a *format specifier*. The format() function can also be used to format floating-point numbers in scientific notation. Look at the result of the expression given below.

```
>>> format(3**50,'.5e')
'7.17898e+23'
```

The result is formatted in scientific notation with five decimal places of precision. This feature is especially useful when displaying results in which only a certain number of decimal places is needed. Finally, the format() function can also be used to insert a comma in the number as shown below.

```
>>> format(123456.8901,',.2f')
'123,456.89'
```

1.3.1.4 Simple operations on numbers

Python can carry out simple operations on numbers. To perform a calculation, simply enter numbers and the type of operations that needs to be performed on them directly into the Python console, and it will print the answer, as shown below.

```
>>> 17 + 56    >>> 90 + 50 - 40    >>> 35 * 15    >>> 108 / 12    >>> -10 * 14
73             100                 525            9.0             -140
```

The spaces around the plus and minus signs here are optional. They are just added to make the statement more readable. The code will execute even if you remove the spaces.

Dividing a number by zero in Python generates an error, and no output is produced as shown below.

```
>>> 117 / 0
```

Traceback (most recent call last):

```
  File "<pyshell#7>", line 1, in <module>
    117 / 0
```

ZeroDivisionError: division by zero

When two numbers are divided always a floating-point number is produced.

```
>>> 15 / 5        >>> 75 / 15.0        >>> 39.0 / 3        >>> 24.0 / 2.0
3.0               5.0                  13.0                12.0
```

You can easily work with a floating-point number and an integer because Python automatically converts the integer to a float. This is known as ***implicit conversion or type coercion.*** *An implicit conversion is performed by the compiler without programmer's intervention.*

Quotient and Remainder: When diving two numbers, if you want to know the quotient and remainder, use the floor division (//) and modulo operator (%), respectively. These operators can be used with both floats and integers. Observe the following statements and their output. When we divide 78 by 5, we get a quotient of 15 and a remainder of 3.

```
>>> 18 // 4    >>> 18 % 4    >>> 324.0 // 6.0    >>> 234.567 % 6.5
4              2             54.0                0.5670000000000073
```

Exponentiation: Besides, +, - , *, / Python also supports ** operator. The ** operator is used for exponentiation, i.e., raising of one number to the power of another. Consider the statements given below and observe the output.

```
>>> 11 ** 3     >>> 5.25 ** 4
1331            759.69140625
```

1.3.2 Strings

A *string* is a group of characters. We have already printed a string in our first program in which we had printed "HELLO WORLD !!!". In Python, there are three ways in which a string can be used.

Using Single Quotes ('): For example, a string can be written as 'HELLO'.

Using Double Quotes ("): Strings in double quotes are exactly same as those in single quotes. Therefore, 'HELLO' is same as "HELLO".

```
All spaces and tabs within a string are preserved in quotes (single quote as
well as double).
```

Using Triple Quotes (''' '''): A multi-line string is specified using triple quotes. We can use as many single quotes and double quotes as required in a string within triple quotes. An example of a multi-line string can be given as,

```
>>> ''' HELLO WORLD !!!
'GOOD MORNING'
"WELCOME TO THE WORLD OF 'PYTHON PROGRAMMING' "
HAPPY LEARNING....'''
' HELLO WORLD !!!\n\'GOOD MORNING\'\n"WELCOME TO THE WORLD OF \'PYTHON
PROGRAMMING\' "\nHAPPY LEARNING....'
```

Note that all the characters, spaces, tabs, new lines and quotes (single as well as double) are preserved within triple quotes.

```
>>> 'Hello'                >>> "HELLO"                >>> '"HELLO"'
'Hello'                    'HELLO'                    'HELLO'
```

Irrespective of the way in which a string is specified, all strings are ***mutable****. This means that once you have created a string, you cannot change it.*

1.3.2.1 String literal concatenation

Python concatenates two string literals that are placed side by side. Consider the code below wherein Python has automatically concatenated three string literals.

```
>>> 'HELLO' 'WORLD'
'HELLOWORLD'
```

1.3.2.2 Unicode strings

Unicode is a standard way of writing international text. That is, if you want to write some text in your native language like Hindi, then you need to have a Unicode-enabled text editor. Python allows you to specify Unicode text by prefixing the string with a u or U. For example,

```
>>> u"Shubh Prabhat"
'Shubh Prabhat'
```

The 'U' prefix specifies that the file contains text written in language other than English.

1.3.2.3 Escape sequences

Some characters (like, ", \) cannot be directly included in a string. Such characters must be escaped by placing a backslash before them as given below.

```
>>> print('How's life?')
      SyntaxError: invalid syntax
>>> print('How\'s life?')
How's life?
```

The reason for the error was that Python got confused as to where the string starts and ends. So, we need to clearly specify that this single quote does not indicate the end of the string. This indication can be given with the help of an ***escape sequence*** as specified in the second string – *a single quote preceded by a backslash.*

Similarly, to print a double quotes in a string enclosed within double quotes, we must precede the double quotes with a backslash as given below.

> **Remember**
>
> When a string is printed, the quotes around it are not displayed

```
>>> print("Sheena asked,"Will you come with me?"")
SyntaxError: invalid syntax
>>> print("Sheena asked,\"Will you come with me?\"")
Sheena asked,"Will you come with me?"
```

An escape sequence is treated as a single character.

Other useful escape sequences are:

Table 1: || Some of the escape sequences used in Python

Escape sequence	Purpose	Example	Output
\\	Prints Backslash	print("\\")	\
\'	Prints single-quote	print("\'")	'
\"	Prints double-quote	print("\"")	"
\a	Rings bell	print("\a")	Bell rings
\f	Prints form feed character	print("Hello\fWorld")	Hello World
\n	Prints newline character	print("Hello\nWorld")	Hello World
\t	Prints a tab	print("Hello\tWorld")	Hello World
\o	Prints octal value	print("\o56")	.
\x	Prints hex value	print("\x65")	e

1.3.2.4 Multi-line strings

When specifying a string, if a single backslash (\) at the end of the line is added, then it indicates that the string is continued in the next line, but no new line is added otherwise. For example,

```
>>> print("Hello World,\
Good Morning !!!")
Hello World,Good Morning !!!
```

Raw strings are not processed in any special way, not even in the escape sequences

1.3.2.5 Raw strings

If you want to specify a string that should not handle any escape sequences and want to display exactly as specified, then you need to specify that string as a *raw string*. A raw string is specified by prefixing r or R to the string.

```
>>> R"How\'s life at your end?"
"How\\'s life at your end?"
```

1.3.2.6 String formatting

We have already used the built-in format() function to format floating-point numbers. The same function can also be used to control the display of strings. The syntax of format() function is given as,

```
format(value, format_specifier)
```

where, value is the value or the string to be displayed, and format_specifier can contain a combination of formatting options.

Example: Commands to display 'PYTHON' left-justified, right-justified and centre-aligned in a field width of 30 characters.

```
>>> format('PYTHON',        >>> format('PYTHON',        >>> format('PYTHON',
      '<30')                      '>30')                      '^30')
      'PYTHON                        '                        PYTHON'                        '            PYTHON    '
```

Here, the '<' symbol means to left justify. Similarly, to right justify, the string use the '>' symbol and the '^' symbol to centrally align the string.

We have seen above that format() function uses blank spaces to fill the specified width. But you can also use the format() function to fill the width in the formatted string using any other character as shown below.

```
>>> print('PYTHON', format('-','-<10'),'PROGRAMMING')
PYTHON----------PROGRAMMING
```

1.3.2.7 String concatenation

Like numbers, we can also add two strings in Python. The process of combining two strings is called *concatenation*. Two strings whether created using single or double quotes are concatenated in the same way.

```
>>> 'HI... and .....'
      + 'BYE'
'HI... and .....BYE'
```

```
>>> '''PYTHON'''
+ '''PROGRAMMING'''
'PYTHONPROGRAMMING'
```

```
>>> '''PYTHON'''
+ '''PROGRAMMING'''
'PYTHON PROGRAMMING'
```

1.3.2.8 Slice a string

A substring of a string is called a **slice**. You can extract subsets of strings by using the slice operator ([ ] and [:]). You need to specify index or the range of index of characters to be extracted. The index of the first character is 0, and the index of the last character is n-1, where n is the number of characters in the string (as shown in Figure 1.2).

	P	Y	T	H	O	N	
Index from the start	0	1	2	3	4	5	
	-6	-5	-4	-3	-2	-1	Index from the end

Figure 1.2 String Indexes

The syntax of slice operation is **s[start:end:stride]**, where start specifies the beginning index of the sub string and end is the index of the last character of the string s. *Omitting either start or end index by default takes start or end of the string. Omitting both means the entire string.*

If you want *to extract characters starting from the end of the string, then you must specify the index as a negative number.* For example, the index of the last character is -1.

1.3.2.9 Specifying stride while slicing strings

In the slice operation, you can specify a third argument as the ***stride.*** The stride specifies the number of characters to move forward after the first character is retrieved from the string. By default, the value of stride is 1, which means that every character between two index numbers is retrieved. If stride is 2, then every second character is accessed; if stride is 3, then every third character is accessed, so on and so forth.

```
# Slice operation on string
>>> str = "Python Programming is Fun"
>>> str[0]                  # prints the first character
P
>>> str[4:10]               # prints characters from 4 to 9
on Pro
>>> str[5:]                 # prints all characters starting from fifth
                              character
n Programming is Fun
>>> str[-1]                 # prints the last character
n
>>> str[:-1]                # prints all except the last character
Python Programming is Fun
>>> str[-7:]                # prints last seven character
>>> str[3:15:2]             # prints every 2nd character from 3rd - 15th
                              character
'hnPorm'
```

Did you notice that when we use the slice operator, elements are accessed from left towards right. For any index n (positive or negative), s[:n] + s[n:] = s, this means that the slice operation always partitions the string into two parts in such a way that all characters are conserved.

Even the whitespace characters are skipped as they are also a part of the string. ***If you omit the first two arguments and only specify the third one, then the entire string is used in steps.*** We can even have a negative value in the stride. For example, if the value of stride is -1, then the string is printed in reverse order.

```
# print every third
  character

str = "Python programming
  is fun"

print(str[::3])

OUTPUT

Ph oai n
```

```
# print string in reverse

str = "Python programming
  is fun"

print(str[::-1])

OUTPUT

nuf si gnimmargorp nohtyP
```

```
# print every second
character in the

# reversed string

str = "Python programming
  is fun"

print(str[::-2])

OUTPUT

nfs nmagr otP
```

1.4 Type conversion

In Python, it is just not possible to complete certain operations that involves different types of data. For example, it is not possible to perform '4' + 7 since one operand is an integer and the other is of string type.

Another situation in which type conversion is a must is when you want to accept a non-string value (integer or float) as an input. The input() function which accepts input(s) from the user takes it as a string. In case you the user to enter a numeric value, then the string value must be explicitly type casted to numbers (integers or floats) so that calculations can be performed on them. In such situations, you must perform conversions between data types.

```
>>> "7"+"4"
'74'
```

```
>>> int("7")+int("3")
10
```

```
x = input("Enter the first number: ")

y = input("Enter the second number: ")

print(x + y)

OUTPUT

Enter the first number: 7

Enter the second number: 4

74
```

```
x = int(input("Enter the first
    number: "))

y = int(input("Enter the second
    number: "))

print(x + y)

OUTPUT

Enter the first number: 7

Enter the second number: 4

11
```

Python provides several built-in functions to convert a value from one data type to another. These functions return a new object representing the converted value. Some of them are given in Table 2.

Table 2: || Functions for Type Conversions

FUNCTION	DESCRIPTION	EXAMPLE
int(x)	Converts x to an integer	int(3.5) gives 3
float(x)	Converts x to a floating point number	float('123') gives 123.0
str(x)	Converts x to a string	str(123.45) gives '123.45'
tuple(x)	Converts list x to a tuple	tuple([1,2,3]) gives (1, 2, 3)
list(x)	Converts tuple x to a list	list((1,2,3)) gives [1, 2, 3]
set(x)	Converts x to a set	set([1,2,3]) gives (1, 2, 3)
ord(x)	Converts a single character to its integer value.	ord('D') gives 68
oct(x)	Converts an integer to an octal string.	oct(9) gives '0o11'
hex(x)	Converts an integer to a hexadecimal string.	hex(1234) gives '0x4d2'
chr(x)	Converts an integer to a character.	chr(70) gives 'F'
complex(x)	Converts to a complex number	complex(3,-8) gives (3-8j)

However, before using type conversions to convert a floating-point number into an integer number, remember that int() converts a float to an int by truncation (discarding the fractional part) and not by rounding to the nearest whole number. The round() works more appropriately by rounding a floating-point number to the nearest integer as shown below. The round() can even take a second, optional argument which is usually a number that indicates the number of places of precision to which the first argument should be rounded.

```
>>> int(3.7)     >>> round(3.7)     >>> round(1234.56789012,2)
3                4                  1234.57
```

Note that each argument passed to a function has a specific data type. If you pass an argument of the wrong data type to a function, it will generate an error. For example, you cannot find the square root of a string. If you do not know what type of arguments a function accepts, you should use the help() before using the function.

1.5 Variables and identifiers

Using just literal constants, nothing much can be done in programs. For developing little complex programs, we must store information to manipulate it as and when required. This is where *variables* can help.

Variable, in simple terms, means something that may change. We can store any piece of information in a variable, and this information may change. For example, a variable today_temp may have value = 30 today, but tomorrow it may be 29 or 31.

Thus, we see that in Python, variable represents a named location that has a value, which can be processed as and when required (like for calculating values).

To be identified easily, each variable is given an appropriate name. Variable names are examples of **identifiers**. *Identifiers* as the name suggests are names given to identify something. This something can be a variable, function, class, module or other object. For naming any identifier, there are some basic rules that you must follow. These rules are:

- The first character of an identifier must be an underscore ('_') or a letter (upper or lowercase).
- The rest of the identifier name can be underscores ('_'), letters (upper or lowercase), or digits (0-9).
- Identifier names are case-sensitive. For example, myvar and myVar are **not** the same.
- Punctuation characters such as @, $ and % are not allowed within identifiers.

> **Remember**
>
> Python is a case-sensitive language

Examples of valid identifier names are sum, __my_var, num1, r, var_20, First, etc.

Examples of invalid identifier names are 1num (starting with a digit), my-var (punctuation and special characters not allowed), %check (first character should be an alphabet or an underscore), Basic Sal (space not allowed), H#R&A (special characters not allowed), etc.

1.6 Creating variables

To create a variable in Python, just assign a value to the identifier using the equal to sign (also known as the assignment operator). For example, the following statements creates variables with different values in Python.

```
num = 7
float_num = 12.34
ch = 'A'
str = "ABC"
print(num)
print(float_num)
print(ch)
print(str)
OUTPUT
7
12.34
A
ABC
```

When we create a variable, Python creates labels referring to those values as shown in Figure 1.3.

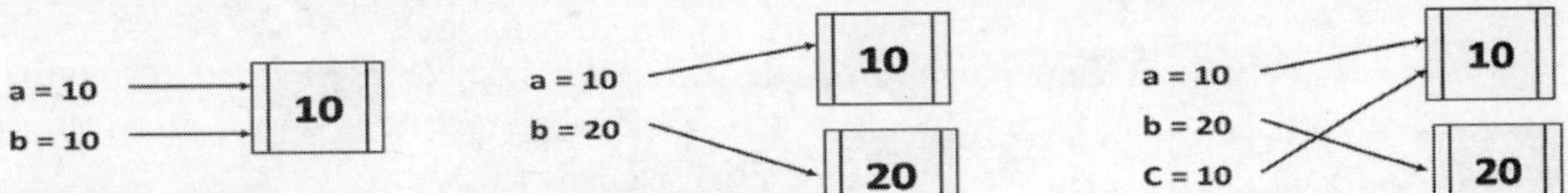

Here, both variables a and b have the same value. A label with value 10 is created and both variables point to the same label.

Here, the value of variable is changed. Both variables a and b have different values. A label with value 10 and another with label 20 is created and both variables point to their label.

Here, both variables a'and b have different values. A label with value 10 and another with label 20 is created and both variables point to their label. When the variable c is created with same value as that of a, it points to the label to which a is pointing.

Figure 1.3 Creating labels

Do you know that Python IDLE remembers variables and their values? Just type the following lines in the command console of IDLE and observe the output.

```
>>> x = 10
>>> y = 20
>>> str1 = "HELLO"
>>> print(str1)
HELLO
>>> print(x * y)
200
```

1.7 Data types of identifiers

In any programming language, data type is a classification that specifies which type of value a variable has. It also specifies the type of mathematical, relational or logical operations that can be applied to it without causing an error. For example, a string data type is used to hold textual data. An integer is a data type that can store whole numbers.

Python has various standard data types that are used to define the operations possible on them and the storage method for each of them. Based on the data type of a variable, the interpreter reserves memory for it and also determines the type of data that can be stored in the reserved memory.

> **Remember**
>
> Python is a purely object-oriented language. It refers to everything as an object including numbers and strings

The five standard data types supported by Python includes – numbers, string, list, tuple and dictionary. We can even create our own data types in Python (like classes). In this chapter, we will learn about numbers and strings. Other data types will be explored in subsequent chapters.

1.7.1 Assigning or initialising values to variables

In Python, programmers need not explicitly declare variables to reserve memory space. The declaration is done automatically when a value is assigned to the variable using the equal sign (=). The operand on the left side of equal sign is the name of the variable, and the operand on its right side is the value to be stored in that variable.

Program to display data of different types using variables and literal constants

```
age = 27
salary = 1234567
gender = 'M'
name = "Siva"

print("NAME: " + name)
print("AGE: " + str(age))          # To convert integer to a string
print("SALARY: " + str(salary))
print("GENDER: " + gender)         # To concatenate or to join two strings
```

OUTPUT

```
NAME: Siva
AGE: 27
SALARY: 1234567
GENDER: M
```

To run this program, type the code in IDLE. Save it with a suitable name with an extension .py. Press F5 or click on *Run* and then on *Run Module*.

In the code, the program assigns literal constant 27 to the variable age using the assignment operator (=). Similarly, we have assigned literal constants to other variables and then printed their values.

In Python, you can reassign variables as many times as you want to change the value stored in them. You may even store value of one data type in a statement and then a value of another data in a subsequent statement. This is possible because Python variables do not have specific types, so you can assign an integer to a variable and later assign a string to the same variable.

Program to re-assign values to a variable

```
age = 27                  age is an integer
print("AGE: ", age)
age = 'TWELVE'            age is a string
print("AGE: ", age)

age = 15.6                age is a floating point number
print("AGE: ", age)
```

```
OUTPUT

AGE: 27

AGE: TWELVE

AGE: 15.6
```

While re-assigning values to variables, be cautious for ensuring that right type of value is used in operations. This is very much evident from the code given below.

```
a = 10
a = a*10
print(a)
a = "PYTHON"
a = a/10
print(a)
```

```
OUTPUT
100
Traceback (most recent call last):
  File "C:\Python37\try.py", line 5, in <module>
    a = a/10
TypeError: unsupported operand type(s) for
/:'str' and 'int'
```

The type() Function

The type() function having the syntax type(object) is used to determine data type of object. This function should be used to ensure that right type of values are being used in the expressions.

```
num = 10
print(type(num))
val = 3.4
print(type(val))
ch = 'a'
print(type(ch))
str = "abc"
print(type(str))
```

```
OUTPUT
<class 'int'>
<class 'float'>
<class 'str'>
<class 'str'>
```

Lvalue and the Rvalue

As the name suggests, expressions that come on the left side of the assignment operator are known as the lvalue. Correspondingly, expressions that come on the right side of the assignment operator is known as the rvalue.

This means that, lvalues are those objects to which values can be assigned. And, rvalues are the literals or expressions that evaluate a value comes on the right-hand side of the assignment operator.

Remember that,

- literals or expressions that evaluate a value cannot come on the left-hand side of the assignment operator.
- Variable names can come on the left-hand side of the assignment operator.

VALID LVALUE AND RVALUE	INVALID LVALUE AND RVALUE
a = 10	10 = a
B = a * 20	a * 20 = b

1.7.2 Multiple assignment

Python allow programmers to assign a single value to more than one variable simultaneously. For example,

```
sum = flag = a= b = 0
```

In the above statement, all four integer variables are assigned a value 0. You can also assign different values to multiple variables simultaneously as shown below.

```
sum, a, b, mesg = 0, 3, 5, "RESULT"
```

Here, variable sum, a and b are integers (numbers) and mesg is a string. sum is assigned a value 0, a is assigned 3, b is assigned 5 and mesg is assigned "RESULT".

Remember that *trying to reference a variable that has not been assigned any value causes an error.* This may happen if you have mistakenly used a variable without assigning it a value prior to its use or have deliberately deleted or removed a variable using the del statement and then trying to use it later in your code. The examples given below illustrate this concept.

Also remember that, right-hand side expression is evaluated before assignment is done, and if there are multiple expressions in a statement separated by commas, then expressions on the RHS are evaluated from *left to right* and assigned in same order.

```
x,y = 10,20
y,y = y+5, y-20
# last value of y persists
print("x = ",x, " y = ",y)
OUTPUT
x =  10  y =  0
```

Programs to assign and access variables

```
>>> name = "Kartik"
>>> age = 15
>>> print(name)
Kartik
>>> print(grade)
Traceback (most recent call last):
  File "<pyshell#8>", line 1, in <module>
    print(grade)
NameError: name 'grade' is not defined
```

Variable not declared prior to use

```
>>> name = "Kartik"
>>> age = 15
>>> grade = 'O'
>>> print(name)
Kartik
>>> del age
>>> print(age)
Traceback (most recent call last):
  File "<pyshell#14>", line 1, in <module>
    print(age)
NameError: name 'age' is not defined
```

Variable being used after it is deleted

1.7.3 Data type Boolean

> **Remember**
> Boolean variables are also created by comparing values using the == operator

Boolean is another data type in Python. A variable of Boolean type can have one of the two values – *True* or *False*. Similar to other variables, the Boolean variables are also created while we assign a value to them or when we use a relational operator on them.

`>>>Boolean_var = True`
`>>> Boolean_var`
`True`
	`>>> 30 == 50`
	`False`
		`>>> "HELLO" == 'HELLO'`
		`True`

`>>> 10 != 10` `False`	`>>"Python3.7" != "Python3.4"` `True`	`>>> 50 > 80` `False`
`>>> 20 <= 20` `True`	`>>> 13 == 13.0` `False`	`>>> 13 >= 13.0` `True`

1.8 Input operation

Real-world programs need to be interactive. By interactive, we mean that you need to take some sort of input or information from the user and work on that input to give the desired result.

To take input from the users, Python makes use of the input() function. The input() function prompts the user to provide some information on which the program can work and give the result. However, we must always remember that the *input function takes user's input as a string.* So, whether you input a number or a string, it is treated as a string only.

Program to read variables from the user

```
name = input("What's your name? ")
age = input("Enter your age: ")
print(name + ", you are " + age + " years old")
```

```
OUTPUT
What's your name? Goransh
Enter your age: 13
Goransh, you are 13 years old
```

To read integers or floating-point numbers using the input() function, you must use the int() and the float() function, respectively. The int() function is used to convert a non-integer value to integer. Similarly, the float() function is used to convert a non-floating-point value into a floating-point value. Hence, the output of the input() function which returns a string value can be passed to the int() or float() function to get a numeric value.

```
a= int(input("Enter a number: "))
a = a + 10
print(a)
OUTPUT
Enter a number : 10
20
```

```
marks = float(input("Enter your total marks: "))
avg = marks/5.0
print(avg)
OUTPUT
Enter your total marks : 495
99.0
```

1.9 Comments

Comments are added in a program to describe the statements in the program code. They make the program easily readable and understandable by the programmer as well as other users who are seeing the code. In Python, a hash sign (#) that is not inside a string literal begins a comment. *All characters following the # and up to the end of the line are part of the comment.*

Program to use comments

```
# Program to find the cost of a dozen pens

price_1 = int(input("Enter the price of 1 pen: "))
price_12 = price_1 * 12 # dozen means 12
print("Price of a dozen pens = ", price_12)
```

```
OUTPUT

Enter the price of 1 pen: 10
Price of a dozen pens = 120
```

Some important points to remember about comments are:

- Comments are the non-executable statements in a program
- The interpreter simply ignores the comments
- When the program is run, comments are not displayed
- Comments can be either typed in a new line or on the same line after a statement or expression
- A program can have any number of comments

1.9.1 Multi-line comments

In Python, multi-line comments are also known as docstring. They can be specified in two ways–first, by using three single quotes (or apostrophe), secondly, by using three double quotes. They are used when explanation of the statements cannot be sufficiently given in one line. The code given below demonstrates the use of multi-line comments.

```
'"adding two
numbers"'
sum = 2 + 3
print(sum)
""" calculating average
of the two numbers
"""
avg = sum/2.0
print(avg)
OUTPUT
5
2.5
```

Did you notice that comments are not printed?

1.10 Reserved words

In every programming language, there are certain words which have a pre-defined meaning. These words also known as reserved words or keywords cannot be used for naming identifiers. Table 3 shows a list of Python keywords.

All the Python keywords contain lowercase letters only

Table 3: || Reserved Words

and	assert	Break	class	continue	def	del	elif	else	except
exec	finally	for	from	global	if	import	in	is	lambda
not	or	pass	print	raise	return	try	while	with	yield

1.11 Indentation

Whitespace at the beginning of the line is called ***indentation***. These whitespaces or the indentation is very important in Python. In a Python program, the leading whitespace including spaces and tabs at the beginning of the logical line determines the indentation level of that logical line.

The level of indentation groups statements to form a block of statements. This means that statements in a block must have the same indentation level. Python very strictly checks the indentation level and gives an error if indentation is not correct.

In the above code, there is a tab at the beginning of the second line. The error indicated by Python tells us that there is an indentation error. Python does not allow users to arbitrarily start new blocks of statements.

```
a = 10
    a = a + 1    # Indentation Error
print(a)
```

```
a = 10
a = a + 1
print(a)
OUTPUT
11
```

Like other programming languages, Python does not use curly braces ({...}). Therefore, to indicate blocks of code for class and function definitions or for flow control (discussed later in the book). It uses only indentation to form a block. *All statements inside a block should be at the same indentation level.*

Remember

Use a single tab for each indention level

1.12 Operators and expressions

Operators are the constructs that are used to manipulate the value of operands. Some basic operators include +, -, * and /. An expression in a programming language is any valid combination of tokens that represents a value. There are two types of expressions,

Simple expressions in which there are only values. For example, 29.

Complex expression in which one or more operators are used on operand(s) to generate a value. For example, in the expression sum = 2 + 4, 2 and 3 are operands and + is the operator. 10 * 8 / 2 is another example of a complex expression.

> Operands are values on which operators are applied to generate a value

However, expressions can also be classified as arithmetic expressions, logical expressions, string expressions and relational expressions, where

- Arithmetic expressions consist of numbers and arithmetic operators.
- Logical expressions have literals or variables and logical operators.
- Relational expressions have literals or variables and relational operators.
- String expressions have string operands and string operators (like, * and +).

Different operators supported by Python include:

a. Arithmetic Operators
b. Comparison (Relational) Operators
c. Assignment Operators
d. Logical Operators
e. Unary Operators
f. Bitwise Operators
g. Membership Operators
h. Identity Operators

1.12.1 Arithmetic operators

Some basic arithmetic operators are +, -, *, /, %, ** and //. You can apply these operators on numbers as well as on numeric variables to perform corresponding operations. For example, if a = 10 and b = 20, then look at the Table 4 to see the result of operations.

Table 4: || Arithmetic Operators

Operator	Description	Example	Output
+	Addition – Adds the operands	>>> print(a + b)	30
-	Subtraction – Subtracts operand on the right from the operand on the left of the operator	>>> print(a – b)	-10
*	Multiplication – Multiplies the operands	>>> print(a * b)	200
/	Division – Divides operand on the left side of the operator with the operand on its right. The division operator returns the quotient.	>>> print(b / a)	2.0
%	Modulus – Divides operand on the left side of the operator with the operand on its right. The modulus operator returns the remainder.	>>> print(b % a)	0

//	Floor Division – Divides the operands and returns the quotient. It also removes the digits after the decimal point. If one of the operands is negative, the result is floored (rounded away from zero towards negative infinity):	>>> print(24//5)
		>>> print(24.0//5.0)
		>>> print(-37//4)
		>>> print(-17.0//3)
			4
			4.0
			
			-10
			-5.0

**	Exponent – Performs exponential calculation. That is raises operand on the right side to the operand on the left of the operator.	>>> print(a**b)	10^{20}

1.12.2 Comparison operators

Comparison operators also known as *relational operators* are used to compare the values on its either sides and determines the relation between them. For example, assuming a = 10 and b = 20, we can use the comparison operators on them as specified in Table 5.

Table 5: || Comparison Operator

Operator	Description	Example	Output
==	Returns true if the two values are exactly equal.	>>> print(a == b)	False
!=	Returns true if the two values are not equal.	>>> print(a != b)	True
>	Returns true if the value at the operand on the left side of the operator is greater than the value on its right side	>>> print(a > b)	False
<	Returns true if the value at the operand on the right side of the operator is greater than the value on its left side.	>>> print(a < b)	True
>=	Returns true if the value at the operand on the left side of the operator is either greater than or equal to the value on its right side.	>>> print (a >= b)	False
<=	Returns true if the value at the operand on the right side of the operator is either greater than or equal to the value on its left side.	>>> print (a <= b)	True

1.12.3 Assignment and in-place or shortcut operators

Assignment operator as the name suggests assigns value to the operand. In-Place operators also known as *shortcut operators* that includes +=, -=, *=, /=, %=, //= and **= allow you to write code like num = num + 10 more concisely, as num += 3. Different types of assignment and in-place operators are given in Table 6.

> **Remember**
>
> Comparison operators (<, >) can also be used to compare strings lexicographically

Table 6: || Assignment and In - Place Operator

Operator	Example
=	c = a, assigns value of a to c
+=	a += b is same as a = a + b
-=	a –= b is same as a = a - b
*=	a *= b is same as a = a * b
/=	a /= b is same as a = a / b
%=	a %= b is same as a = a % b
//=	a //= b is same as a = a // b
**=	a**= b is same as a = a** b

Example: Application of the += operator on strings

```
>>> str1 = "PYTHON"
>>> str2 = "PROGRAMMING"
>>> str1 += str2
>>> print(str1)
PYTHONPROGRAMMING
```

1.12.4 Unary operators

Unary operators act on single operands. Unary minus operator is strikingly different from the arithmetic operator that operates on two operands and subtracts the second operand from the first operand. When an operand is preceded by a unary minus sign, its value is negated.

For example, if a number is positive, it becomes negative when preceded with a unary minus operator. Similarly, if the number is negative, it becomes positive after applying the unary minus operator. Consider the given example.

> **Remember**
>
> Unlike other programming languages, Python does not support prefix and postfix increment as well decrement operators

```
>>> a = -5          >>> a = 5
>>> b = -a          >>> b = -a
>>> print(b)        >>> print(b)
OUTPUT              OUTPUT
5                   -5
```

1.12.5 Bitwise operators

As the name suggests, bitwise operators perform operations at bit level. These operators include bitwise AND, bitwise OR, bitwise XOR and shift operators. Bitwise operators expect their operands to be of integers and treat them as a sequence of bits.

Bitwise AND (&): When we use the bitwise AND operator, the bit in the first operand is ANDed with the corresponding bit in the second operand. The bitwise-AND operator compares each bit of its first operand with the corresponding bit of its second operand. If both bits are 1, the corresponding bit in the result is 1 and 0 otherwise.

Bitwise OR (|): When we use the bitwise OR operator, the bit in the first operand is ORed with the corresponding bit in the second operand. The bitwise-OR operator compares each bit of its first operand with the corresponding bit of its second operand. If one or both bits are 1, the corresponding bit in the result is 1 and 0 otherwise.

Bitwise XOR (^): When we use the bitwise XOR operator, the bit in the first operand is XORed with the corresponding bit in the second operand. That is, the bitwise-XOR operator compares each bit of its first operand with the corresponding bit of its second operand. If one of the bits is 1, the corresponding bit in the result is 1 and 0 otherwise.

Bitwise NOT (~): The bitwise NOT, or complement, is a unary operation and performs logical negation on each bit of the operand. By performing negation of each bit, it actually produces the ones' complement of the given binary value. Bitwise NOT operator sets the bit to 1, if it was initially 0 and sets it to 0, if it was initially 1.

The truth tables of these Bitwise operators are summarised in Table 7.

Table 7: || Truth tables for Bitwise operators

A	B	A&B	A	B	A|B	A	B	A^B	A	!A
0	0	0	0	0	0	0	0	0	0	1
0	1	0	0	1	1	0	1	1	1	0
1	0	0	1	0	1	1	0	1		
1	1	1	1	1	1	1	1	0		

```
>>> x = 6
>>> y = 8
>>> print(x&y)
OUTPUT
0
```

```
>>> x = 6
>>> y = 8
>>> print(x|y)
OUTPUT
14
```

```
>>> x = 6
>>> y = 8
>>> print(x^y)
OUTPUT
14
```

```
>>> x = 6
>>> print(~x)
-7
```

You can check the result of bitwise operator by converting a number into binary using the **bin() function**. For example, >>> bin(15) will give '0b1111'. >>> bin(7) gives '0b111'. >>> 15 & 7 gives 7, as 1 1 1 1 & 0 1 1 1 gives 0 1 1 1.

1111
0111
0111

1.12.6 Shift operators

Python supports two bitwise shift operators. They are shift left (<<) and shift right (>>). These operations are used to shift bits to the left or to the right. The syntax for a shift operation can be given as: **operand op num**

where, the bits in operand are shifted left or right depending on the operator (left if the operator is << and right if the operator is >>) by number of places denoted by num.

```
If we left shift 01011101,
then after first left shift
we will get, 10111010.
After second left shift, we
will get, 01110100.
```

```
If we right shift 01011101, then after first
right shift we will get, 00101110.
After second left shift, we will get, 00010111.
```

```
>>> x = 5
>>> y = 4
>>> x << y
80
```

```
>>> x = 80
>>> y = 4
>>> x >> y
5
```

When we apply a left shift, every bit in x is shifted to the left by one place. Therefore, the MSB (most significant bit) of x is lost, the LSB of x is set to 0.

If you observe carefully, you will notice that ***shifting once to the left multiplies the number by 2.*** On the contrary, when we apply a right shift, every bit in x is shifted to the right by one place. Therefore, the LSB of x is lost, the MSB of x is set to 0. ***When we shift once to the right, it divides the number by 2.***

Remember

Bitwise operator cannot be applied to float or double variables

1.12.7 Logical operators

Python supports three logical operators – logical and, logical or, and logical not. As in case of arithmetic expressions, the logical expressions are evaluated from left to right.

Logical and: Logical AND operator is used to simultaneously evaluate two conditions or expressions with relational operators. If expressions on both the sides (left and right side) of the logical operator are true, then the whole expression is true else it is false. For example, (a > b) and (a > c) will return TRUE only if the value of a is greater than the values of b and c.

The and operator tests the second operand only if the first operand is true.

Logical or: Logical or operator .is used to simultaneously evaluate two conditions or expressions with relational operators. If one or both the expressions of the logical operator are true, then the whole expression is true. This means that the expression is false only if both the expressions are false. For example, (a > b) or (a != b) will return TRUE if a is either greater than b or less than b. It will return FALSE if a is equal to b.

> **Remember**
>
> Truth table of logical and, or and not is exactly same as that of Bitwise AND, OR and NOT operators

Logical not: The logical not operator takes a single expression and negates the value of the expression. Logical NOT produces a zero if the expression evaluates to a non-zero value and produces a 1 if the expression produces a zero. In other words, it just reverses the value of the expression. For example,

```
>>> a = 10
>>> b = not a        a is non-zero (or TRUE) so b is FALSE
>>> print(b)
False
```

```
>>> a = 0
>>> b = not a        a is zero (or FALSE) so b is TRUE
>>> print(b)
True
```

It can be noted that the *logical expressions operate in a shortcut (or lazy) fashion and stop the evaluation when it knows the final outcome for sure.* For example, in a logical expression involving logical AND, if the first operand is false, then the second operand is not evaluated as it is certain that the result will be false. Similarly, for a *logical expression involving logical OR, if the first operand is true, then the second operand is not evaluated as it is certain that the result will be true.*

1.12.8 Membership operators

Python supports two types of membership operators – **in** and **not in**. These operators, as the name suggests, test for membership in a sequence such as strings, lists or tuples that will be discussed in later chapters and are listed below.

```
>>> str1 ="HELLO"
>>> 'L' in str1
True
>>> 'T' in str1
False
```

```
>>> str1 = "HELLO"
>>> 'e' not in str1
True
>>> 'E' not in str1
False
```

in operator: The operator returns true if a variable is found in the specified sequence and false otherwise.

not in operator: The operator returns true if a variable is not found in the specified sequence and false otherwise.

```
>>> a = "r"
>>> str = "Good Morning"
>>> a in str
True
>>> 'R' in str
False
```

1.12.9 Identity operators

Python supports two types of identity operators. These operators compare the memory locations of two objects and are given as follows.

is Operator: Returns true if operands or values on both sides of the operator point to the same object and false otherwise. For example, if a is b returns TRUE if id(a) is same as id(b).

is not Operator: Returns true if operands or values on both sides of the operator do not point to the same object and false otherwise. For example, if a is not b returns TRUE if id(a) is not same as id(b).

```
The id() function returns a unique id of the object. Every object in Python has its own unique id which is assigned to the object when it is created. This id is the object's memory address, and will be different for each time you run the program.
```

we have learnt that Python creates labels when a variable is created. Two variables with the same value refer to the same label and thus have the same id. This concept can be understood by the following example.

```
>>> a = 10
>>> b = 10
>>> a is b
True
>>> a = 20
>>> b = 10
>>> a is b
False
```

When the is operator returns True, it also indicates that the equality operator will also return True. But this is not always true the other way. That is, two objects having the same value and returning True with equality operator may return False with the is operator. This generally happens in three cases.

- First, when input is taken from the user.
- Second, with integer literals having several digits.
- Third, with floating-point and complex numbers.

In all the cases, Python creates two different objects even if they have same value. This is illustrated below.

```
CASE 1:                                  CASE 2:             CASE 3:
>>> s1 = "HELLO"                         >>> n1 = 1234567    >>> n1 = 1.23
>>> s2 = input("Enter a string: ")       >>> n2 = 1234567    >>> n2 = 1.23
Enter a string : HELLO                   >>> n1 == n2        >>> n1 == n2
>>> s1 == s2                             True                True
True                                     >>> n1 is n2        >>> n1 is n2
>>> s1 is s2                             False               False
False
```

1.12.10 Operators precedence and associativity

Table 8 lists all operators from highest precedence to lowest. When an expression has more than one operator, then it is the relative priorities of the operators with respect to each other that determine the order in which the expression will be evaluated.

Remember that

Operators are associated from left to right. This means that operators with same precedence are evaluated in a left to right manner.

Parentheses can change the order in which an operator is applied. The operator in parenthesis is applied first even if there is a higher priority operator in the expression.

Table 8: || Operator Precedence Chart

OPERATOR	DESCRIPTION
()	Parenthesis (for grouping)
**	Exponentiation
~,+,-	Complement, unary plus and minus
*,/,%,//	Multiply, divide, modulo and floor division
+,-	Addition and subtraction
>>, <<	Right and left bitwise shift
&	Bitwise 'AND'
^|	Bitwise exclusive 'OR' and regular 'OR'
<=, <,>,>=	Comparison operators
<>, ==, !=	Equality operators
=,%=,/=,//=, -=, +=, *=, **=	Assignment operators
Is, is not	Identity operators
In, not in	Membership operators
Not, or, and	Logical operators

```
>>>5*6+3
33
>>>5+6*3
23
```

* Has higher precedence than +. Hence, first the operands will be multiplied and then addition will be performed.

Let us try some more codes to see how operator precedence works in our expressions.

>>> (50+40)*10/20 45.0	>>> ((50+40)*20)/10 180.0	>>> (50+40)*(20/10) 180.0
>>> 50+ (40*10)/20 70.0	>>>(False==False) or True True	>>> False==(False or True) False
>>> 50*100/5//4 250.0	>>> (((50*100)/5)//4) 250.0	>>> 50*(100/(5//4)) 5000.0

1.13 Expressions in Python

In any programming language, an expression is any legal combination of symbols (like variables, constants and operators) that represents a value. Every language has its own set of rules that define whether an expression is valid or invalid in that language. *In Python, an expression must have at least one operand (variable or constant) and can have one or more operators. On evaluating an expression, we get a value.*

Operand is the value on which operator is applied. These operators use constants and variables to form an expression. A * B + C – 5 is an example of an expression, where, +, *, - are operators; A, B and C are variables and 5 is a constant. Some valid expressions in Python are: x = a / b, y = a * b, z = a^ b, x = a > b, etc. When an expression has more than one operator, then the expression is evaluated using the operator precedence chart.

An example of an illegal expression can be a+ –b or <y++. When the program is compiled, the validity of all expressions is checked. If an illegal expression is encountered, an error message is displayed.

In Python, we can categorise expressions based on the data type of the result obtained on evaluating an expression. These types of expressions include,

Constant Expressions that involves only constants. Example: 8 + 9 - 2

Integral Expressions that produces an integer result. Example:

a=10, b=5

c = a * b

Floating-Point Expressions produces floating-point results. Example: a * b / 2

Relational Expressions returns either true or false value. Example: c = a > b

Logical Expressions combines two or more relational expressions and returns a value as *true* or *false*. Example: a > b and y != 0.

Bitwise Expressions manipulates data at bit level. Example: x = y & z.

Assignment Expressions assigns a value to a variable. Example: c = 10.

> **Remember**
>
> Deleted variables can be used again in the code if and only if you reassign them some value

1.14 Decision control statements

Till now, we have executed simple statements in Python. Such statements are executed sequentially from the first line of the program to the last. That is, the second statement is executed after the first, the third statement is executed after the second, so on and so forth. This way of execution is known as **sequential control flow**.

However, in some cases, we want to either execute only a selected set of statements (i.e., selection control) or execute a set of statements repeatedly (i.e., iterative control). In such cases, decision control system comes into picture.

A ***decision control statement*** is a statement that determines the flow of control in a program. Flow of control means which instruction would be executed next. A decision control statement can either skip one or more instructions. The three fundamental methods of control flow in a programming language are *sequential, selection and iterative control.*

Selection and iterative control are a part of decision control system. Thus, a decision control statements can alter (change) the flow of a sequence of instructions. And, this type of conditional processing help users to extend the usefulness of programs.

Programmers can make programmes that determine which statements of the code should be executed and which should be ignored in certain circumstances. Figure 1.4 shows the categorisation of decision control statements.

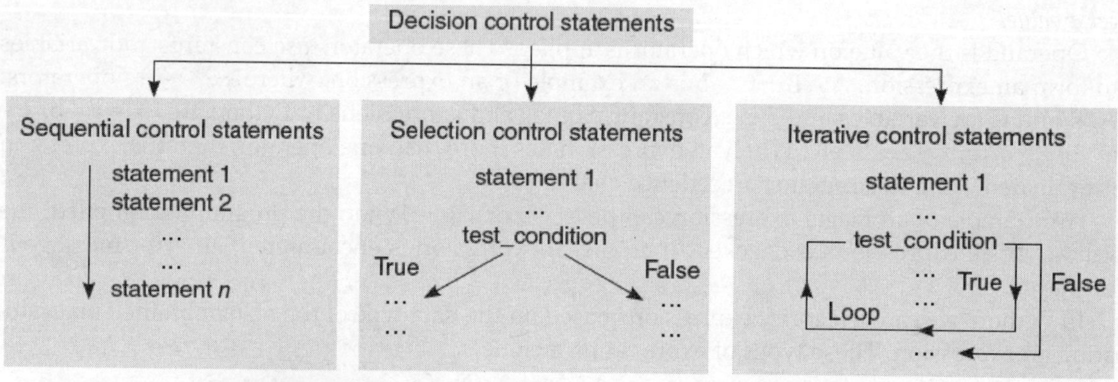

Figure 1.4 Categorisation of decision control statements

1.15 Selection/conditional branching statements

The decision control statements usually jump from one part of the code to another depending on whether a particular condition is satisfied or not. That is, they execute statements selectively based on certain decisions. Such type of decision control statements is known as ***selection control statements*** or *conditional branching statements*. Python language supports different types of conditional branching statements which are as follows:

- If statement
- If-else statement
- Nested if statement
- If-elif-else statement

1.15.1 If statement

If statement is the simplest form of decision control statements that is frequently used in decision-making, an if statement is a selection control statement based on the value of a given Boolean expression. The general form of a simple if statement is shown in Figure 1.5.

> Python is a case sensitive language. So, 'if' is not same as 'IF'

```
SYNTAX OF IF STATEMENT

if test_expression:
    statement1

    ........

    Statement n
statement x;
```

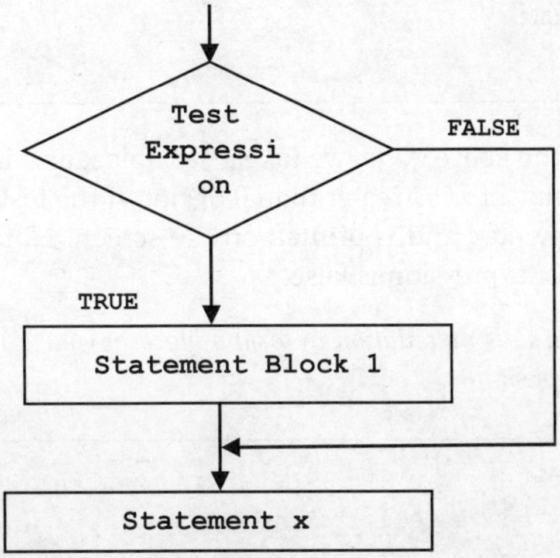

Figure 1.5 If statement construct

The if block may include 1 or more statements. According to the figure, first, the test expression is evaluated. If the test expression is true, the statement of if block (statement 1 to n) are executed, otherwise these statements will be skipped and the execution will jump to statement x.

Implementing if statement in Python

Always remember the following points while implementing an if construct in Python.

- The statement in an if block is any valid statement in Python.
- The test expression is any valid expression that may include logical operators.
- **A header in Python is a specific keyword followed by a colon.** In the figure, the if statement has a header, **"if text_expression":** having keyword if.
- The group of statements following a header is called a **suite**. After the header, all instructions that are indented at the same level forms a suite.
- While four spaces are is commonly used for each level of indentation, any number of spaces may be used.

> Header and its suite are together known as a clause

Example: Program to increment a number if it is positive

```
x = 10          #Initialize the value of x
if(x>0):        #test the value of x
          x = x + 1 #Increment the value of x if it is > 0
print(x)        #Print the value of x
OUTPUT:
x = 11
```

Remember to properly indent the statements that are dependent on the previous statements.

In the above code, we take a variable x and initialise it to 10. In the test expression, we check if the value of x is greater than 0 or not. If the test expression evaluates to true, then the value of x is incremented and is printed on the screen. Note that the print statement will be executed even if the test expression is false.

Python uses indentation to form a block of code. Other languages such as C and C++, use curly braces to accomplish this.

Write a program to determine whether a person is eligible to vote.

```
age = int(input("Enter the age: "))
if(age>=18):
    print("You are eligible to vote")
OUTPUT
Enter the age: 35
You are eligible to vote
```

Write a program to determine the character entered by the user.

```
char = input("Press any key: ")
if(char.isalpha()):
    print("The user has entered a character")
if(char.isdigit()):
    print("The user has entered a digit")
if(char.isspace()):
    print("The user entered a white space
character")
OUTPUT
Press any key: 7
The user has entered a digit
```

1.15.2 If-else statement

Although if-statement plays a vital role in conditional branching, its usage is very limited. Its simplicity is also its drawback. In the if-statement, the test expression is evaluated, if the result is true, the statement(s) followed by the expression is executed. But, if the expression is false, nothing useful happens. So, using an if-else statement solves our problem. The general form of a simple if-else statement is shown in Figure 1.6.

SYNTAX OF IF-ELSE STATEM

```
if (test expression):
        statement block 1

else:
        statement block 2

statement x;
```

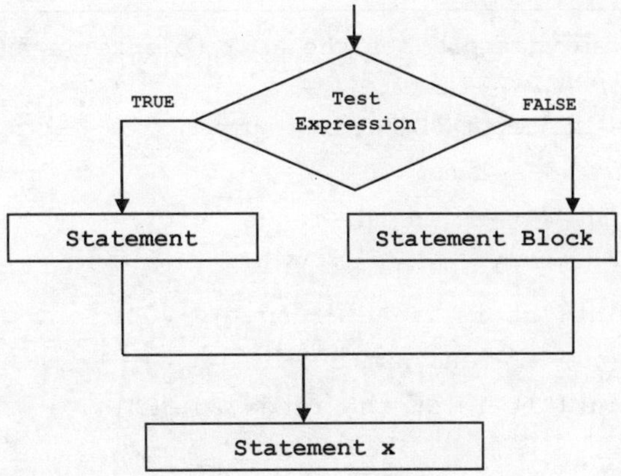

Figure 1.6 IF-Else statement construct

In the above syntax, we have written statement block. A statement block may include one or more statements. According to the if-else construct, first the test expression is evaluated. If the expression is true, statement block 1 is executed and statement block 2 is skipped. Otherwise, if the expression is false, statement block 2 is executed and statement block 1 is ignored. In any case, after the statement block 1 or 2 gets executed, the control will pass to statement x. Therefore, statement x is executed in every case.

Write a program to determine whether a person is eligible to vote or not. If he is not eligible display how many years are left to be eligible.

```
age = int(input("Enter the age: "))

if(age>=18):

       print("You are eligible to vote")

else:

   yrs = 18 - age

   print("You have to wait for " + str(yrs) +" years")
```

OUTPUT

```
Enter the age: 10

You have to wait for 8 years
```

Write a program to find larger of two numbers.

```
a = int(input("Enter the value of a: "))
b = int(input("Enter the value of b: "))

if(a>b):

      large = a

else:

      large = b

print("Large = ",large)
```

OUTPUT

```
Enter the value of a: 50

Enter the value of b: 30

Large = 50
```

1.15.3 Nested if statements

A statement that contains other statements is called a ***compound statement***. To perform more complex checks, if statements can be nested, that is, it can be placed one inside the other. In such a case, the inner if statement is the statement part of the outer one. Nested if statements are used to check if more than one conditions are satisfied. Consider the code given below to understand this concept.

Program that prompts the user to enter a number and then print its interval

```
num = int(input("Enter any number from 0-30: "))
if(num>=0 and num<10):
   print("It is in the range 0-10")
elif(num>=10 and num<20):
   print("It is in the range 10-20")
elif(num>=20 and num<30):
   print("It is in the range 20-30")
```

OUTPUT

```
Enter any number from 0-30: 25
It is in the range 20-30
```

If statements can be nested resulting in multi-way selection. You can do the same program using if-else and if-elif-else statements.

1.15.4 If-elif-else statement

Python supports if-elif-else statements to test additional conditions apart from the initial test expression. The if-elif-else construct works in the same way as a usual `if-else` statement. If-elif-else construct is also known as **nested-if construct**. The elif (short for else if) statement is a shortcut to if and else statements. ***A series of if and elif statements have a final else block, which is executed if none of the if or elif expressions is True.*** Its syntax is given in Figure 1.7.

COMPARING FLOATING POINT NUMBERS

Never test floating point numbers for exact equality. This is because floating point numbers are just approximations, so it is always better to test floating point numbers for 'approximately equal' rather than testing for exactly equal.

We can test for approximate equality by subtracting the two floating point numbers (that are to be tested) and comparing their absolute value of the difference against a very small number, epsilon.

SYNTAX OF IF-ELIF-ELSE STATEMENT

```
if ( test expression 1)
        statement block 1
elif ( test expression 2)
        statement block 2
...........................
elif (test expression N)
        statement block N
else
        Statement Block X
Statement Y
```

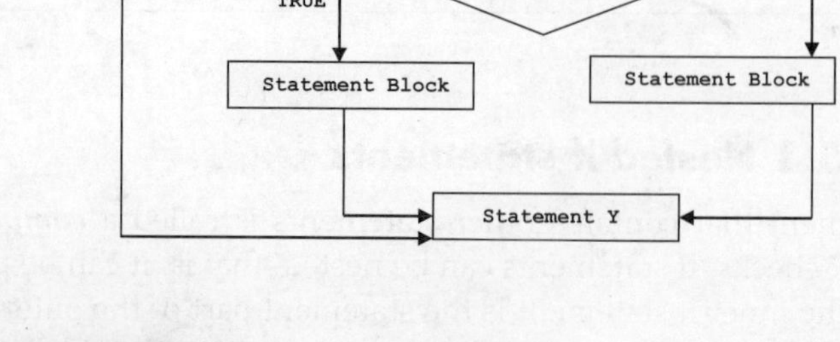

Figure 1.7 if-elif-else Syntax

Note that it is not necessary that every if statement should have an else block as Python supports simple if statements also. After the first test expression or the first if branch, the programmer can have as many `elif` branches as he/she wants depending on the expressions that have to be tested. The final else block is called if none of the if or elif expressions is True.

```
Remember
The elif and else
parts are optional
```

To test whether a number entered by the user is negative, positive or equal to zero.

```
num = int(input("Enter any number: "))
if(num==0):
        print("The value is equal to zero")
elif(num>0):
        print("The number is positive")
else:
        print("The number is negative")
```

OUTPUT

```
Enter any number: -10
The number is negative
```

Write a program to determine whether the character entered is a vowel or not.

```
ch = input("Enter any character: ")
if(ch=="A" or ch=="E" or ch=="I" or
ch=="O" or ch=="U"):
        print ch, "is a vowel")
elif(ch=="a" or ch=="e" or ch=="i" or
ch=="o" or ch=="u"):
        print(ch, "is a vowel")
else:
        print(ch,"is not a vowel")
```

OUTPUT

```
Enter any character: h
h is not a vowel
```

In the program to test whether a number is positive or negative, note that if the first test expression evaluates a true value, then rest of the statements in the code will be ignored and after executing the print statement that displays 'The value is equal to zero', the control will jump to return 0 statement.

Keep the logical expressions simple and short. For this, you may use nested if statements.

Python assumes any non-zero and non-null values as TRUE. Similarly, all values that are either zero or null, are assumed as FALSE value.

```
Use the AND/OR operators to form a compound
relation expression. In Python, the following
expression is invalid.
        if (60 ≤ marks ≤ 75):
The correct way to write is,
        if ((marks ≥ 60) and (marks ≤ 75):
```

1.16 Iterative statements

Python supports basic loop structures. Iterative statements are used to repeat the execution of one or more statements. In Python, iterative statements are implemented through while loop and for loop.

SYNTAX OF WHILE LOOP

```
statement x

while (condition):
   statement block

statement y
```

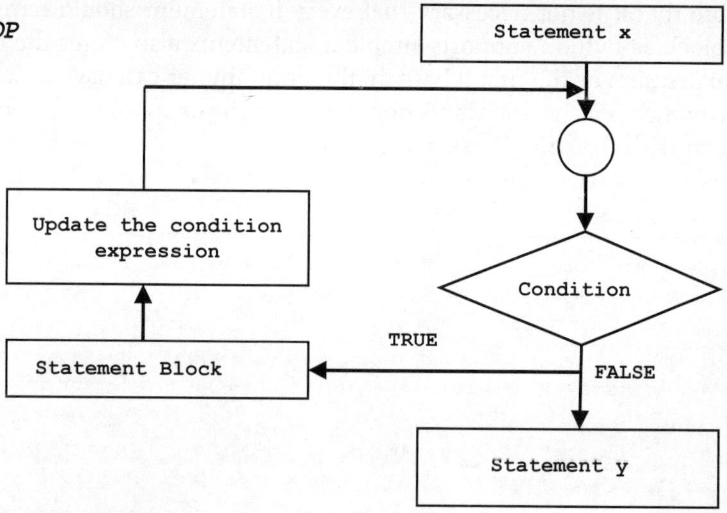

Figure 1.8 The while loop construct

1.16.1 While loop

The while loop provides a mechanism to repeat one or more statements while a particular condition is true. Figure 1.8 shows the syntax and general form of representation of a while loop.

> Iterative statements are used to repeat the execusion of a list of statements, depending on the value of an integer expression

Note in the while loop, the condition is tested before any of the statements in the statement block is executed. If the condition is true, only then the statements will be executed otherwise; if the condition is false, the control will jump to statement y, which is the immediate statement outside the while loop block.

We must update the condition with every iteration of the loop. This is necessary because it is this condition, which determines when the loop will end. If we do not update the condition, then it will never become false. This will result in an infinite loop which is never desirable.

A while loop is also referred to as a top-checking loop since control condition is placed as the first line of the code. If the control condition evaluates to false, then the statements enclosed in the loop are never executed. Look at the following example code.

To print first 10 numbers using a while loop.

```
i = 0
while(i<=10):
        print(i,end='')
        i = i+1
```

OUTPUT:

```
0 1 2 3 4 5 6 7 8 9 10
```

Write a program to calculate the sum and average of first 10 numbers.

```
i = 0
s = 0
while(i<=10):
  s = s+i
  i = i+1
avg = float(s)/10
print("The sum of first 10 numbers is:",s)
print("The average of first 10 numbers is:", avg)
```

OUTPUT

```
The sum of first 10 numbers is: 55
```

In the program initially i = 0 and is less than 10, that is the condition is true, so in the while loop, the value of i is printed and the condition is updated so that with every execution of the loop, the condition becomes more approachable. Always remember that, when writing a while loop,

First, the loop control variable must be initialised before entering the loop.

Second, the test expression that decides whether the statement(s) in the loop will be executed or not is evaluated.

Third, the statement(s) inside the loop are executed if the test expression is True.

Fourth, the loop control variable is updated.

```
i = 0
sum = 0
avg = 0.0
while(i<=10):
    sum = sum + i
avg = sum/10
print("\n The sum of first 10 numbers = ", sum)
print("\n The average of first 10 numbers = ", avg)
```

```
The infinite loop is a
loop which never stops
running. Its condition
always True.
```

while loop is very useful for designing interactive programs in which the number of times the statements in loop has to be executed may or may not be known in advance. Let us look at a program which results in an infinite loop. Although the program is supposed to calculate the average of first 10 numbers, the condition never becomes false, and the desired output is *not* generated. Once you have entered the infinite loop, either press Ctrl + C keys on the keyboard or press the close button of the Python shell window.

1.16.2 For loop

Like the while loop, the for loop provides a mechanism to repeat a task until a particular condition is true. For loop is usually known as a determinate or definite loop because the programmer knows exactly how many times the loop will repeat. The number of times the loop has to be executed can be determined mathematically by checking the logic of the loop.

The for..in statement is a looping statement used in Python to iterate over a sequence of objects, i.e., go through each item in a sequence. Here, by sequence, we mean just an ordered collection of items. The flow of statements in a for loop can be given as in Figure 1.9.

When a for loop is used, a range of sequence is specified (only once). The items of the sequence are assigned to the loop control variable one after the other. The for loop is executed for each item in the sequence. With every iteration of the loop, a check is made to ensure if the loop control variable has been assigned all the values in the sequence. If all the values have not been assigned, the statement block of the loop is executed else, the statements comprising the statement block of the for loop are skipped and the control jumps to the immediate statement following the for loop body. Note that every iteration of the loop must make the loop control variable closer to the end of the sequence.

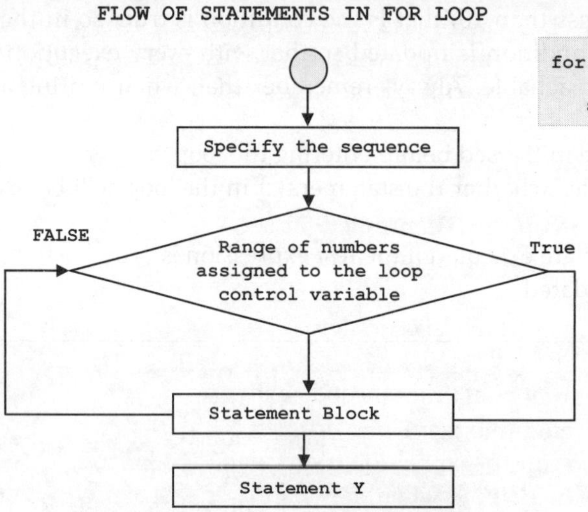

SYNTAX OF FOR LOOP

```
for loop_contol_var in sequence:
    statement block
```

Figure 1.9 For loop construct

Let us print all the characters in a string using the for loop. We know that a string is a sequence of characters. So, the for loop statement(s) will be executed for each character in the string.

```
for i in "PYTHON":
    print(i, end = ' ')
Ans. P Y T H O N
```

1.17 The range() function

The range() is a built-in function in Python that is used to iterate over a sequence of numbers. The syntax of range() is **range(beg, end, [step])**

The **range()** generates a sequence of numbers starting with **beg** (inclusive) and ending with one less than the number **end**. The **step** argument is optional (hence, written in brackets). By default, every number in the range is incremented by 1, but we can specify a different increment using step. It can be both negative and positive but not zero.

> Step can be either positive or negative but cannot be zero

Programs to print first n numbers using the `range()` in a for `loop`

```
for i in range(1, 5):
        print(i, end= ' ')
OUTPUT
1 2 3 4
```

Print numbers in the same line

beg step

```
for i in range(1, 10, 2):
print (i, end= '
OUTPUT
1 3 7 9
```

end

The range() function had produced values 1, 2, 3 and 4. Did you notice that the statement(s) of the for loop is executed for each value of the loop control variable (which is i, here). Initially, i is 1, in the next iteration it is 2, so on and so forth. The loop continues until all the values in the sequence are processed.

1.18 Selecting an appropriate loop

Loops can be either counter-controlled or condition controlled (or sentinel-controlled). When we know in advance, the number of times the loop should be executed, we use a counter-controlled loop. Counter is a variable that must be initialised, tested and updated for performing the loop operations. Such a counter-controlled loop in which the counter is assigned a constant or a value is also known as a ***definite repetition loop***.

When we do not know in advance the number of times the loop will be executed, we use a condition-controlled (or sentinel-controlled or indefinite loop) loop. In such a loop, a special value called the *sentinel value* is used to change the loop control expression from true to false. For example, when data are read from the user, the user may be notified when they want the execution to stop. A programmer may specify to stop the loop a -1 (or any other value) should be entered, they may enter -1. This value is called a ***sentinel value***. A condition-controlled loop is often useful for indefinite repetition loops as they use a true/false condition to control the number of times the loop is executed.

If you require to have a *counter-controlled loop, then choose for loop else if you need to have a sentinel-controlled loop then go for a while loop*. Table 9 shows the comparison between the counter-controlled and condition-controlled loops.

Table 9: || Comparison between Condition-controlled and Counter-controlled Loops

```
i = 0
while(i<=10):
    print(i, end = '')
    i+=1
```

Counter-controlled

```
i = 0
while(1):
    print(i, end = '')
    i+=1
    if(i==11):
        break
```

Condition-controlled

```
for i in range(11):
    print(i, end = '')
```

Counter-controlled

Attribute	Counter controlled loop	Condition controlled loop
Number of execution	Used when number of times the loop has to be executed is known in advance.	Used when number of times the loop has to be executed is not known in advance.
Condition variable	In counter controlled loops, we have a counter variable.	In Condition controlled loops, we use a sentinel variable.
Value and limitation of variable	The value of the counter variable and the condition for loop execution, both are strict.	The condition for loop execution is strict but the value of the sentinel variable may vary.

1.19 Nested loops

Nested loop means that a loop is placed inside another loop. Although both for and while loop can be nested, we usually use nested for loops as they are easiest to control. In such a case, the inner for loop can be used to control the number of times a particular set of statements will be executed, and the outer for loop can be used to control the number of times the inner loop is repeated. In Python, loops can be nested to any desired level.

Write a program to print the following pattern.

```
Pass 1- 1 2 3 4 5
Pass 2- 1 2 3 4 5
Pass 3- 1 2 3 4 5
Pass 4- 1 2 3 4 5
Pass 5- 1 2 3 4 5
for i in range(1,6):
    print("PASS",i,"- ",end='')
    for j in range(1,6):
        print(j, end='')
    print()
```

Write a program to print the following pattern.

```
**********
**********
**********
**********
**********
for i in range(5):
    print()
    for j in range(5):
        print("*",end='')
```

1.20 Break statement

The *break* statement is used to terminate the execution of the nearest enclosing loop in which it appears. The break statement is widely used with for loop and while loop. When compiler encounters a break statement, the control passes to the statement that follows the loop in which the break statement appears. Its syntax is quite simple, just type keyword **break**.

```
Program to demonstrate the break statement
i = 1
while i <= 10:
    print(i, end='')
    if i==5:
        break
    i = i+1
print("\n Done")
OUTPUT
1 2 3 4 5
Done
```

Note that the code is meant to print first 10 numbers using a while loop, but it will actually print only numbers from 0 to 4. As soon as i becomes equal to 5, the break statement is executed and the control jumps to the statement following the while loop.

Hence, the **break** *statement is used to exit a loop from any point within its body, bypassing its normal termination expression.* When the `break` statement is encountered inside a loop, the loop is immediately terminated, and program control is passed to the next statement following the loop. Figure 1.10 shows the transfer of control when the break statement is encountered.

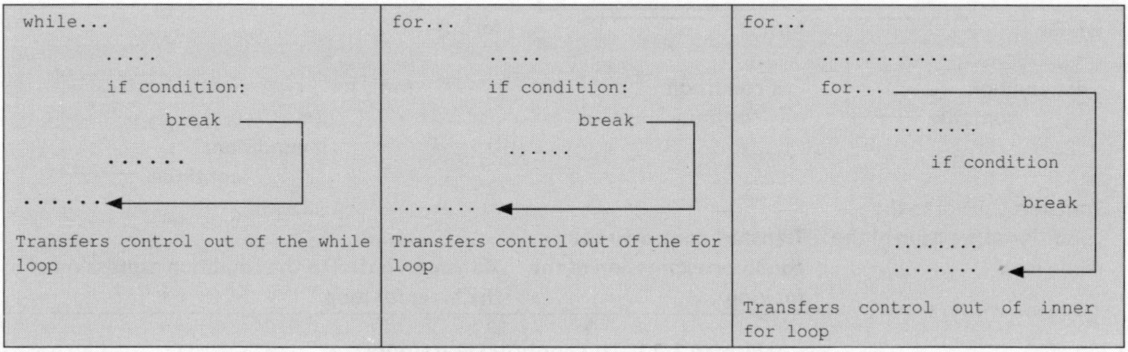

Figure 1.10 The break statement

1.21 The continue statement

Like the break statement, the continue statement can only appear in the body of a loop. When the compiler encounters a continue statement, then the rest of the statements in the loop are skipped and the control is unconditionally transferred to the loop-continuation portion of the nearest enclosing loop. Its syntax is quite simple, just type keyword **continue** as shown below.

```
Program to demonstrate the continue statement
for i in range(1,11):
      if(i==5):
           continue
     print(i, end='')
print("\n Done")
OUTPUT
1 2 3 4 6 7 8 9 10
Done
```

When the continue statement is encountered in the while and for loop, the control is transferred to the statement that tests the controlling expression. However, if placed with a for loop, the continue statement causes a branch to the code that updates the loop variable.

Note that the code is meant to print numbers from 0 to 10. But as soon as I becomes equal to 5, the continue statement is encountered, so rest of the statement(s) in the for loop are skipped. In the output, there is no 5... 5 could not be printed as continue caused early increment of i and skipping of statement that printed the value of i on screen). Figure 1.11 illustrates the use of continue statement in loops.

Hence, the continue statement is the opposite of the break statement. It forces the next iteration of the loop thereby skipping any statements that were a part of the loop. The continue statement is usually used to restart a statement sequence when an error occurs.

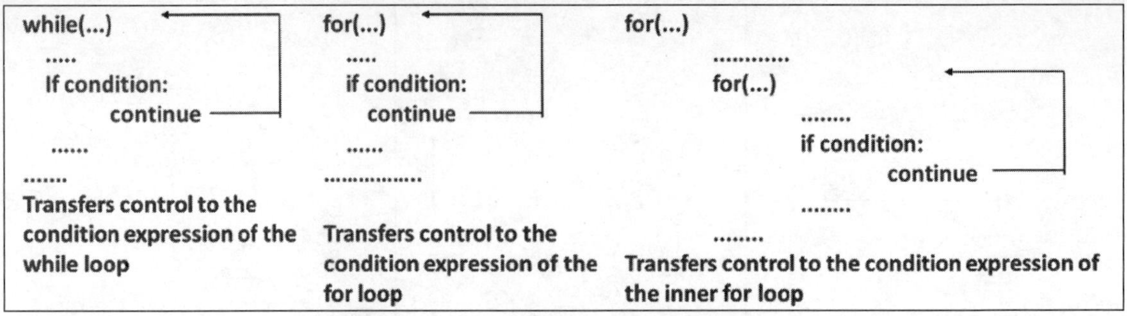

Figure 1.11 The continue statement

1.22 The pass statement

Pass statement is used when a statement is required syntactically, but no instruction has to be executed. It specifies a *null* operation or simply **No Op**eration (NOP) statement. Nothing happens when the pass statement is executed. Syntax of pass statement is simple, just type the keyword **pass**.

```
Program to demonstrate pass statement

for i in range(5):

    pass #The statement is doing nothing

    print(i,end = '')

print("Done")

OUTPUT

0 1 2 3 4 Done
```

The pass statement is used as a placeholder for future statements. For example, if we have a loop that is not implemented yet, but we may wish to write some code in it in the future. Then, we can use the pass statement instead of an empty body of the loop. Although the pass statement will not do anything, it will make the program syntactically correct. This is shown in the code.

Difference between comment and pass statements In Python programming, *pass* is a null statement. While the interpreter ignores a comment entirely, *pass* is not ignored. ***Comment is not executed, but pass statement is executed but nothing happens.***

1.23 The *else* statement used with loops

We have studied if-else block in the previous chapter. We can also have an *else* statement associated with the loop statements. *If the* **else** *statement is used with a for loop, the else statement is executed when the loop has completed iterating. But when used with the while loop, the else statement is executed when the condition becomes false.*

```
for i in range(3):
    print(i, end=")
else:
    print("Done")
OUTPUT
0 1 2 3 Done
```

```
i = 10
while(i<0):
    print(i)
    i=i+1
else:
    print(i, "is not negative so loop did not execute")
OUTPUT
i is not negative so loop did not execute
```

Key Terms

Clause: Combination of header and its suite.
Decision control flow: A type of flow control in which either a selected set of statements are executed or a particular set of statements is executed repeatedly.
Definite repetition loop: A counter-controlled loop in which the counter is assigned a constant or a value is also known as a definite repetition loop.
Docstring: In Python, multi-line comments are also known as docstring.
Expression: An expression in a programming language is any valid combination of tokens that represents a value.
Flow control: Flow control means which statement would be executed next.
Identifiers: Names given to identify a variable, function, class, module or any other object.
Iterative statement: Statements that repeat the execution of a block of statements depending on the value of an integer expression.
Keywords: Reserved words in a programming language that have a pre-defined meaning.
Lvalue: Expressions that come on the left side of the assignment operator.
Nested (or compound) statement: A statement that contains other statements is called a compound statement.
Nested loop: A loop that is placed inside another loop.
Operands: Values on which the operator is applied.
Operators: Constructs used to manipulate the value of operands.
Rvalue: Expressions that comes on the right side of the assignment operator.
Selection control statements: Decision control statements that allow the flow control to jump from one part of the code to another depending on whether a particular condition is satisfied or not. Since they execute statements selectively based on certain decisions, such type of decision control statements is known as selection control statements or *conditional branching statements*.
Sequential control flow: A programming style in which the statements in a program are executed one after the other.
Slice: A substring of a string is called a slice.
String: A string is a group of characters.
String concatenation: The process of combining two strings.
Suite: Group of statements following the header.
Unary operator: Operator applied on a single operand.
Variable: Variable means something that may change. In Python programs, any piece of information can be used to store information that may change

Chapter Highlights

- Python is a high-level, interpreted, interactive, object-oriented and reliable language.
- If you want to execute the program in Python shell, then just press the **F5** key or click on Run Menu and then select **Run Module**.
- The character set of a language is a set of valid characters that the language can recognise. Such characters may be digits, alphabets or any other symbol.
- Tokens are the small units of the programming language. Python supports literals, keywords, identifiers and operators as tokens.
- Number as the name suggests, refers to a numeric value. You can use four types of numbers in Python programs. These include integers, long integers, floating-points and complex numbers.
- When two very large floating-point numbers are multiplied, it may result in an *arithmetic overflow*. Arithmetic overflow is a condition that occurs when a calculated result is too large.
- Arithmetic underflow occurs when two floating-point numbers are divided. It is a condition that occurs when a calculated result is too small in magnitude to be represented.
- Any floating-point value may contain an arbitrary number of decimal places, so it is always recommended to use the built-in format() function to produce a string version of a number with a specific number of decimal places. It can also be used to control the display of strings.
- A raw string does not handle any escape sequences. It is specified by prefixing r or R to the string.
- To create a variable in Python, just assign a value to the identifier using the equal to sign.
- When we create a variable, Python creates labels referring to those values.
- Variables can hold values of different types called data types.
- Based on the data type of a variable, the interpreter reserves memory for it and also determine the type of data that can be stored in the reserved memory.
- The five standard data types supported by Python includes–numbers, string, list, tuple and dictionary.
- In Python, you can reassign variables as many times as you want to change the value stored in them. You may even store value of one data type in a statement and then a value of another data in a subsequent statement.
- The type() function is used to determine data type of object.
- Python allow programmers to assign a single value to more than one variable simultaneously.
- Trying to reference a variable that has not been assigned any value causes an error. This may happen if you have mistakenly used a variable without assigning it a value prior to its use or have deliberately deleted or removed a variable using the del statement and then trying to use it later in your code.
- A variable of Boolean type can have one of the two values – True or False.
- Comments are added in a program to describe the statements in the program code. They make the program easily readable and understandable by the programmer as well as other users who are seeing the code.
- To take input from the users, Python makes use of the input() function.
- Whitespace at the beginning of the line is called indentation. These whitespaces the beginning of the logical line determines the indentation level of that logical line.
- Comparison operators also known as relational operators are used to compare the values on its either sides and determines the relation between them.

- ✶ Unary operators act on single operands. When an operand is preceded by a unary minus sign, its value is negated.
- ✶ Python supports two bitwise shift operators. They are shift left (<<) and shift right (>>). These operations are used to shift bits to the left or to the right. The syntax for a shift operation can be given as: operand op num.
- ✶ Python supports two types of membership operators- in and not in. These operators test for membership in a sequence such as strings, lists, or tuples.
- ✶ The test expression is any valid expression that may include logical operators.
- ✶ After the header, all instructions that are indented at the same level, form a suite.
- ✶ Python uses indentation to form a block of code.
- ✶ An if-else statement specifies what has to be done if the statement is true as well as when it is false.
- ✶ Nested if statements are used to check if more than one conditions are satisfied.
- ✶ A series of if and elif statements have a final else block, which is executed if none of the if or elif expressions is True.
- ✶ In Python, iterative statements are implemented through while loop and for loop.
- ✶ The while loop provides a mechanism to repeat one or more statements while a particular condition is true.
- ✶ The value of the loop control variable is updated with every iteration of the loop.
- ✶ The for loop provides a mechanism to repeat a task until a particular condition is true.
- ✶ The for..in statement is a looping statement used in Python to iterate over a sequence of objects.
- ✶ The range() is a built-in function in Python that is used to iterate over a sequence of numbers.
- ✶ Loops can be either counter-controlled or condition controlled (or sentinel-controlled) loops.
- ✶ When we do not know in advance the number of times the loop will be executed, we use a condition-controlled loop.
- ✶ The break statement is used to terminate the execution of the nearest enclosing loop in which it appears.
- ✶ When the compiler encounters a continue statement then the rest of the statements in the loop are skipped and the control is unconditionally transferred to the loop-continuation portion of the nearest enclosing loop.
- ✶ Pass statement is used when a statement is required syntactically but no instruction has to be executed. It specifies a null operation or simply No Operation (NOP) statement.
- ✶ If the else statement is used with a for loop, the else statement is executed when the loop has completed iterating. But when used with the while loop, the else statement is executed when the condition becomes false.

Review Questions

1. Explain the features of Python.
2. What do you understand by the term Python character set?
3. Write a short note on literals in Python.
4. What problems can popup while dealing with floating-point numbers?
5. With the help of an example, explain the use of format() function.

6. What is a string in Python? Explain the different ways in which you can define a string.
7. Differentiate between implicit conversion and type conversion.
8. What is an escape sequence? Give examples. Why are they called so?
9. Write the commands to display the text "I love programming" in a width of 50 characters when the text is left-justified, right justified and centre aligned.
10. Write a command to print the string in reverse.
11. Justify the statement – "Python is a free and open-source programming language".
12. Which of the following expressions would result in overflow or underflow error? Justify your answer.
    a. 1.23e + 150*4.56e + 100
    b. 6.78e – 100/4.67e + 200
13. Identify the expressions which will involve coercion and the ones which will involve explicit type conversion.
    a. 5.0+2
    b. 6.5*3.0
    c. 7.0+float(8)
    d. 6.2*5.0
    e. 5.7+int(9.0)
14. Find and correct the error (if any).
    a. >>> print('It is Teacher's Daty today ')
    b. >>> print("Rohan knows "Hindi", "English", "Punjabi"")
15. What are identifiers? List some rules that must be kept in mind while naming an identifier.
16. With the help of a diagram explain what happens when a variable is created in Python.
17. With the help of an example explain how variables can be re-assigned values in Python.
18. Can we re-assign a value of another data type to a variable? If yes, why?
19. Differentiate between lvalue and rvalue.
20. What do you understand by the term multiple assignment?
21. What are Boolean variables? How are they created?
22. What are comments? How are they written in Python?
23. What is a docstring? How is it defined in a Python program?
24. Why is indentation necessary in Python?
25. Logical expressions operate in a shortcut (or lazy) fashion. Justify this statement.
26. The statement print "Python # Programming" will be executed or not?
    If yes justify its output.
    Hint: The # inside a string, so it is just considered as a character and not as comment.
27. Differentiate between = and ==.
    Hint: The = is used to assign value but the == is used to test if two things have the same value.
28. Which data type will you use to represent the following data values?
    a. Number of days in a week.
    b. The circumference of a circle
    c. You school fees
    d. Distance between moon and the earth
    e. Your favorite book
    f. Whether you will give the entrance exam of not
29. Which type of value will you use for storing the following information?
    a. Employee ID
    b. Employee Name
    c. Employee Salary
    d. Phone Number

30. Which of the following are correct type conversions?
  a. int (8.2+6.3)
  b. str (5.6 * 6.7)
  c. float ("12"+"3.4")
  d. str (6/4)

31. Express the following floating-point numbers in scientific notation:
  a. 123.456789 b. 0.000123456
  c. 1.234567

32. Evaluate the following arithmetic expressions using the rules of operator precedence in Python.
  a. 4+5*10 b. 6+7*2+5
  c. 20//4*2 d. 5*6**3
  e. 24//6//3 f. 4**2**3
  g. 100-(15*3) h. 50%7 i. –(100/6)+5

33. Write the following values in the exponential notation
  a. 1230.4567
  b. 0.00000056009
  c. 7000809.000000000003

34. Evaluate the following expressions
  a. True and False
  b. (100<10) and (100>50)
  c. True or False
  d. (100<10) or (100>200)
  e. not(True) and False
  f. not (100<10) or (100>50)
  g. not(True and False)
  h. not (100<10 or 100>50)
  i. not True and False
  j. 100<10 and not 100>50
  k. not True and False or True
  l. not (100<10 or 50<200)

35. Which of the following results in True?
  a. >>>90 == 90 and 11==11
  b. >>>31==51 and 71==31
  c. >>>72!=12 and 25==25
  d. >>>54<51 and 61>86
  e. 15<20 or 20

36. Identify the correct arithmetic expression in Python
  a. 10(13+76) b. (15*16)(47+18)
  c. 14*(33-52) d. 15***2

37. Give an appropriate Boolean expression for each of the following.
  a. Check if variable var is greater than or equal to 10, and less than 100.
  b. Check if variable var is less than 100 and greater than or equal to 10, or it is equal to 50.
  c. Check if either the name 'Kalam' or 'Azad' appears in a list of names assigned to variable names.
  d. Check if the name 'Abdul' appears and the name 'Maulana' does not appear in a list of names assigned to variable names.

38. Write the data types of the following:

a. type(5+4) b. (20*345)
c. type(987/45) d. type(2345//12)
e. type(123%34)

39. Identify the data types of the following literals: 9, 29.4, 5j, 3+7i

40. Write the following expressions in Python:

$$\frac{-b \pm \sqrt{b^2 - 4ac}}{2a} \qquad \sqrt{a^2 + b^2}$$

$$\frac{\pi}{2}rh \qquad x^2yz \qquad (a - b)2 = a2 - 2ab + b2$$

d = amn/a-3 (em)n = emn

41. Differentiate between

a. bool('0') and bool('')
b. bool(0k) and bool('0k')

42. What is flow control?

43. Differentiate between sequential control flow and selection control flow.

44. Why do we need decision control statements?

45. With the help of a flowchart, explain the syntax of the following statement:

a. If b. if-else
c. if-el-if d. nested if

46. What are conditional branching statements? How does Python support such statements?

47. How will you identify the suite of an if-statement?

48. With the help of an example explain why if-else statement is better than a simple if-statement.

49. What do you mean by a nested-if statement? How is it implemented In Python?

50. Why should we not floating-point numbers to test for exact equality?

51. Change the indentation to make the code syntactically correct.

```
if condition1:
statement1
elif condition2:
statement2
elif condition3:
statement3
elif condition4:
statement4
```

52. Under what conditions, programming will be printed?

```
if a < 10:
   print("Python")
elif a < 20:
   print("Programming")
else:
   print("is fun..")
```

53. With the help of a flowchart, explain the construct of a while-loop.
54. Why is the value of the loop control variable updated with every iteration of the loop?
55. With the help of a flowchart, explain the construct of a for-loop.
56. With the help of an example explain the use of range() function.
57. Differentiate between a condition-controlled and a counter-controlled loop.
58. With the help of an example, explain the use of break statement.
59. What happens when the pass statement executes?
60. Differentiate between the comment and the pass statements.
61. When is the else statement with loops executed?
62. What will happen if we replace the break statement in the code with a 'continue' statement?
63. Fill in the blanks to complete the code:
   a. create a loop that increments the value of x by 3 and prints the odd values from 0-100.

```
x = 0
___x <= ___
   ___(x)
   x += 2
```

   b. to create a for loop that prints only the even values in the range 0-50:

```
___ i in range(______):
    print(___)
```

64. Identify the definite and indefinite loop.

```
n = input('Enter a number:')
while n != -1:
    n = input('Enter a number:')
```

```
x = 0
while x<10:
    print 10**num
    n = n+1
```

65. Correct the code to produce the desired output.

```
for i in range(10,0):
    print(i)
```

```
i=10
while(i>0):
    print(i)
    i-1
```

```
i=10 ; result = 1
while(i>0):
    result = result+i**2
    i = i+1
print(result)
```

66. The following for loops are written to print numbers from 1 to 10. Are these loops correct? Justify your answer

```
for i in range(10):
    print(i)
```

```
for i in range(10):
    num = i+1
    print(num)
```

```
for i in range(10):
    print(i)
    i = i+1
```

67. Write the following piece of code using for loop.

```
i = 20
while i>0:
    print(i)
    i = i-2
```

Programming Exercise

1. Write a program to calculate the body mass index (BMI) of a person. (BMI = kg/m^2, where kg is person's weight and m is his/her height in meters)
2. Write a program to perform string concatenation.
3. Write a program to demonstrate printing a string within single quotes, double quotes and triple quote.
4. Write a program to print the ASCII value of a character.
5. Write a program to read a character in upper case and then print it in lower case.
6. Write a program to swap two numbers using a temporary variable.
7. Write a program to read the address of a user. Display the result by breaking it in multiple lines.
8. Write a program to calculate simple interest and compound interest.
9. Write a program that prompts users to enter two integers x and y. The program then calculates and displays x^y.
10. Write a program that prompts user to enter his first name and last name and then displays a message "Greetings!!! First name Last name".
11. Write a program to calculate salary of an employee given his basic pay (to be entered by the user), HRA = 10 per cent of basic pay, TA = five per cent of basic pay. Define HRA and TA as constants and use them to calculate the salary of the employee.
12. Write a program to prepare a grocery bill. For that enter the name of the items purchased, quantity in which it is purchased and its price per unit. Then, display the bill in the following format.

    ```
    ************ B I L L *********************
    Item Quantity     Price Amount
    *********************************************

    Total Amount to be paid
    *********************************************
    ```

13. Momentum is calculated as, $e = mc^2$, where m is the mass of the object and c is its velocity. Write a program that accepts an object's mass (in kilograms) and velocity (in meters per second) and displays its momentum.
14. Write a program that calculates number of seconds in a day.
15. Write a program to read and display the details of a student. While printing use '-' to separate two values.
16. Write a program that prompts the user to enter the first name and the last name. Then, display the following message.
    Hello *firstname lastname*
    Welcome to Python!
17. Write a program to check whether a number is divisible by 10 or not. If the number is not divisible then print how much should be added to it to make it completely divisible by 10.
18. Write a program to verify whether a candidate is eligible to appear for an exam or not. The minimum and maximum age of person appearing for the exam is 21 and 35, respectively.
19. Write a program that prompts user to enter an angle and then prints its quadrant.
20. Write a program that prompts user to enter a number between 1 and 12 and then displays the corresponding month of the year.

21. Write a menu driven program that prompts user to enter two sides of a rectangle. The user can then choose from a given set of options, if he/she needs to calculate perimeter, area or diagonal of the rectangle.
22. Write a program that prompts users to enter a character (A, B, C, D, E). Then using if-elif-else construct display Outstanding, Very Good, Good, Average and Fail, respectively.
23. Write a program that determines whether a student is eligible for PG course or not. To be eligible, the student must have obtained more than 80% in X and XII examination, and 70% plus marks in graduation. If the student changes his stream (Science, Commerce, Arts), then deduct 5% from his graduation score.
24. Write a program to read a floating-point number and an integer. If the value of the floating-point number is greater than 3.14, then multiply the value of the integer with 100.
25. Write a program that prompts user to enter two integers. Divide the greater number with the smaller one and print the remainder and quotient thus obtained.
26. Write a program that accepts the current date and the date of birth of the user. Then, calculate the age of the user and display it on the screen. Note that the date should be displayed in the format specified as dd/mm/yy.
27. Write a code to calculate the amount to be paid by a customer by considering the following points.

```
If the amount_to_be_paid >=30000, then discount = 30%.
If the amount_to_be_paid >=20000, then discount = 20%.
If the amount_to_be_paid >=10000, then discount = 10%.
Otherwise, discount = 5%
```

28. Write a program that prompts user to enter his/ her age (15–18 years) and then display the perfect height and weight for that age.

Age	Height (kgs)	Weight (cms)
15	56	170
16	60	173
17	64	175
18	66	176

29. Write a program that prompts user to enter his/her body temperature. Check and display whether the user has normal body temperature, high fever or low fever.
30. Write a program that prompts user to enter a number. Display the square root of the number. Remember that square root of negative numbers is not defined.
31. Write a program that prompts user to enter lengths of three sides. Check whether these are the sides of a triangle.
32. Hint: sides of a triangle follow the rule, a + b > c. Similarly, b + c > a and a + c > b.
33. Write a program that prompts user to enter the angles of a triangle. Check whether the triangle is acute, obtuse or right angled.
34. Write a program to check whether a number entered by user is positive, negative or equal to zero.
35. Write a program that prompts user to enter the distance between his/her home and school. If the distance is in kilometers, display it in meters and vice versa.
36. Write a program that prompts users to enter status code `'S'`, `'M'`, `'D'` or `'U'` and returns the string `'Separated'`, `'Married'`, `'Divorced'` or `'Unmarried'`, respectively. In case an inappropriate letter is passed, print an appropriate message.

37. An employee's total weekly pay is calculated by multiplying the hourly wage and number of regular hours plus any and overtime pay, which in turn is calculated as total overtime hours multiplied by 1.5 times the hourly wage. Write a program that takes as inputs the hourly wage, total regular hours and total overtime hours and prints an employee's total weekly pay.
38. Write a program to calculate electricity bill based on following information.

Consumption Unit	Rate of Charge
0–150	Re 3 per unit
151–350	Rs 100 plus Rs 3.75 per unit exceeding 150 units
301–450	Rs 250 plus Rs 4 per unit exceeding 350 units
451–600	Rs 300 plus Rs 4.25 per unit exceeding 450 units
Above 600	Rs 400 plus Rs 5 per unit exceeding 600 units

39. Write a program to check whether a number is divisible by 10 or not. If the number is not divisible, then print how much should be added to it to make it completely divisible by 10.
40. Write a program to verify whether a candidate is eligible to appear for an exam or not. The minimum and maximum age of person appearing for the exam is 21 and 35, respectively.
41. Write a program that prompts user to enter an angle and then prints its quadrant.
42. Write a program that prompts user to enter a number between 1-12 and then displays the corresponding month of the year.
43. Write a menu driven program that prompts user to enter two sides of a rectangle. The user can then choose from a given set of options, if he/she needs to calculate perimeter, area or diagonal of the rectangle.
44. Write a program that prompts users to enter a character (A, B, C, D, E). Then, using if-elif-else construct display Outstanding, Very Good, Good, Average and Fail, respectively.
45. Write a program that determines whether a student is eligible for PG course or not. To be eligible, the student must have obtained more than 80% in X and XII examination and 70% plus marks in Graduation. If the student changes his stream (Science, Commerce, Arts), then deduct 5% from his graduation score.
46. Write a program to read a floating-point number and an integer. If the value of the floating-point number is greater than 3.14, then multiply the value of the integer with 100.
47. Write a program that prompts user to enter two integers. Divide the greater number with the smaller one and print the remainder and quotient thus obtained.
48. What output will be generated when the expression 5 or 100/0 is evaluated? What change can you do so that Python reports a Divide-by-Zero Error?
49. Write a program that prompts user to enter lengths of three sides. Check whether these are the sides of a triangle.
50. Hint: sides of a triangle follow the rule, a + b > c. Similarly, b + c > a and a + c > b.
51. Write a program that prompts user to enter the angles of a triangle. Check whether the triangle is acute, obtuse or right angled.
52. Write a program to check whether a number entered by user is positive, negative or equal to zero.

53. Write a program that converts a decimal number into its equivalent octal value.

54. Write a program that converts an octal number into its equivalent decimal value.

55. Write a function that accepts two positive numbers n and m where m<=n, and returns numbers between 1 and n that are divisible by m.

56. Write a program to convert time in hours into minutes and vice versa.

57. Write a program to calculate conveyance charges to be paid by the users. Enter the type of car as a character (like s for sedan, p for prime, m for mini) and distance in kms. Calculate charges as given below: sedan – 17 Rs per km, prime – 12 Rs per km and mini – 10 Rs per km.

58. Modify the above program to calculate the conveyance charges. Read the kms when the user sits in the car and the time of his/her exit. Calculate the difference between the two readings and calculate the charges based on following rules.

Car Type	Rate till first 5 kms	Rate after first 5 kms
Mini	10	10
Prime	20	12
Sedan	30	17

59. Write a program to sum the series
$1^2/1 + 2^2/2 + 3^2/3 + \ldots + n^2/n$.

60. Write a program that prints cube of numbers in the range `(1,n)`.

61. Write a program that prompts user to enter the distance between his/her home and school. If the distance is in kilometers, display it in meters and vice versa.

62. Write a program that displays Python Programming as
a. `python programming`
b. `PYTHON PROGRAMMING`
c. `pYTHON pROGRAMMING`

63. Write a program that prompts users to enter numbers. Once the user enters -1, it displays the count, sum and average of even numbers and that of odd numbers.

64. Write a program to display the sin(x) value where x ranges from 0 to 360 in steps of 45.

65. Write a program that displays all the numbers from 1-100 that are not divisible 7 as well as by 11.

66. Write a program that accepts any number and prints the number of digits in that number.

67. Write a program that prints numbers from 100 to 1 in steps of 4.

68. Write a program to generate the following pattern:

```
* * * * *
*       *
*       *
*       *
* * * * *
```

69. Write a program to generate the following pattern:

```
$ * * * *
* $     *
*   $   *
*     $ *
* * * * $
```

70. Write a program to generate the following pattern:

```
$ * * * $
* $   $ *
*   $   *
* $   $ *
$ * * * $
```

71. Write a program that reads integers until the user wants to stop. When the user stops entering numbers, display the largest of all the numbers entered.

72. Write a program to generate the Fibonacci series.

73. Write s program to print first 20 even numbers in descending order.

74. Write a program to print the sum of the following series:

a. $-x + x^2 - x^3 + x^4 + \ldots$

b. $1 - x + x^2/2! - x^3/3! + \ldots$

75. Write a program to print the following pattern

a.
```
  *
 * *
* * *
 * *
  *
```

b.
```
*
* *
* * *
* *
*
```

c.
```
  *
 * *
*   *
 * *
  *
```

d.
```
*
* *
*   *
* *
*
```

e.
```
   A
  ABA
 ABCBA
ABCDCBA
```

f.
```
    1
  2 1 2
3 2 1 2 3
```

g.
```
12345
2345
345
45
5
```

h.
```
1
12
123
1234
12345
```

Fill in the Blanks

1. Python files are stored with a ____ extension.
2. The ______ function prints one or more literals (or values) followed by a newline.
3. To execute Python script file, ______ key is pressed.
4. ______ are the small units of the programming language.
5. Large floating-point numbers are efficiently represented in ________ notation.
6. ______ denotes that an arithmetic overflow has occurred.
7. ______ function is used to produce a string version of a number with specific number of decimal places.
8. The ____ prefix specifies that the file contains text written in language other than English.
9. A ________ is specified by prefixing r or R to the string.
10. The process of combining two strings is called __________.
11. The ______ specifies the number of characters to move forward after the first character is retrieved from the string.

12. A line in Python can have maximum ____ characters.
13. ____ are used to store values.
14. Names given to identify a variable, function, class, module or any other object are generally known as ________.
15. >>>not 10 ==10 gives the answer _______.
16. >>>not 100>700 gives _____.
17. A variable in Python is assigned a value by using the ________ operator.
18. When we create a variable, Python creates _____ referring to those values.
19. Variables can hold values of different types called ________.
20. ________ are those objects to which values can be assigned.
21. To take input from the users, Python uses the _______ function.
22. The _____ function is used to convert a non-integer value to integer.
23. In Python, multi-line comments are also known as _______.
24. The level of ______ groups statements to form a block of statements.
25. Values on which the operator is applied is called ________.
26. _______ operator is used to negate the value of the operand on which it is applied.
27. ________ expressions operate in a shortcut (or lazy) fashion and stop the evaluation when it knows the final outcome for sure.
28. 1. if a is b returns TRUE, then __________.
29. _________ can change the order in which an operator is applied.
30. Literals of the form a + bi are called ____________.
31. 123.45E-9 is equal to _______.
32. ___________ converts an integer to a floating-point number.
33. The ___ operator returns the quotient after division.
34. To find x^y, you will use _____ operator.
35. ________ is a group of characters.
36. Variable names can contain only ________, __________ and __________.
37. >>>90 != 70 gives output _______.
38. 29%0 = ________.
39. int("10"+"20") will give ______.
40. ________ operator treats operand as a sequence of bits.
41. >>> print (format(12356.265901, '.3f')) will result in the value ______.
42. _________ means which statement would be executed next.
43. ________ is the simplest form of decision control statements.
44. Header and its suite together forms a _________.
45. Python uses _________ to form a block of code.
46. A __________ statement contains other statements.

47. A series of if and elif statements have a final _______ block.
48. _____ and _____ operators are used to form a compound relational expression.
49. ______ is a short form of "else if" statement. Ans elif
50. Python uses __________ to form a block of code.
51. A series of if elif statements have a final ______ block, which is executed if none of the if or elif expressions is True.
52. Python assumes any non-zero and non-null values as ________.
53. ________ begin with a keyword and end with a colon.
54. x = 10
    y = 20
    __x>y__
    print print("In if")
    ______
        print ("In else")
55. Fill the blanks to print *Python* on the screen.
    x = 10
    y = 50
    if x>10 __ y<100:
    ___("Python")
56. __________ statements are used to repeatedly execute one or more statements in a block
57. In Python, iterative statements are implemented through _______ and ______ loops.
58. An _________ loop will occur if the condition of while loop never becomes false.
59. The for loop provides a mechanism to repeat a task until a particular condition is ______.
60. The _______function in Python that is used to iterate over a sequence of numbers.
61. When we know in advance the number of times the loop should be executed, we use a _________ controlled loop.
62. When we do not know in advance the number of times the loop will be executed, we use a _________ controlled loop.
63. When ______ statement is encountered, rest of the statements in the loop are skipped and the control is unconditionally transferred to the loop-continuation portion of the nearest enclosing loop.
64. ______ statement specifies a null operation.
65. The ______ statement is executed when the for loop has completed iterating.

State True or False

1. Integers can be specified as octal and hexadecimal numbers also.
2. Arithmetic underflow is a condition that occurs when a calculated result is too large.
3. Strings are mutable in Python.

4. When specifying a string, if a single backslash (\) at the end of the line is added then it indicates that the string is continued in the next line, but no new line is added otherwise.
5. A Unicode string does not handle any escape sequences. It is specified by prefixing r or R to the string.
6. format() function can be used to control the display of strings.
7. The default value of stride is 0.
8. Whitespace characters are also counted as a character in the string.
9. Computational thinking means thinking like a computer or to give instructions to a computer.
10. Coding is not a part of computational thinking.
11. Computational thinking involves considering different options carefully before deciding upon he best one.
12. \r represents a newline.
13. An escape sequence is treated as a single character.
14. In Python, a semi-colon is used to terminate every statement.
15. Python allows writing multiple statements in a single line.
16. The first character of an identifier must be a dollar sign ($).
17. Python is a case-sensitive language.
18. Based on the data type of a variable, the interpreter reserves memory.
19. While re-assigning values to a variable, the data type must not change.
20. Python variables do not have specific data types.
21. Comments are written to make the program easily readable and understandable.
22. Comments are the executable statements in a program.
23. When the program is run, comments are not displayed.
24. All keywords are written in uppercase characters.
25. Statements in a block must have the same indentation level.
26. Arithmetic operators also known as relational operators.
27. Relational operators can be used to compare strings.
28. Python does not support prefix and postfix increment/decrement operators.
29. Bitwise OR operator produces the ones' complement of the given binary value.
30. Shifting once to the right multiplies the number by 2.
31. The is operator returns true if operands or values on both sides of the operator does not point to the same object and false otherwise.
32. INT = 2; print(INT) will give an error.
33. The id() function can be used to print the address of the variable.
34. A sequential control program can skip one or more statements.
35. In selection control statements, all the statements are executed from the first one to the last.

36. Group of statements following the header is known as a clause.
37. After the header, all instructions that are indented at the same level forms a suite.
38. It is mandatory to use four spaces to define each level of indentation.
39. The final else block in an if-elif-else statement is executed when none of the if or elif expressions is True.
40. You can use floating-point numbers for checking for equality in the test expression.
41. Indentation identifies a statement block.
42. Statements within a suite can be indented a different amount.
43. elif and else blocks are optional.
44. The while loop repeats one or more statements while a particular condition is false.
45. Iterative Statement repeats the execution of a block of statements depending on the value of an expression that evaluates to an integer value only.
46. In the while loop, the condition is tested after statement block is executed at least once.
47. The value of the loop control variable is updated with every alternate iteration of the loop.
48. An infinite loop will occur if the condition of while loop is always false.
49. The for loop is executed for each item in the sequence.
50. Every iteration of the loop must make the loop control variable farther from the end of the sequence.
51. The step argument in the range() function is optional.
52. Sentinel value is used in counter-controlled loop.
53. Both for and while loop can be nested.
54. The break and continue statements can only appear in the body of a loop.
55. In a for loop, the continue statement causes a branch to the code that updates the loop variable.
56. The pass statement is a non-executable statement that is ignored by the compiler.
57. The number of times the loop control variable is updated is equal to the number of times the loop iterates.
58. In a while loop, the loop control variable is initialised in the body of the loop.

Give the Output

1.
```
print("Hello")
print("My Dear Students", end = ' ')
print("Let us learn Python")
print("Programming")
```
2.
```
>>> format(10**25,'.2e')
```
3.
```
>>> format(987654321.315978,',.3f')
```
4.
```
>>> 'PYTHON'
```
5.
```
>>> "PROGRAMMING IN PYTHON"
```
6.
```
>>> ''' I ENJOY PROGRAMMING
IN
PYTHON'''
```

7. `>>> 'PYTHON' "PROGRAMMING"`
8. ```
   >>> print("Python Programming \ is
   FUN !!!!")
   ```
9. `>>> print(R'It is Teacher's Day today ')`
10. `>>> "I" + 'LOVE' + '''PROGRAMMING'''`
11. ```
    str = "I Love Programming in Python"
    print(str[0])
    print(str[7])
    print(str[-5])
    print(str[7:10])
    print(str[::2])
    print(str[3:11:3])
    print(str[:-7])
    print(str[-6:])
    ```
12. `>>> print(type(int('10')))`
13. `>>> str(print())+"abc"`
14. `>>> print(print("abc"))`
15. `>>> str(print("abc"))+"xyz"`
16. `>>> print(print("abc",end=" "))`
17. `(10<20) and (20 < 10) or (5 < 30) and not (15 < 40)`
18. ```
    x,y,z = 10,20,30
    y,z,x = x+5, y+7, z-3
    print("x = ",x, " y = ",y, "z = ",z)
    ```
19. ```
    x,y = 10,20
    y,z = x+5, y-20
    print("x = ",x, " y = ",y," z = ",z)
    ```
20. `>>> 350 + 230 - 170`
21. `>>> (51 + 9.7 - 4) * 100`
22. `>>> 110%(95//3)`
23. `>>> 'Python Programming is fun…'`
24. `>>>"Python Programming is fun…"`
25. `>>>'"Python… \n Programming?"'`
26. `>>> print("Python \n Programmiung")`
27. `>>> print("PYTHON !!!!"*3)`
28. `>>>x = 100 ; x *= 3     ; print(x)`
29. `>>> s1 = "HELLO"; s1 += "WORLD"; print(s1)`
30. ```
    days = "Mon Tue Wed Thu Fri Sat Sun"
    months = "Jan\nFeb\nMar\nApr\nMay\nJun\nJul\nAug"
    print("Days are : "+ days)
    print("Months are: "+ months)
    print(""" There's a new dream today.
    I'll tell you some other day.
    Come on, let's enjoy. """)
    ```
    ```

31. ```
    # print ABCD
    Nothing
    ```
32. ```
    >>>n1 = 20
    >>>n2 = 30
    >>>del num1
    >>>n2 = 40
    >>>n1 = 50
    >>>print(num1 - num2)
    ```
33. ```
    >>> num1 = "7"
    >>> num1 += "10"
    >>> num2 = int(num1) + 3
    >>> print (float(num2))
    ```
34. ```
    name = input("Enter a word :")
    print ('HELLO' + name)
    ```
35. ```
    n1 = 90
    n2 = n1 + 50
    n2 = int(str(n2) + "40")
    print(num2)
    ```
36. `>>> abs(100-200) * 3`
37. `>>>float("5678" * int(input("Enter a number:")))`
38. `>>> int = 2; print(int)`
39. ```
    a,b = 10,20
    b,a = a *5, b /2
    print("a = ",a, " and b = ", b)
    ```
40. ```
    a,b = 10,20
    a,b,a = a*10, b*5,a*20
    print("a = ",a, " and b = ", b)
    ```
41. ```
    x =10
    print(id(x))
    x = x + 10
    print(id(x))
    x = x - 10
    print(id(x))
    ```
42. `0 or 10`
43. `10 or 0`
44. `0 or 0`
45. `"abc" or ""`
46. `'' or ''`
47. `'k' or 'r'`
48. `10 ** 3 ** 2`
49. `7 -5 -12 > -5 *3 +8`
50. `len(str(7 -5 -12 > -5 *3 +8)) == len('true')`

51. `bool('0') and (10 < 20)`

52. `23%5 is 23%5`

53. `20 or len(20)`

54. `10 == 10.0`

55. `10 == int(10)`

56. `str(10)==str('10.0')`

57. `'R' == 'R'`

58. `70/(7-(2+4))or 4<5`

59. `5 < 9 or 60/(10-(6+4))`

60. `len("abcd") == 30/6 or 30/10`

61. `2 * (5 *(len("007")))`

62. `30 < 70 and 40 > 50`

63. `N = 1 + 1 + 1 == 0.3; print(N)`

64.
```
a = True; b = 0<5
a==b       ;       a is b
```

65.
```
print(bool(int('0')))
print(bool(str(0)))
print(bool(float('0.0')))
print(bool(str(0.0)))
```

66.
```
a,b,c = 12,13,16
d = a + b *c/b
print(d)
```

67.
```
if(5.0 < 9.0):
                print("DONE")
```

68.
```
years = 99
if(years == 100):
          print("Century")
elif(years == 75):
          print("Platinum Jublee")
elif(years == 50):
          print("Half Century")
elif(years == 25):
          print("Silver Jublee")
elif(years == 10):
          print("Decade")
else:
     print("Long way to go....")
```

69.
```
years = 99
if years > 30:
    print("30")
if years < 50:
    print("50")
if years == 7:
    print("70")
```

70.
```
num = int((10*6 + 10 - 20) > 0)
if num == 50:
   print("You win...")
else:
   print("Try Again")
```

71.
```
num = 3
if (num ** 3) > (5%2 - 3 * 4 /2):
   if (num // 4) >= 2:
       print("You win")
   else:
       print("Try Again")
```

72.
```
num = 3
if num == 2:
   print("Yes")
elif num == 4:
   print("Yes")
elif num == 8:
   print("Yes")
else:
   print("Number is not an even number")
```

73.
```
if(10 == 100) and (100 + 200 > 300):
   print("Win Win..")
else:
   print("Oh No !!!")
```

74.
```
if not True:
   print("WRONG")
elif not((10+10 - 20 * 3) == 30):
   print("Really !")
else:
   print("May Be")
```

75.
```
if (10 << ((41 - 40 // 2 + 1)%2)) == 60:
    print("WoW")
else:
    print("Gosh")
```

76.
```
a = 5
b = 70
if not 10 + 10 == b or a == 40 and
     70 == 80:
   print("Yeah")
elif a != b:
   print("Nope")
```

77.
```
num = 10
if num > 30:
    if num > 40:
        print("Python")
    else:
        print("Programming")
elif num < 20:
    if(num!=0):
        print("is fun..")
print("Isnt it !!!")
```

78.
```
weather = 'foggy'
if weather == 'sunny':
    print("Take your shades")
elif weather == 'raining':
    print("Take your umbrella")
else:
    print("Stay at home")
```

79.
```
for letter in "HELLO":
        pass
```

80.
```
i=1
while i<=6:
  print(i),
i=i+1
print("Done")
```

81.
```
i=0
while i<10:
  i = i + 1
  if(i == 5):
     print("\n Continue")
     continue
  if(i==7):
     print("\n Breaking")
     break
  print(i),
  print("\n Done")
```

82.
```
for i in range(5):
    print("hello!", end= " ")
```

83.
```
for i in range(10):
    if not i%2==0:
        print(i+1)
```

84.
```
for i in range(10,0,-1):
    print(i, end = ' ')
```

85.
```
for i in range(5,25,3):
    print(i, end = ' ')
```
86.
```
for i in "PYTHON":
    print(i,'-',end=' ')
```
87.
```
for i in range(10):
    pass
print(i)
```
88.
```
while True:
str = input("Enter a string (Bye to exit) : ")
    if str == "bye":
        break
    print(str)
else:
    print("Exiting......")
```
89.
```
for i in range(1,20):
    if i%5==0:
        break
    else:
        print(i)
for i in range(1,20):
    if i%5==0:
        continue
    else:
        print(i)
while(4>5):
    print("DONE")
else:
    print("NOT DONE")
```
90.
```
for i in range(1,5):
    for j in range(1,i):
        print('#',end = ' ')
    print()
```
91.
```
while(5*2 > 10):
    print("JUST DO IT")
else:
    print("DONE")
```
92.
```
a = 10; b = 0
while(a>b):
    print(a,b)
    a=a-1
    b=b+1
```

93.
```
run = True
a = 100
while run == True:
    print(a)
    a = a - 10
    if a < 40:
        run = False
```

94.
```
for i in range(100,50,-10):
    print(i)
```

95.
```
for i in range(100,50,-10):
    print(i)
```

96.
```
x = 10; y = 5
for i in range(x-y*2):
    print("%")
```

Find Out the Error, If Any

1. >>>10+'20'+30+'40'
2. >>>'10'*'20'
3. >>>'PYTHON'*7.0
4. x = 10
   print(x)
5. x = 123.456
   print('%'+x)
6. x = 1; y = 2;
   print(x+y+z)
7. if = 5; print(if)
8. a = 10; b = 20; print(a;b)
9. x =10
   y = x * 30
   x = "PYTHON"
   z = x/10
10. name = int(input("Enter your name : "))
    print("HELLO", name)
11. print(len(bool(0)))
12. >>> print("HELLO"/2)
13. >>> print(type(int("HELLO")))
14.
```
while(i<10):
    print(i)
```

CHAPTER 2

Revisiting Data Structures in Python

In this chapter, we will quickly revise Python strings and lists. We will read different operations, functions and methods that can be applied on these non-primitive data structure in Python.

2.1 Introduction to Python strings

The Python string data type is a sequence made up of one or more individual characters, where a character could be a letter, digit, whitespace or any other symbol enclosed within single, double or even triple quotes. Python has a built-in string class named 'str' that has many useful features. We can create a variable of string type in many ways, for example,

```
lang = "Python"  gender = 'F'  choice = lang  message = str("How are you?")
```

We have already seen that escape sequences works with each type of string literals. A multiple-line text within quotes must have a backslash (\) at the end of each line to escape the newline.

2.2 String indexing

Individual characters in a string are accessed using the subscript ([ ]) operator. The expression in brackets is called an *index*. The index specifies the character to be accessed from the given set of characters in the string.

The index of the first character is 0 and that of the last character is n-1 where n is the number of characters in the string. *If you try to exceed the bounds (below 0 or above n-1), then an error is raised.*

2.3 Finding the number of characters in a string

Python determines the size or the length of a string by counting the number of characters in it. For example, len("abcd") is 4 since there are four characters. Although this calculation is simple, some points must be considered while counting.

a. An escape sequence is counted as a single character.

b. In a multi-line string created with triple quotes, the End-Of_Line **(EOL)** character at the end of the line is also counted. Usually, the EOL is the carriage return character when the Enter key is pressed.

c. In a multi-line string, backslash character at the end of the line is not counted.

```
>> len("\n")  >>> len("HELLO \t WORLD") >>> len("Neeru\'s Pen") >>> len("Neeru's Pen")
1             13                          11                        11
>>> str1 = '''A >>> len(str1)             >>> str2 = '''A\
B             7                           B\
C                                         C\
D'''                                      D'''
```

2.4 Traversing a string

String is a sequence type (sequence of characters). It can be traversed in two ways. First, by accessing each character in the string. Second, by accessing element at each index. The len() function returns the length of the string. That is, number of characters in the string. We can then use for loop in which the loop control variable varies from 0 to n-1, where n is the number of characters in the string.

Whichever method you use, always remember that if you try to access a character *with index less than 0 and/or greater than n-1 then an IndexError:* string index out of range error will be generated.

```
# traversing string                           # traverse string using index
lang = "PYTHON"                               lang = "PYTHON"
for i in lang:                                for i in range(len(lang)):
    print(i, end = '') # print each character     print(lang[i], end = '')
OUTPUT                                        OUTPUT
PYTHON                                        PYTHON
```

In the first code, the for loop executes for every character in str. The loop starts with the first character and automatically end when the last character is accessed. In the second code, the string is traversed using index of each character (rather than the character itself). We can also iterate through the string using while loop.

```
# traversing string using while loop
lang = "PYTHON"
index = 0
l = len(lang)
while index < l:
  ch = lang[index]
  print(ch, end = '')
  index += 1
OUTPUT
PYTHON
```

```
# access string out of index
lang = "PYTHON"
l = len(lang)
print(lang [l+1]) # not a part of string
OUTPUT
Traceback (most recent call last):
  File "C:\Users\Python37\try.py", line 3, in
<module>
    print(lang[l+1])
IndexError: string index out of range
```

In the above program, the while loop traverses the string and displays each character. The loop condition is index < len(lang), so the moment index becomes equal to the length of the string, the condition evaluates to false, and the body of the loop is not executed. As we said earlier, index of the last character is len(message) – 1.

Points to remember

- Even the whitespace characters, exclamation mark and any other symbol (like ?, <,>,*, @, #, $, %, etc.) that forms a part of the string would be assigned its own index number.
- Index can either be an integer or an expression that evaluates to an integer.
- A character cannot be used for string indexing.

```
# indexing string in different ways
msg = "PYTHON PROGRAMMING IS FUN"
i = 2
print(msg[i]) # index is an integer
print(msg[i*3+2]) # index is an expression that evaluates to an
integer
print(msg['N']) # character as an index
OUTPUT
T
R
Traceback (most recent call last):
 File "C:\Users\Python37\try.py", line 5, in <module>
   print(msg['N']) # character as an index
TypeError: string indices must be integers
```

2.5 Concatenating, appending and multiplying strings

The word **concatenate** means to join together. Python allows you to concatenate two strings using the + operator as shown below.

Append means to add something at the end. In Python, one string can be added at the end of another string using the += operator.

```
# String Concatenation

str1 = "Python"

str2 = "Programming"

str3 = str1 + str2 # string concatenation

print("The concatenated string is: ", str3)

OUTPUT

The concatenated string is: PythonProgramming
```

```
# Appending and concatenating strings

str1 = "Good morning, "

name = input("\n Enter your name: ")

str1+= name # appending strings

str2 = str1 + ". Welcome to Python Programming."

print(str2)

OUTPUT

Enter your name: Priya

Good morning, Priya. Welcome to Python Programming.
```

We can **multiply** a string using the * operator. When a string is multiplied with an integer number n, then the string is repeated n number of times. The order of string and integer is not important. Therefore, `5*"HI" is same as "HI" * 5.`

However, remember that you cannot multiply two strings. Also, you cannot multiply a string with a floating-point number.

```
# multiplying string
str = "I WILL DO IT"
print(str * 3) # multiplying string
OUTPUT
I WILL DO IT I WILL DO IT I WILL
   DO IT
```

```
# multiplying string
str = "PYTHON" * '3'
print(str)
OUTPUT
Traceback (most recent call
   last):
File "C:\Users\Python37\try.
   py", line 2, in <module>

   str = "PYTHON" * '3'
TypeError: can't multiply
   sequence by non-int of type
   'str'
```

```
# multiplying string
str = "HELLO" * 3.0
print(str)
OUTPUT
Traceback (most recent call
   last):
File "C:\Users\Python37\try.
   py", line 2, in <module>

   str = "HELLO" * 3.0
TypeError: can't multiply
   sequence by non-int of
   type 'float'
```

2.6 The str() function

The str() function is used to convert values of any other type into string type. This helps the programmer to concatenate a string with any other data, which is otherwise not allowed.

```
# concatenating string and a number
roll_no = 9
name = "Aditi"
print(name+ "is roll number" + roll_no)
OUTPUT
Traceback (most recent call last):
  File "C:\Users\
TypeError: can only concatenate str (not "int") to str
```

```
# concatenating string and a number
roll_no = 9
name = "Aditi"
print(name + "is roll number" + str(roll_no))
OUTPUT
Aditi is roll number 9
```

2.7 Strings are immutable

Python strings are immutable. This means that once a string is created, it cannot be changed. If you try to modify an existing string variable, a new string is created.

Every object in Python is stored in memory. You can find out whether two variables are referring to the same object or not by using the id(). The **id()** returns the memory address of that object. Since both str1 and str2 points to same memory location, they both actually point to the same object.

In Python, every two objects having the same value have the same id. The moment the value of one object is changed, a new object is created with a different id.

From the output, it is very clear when values of str1 and str2 were same; their IDs were same as they were pointing to the same object. When we changed the value of str2 and later of str3, the ids of the object changed.

Now can you guess the output of the following code?

```
str = "PYTHON"
str[3] = 'A'
print(str)
```

Yes, the code will result in an error – TypeError: 'str' object does not support item assignment simply because strings are immutable. It does now allow any changes. If you want to make any kind of changes you must create a new string as shown below.

Always remember that we cannot delete or remove characters from a string. But can delete the entire string using the keyword del.

```
# Checking object's ID
str1 = "Python"
str2 = "Python"
str3 = "Programming"
# ID of str1 and str2 will be same
print("ID OF STR1 = ",id(str1))
print("ID OF STR2 = ",id(str2))
print("ID OF STR3 = ",id(str3))
# changing the value of str2
str2 = "Programming"
# ID of str2 and str3 will be same
print("\n\n ID OF STR1= ",id(str1))
print("ID OF STR2 = ",id(str2))
print("ID OF STR3 = ",id(str3))
# changing the value of str3
str2 = "Programming is fun"
# All IDs will be different
print("\n\n ID OF STR1 = ",id(str1))
print("ID OF STR2 = ",id(str2))
print("ID OF STR3 = ",id(str3))
OUTPUT
ID OF STR1 = 3091055531600
ID OF STR2 = 3091055531600
ID OF STR3 = 3091069698480

ID OF STR1 = 3091055531600
ID OF STR2 = 3091069698480
ID OF STR3 = 3091069698480

ID OF STR1 = 3091055531600
ID OF STR2 = 3091070019384
ID OF STR3 = 3091069698480
```

2.8 String formatting operator

This string formatting operator (%) takes a format string on the left (that has %d, %s, etc.), and the corresponding values in a tuple (will be discussed in subsequent chapter) on the right. The format operator, % allow users to construct strings, replacing parts of the strings with the data stored in variables. The syntax for the string formatting operation is:

A tuple is made of values separated by commas inside parentheses

```
"<FORMAT>" % (<VALUES>)
```

The statement begins with a *format* string consisting of a sequence of characters and *conversion specifications*. Conversion specifications start with a % operator and can appear anywhere within the string. Following the format string is a % sign and then a set of values, one per conversion specification, separated by commas and enclosed in parenthesis. If there is a single value, then parentheses are optional.

```
# Formatting strings
roll_no = 23
name = "Aarish"
print("ROLL NO. = %d Name = %s" %(roll_no, name))
print("ROLL NO. = %d Name = %s" %(39, "Anika"))
OUTPUT
ROLL NO. = 23 Name = Aarish
ROLL NO. = 39 Name = Anika
```

In the output, we can see that %s has been replaced by a string and %d has been replaced by an integer value. You can either supply these values directly or by using variables. Table 1 lists other string formatting characters.

Note that the number and type of values in the tuple should match the number and type of format sequences or conversion specifications in the string, otherwise an error is returned.

```
# number of arguments don't match
>>> '%d %f %s' % (15, 92.75)
Traceback (most recent call last):
  File "<pyshell#0>", line 1, in <module>
   '%d %f %s' % (15, 92.75)
TypeError: not enough arguments for format string
```

```
# type of argument don't match
>>> '%d %f %s' % (92, "Myra", "Sood")
Traceback (most recent call last):
  File "<pyshell#1>", line 1, in <module>
   '%d %f %s' % (92, "Myra", "Sood")
TypeError: must be real number, not str
```

Table 1: || Formatting symbols

Format symbol	Purpose
%c	Character
%d or %i	Signed decimal integer
%s	String
%u	Unsigned decimal integer
%o	Octal integer
%x or %X	Hexadecimal integer (x for lower case characters a-f and X for upper case characters A-F)
%e or %E	Exponential notation
%f	Floating point number
%g or %G	Short numbers in floating point or exponential notation

In the code, we have set the width of each column independently using the string formatting feature of Python. The - after each % in the conversion string indicates left justification. The numerical values specify the minimum length. Therefore, %-15d means it is a left justified number that is at least 15 characters wide.

```
# String Formatting for printing power of number
i = 1
print("%-4s%-5s%-6s%-8s%-13s" % ('i', 'i**2', 'i**3', 'i**4', 'i**5'))
while(i <= 5):
  print("%-4d%-5d%-6d%-8d%-13d" % (i, i**2, i**3, i**4, i**5))
  i+=1
OUTPUT
i   i**2 i**3  i**4    i**5
1   1    1     1       1
2   4    8     16      32
3   9    27    81      243
4   16   64    256     1024
5   25   125   625     3125
```

2.9 The format() function

The format() function is also used for formatting strings. Format strings have curly braces {} as placeholders or replacement fields which gets replaced. We can even use positional arguments or keyword arguments to specify the order of fields that have to be replaced. Consider the code given below and carefully observe the sequence of fields in the output and then compare the sequence as given in the arguments of format() function.

2.10 Built-in string methods and functions

Strings are an example of Python **objects**. An object is an entity that contains both data (the actual string itself) as well as functions to manipulate that data. These functions are available to any **instance** (variable) of the object.

```
# format() function with strings
str1 = "{},{}{}".format('Python','is','Easy')
print("\n The default sequence of arguments is : " + str1)
str2 = "{1} {0} {2}?".format('Python','Is','Easy')
print("\n The positional sequence of arguments (1, 0 and 2) is : " + str2)
str3 = "{c}, {b} very {a}".format(a='Python', b='Is',c='Easy')
print("\n The keyword sequence of arguments is : " + str3)
OUTPUT
The default sequence of arguments is : Python, is Easy
The positional sequence of arguments (1, 0 and 2) is : Is Python Easy?
The keyword sequence of arguments is : Easy, Is very Python
```

Python supports many built-in methods to manipulate strings. A method is just like a function. The only difference between a function and method being that method is invoked or called on an object. For example, if the variable str is a string, then you can call the upper() method as str.upper() to convert all the characters of str in upper case. Table 2 discusses some of the most commonly used string methods.

Table 2: || Commonly Used String Functions and Methods

Function	Usage	Example

capitalise()	This function is used to capitalise first letter of the string.	`str = "python"`
		`print(str.capitalize())`
		`OUTPUT`
		`Python`

centre(width, fillchar)	Returns a string with the original string centred to a total of width columns and filled with fillchar in columns that do not have characters	`str = "python"`
		`print(str.center(15, '*'))`
		`OUTPUT`
		`*****python****`

count(str, beg, end)	Counts number of times str occurs in string. You can specify beg and end to specify as 0 to len of string to search the entire or with any other value to just search a part of the string.	`str = "se"`
		`message = "He sells sea shells on the sea shore"`
		`print(message.`
		`count(str,0,len(message)))`
		`OUTPUT`
		`3`

endswith(suffix, beg, end)	Checks if string ends with suffix; returns true if so and false otherwise. You can either set beg = 0 and end to length of the message to search entire string or use any other value to search a part of it.	`message = "He sells sea shells on the sea shore"`
		`print(message.endswith("ore", 0,len(message)))`
		`OUTPUT`
		`True`

startswith(prefix, beg, end)	Checks if string starts with prefix; returns true if so and false otherwise. You can either set beg = 0 and end to length of the message to search entire string or use any other value to search a part of it.	`message = "He sells sea shells on the sea shore"`
		`print(message.startswith("sea", 0,len(message)))`
		`OUTPUT`
		`False`

find(str, beg, end)	Checks if str is present in string. If found it returns the position at which str occurs in string otherwise returns -1. You can either set beg = 0 and end to length of the message to search entire string or use any other value to search a part of it.	`message = "He sells sea shells on the sea shore"`
		`print(message.`
		`find("sea",0,len(message)))`
		`OUTPUT`
		`9`

index(str, beg, end)	Same as find but raises an exception if str is not found	`message = "He sells sea shells on the sea shore"`
		`print(message.index("in", 0, len(message)))`
		`ValueError: substring not found`

rfind(str, beg, end)	Same as find but start searching from the end. So it will return index of the last occurrence of str in the main string.	`message = "He sells sea shells on the sea shore"`
		`print(message.rfind("sea", 0, len(message)))`
		`OUTPUT`
		`27`

Table 2: || *(Continued)*

Function	Usage	Example

rindex(str, beg, end)	Same as rindex but start searching from the end and raises an exception if str is not found	`message = "He sells sea shells on the sea shore"`
		`print(message.rindex("gg", 0, len(message)))`
		`OUTPUT`
		`ValueError: substring not found`

isalnum()	Returns true if string has at least 1 character and every character is either a number or an alphabet and false otherwise.	`message = "JamesBond007"`
		`print(message.isalnum())`
		`OUTPUT`
		`True`

isalpha()	Returns true if string has at least 1 character and every character is an alphabet and false otherwise.	`message = "JamesBond007"`
		`print(message.isalpha())`
		`OUTPUT`
		`False`

isdigit()	Returns true if string contains only digits and false otherwise.	`message = "108"`
		`print(message.isdigit())`
		`OUTPUT`
		`True`

islower()	Returns true if string has at least 1 character and every character is a lowercase alphabet and false otherwise.	`message = "Python"`
		`print(message.islower())`
		`OUTPUT`
		`False`

isspace()	Returns true if string contains only whitespace characters and false otherwise.	`message = "   "`
		`print(message.isspace())`
		`OUTPUT`
		`True`

isupper()	Returns true if string has at least 1 character and every character is an uppercase alphabet and false otherwise.	`message = "PYTHON"`
		`print(message.isupper())`
		`OUTPUT`
		`True`

len(string)	Returns the length of the string	`str = "PYTHON"`
		`print(len(str))`
		`OUTPUT`
		`6`

ljust(width[, fillchar])	Returns a string left-justified to a total of width columns. Columns without characters are padded with the character specified in the fillchar argument	`str = "PYTHON"`
		`print(str.ljust(10, '*'))`
		`OUTPUT`
		`PYTHON****`

(continued)

Table 2: || (Continued)

Function	Usage	Example

rjust(width[, fillchar])	Returns a string right-justified to a total of width columns. Columns without characters are padded with the character specified in the fillchar argument	`str = "PYTHON"`
		`print(str.rjust(10, '&'))`
		`OUTPUT`
		`&&&&PYTHON`

zfill (width)	Returns string left padded with zeros to a total of width characters. It is used with numbers and also retains its sign (+ or -).	`str = "5678"`
		`print(str.zfill(10))`
		`OUTPUT`
		`0000005678`

lower()	Converts all characters in the string into lowercase.	`str = "PYTHON"`
		`print(str.lower())`
		`OUTPUT`
		`python`

upper()	Converts all characters in the string into uppercase.	`str = "python"`
		`print(str.upper())`
		`OUTPUT`
		`PYTHON`

lstrip()	Removes all leading whitespace in string.	`str = "PYTHON"`
		`print(str.lstrip())`
		`OUTPUT`
		`PYTHON`

rstrip()	Removes all trailing whitespace in string.	`str = "PYTHON"`
		`print(str.lstrip())`
		`OUTPUT`
		`PYTHON`

strip()	Removes all leading and trailing whitespace in string.
	The strip() function when used with a string argument will strip (from both ends) any combination of the specified characters in the string
		`str = "PYTHON"`
		`print(str.strip())`
		`str = "abcPYabcTHONabc"`
		`print(str.strip("abc"))`
		`OUTPUT`
		`PYTHON`
		`PYabcTHON`

max(str)	Returns the highest alphabetical character (having highest ASCII value) from the string str.	`str = "PyThoN pRoGrAmMiNg"`
		`print(max(str))`
		`OUTPUT`
		`y`

min(str)	Returns the lowest alphabetical character (lowest ASCII value) from the string str.	`str = "PyThoNpRoGrAmMiNg"`
		`print(min(str))`
		`OUTPUT`
		`A`

Table 2: || (Continued)

Function	Usage	Example

replace(old, new [, max])	Replaces all or max (if given) occurrences of old in string with new	`str = "She sells sea shells on the sea shore"`
		 `print(str.replace("se", "SE"))`
		 `OUTPUT`
		 `She SElls SEa shells on the SEa shore`

title()	Returns string in title case	`str = "she sells sea shells on the sea shore"`
		 `print(str.title())`
		 `OUTPUT`
		 `She Sells Sea Shells On The Sea Shore`

swapcase()	Toggles the case of every character (upper case character becomes lower case and vice versa)	`str = "PyThoNpRoGrAmMiNg"`
		 `print(str.swapcase()) OUTPUT`
		 `pYtHOnPrOgRaMmInG`

split(delim)	Returns a list of substrings separated by the specified delimiter. If no delimiter is specified then by default it splits strings on all whitespace characters	`str = "She, sells, sea shells, on the, sea shore"`
		 `print(str.split(','))`
		 `OUTPUT`
		 `['She', 'sells', 'sea shells', 'on the', 'sea shore']`

join(list)	It is just the opposite of split. The function joins a list of strings using the delimiter with which the function is invoked.	`str = ['Power','of','the', 'Universe','HE-MAN']`
		 `print('#'.join(str))`
		 `OUTPUT`
		 `Power#of#the#Universe#HE-MAN`

str.splitlines()	Returns a list of the lines in the string. This method uses the newline characters like \r, \n to split lines.	`print('Python is \n\n a very \r simple language\r\n'.splitlines())`
		 `OUTPUT`
		 `['Python is ', '', ' a very ', ' simple language']`

2.11 Comparing strings

In Python, string can be compared using relational operators like >, <, <=, <=, ==, !=. The comparison is done lexicographically, i.e., using ASCII value of the characters. The ASCII values of A-Z are 65-90, ASCII code for a-z is 97-122 and for 0-9, the code is 48-57. This means that bread is greater than Bread because the ASCII value of 'b' is 98 and 'B' is 66.

```
>>> "PYTHON" == "python"   >>> "PYTHON" >= "python"   >>> "SMILE" < "laughter"   >>> "GIVE" != "EXPECT"
False                      False                      True                       True
```

Did you notice that String values are ordered using lexographical (dictionary) ordering? Basically, internally, the comparison is done.

2.12 ord() and chr() functions

ord() function returns the ASCII code of the character and **chr()** function returns character represented by an ASCII number.

```
ch = 'P'
print(ord(ch))
OUTPUT
80
```

```
ch = 'y'
print(ord(ch))
OUTPUT
121
```

```
print(chr(79))
OUTPUT
O
```

```
print(chr(117))
OUTPUT
u
```

2.13 In and not in operators

in and not in operators can be used with strings to determine whether a character or a string is present in another string. Therefore, the in and not in operator are also known as membership operators.

```
# using in operator
str1 = "Python programming is fun"
str2 = "is"
if str2 in str1:
   print("Found")
else:
   print("Not Found")
OUTPUT
Found
```

```
# using not in operator
str1 = "Arav is a very naughty boy"
str2 = "good"
if str2 not in str1:
   print("Arav is not a good boy.")
else:
   print("Arav is a very good boy.")
OUTPUT
Arav is not a good boy.
```

You can also use the in and not in operators to check whether a character is present is in a word. Also remember that a string is a substring of itself.

```
>>> 'y' in "PYTHON"
False
```

```
>>> 'N' in "PYTHON"
True
```

```
>>> 'PYTHON' in 'PYTHON'
True
```

```
>>> 'V' in 'V'
True
```

2.14 Lists

List is a versatile data type available in Python, in which elements are written as a list of comma-separated values (items) between square brackets. Lists in Python are mutable as we can change the value of its elements. This is in striking contrast with strings which were immutable.

The key feature of list is that it can have elements that belong to different data types. The syntax of defining a list can be given as, **List_variable = [val1, val2,.....]**

```
list_A = [1,2,3,4,5]
print(list_A)
[1, 2, 3, 4, 5]
```

```
list_B = ['A', 1, 'C', 2, 'E']
print(list_B)
['A', 1, 'C', 2, 'E']
```

```
list_C = ["HELLO","WORLD"]
print(list_C)
['HELLO', 'WORLD']
```

```
list_D = [1, 'a', 'HELLO']
print(list_D)
[1, 'a', 'HELLO']
```

We can even create an empty list by writing **list_variable = [].** An empty list is equivalent to False when use with logical operators.

```
>>> list = []
>>> list == True
False
```

2.15 Accessing values in lists

Like strings, lists can also be sliced and concatenated. To access values in a list, square brackets are used to slice along with the index or indices to get value stored at that index. As discussed earlier, the syntax for the slice operation is **seq = List[start:stop:step].**

For example, seq = List[::2] *# get every other element, starting with index 0*

seq = List[10::3] *# get every third element, starting with index 10*

seq = List[-3] *# get third element from the end*

seq = list_A[-3] # 3rd element from the end

seq = List[3:] *# get all elements starting from the third index from the beginning*

```
num_list = [2,4,6,8,10,12,14,16,18,20]
print("num_list is: ", num_list)
print("First element in the list is", num_list[0])
print("num_list[2:5] = ", num_list[4:7])
print("num_list[::2] = ", num_list[::3])
print("num_list[1::3] = ", num_list[1::2])
```

```
OUTPUT
num_list is: [2, 4, 6, 8, 10, 12, 14, 16, 18, 20]
First element in the list is 2
num_list[2:5] = [10, 12, 14]
num_list[::2] = [2, 8, 14, 20]
num_list[1::3] = [4, 8, 12, 16, 20]
```

If the start and end values of the slice operation are beyond the size of the list, then all the elements within the specified range are returned. For example, consider the example given below in which the start and end values are out of range of the size of the list.

Note that the valid index range of the list is 0-4. Values -9 and 9 are beyond the size of the list, so the entire list is returned as 0 to 4 lies within the range -9 to 9. But in the second case, when start = -3 and end = 9, -3 lies in the valid range, which is the third element from the end, hence the result.

```
I = [1,2,3,4,5]
print(I[-9:9])
OUTPUT
[1, 2, 3, 4, 5]
```

```
I = [1,2,3,4,5]
print(I[-3:9])
OUTPUT
[3, 4, 5]
```

2.16 The eval() function

The eval() function is used to evaluate and return the result of an expression as string.

```
>>> eval("10 == 10")
True
>>> eval("20 <= 10")
False
>>> eval("30-5*4+20")
30
>>> eval(" 'HELLO' * 3")
'HELLOHELLOHELLO'
```

We can use the eval() function to read value(s) of any type, but it is use is discouraged as we may get unforeseen problems as a result of using this function.

2.17 Updating values in lists

```
Example: Let's write a program that uses the eval() function to accept a list of numbers and print the sum of the elements.
list = eval(input("Enter values: "))
print(list)
sum(list)
print("SUM = ",sum(list))
OUTPUT
Enter values [1,2,3,4,5,6,7,8,9,10]
[1, 2, 3, 4, 5, 6, 7, 8, 9, 10]
SUM = 55
```

```
Example: Using the eval() function to accept input of different types.
a = eval(input("Enter an integer : "))
print(type(a))
b = eval(input("Enter a float: "))
print(type (b))
c = eval(input("Enter a tuple: "))
print(type(c))
d = eval(input("Enter a list: "))
print(type(d))
OUTPUT
Enter an integer : 1
<class 'int'>
Enter a float : 2.3
<class 'float'>
Enter a tuple : (4,5,6)
<class 'tuple'>
Enter a list : [7,8,9]
<class 'list'>
```

Once created, one or more elements of a list can be easily updated by giving the slice on the left-hand side of the assignment operator. You can also append new values in the list and remove existing value(s) from the list using the append() method and del statement, respectively.

```
num_list = [2,4,6,8,10,12,14,16,18,20]
print("List is:", num_list)
num_list[5] = 100
print("List after udpation is:", num_list)
num_list.append(200)
print("List after appending a value is", num_list)
del num_list[3]
print("List after deleting a value is ", num_list)
```

```
OUTPUT
List is : [2, 4, 6, 8, 10, 12, 14, 16, 18, 20]
List after udpation is : [2, 4, 6, 8, 10, 100, 14, 16, 18, 20]
List after appending a value is [2, 4, 6, 8, 10, 100, 14, 16, 18, 20, 200]
List after deleting a value is [2, 4, 6, 10, 100, 14, 16, 18, 20, 200]
```

If you know exactly which element(s) to delete, use the del statement otherwise use the remove() method to delete the unknown elements.

```
num_list = [2,4,6,8,10,12,14,16,18,20]
del num_list[3:6] # deletes numbers at index 3,4,5
print(num_list)
del num_list[:] #deletes all the numbers from the list
print(num_list) # an empty list is printed
OUTPUT
[2, 4, 6, 14, 16, 18, 20]
[]
```

```
del(num_list)
print(num_list)    # the list no longer exists
OUTPUT
Traceback (most recent call last):
 File "C:\Users\Reema\Python\Python37\try.py",
line 5, in <module>
 print(num_list) # the list no longer exists
NameError: name 'num_list' is not defined
```

Note that when we write del num_list, the entire variable is deleted. If you make any attempt to use this variable after the del statement then an error will be generated.

2.18 Relational operations on lists

We can compare two list objects using relational operators like ==, >,<,>=,<=!=, etc. Python compares elements of a list in lexicographical order. Each element of the list is compared with the corresponding element in the other list. However, to use operators like >=,<=,>,< the two values must be of compatible type otherwise an error will be generated.

```
l1 = [1,2,3]
l2 = [1,2,3]
l3 = [1,[2,3]]
print(l1==l2)
print(l1==l3)
OUTPUT
True
False
```

```
l1 = [1,2,3]
l2 = [1,3,3]
print(l1>=l2)
print(l1<=l2)
OUTPUT
False
True
```

```
l1 = [1,2,3,4]
l2 = [1,2,3]
print(l1>=l2)
OUTPUT
True
```

```
l1 = [1,2,3,4]
l2 = ['a','b','c']
l3 = [1.0,2.0,3.0]
print(l1>=l3)
print(l2>=l3)
OUTPUT
True
Traceback (most recent call last):
  File "C:\Python37\try.py", line 5, in
<module> print(l2>=l3) TypeError: '>=' not
supported between instances of 'str'
and 'float'
```

2.19 Nested lists

Nested list means a list within another list. We have already said that a list has elements of different data types. So besides other elements, a list can also have another list as its element. For example, **list1 = [1,2,'a',[5.0,6,"ABCD"],"BYE"]**. Here, list1 is a list that has another list at index 3.

To ***insert items from another list*** at a particular location, we can use the slice operation. This would create a nested list that is, list within another list.

Remember that you can specify an element in the nested list by using a set of indices. For example, assuming that the inner list starts at index 3 in the main list, to print the second element of the nested (or the inner) list, we will write print list[3][1]. The first index specifies the starting location of the nested list in the main list and the second index specifies the index of the element within the nested list. The code given below clarifies this concept.

```
# Creating a Nested List

list1= [1,2,'a',[5.0,6,"ABCD"],
"BYE"]

i=0

while i<(len(list1)):

  print("List1[",i,"] = ",list1[i])

  i+=1

OUTPUT

List1[0] = 1

List1[1] = 2

List1[2] = a

List1[3]= [5.0, 6, 'ABCD']

List1[4] = BYE
```

```
# Inserting a list within another list-creating a nested list

num_list = [2,4,12,14]

print("Original List : ", num_list)

num_list[2] = [6,8,10]

print("After inserting another list, the updated list is : ", num_list)

print("Second element of nested list is : ",num_list[2][1])

OUTPUT

Original List: [2, 4, 12, 14]

After inserting another list, the updated list is : [2, 4, [6, 8, 10), 14]

Second element of nested list is : 8
```

2.20 List aliasing and cloning

When one list is assigned to another list using the assignment operator (=), then a new copy of list is not made. Instead, assignment makes the two variables point to the one list in memory. This is also known as ***aliasing***.

Cloning lists: If you want to modify a list and also keep a copy of the original list, then you should create a separate copy of the list (not just the reference). This process is called ***cloning*. The slice operation is used to clone a list.**

```
list1= [1,2,3,4,5,6,7,8,9,10]

print("List1 = ", list1)

list2 = list1 #list aliasing

print("List2 = ", list2)

list3 = list1[2:5] #list cloning

print("List3 = ", list3)
```

```
OUTPUT

List1 = [1, 2, 3, 4, 5, 6, 7, 8, 9, 10]

List2 = [1, 2, 3, 4, 5, 6, 7, 8, 9, 10]

List3 = [3, 4, 5]
```

2.21 Deleting elements

We can delete one or more elements from the list by using the **del** statement. The syntax to remove a single element from the list is del **list_variable[index].** And to remove more than one element from the list, we use the syntax, **del[start:stop].** Finally, to remove the entire list, we need to write **del list_variable.**

```
l = [1,2,3,4,5,6,7,8,9,10]
print(l)
# deleting third element
del l[2]
print(l)
# deleting fourth, fifth, sixth and seventh elements from the list
del l [2:6]
print(l)
# deleting the entire list
print("Deleting List .......")
del l
print(l)
OUTPUT
[1,2,3,4,5,6,7,8,9,10]
[1,2,4,5,6,7,8,9,10]
[1,2,8,9,10]
Deleting List.......
Traceback (most recent call last): File "C:\Python37\try.py", line
12, in <module>        print(l)
NameError: name 'l' is not defined
```

2.22 Deep copies and shallow copies in Python

When copying lists or any other object in Python, we can make a deep copy of the original object or a shallow copy. *A deep copy makes a new and separate copy* of an *entire* object or list with its own unique memory address. Therefore, any changes made in the new copy of the object/list will not be reflected in the original one.

A deep copy creates a new list or object by recursively copying the elements from the original object to the new one. So, both the objects are completely independent of each other. This is similar to the concept of passing by value in languages like C++, Java and C#.

But, although a shallow copy also makes a separate new object or list, instead of copying the elements to the new object, *it simply copies the references to their memory addresses.* Hence, changes made in the original object would also be reflected in the copied object and vice versa. Therefore, both the copies are dependent on each other. This is similar to the concept of passing by reference in programming languages like C++, C# and Java.

Talking in terms of lists, ***the assignment operator is used to create a shallow copy of the list and the list() creates a deep copy*** as illustrated below.

```
# Creating a shallow copy of a list
l1 = [1,2,3,4,5]
l2 = l1
print("L1 = ", l1)
print("L2 = ", l2)
l1[2] = 10
print("L1 = ", l1)
print("L2 = ", l2)
OUTPUT
L1 = [1, 2, 3, 4, 5]
L2 = [1, 2, 3, 4, 5]
L1 = [1, 2, 10, 4, 5]
L2 = [1, 2, 10, 4, 5]
```

```
# Creating a deep copy of a list
l1 = [1,2,3,4,5]
l2 = list(l1)
print("L1 = ", l1)
print("L2 = ", l2)
l1[2] = 10
print("L1 = ", l1)
print("L2 = ", l2)
OUTPUT
L1 = [1, 2, 3, 4, 5]
L2 = [1, 2, 3, 4, 5]
L1 = [1, 2, 10, 4, 5]
L2 = [1, 2, 3, 4, 5]
```

2.23 Basic list operations

Lists behave in the similar way as strings when operators like + (concatenation) and * (repetition) are used. It works similar in case of operations discussed in Table 3.

Table 3: || Operations on lists

Operation	Description	Example	Output
len	Returns length of list	`len([1,2,3,4,5,6,7,8,9,10])`	`10`
concatenation	Joins two lists	`[1,2,3,4,5] + [6,7,8,9,10]`	`[1, 2, 3, 4, 5, 6, 7, 8, 9, 10]`
repetition	Repeat elements in the list	`"Love", "Python"*2`	`['Love', 'Python', 'Love', 'Python']`
in	Checks if the value is present in the list	`'a' in ['a','e', 'i','o','u']`	`True`
not in	Checks if the value is not present in the list	`9 not in [0,2,4,6,8]`	`True`
max	Returns maximum value in the list	`>>> num_list = [1,0,3,7,4,2,4,9]` `>>> print(max(num_list))`	`9`
min	Returns minimum value in the list	`>>> num_list = [1,0,3,7,4,2,4,9]` `>>> print(min(num_list))`	`0`

Table 3: || *(Continued)*

Operation	Description	Example	Output
sum	Adds the values in the list that has numbers	`num_list = [1,2,3,4,5,6,7,8,9,10]` `print("SUM = ", sum(num_list))`	`SUM = 55`
all	Return True if all elements of the list are true (or if the list is empty)	`>>> num_list = [8,9,0,10]` `>>> print(all(num_list))`	`False`
any	Return True if any element of the list is true. If the list is empty, returns False	`>>> num_list = [,0,1,2,4,9]` `>>> print(any(num_list))`	`True`
List	Convert tuple, string or to a list	`>>> list1 = list("PYTHON")` `>>> print(list1)`	`['P', 'Y', 'T', 'H', 'O', 'N']`

Sorted	Return a new sorted list. The original list is not sorted.	`>>> list1 = [1,0,3,7,4,2,9]`
		`>>> list2 = sorted(list1)`
		`>>> print(list2)`
			`[0,1,2,3,4,7,9]`

2.24 List methods

Python has various methods to help programmers work efficiently with lists. Some of these methods are summarized in Table 4.

Table 4: || List methods

Method	Description	Syntax	Example	Output

append()	Appends an element to the list. In insert(), if the index is 0, then element is inserted as the first element and if we write, list.insert(len(list), obj), then it inserts obj as the last element in the list. That is, if index= len(list) then insert() method behaves exactly same as append() method.	`list.append(obj)`	`num_list = [1,2,3,4]`
			`num_list.append(5)`
			`print(num_list)`
				`[1, 2, 3, 4, 5]`

count()	Counts the number of times an element appears in the list	`list.count(obj)`	`num_list = [1,2,3,4,3,2,4,6]` `print( num_list.count(4))`	`1`
index()	Returns the lowest index of obj in the list. Gives a ValueError if obj is not present in the list	`list.index(obj)`	`num_list = [1,2,3,4,3,2,4,6]` `print(num_list.index(3))`	`2`

(continued)

Table 4: || *(Continued)*

Method	Description	Syntax	Example	Output

insert()	Inserts obj at the specified index in the list.	`list.insert(index, obj)`	`num_list = [1,2,3,4,5]`
			`num_list.insert(3, 0)`
			`print(num_list)`
				[1, 2, 3, 0, 4, 5]

pop()	Removes the element at the specified index from the list. Index is an optional parameter. If no index is specified then removes the last object (or element) from the list.	`list.pop([index])`	`num_list = [1,2,3,4,5]`
			`print(num_list.pop())`
			`print(num_list)`
				5
				[1, 2, 3, 4]

remove()	Removes or deletes obj from the list. ValueError is generated if obj is not present in the list. If multiple copies of obj exists in the list then the first value is deleted.	`list.remove(obj)`	`num_list = [0,1,2,3,4,5]`
			`num_list.remove(0)`
			`print(num_list)`
				[1, 2, 3, 4, 5]

reverse()	Reverse the elements in the list.	`list.reverse()`	`num_list = [1,2,3,4]`
			`num_list.reverse()`
			`print num_list`
				[4, 3, 2, 1]

sort()	Sorts the elements in the list	`list.sort()`	`num_list = [3,5,0,4,1]`
			`num_list.sort()`
			`print(num_list)`
				[0, 1, 3, 4, 5]

extend()	Adds the elements in a list to the end of another list. Using + or += on a list is similar to using extend().	`list1.extend(list2)`	`num_list1 = [1,2,3]`
			`num_list2 = [4,5,6]`
			`num_list1.extend(num_list2)`
			`print(num_list1)`
				[1, 2, 3, 4, 5, 6]

Recall the difference between a function and a method. A **function** is a piece of code that is directly called by name. It may or may not accept parameters and may or may not return data. All data that are to be used by a function are explicitly passed (or made global). *Example, len(list1).*

However, a **method** is a piece of code that is called by name of the object followed by a dot operator and name of the method. Example, *list1.sort()*.

Key points to remember

- The sort() method uses ASCII values to sort the values in the list. Since lower case characters' ASCII value starts from 97and upper case character's starts from 65, upper case characters appear before lower case characters when sorting is done.
- Items in a list can also be deleted by assigning an empty list to a slice of elements as shown below.

- The range() function can be used to print index as shown in the code given below.

```
list1 = ['1', 'a', "Abc", '2', 'B', "def"]
list1.sort()
print(list1)
OUTPUT
['1', '2', 'Abc', 'B', 'a', 'def']
```

```
list = ['P','r','o','g','r','a','m','m','i','n','g']
list[3:6] = []
print(list)
OUTPUT
['P', 'r', 'o', 'm', 'm', 'i', 'n', 'g']
```

```
list = ['B','Y','E']
for i in range(len(list)):
    print("index: ", i)
OUTPUT
index : 0
index : 1
index : 2
```

- If you give an index out of range or the legal indices, then an **IndexError** will be generated. For a list, the legal indices include index from 0 to length of the list – 1. Consider the example, given below.

```
list = [1,'a',3.4,"PYTHON"]
print(len(list))
# error because length is 4 and we are accessing access an index out of range
print(list[4])
OUTPUT
4
Traceback (most recent call last):
  File "C:\Python37\try.py", line 4, in <module>
    print(list[4])
IndexError: list index out of range
```

- The + operator can also be used to join two lists. But if you try to join a number or string or any other data with a list using the + operator, **TypeError** will be generated.

```
l1 = [1, 2, 3, 4, 5]
l2 = l1+6
print(l2)
OUTPUT
Traceback (most recent call last):
  File "C:\Python37\try.py", line 2, in <module>
  l2 = l1 + 6
TypeError: can only concatenate list (not "int") to list
```

```
# Correct Way
l1 = [1,2,3,4,5]
l2 = l1 + [6]
print(l2)
OUTPUT
[1, 2, 3, 4, 5, 6]
```

- Like strings, lists can also be repeated using the * operator.
- While the append() method adds a single element to a list, the extend() method is used to add multiple elements from one list to another list.

```
# Repeating a list
l1 = ['B','Y','E']
l2 = l1 * 3
print(l2)
OUTPUT
['B', 'Y', 'E', 'B', 'Y', 'E', 'B', 'Y', 'E']
```

```
# Difference between append() and extend()
l1 = [1,2,3,4,5]
l1.append(6)
l1.extend([7,8])
print(l1)
OUTPUT
[1, 2, 3, 4, 5, 6, 7, 8]
```

In the insert() method, if we specify a negative index that is not in the set of valid indices, the element is added in the beginning of the list.

```
l1 = [1,2,3,4,5]
l1.insert(-10,123)
print(l1)
OUTPUT
[123, 1, 2, 3, 4, 5]
```

In the pop() method, it is called on an empty list then, and IndexError will be generated.

```
l1 = []
l1.pop()
OUTPUT
Traceback (most recent call last):
  File "C:\ Python37\try.py", line 2, in <module>    l1.pop()
IndexError: pop from empty list
```

2.25 Tuple

A tuple is very similar to lists but differs in two things.

- First, a tuple is an immutable object. This means that while you can change the value of one or more elements in a list, you cannot change the values in a tuple.
- Second, tuples use parentheses to define its elements, whereas lists use square brackets.

2.26 Creating tuple

Creating a tuple is very simple and almost similar to creating a list. You need to just put the different comma-separated values within a parenthesis.

```
# Creates an empty tuple
Tup1 = ()
print(Tup1)
OUTPUT
()

# Creates a tuple with a single element
Tup1 = (5,)
print(Tup1)

OUTPUT
5

# Tuple of integers

Tup1 = (1,2,3,4,5)
print(Tup1)
OUTPUT
(1,2,3,4,5)

# Creates a tuple of

# mixed values
Tup5 = (1,"abc",2.3,'d')
print(Tup5)
OUTPUT
(1, 'abc', 2.3, 'd')

# A tuple of characters
Tup1 = ('a','b','c', 'd')
print(Tup1)

OUTPUT
('a', 'b', 'c', 'd')

# Creates a tuple of strings
Tup1=("abc","def", "ghi")

print(Tup1)

OUTPUT
('abc', 'def', 'ghi')

# Tuple of floating point
# numbers

Tup1 =
(1.2,2.3,3.4,4.5)
print(Tup1)
OUTPUT
(1.2, 2.3, 3.4, 4.5)
```

Key points to remember:

- Any set of comma-separated, values written without an identifying symbol like brackets or parentheses, etc., is treated as a tuple by default.

```
print('A', "bcd", 5, 6.7)
OUTPUT
A bcd 5 6.7

a,b,c = 10, 20,30
print(a,b,c)
OUTPUT
10 20 30
```

- If you want to create a tuple with a single element, you must add a comma after the element. In the absence of a comma, Python treats the element as an ordinary data type.

```
# comma after first element
Tup = (15,)
print type(Tup)
OUTPUT
<type 'tuple'>

# comma missing
Tup = (10)
print type(Tup)
OUTPUT
<type 'int'>
```

- We can use the eval() function to input a tuple. But while specifying the input elements, enclose them within parentheses as shown in the code.

```
# eval() Function to read Tuple
Tup = eval(input("Enter values of the tuple : "))
print(Tup)
print(type(Tup))
OUTPUT
Enter values of the tuple : (1,2,'a','bcd',7.8)
(1, 2, 'a', 'bcd', 7.8)
<class 'tuple'>
```

- We can also use the tuple() function to create a tuple with the specified sequence.

```
# Using the tuple() Function
tup = tuple("abc")
print(tup)
tup = tuple([1,2,3])
print(tup)
OUTPUT
('a', 'b', 'c')
(1, 2, 3)
```

2.27 Utility of tuples

In real-world applications, tuples are extremely useful for representing *records* or structures as we call in other programming languages. These structures store related information about a subject together. The information belongs to different data types. For example, a tuple that stores information about a student will have roll_no, name, course, total_marks, avg, etc. If you carefully observe these individual elements, you will see that they belong to different data types. For example, roll_no can be an integer or an alphanumeric value, name and course will be string, total_marks and avg can be floating point numbers.

Some built-in function returns a tuple. For example, the **divmod()** function returns two values, quotient as well as the remainder after performing the divide operation.

```
Program to illustrates
divmod() function
quo, rem = divmod(157,4)
print("Quotient = ",quo)
print("Remainder = ",rem)
OUTPUT
Quotient = 39
Remainder = 1
```

```
Tup1 = (1,20,3,40,5,60,7,80,9,100,11,120)
print("Tup[4:8] = ", Tup1[4:8])
print("Tup[:5] = ", Tup1[:5])
print("Tup[3:] = ", Tup1[3:])
print("Tup[:] = ", Tup1[:])
print("Tup[:-4]= ", Tup1[:-4])
print("Tup[-1:5] = ", Tup1[-1:5])
print("Tup[::-2] = ", Tup1[::-2])
OUTPUT
Tup[4:8] = (5, 60, 7, 80)
Tup[:5] = (1, 20, 3, 40, 5)
Tup[3:] = (40, 5, 60, 7, 80, 9, 100, 11,
120)
Tup[:] = (1, 20, 3, 40, 5, 60, 7, 80, 9,
100, 11, 120)
Tup[:-4] = (1, 20, 3, 40, 5, 60, 7, 80)
Tup[-1:5] = ()
Tup[::-2] = (120, 100, 80, 60, 40, 20)
```

2.28 Accessing values in a tuple

```
# Slice operation on a tuple
tup = (1,'a',2,'bcd',
3.4,5,'e',6.7,'efg')
print(tup[3])
print(tup[10-4*2+5])
print(tup[-5])
print(tup[3:6])
print(tup[2:7:2])
print(tup[-10:10])
OUTPUT
bcd
6.7
3.4
('bcd', 3.4, 5)
(2, 3.4, 'e')
(1, 'a', 2, 'bcd', 3.4, 5, 'e',
6.7, 'efg')
```

Again, like other sequences (like strings and lists), indices in a tuple starts at 0. Slice operation, concatenation and other operations possible with other sequences can also be applied on tuples.

> You can't delete elements from a tuple. Methods like remove or pop do not work with tuple.

In the slice operation, we can also use negative indices, strides and even expressions.

When accessing a tuple, if the index is out of the range of legal indices of the tuple, then Python raises an IndexError.

The start and stop parameters of the slice operation specify the boundaries of elements to be accessed. All elements falling within the boundary are returned.

```
tup = (1,2,3)
print(tup[10])
OUTPUT
Traceback (most recent call last):
 File "C:\Python37\try.py", line 2, in
<module> print(tup[10])
IndexError: tuple index out of range
```

```
tup = (1,2,3)
print(tup[-10:10])
OUTPUT
(1, 2, 3)
```

2.29 Updating tuple

We have already said that ***tuple is immutable***. So, you cannot change the value(s) in the tuple. You can only extract values from a tuple to form another tuple.

```
# Updating tuple
tup = (1,'a',2,'bcd',3.4,5,'e')
tup[3] = 'Not Possible'
print(tup)
OUTPUT
Traceback (most recent call last):
  File "C:\Python37\try.py", line 2, in <module>
   tup[3] = 'Not Possible'
TypeError: 'tuple' object does not support item
assignment
```

2.30 Deleting elements in tuple

Since tuple is an immutable data structure, you cannot delete value(s) from it. Of course, you can create a new tuple that has all elements in your tuple except the ones you do not want (those you wanted to be deleted). However, the entire tuple can be deleted by using the del statement.

```
Tup1 = (1,2,3,4,5)
Tup2 = (6,7,8,9,10)
Tup3 = Tup1+ Tup2
print(Tup3)
OUTPUT
(1, 2, 3, 4, 5, 6,
7, 8, 9, 10)
```

```
Tup1 = (1,2,3,4,5)
del Tup1[3] # delete an element
print(Tup1)
OUTPUT
Traceback (most recent call last):
 File "C:\Users\Python37\try.py",
 line 2, in
<module>
  del Tup1[3]
TypeError: 'tuple' object doesn't
support item deletion
```

```
Tup1 = (1,2,3,4,5)
# delete tuple
del Tup1
print(Tup1)
OUTPUT
Traceback (most recent call last):
 File "C:\Users\Python37\try.py", line 4, in
<module>
  print(Tup1)
NameError: name 'Tup1' is not defined
```

2.31 Joining tuples

Like lists, two or more tuples can be joined using the + operator. The + operator requires that both the operands must be of tuple types. Numbers or any other type values cannot be added to a tuple. To add a single element to a tuple, we must use comma after the value.

```
# Joining Tuples
tup1 = (1,2,3)
tup2 = (4,5,6)
tup3 = tup1 + tup2
print(tup3)
OUTPUT
(1, 2, 3, 4, 5, 6)
```

```
# Joining tuples with a
# non-number value
tup1 = (1,2,3)
tup2 = tup1 + 'a'
print(tup2)
OUTPUT
Traceback (most recent call last):
File "C:\Python37\try.py", line 2, in
<module>
tup2 = tup1 + 'a'
TypeError: can only concatenate tuple
(not "str") to tuple
```

```
# Joining single
# value to a tuple
tup1 = (1,2,3)
tup2 = tup1 + (4,)
print(tup2)
OUTPUT
(1, 2, 3, 4)
```

2.32 Unpacking tuples

Creating a tuple from a set of values is called packing. Correspondingly, creating individual values from a tuple is known as unpacking. The syntax of unpacking can be given as,

```
var1, var2, var3, ...., varn = tuple_variable
```

While unpacking a tuple remember that the number of elements in the tuple must match with the number of variables on the left side of the assignment operator.

```
# Unpacking tuple
tup = (1,'a',2.0,'bcd',3)
(a,b,c,d,e) = tup
print("a = ",a, end = ")
print("b = ",b, end = ")
print("c = ",c, end = ")
print("d = ",d, end = ")
print("e = ",e, end = ")
OUTPUT
a = 1 b = a c = 2.0 d = bcd e = 3
```

```
# Packing tuple
a =1; b='a';c=2.0; d='bcd'
tup = (a,b,c,d)
print("tup = ",tup)
OUTPUT
tup = (1, 'a', 2.0, 'bcd')
```

Tuple packing and unpacking are very useful to change the values in a tuple. We know that tuples are immutable objects in Python, so their values cannot be changed. In case, we need to change values; there are three ways, unpacking and packing tuple is just one of them.

The first way is to create a new tuple with modified values.

Second way is to first unpack the tuples into variables. Modify the value of variables. And then, pack those variables to form a tuple.

Third way is to convert a tuple into a list using the list() function. Modify the list values and then use the tuple() function to convert the list into a tuple.

2.33 Basic tuple operations

Like strings and lists, you can also perform operations like concatenation, repetition, etc., on tuples. The only difference is that a new tuple should be created when a change is required in an existing tuple. Table 5 summarises some operations on tuples.

Table 5: || Operations on Tuples

Operation	Expression	Output
Length	len((1,2,3,4,5,6))	6
Concatenation	(1,2,3) + (4,5,6)	(1, 2, 3, 4, 5, 6)
Repetition	('Python..')*3	Python.. Python.. Python..'
Membership	5 in (1,2,3,4,5,6,7,8,9)	True
Iteration	for i in (1,2,3,4,5,6,7,8,9,10): print(i,end=' ')	1,2,3,4,5,6,7,8,9,10
Comparison (Use >, <, ==)	Tup1 = (1,2,3,4,5) Tup2 = (1,2,3,4,5) print(Tup1>Tup2)	False
Maximum	max(1,9,3,6,4,0)	9
Minimum	min(1,9,3,6,4,0)	0
Convert to Tuple (converts a sequence into a tuple)	tuple("PYTHON") tuple([1,2,3,4,5])	('P', 'Y', 'T', 'H', 'O', 'N') (1, 2, 3, 4, 5)

While using the **max()** and **min()** functions, remember that the values in the tuple must be of same type. If the values are not of the same type, then **TypeError** will be returned.

```
# Finding largest and smallest value
tup = (23,75,12,90,82)
print("Largest Value = ",max(tup))
print("Smallest Value = ",min(tup))
OUTPUT
Largest Value = 90
Smallest Value = 12
```

```
# Finding largest and smallest value in a tuple
tup = (23,'a',12.56,90,'bcd')
print("Largest Value = ",max(tup))
print("Smallest Value = ",min(tup))
OUTPUT
Traceback (most recent call last):
  File "C:\Python37\try.py", line 3, in <module>
    print("Largest Value = ",max(tup))
TypeError: '>' not supported between instances
of 'str' and 'int'
```

2.34 Tuple assignment

Tuple assignment is a very powerful feature in Python. It allows a tuple of variables on the left side of the assignment operator to be assigned values from a tuple given on the right side of the assignment operator. Each value is assigned to its respective variable.

In case, an expression is specified on the right side of the assignment operator, first that expression is evaluated and then assignment is done. This feature makes tuple assignment quite versatile. The codes given below shows different ways of tuple assignment.

```
# an unnamed tuple of values assigned to values of
# another unnamed tuple
(val1, val2, val3) = (10,20,30)
print(val1, val2, val3)
Tup1 = (10, 20, 30)
(val1, val2, val3) = Tup1 # tuple assigned to another
tuple
print(val1, val2, val3)
OUTPUT
10 20 30
10 20 30
```

```
# expressions are evaluated before assignment
(val1, val2, val3, val4)= (1+2, 4/3 - 5,6%7,8 **
2)
print(val1, val2, val3, val4)
OUTPUT
3-3.6666666666666667 6 64
```

Note that *when assigning values to a tuple, you must make sure that number of values on both the sides of the assignment operator must be same,* otherwise an error will be generated as shown below.

```
(val1, val2, val3, val4)= (1+2, 6%7, 8 ** 2)
print(val1, val2, val3, val4)
Traceback (most recent call last):
 File "C:\Users\Python37\try.py", line 1, in <module>
  (val1, val2, val3, val4)= (1+2, 6%7, 8 ** 2)
ValueError: not enough values to unpack (expected 4, got 3)
```

2.35 Accessing using index

Like other sequences, we can access an individual element of a tuple by using its index. Correspondingly, we can also get the index of an element, by specifying the element in the index method. The index() method is used to get the index of an element in the tuple. If the element being searched is not present in the list, then error is generated. The syntax of index() is given as, **list.index(obj)**
where, obj is the object whose index has to looked.

Tuples are faster than lists, but they cannot be changed

```
Tup (11, 67, 642, 'AB', "Good
Morning", 4.5)
print(Tup.index('AB'))
OUTPUT
3
```

```
Tup (11, 67, 642, 'AB', "Good Morning", 4.5)
print(Tup.index(5.4))
Traceback (most recent call last):
 File "C:\Users\Python37\try.py", line 2, in
 <module>
  print (Tup.index(5.4))
ValueError: tuple.index(x): x not in tuple
```

2.36 Tuples for returning multiple values

We have learnt that a function can return only a single value. But at times, we need to return more than one value from a function. In such situations, it is preferable to group together multiple values and return them together.

```
Program returning the highest as well as the lowest score.
def max_min_score(vals):
x = max(vals)
y = min(vals)
return (x,y)
score = (99, 98, 90, 97, 89, 86, 93, 82)
(max_score, min_score) = max_min_score(score)
print("Highest Score=", max_score)
print("Highest Score=", min_score)
OUTPUT
Highest Score = 99
Highest Score = 82
```

2.37 Nested tuples

In Python, users can easily define a tuple inside another tuple. Such a tuple is called a nested tuple. Consider the nested table in the code given below that stores and prints the details of employees.

```
# Nested Tuple
Emps = (("Arav", "Back Office", 35000), ("Chaitanya", "Technical Assistant",
50000), ("Dhruvika", "Programmer", 100000))
for i in Emps:
 print(i)
OUTPUT
('Arav', 'Back Office', 35000)
('Chaitanya', 'Technical Assistant', 50000)
('Dhruvika', 'Programmer', 100000)
```

You can even specify a list within a tuple. The code given below prints the name of the topper and her marks in 4 subjects. These marks are specified as list in the tuple Topper.

> Slicing can be done on tuples

```
# List within a nested tuple
Toppers = (("Janvi",[94, 95, 96, 97]),("Khushi",[99, 95, 90, 93]), ("Myra",[91, 95, 93,
94]))
print("Second Topper is: ", Toppers[1])
OUTPUT
Second Topper is: ('Khushi',[99, 95, 90, 931])
```

2.38 The count() method

The count() method returns the number of elements with a specific value in a tuple.

```
# count() method on tuple
tup = (10,7,8,10,9,7,3,8,5,8,1,8)
print(tup.count(8))
tup = ("abc","def","abc","efg")
print(tup.count("abc"))
OUTPUT
4
2
```

Reassigning a value in an tuple causes a TypeError

2.39 The zip() function

`zip` is a built-in function that takes two or more sequences and 'zips' them into a list of tuples. The tuple thus formed has one element from each sequence. The code given below illustrates this concept.

```
# Count number of y using count()
tup = "xyyyyzyyyzxzzedbgsyyy"
print("Number of y = ", tup.count('y'))
OUTPUT
Number of y = 10
```

```
# zip() method
Tup = (2,4,6,8,10)
List1 = ['A','E','I','O','U']
print(list((zip(Tup, List1))))
OUTPUT
[(2, 'A'), (4, 'E'), (6, '1'), (8, 'O'), (10, 'U')]
```

From the output, we see that the ***result of zip() function is a list of tuples*** where each tuple contains a character from the list and an integer from the tuple. The example, we had seen had equal number of values in list and tuple, but ***if the two sequences have different length, then the result has the length of the shorter one*** as illustrate din the code given below. We can even print the elements in a tuple using the for statement as shown below.

If the index specified in the Tuple slice is too big, then an indexError exception is raised

```
# zip() method with unequal parameters
Tup = (2,4,6)
List1 = ['A','E','I','O','U']
print(list((zip(Tup, List1))))
OUTPUT
[(2, 'A'), (4, 'E'), (6, 'I')]
```

```
# printing tuple with for loop
Tup (2,4,6)
List1 = ['A','E','I','O','U']
Tup = list((zip(Tup, List1)))
for i, char in Tup:
  print(i, char)
OUTPUT
2 A
4 E
6 I
```

Key points to remember:

> Unlike lists, tuples do not support remove(), pop(), append(), sort(), reverse(), and insert() methods

- Tuples can be converted into lists and vice-versa using the built-in `tuple()` function that takes a list and returns a tuple with the same elements. Similarly, the `list()` function takes a tuple and returns a list.
- You cannot divide or subtract tuples. If you try to do so you will get a TypeError with 'unsupported operand type'.
- Since tuples are immutable, they do not support methods like `sort` and `reverse`, as these methods modify existing sequence.

```
# list from tuple and vice versa
Tup = (2,4,6)
List1 = list(Tup)
print("LIST = ", List1)
List1 = List1 + [8,10,12]
Tup1 = tuple(List1)
print("TUPLE=", Tup1)
OUTPUT
LIST = [2, 4, 6]
TUPLE = (2, 4, 6, 8, 10, 12)
```

```
# subtracting two tuples
Tup1 = (2,4,6)
Tup2 = (1,3,5)
Tup3 = Tup1 - Tup2
print(Tup3)
OUTPUT
Traceback (most recent call last):
 File "C:\Users\Python37\try.py", line 3, in <module>
  Tup3 = Tup1 - Tup2
TypeError: unsupported operand type(s) for-: 'tuple' and 'tuple'
```

```
# reverse method on tuple
Tup1 = (2,1,4,8,6)
Tup1.reverse()
print(Tup1)
OUTPUT
Traceback (most recent call last):
 File "C:\Users\try.py", line 2, in <module>
   Tup1.reverse()
AttributeError: 'tuple' object has no attribute 'reverse'
```

- However, Python has a built-in function `sorted()`, which takes any sequence as a parameter and returns a new list with the same elements but in a different order. For example, the code given below illustrates this concept.
- You can use string formatting feature to print values in the Tuple. This is shown in the code given below.

```
Program to sort a tuple of values
Tup = (5,1,0,2,8,3,9)
print(sorted(Tup))
OUTPUT
[0, 1, 2, 3, 5, 8, 9]
```

```
# Program to illustrate string formatting with tuple
Tup =("Mira", 12, 94.534)
print("%s studying in class %d scored %.2f aggregate"
%(Tup[0],Tup[1],Tup[2]))
OUTPUT
Mira studying in class 12 scored 94.53 aggregate
```

2.40 Advantages of tuple over list

Although tuples are similar to lists, there are some advantages of implementing a tuple over a list. Some of these advantages are listed below.

- Since tuples are immutable, iterating through tuple is faster than iterating over a list. This means that tuple performs better than a list.
- Tuples can be used as key for a dictionary but lists cannot be used as keys. We will learn about dictionaries in the next chapter.
- Tuples are best suited for storing data that are write protected (you can read the data but cannot write to it).

- Tuples can be used in place of lists where the number of values is known and small.
- If you are passing a tuple as an argument to a function, then the potential for unexpected behaviour due to aliasing gets reduced.
- Multiple values from a function can be returned using a tuple.

> If a negative value is used for the step, the slice is done backwards

2.41 Dictionaries

Dictionary is a data structure in which we store values as a **pair of key and value.** Each key is separated from its value by a colon (:), and consecutive items are separated by commas. The entire set of items in a dictionary is enclosed in curly braces ({}). The syntax for defining a dictionary is

dictionary_name = {key_1: value_1, key_2: value_2, key_3: value_3}

If there are many keys and values in dictionaries, then we can also write just one key-value pair on a line to make the code easier to read and understand. This is shown below.

```
dictionary_name = {key_1: value_1,
                   key_2: value_2,
                   key_3: value_3,
                   }
```

> Using a mutable object as a dictionary key causes a TypeError

While, keys in the ***dictionary must be unique and be of any immutable data type (like strings, numbers, or tuples), there is no stringent requirement for uniqueness and type of values.*** That is, value of a key can be of any type. Remember that, dictionaries are not sequences, rather they are **mappings**. Mappings are collections of objects that store objects by key instead of by relative position.

Dictionary is like an associative array (also known as hashes) in which any key of the dictionary can be associated or mapped to a value.

2.42 Creating dictionary

The syntax to create an empty dictionary can be given as **dictionary_variable = []**, and the syntax to create a dictionary with key-value pairs is: dictionary_variable = {key1 : val1, key2 : val2, ...}. In this syntax, we can specify key-value pairs separated by a colon in curly brackets as shown below.

```
# To create an empty dictionary
Dict = {}

print Dict
OUTPUT
{}
```

```
# Create a dictionary with key-value pairs
Dict = {'EMP_NO': '123', 'Name': 'Aaditya',
'Department': 'SALES'}
print(Dict)
OUTPUT
{'EMP_NO': '123', 'Name': 'Aaditya',
'Department': 'SALES'}
```

Creating dictionary using dict() Method

To create a dictionary with one or more key-value pairs, you can also use the dict() function. The dict() creates a dictionary directly from a sequence of key value pairs. For example, the line of code given below creates a dictionary using a list of key-value pairs.

```
# Creating a dictionary using dict() function
Dict = dict([('EMP_NO','123'),('Name','Aaditya'),('Department','SALES')])
print(Dict)
OUTPUT
{'EMP_NO':'123','Name':'Aaditya','Department':'SALES'}
```

We can enclose the keys and values in a separate tuple and then use them as argument in the zip() function. The output of the zip function can then be passed as an argument to the dict() function so that the dictionary can be created using the two tuples.

Note that in the program, the zip() function clubs first value from the heads tuple with the first value in the vals tuple, then the second value from both the tuples are clubbed, and finally the third value is clubbed.

```
# Creating dictionary using keys and values that
# are stored as tuples
heads = ('Roll No','Name','Marks')
vals = ('101','Mishti',99)
Student = dict(zip(heads,vals))
print(Student)
OUTPUT
{'Roll No': '101', 'Name': 'Mishti', 'Marks': 99}
```

2.43 Accessing values in a dictionary

To access values in a dictionary, square brackets are used along with the key to obtain its value. Note that if you try to access an item with a key, which is not specified in the dictionary, a KeyError is generated.

```
# Accessing dictionary values
Dict = {'EMP_NO': '123', 'Name': 'Aaditya', 'Department': 'SALES'}
print("Dict[EMP_NO] = ", Dict['EMP_NO'])
print("Dict[Name] = ", Dict['Name'])
print("Dict[Department] = ", Dict['Department'])
OUTPUT
Dict[EMP_NO] = 123
Dict[Name] = Aaditya
Dict[Department] = SALES
```

```
# Accessing key which is not present in dictionary
Dict = {'EMP_NO': '123', 'Name': 'Aaditya'}
print("Dict[EMP_NO] = ", Dict['EMP_NO'])
print("Dict[Name] = ", Dict['Name'])
print("Dict[Department] = ", Dict['Department'])
OUTPUT
Dict[EMP_NO] = 123
Dict[Name] = Aaditya
Traceback (most recent call last):
  File "C:\Users\Python37\try.py", line 4, in <module>
  print("Dict[Department] = ", Dict['Department'])
KeyError: 'Department'
```

2.44 Adding an item in a dictionary

To add a new entry or a key-value pair in a dictionary, just specify the key-value pair as you had done for the existing pairs. The syntax to add an item in a dictionary is **dictionary_variable[key] = val.**

2.45 Modifying an item in a dictionary

To modify an entry, just overwrite the existing value with the new value.

```
# adding and modifying values in a dictionary
Dict = {'EMP_NO': '123', 'Name': 'Aaditya'}
print("Original dictionary", Dict)
Dict['Department'] = 'Sales' # new key-value pair added
Dict['Name'] = 'Aadi' # existing value modified
print("Updated Dictionary",Dict)
OUTPUT
Original dictionary {'EMP_NO': '123', 'Name': 'Aaditya'}
Updated Dictionary {'EMP_NO': '123', 'Name': 'Aadi', 'Department': 'Sales'}
```

2.46 Deleting items

One or more items in a dictionary can be deleted using the **del** keyword. To delete or remove all the items in just one statement, use the **clear()** function. Note that the clear() method does not delete the dictionary, it just deletes all the elements inside the dictionary. To remove an entire dictionary from the memory, we can again use the del statement **as del Dict_name.** The syntax to use the del statement can be given as, **del dictionary_variable[key].**

```
# deleting entries and the entire dictionary
Dict = {'EMP_NO': '123', 'Name': 'Aaditya', 'Department': 'Sales'}
print("Original Dictionary", Dict)
del Dict['EMP_NO'] # a particular key-value pair deleted
print("After deleting EMP_NO", Dict)
Dict.clear() # all entries deleted
print("After deleting all entries ", Dict)
del Dict     # delete dictionary
print("Printing Dictionary after deleting it ", Dict)
OUTPUT
Original Dictionary {'EMP_NO': '123', 'Name': 'Aaditya', 'Department': 'Sales'}
After deleting EMP_NO {'Name': 'Aaditya', 'Department': 'Sales'}
After deleting all entries {}
Traceback (most recent call last):
 File "C:\Users\Python37\try.py", line 8, in <module>
 print("Printing Dictionary after deleting it ", Dict)
NameError: name 'Dict' is not defined
```

The pop() method

The pop() method can be used to delete a particular key from the dictionary. The syntax of the pop() method is, **dict.pop(key [, default])**

The pop() method removes an item from the dictionary and returns its value. ***If the specified key is not present in the dictionary, then the default value is returned.*** Since default value is optional, if you do not specify the default value and the key is also not present in the dictionary, then a KeyError is generated.

Another method **popitem()** randomly pops and returns an item from the dictionary. The use of these methods are illustrated in the program given below.

```
# Program to randomly pop an element from a dictionary
Dict = {'EMP_NO': '123', 'Name': 'Aaditya', 'Department': 'Sales'}
print("Original Dictionary", Dict)
print("Name is :  ", Dict.pop('Name'))  # returns Name
print("Dictionary after popping Name is : ", Dict)
print("Salary is :", Dict.pop('Salary',-1)) # returns default value
print("Randomly popping any item : ", Dict.popitem())
print("Dictionary after random popping is : ", Dict)
print("Designation is :", Dict.pop('Designation'))      # generates error
print("Dictionary after popping Designation is : ", Dict)
OUTPUT
Original Dictionary {'EMP_NO': '123', 'Name': 'Aaditya', 'Department': 'Sales'}
Name is : Aaditya
Dictionary after popping Name is : {'EMP_NO': '123', 'Department': 'Sales'}
Salary is : -1
Randomly popping any item : ('Department', 'Sales')
Dictionary after random popping is : {'EMP_NO': '123'}
Traceback (most recent call last):
  File "C:\Users\Python37\try.py", line 9, in <module>
  print("Designation is:", Dict.pop('Designation'))
# generates error
KeyError: 'Designation'
```

Points to remember:

- Keys must have unique values. ***Keys should not be duplicated in a dictionary***. If you try to add a duplicate key, then the last assignment is retained.

```
# Dictionary with duplicate keys
Dict = {'EMP_NO': '123', 'Name' : 'Aaditya','Department' : 'Sales','EMP_NO' : '456'}
print(Dict)
OUTPUT
{'EMP_NO': '456', 'Name': 'Aaditya', 'Department': 'Sales'}
```

- In a dictionary, ***keys should be strictly of a type that is immutable***. This means that a key can be of strings, number or tuple type, but it cannot be a list, which is mutable. In case you try to make your key of a mutable type, then a **TypeError** will be generated.

- The keys() method of dictionary returns a list of all the keys used in the dictionary, in an arbitrary order. Use the sorted() function to sort the keys.

```
# Program to use tuple as keys

Dict = {(1,2),([3,4])}

print(Dict)

OUTPUT

Traceback (most recent call last):

 File "C:\Users\Python37\try.py", line 5, in

<module>

 Dict = {(1,2),([3,4])}

TypeError: unhashable type: 'list'
```

```
# Dictionary with sorted keys

Dict = {'EMP_NO': '123', 'Name': 'Aaditya', 'Department':
'Sales', 'EMP_NO': '456'}

print(sorted(Dict.keys()))

OUTPUT

['Department', 'EMP_NO', 'Name']
```

- The **in keyword** can be used to check whether a single key is in the dictionary.

```
# Program to check single key in a dictionary
Dict = {'EMP_NO': '123', 'Name': 'Aaditya', 'Department': 'Sales', 'EMP_NO': '456'}
if 'Department' in Dict:
   print(Dict['Department'])
OUTPUT
Sales
```

The key-value pairs can be specified as a list or as a tuple. To create a dictionary out of this list or tuple, it must be passed as an argument to the dict() function.

In the program, we have used a tuple having list of keys and values as its elements. In the same way, we could have even used nested tuples.

```
# Dictionary using a tuple of lists having key- value pairs
Student = dict((['RollNp','101'],['Name','Krish'],
['Marks',90]))
print(Student)
OUTPUT
{'Roll Np': '101', 'Name': 'Krish', 'Marks': 90}
```

2.47 Traversing a dictionary

Looping over a Dictionary can be done to access only values, only keys or both using the for loop. We can use the items() method that returns a list of tuples (key,value pair). The keys() method returns a list of keys in the dictionary. The values() method returns a list of values in dictionary.

```
# Program to access items in a dictionary
Dist = {'EMP_NO':'123','Name':'Aaditya','Department':'Sales','EMP_NO':'456'}
print("KEYS:", end = ")
for key in Dict:
 print(key,end = ")  # accessing only keys
print("\nVALUES:", end = ")
for val in Dict.values():
 print(val, end = ") #accessing only values
print("\nDICTIONARY:", end = ")
for key, val in Dict.items():
 print(key, val, "\t", end = ") #accessing keys and values
OUTPUT
KEYS : EMP_NO Name Department
VALUES : 456 Aaditya Sales
DICTIONARY : EMP_NO 456            Name Aaditya   Department Sales
```

2.48 Nested dictionaries

Like any other sequence, we can also have nested dictionary in Python. A nested dictionary has a dictionary defined inside another dictionary.

```
# Program to illustrate nested dictionary
Employees = {'Aman': {'EMP_NO':90, 'Sal':89, 'Desig': 'Analyst'},
     'Sadhvi': {'EMP_NO':91, 'Sal':87, 'Desig': 'Programmer'},
     'Kiyan': {'EMP_NO:92, 'Sal':92, 'Desig': 'Testing
     Professional'}}
for key, val in Employees.items():
  print(key, val)
OUTPUT
Aman {'EMP_NO': 90, 'Sal': 89, 'Desig': 'Analyst'}
Sadhvi {'EMP_NO': 91, 'Sal': 87, 'Desig': 'Programmer'}
Kiyan {'EMP_NO': 92, 'Sal': 92, 'Desig': 'Testing Professional'}
```

2.49 The copy() method

The copy() method of dictionary returns a shallow copy of the dictionary, i.e, the dictionary returned will not have a duplicate copy of the original dictionary but will have the same reference. This means that both the copies of dictionaries will point to the same object (or address) in computer's memory.

```
# Program using copy() method
Emp = {'EMP_NO':90, 'Sal':89, 'Desig': 'Analyst'}
print("Original Emp : ",Emp)
Emp_Copy = Emp.copy()
print("Copied Emp : ", Emp_Copy)
Emp_Copy['Sal'] = 99
print("Emp after modification :", Emp)
print("Copy of Emp after modification :", Emp_Copy)
OUTPUT
Original Emp : {'EMP_NO':90,'sal':89,'Desig':'Analyst'}
Copied Emp : {'EMP_NO':90,'Sal':89,'Desig':'Analyst'}
Emp after modification : {'EMP_NO':90,'Sal':89,'Desig':
'Analyst'}
Copy of Emp after modification : {'EMP_NO':90,'Sal':99,
'Desig': 'Analyst'}
```

2.50 Built-in dictionary functions and methods

Table 6 discusses some methods and functions that can be used on dictionaries in Python.

Table 6: || Methods and functions of dictionaries

Operation	Description	Example	Output
len(Dict)	Returns the length of dictionary. That is, number of items (key-value pairs)	`Emp = {'EMP_NO':90, 'Sal':89, 'Desig': 'Analyst'}` `print(len(Emp))`	3
str(Dict)	Returns a string representation of the dictionary	`Emp = {'EMP_NO':90, 'Sal':89, 'Desig': 'Analyst'}` `print(str(Emp))`	`{'EMP_NO': 90, 'Sal': 89, 'Desig': 'Analyst'}`
Dict.get(key)	Returns the value for the key passed as argument. If the key is not present in dictionary, it will return the default value. If no default value is specified then it will return None	`Emp = {'EMP_NO':90, 'Sal':89, 'Desig': 'Analyst'}` `print(Emp. get('Desig'))`	Analyst

Dict. setdefault(key, value)	Sets a default value for a key that is not present in dictionary	`Emp = {'EMP_NO':90, 'Desig': 'Analyst'}`
		`Emp. setdefault('Sal',0)`
		`print("Emp gets a salary = ", Emp. get('Sal'))`
			Emp gets a salary = 0

(continued)

Table 6: || *(Continued)*

Operation	Description	Example	Output

Dict1. update(Dict2)	Adds the key-value pairs of Dict2 to the key-value pairs of Dict1	`Emp1 = {'EMP_NO':90, 'Desig': 'Analyst'}`
		`Emp2 = {'Name' : 'Krish', 'Sal' : 89}`
		`Emp1.update(Emp2)`
		`print(Emp1)`
			`{'EMP_NO': 90, 'Desig': 'Analyst', 'Name': 'Krish', 'Sal': 89}`

in and not in	Checks whether a given key is present in dictionary or not.	`Emp = {'EMP_NO':90, 'Sal':89, 'Desig': 'Analyst'}`
		`print('Name' in Emp)`
		`print('Name' not in Emp)`
			`False`
			`True`

2.51 Difference between a list and a dictionary

There are two main differences between a list and a dictionary.

- First, a list is an ordered set of items. But, a dictionary is a data structure that is used for matching one item (key) with another (value).
- Second, in lists, you can use indexing to access a particular item. But these indexes should be a number. In dictionaries, you can use any type (immutable) of value as an index. For example, when we write Dict['Name'], Name acts as an index, but it is not a number but a string.
- Third, lists are used to look up a value, whereas a dictionary is used to take one value and lookup another value. For this reason, dictionary is also known as a *lookup table*.
  In fact, the main advantage of a dictionary is that you do not need to search for a value one by one in the entire set of values, you can find a value instantly.
- Fourth, the key-value pair may not be displayed in the order in which it was specified while defining the dictionary. This is because Python uses complex algorithms (called hashing) to provide fast access to the items stored in the dictionary. This also makes dictionary preferable to use over a list of tuples.

Key Terms

Dictionary: A collection of key:value pairs that maps from keys to values. While keys can be of any immutable type, there is no such restriction on its associated value which can be of any type.
Dot notation: Use of the dot operator (.) to access functions inside a module.
Empty string: A string that has no characters and has a length = 0.
Format operator: % operator that takes a format string and a tuple to generate a string that includes values of the tuple formatted as specified by the format string.
Format sequence: Sequence of characters in a format string, like `%d`, that specifies how a value should be formatted.
Format string: String used with the % or format operator that contains format sequences.
Hash function: A function used to compute the location for a key.

Immutable: The property of a sequence whose items cannot be assigned.
Immutable data: Data that cannot be modified. Assigning values to elements or slices of immutable data results in a runtime error.
Index: A variable or value used to access a member of an ordered set.
Invocation: A statement that calls a method.
Key: Data that are *mapped to* a value in a dictionary. Keys are unique data items that are used to look up values in a dictionary.
key-value pair: A pair of items in a dictionary. Key is used to lookup for a value stored in the dictionary.
List: A mutable data structure that can have elements that belong to different data types.
List Aliasing: When one list is assigned to another list using the assignment operator (=), then a new copy of list is not made. Instead, assignment makes the two variables point to the one list in memory. This is also known as aliasing.
List Cloning: The process of creating a separate copy of the list (not just the reference) is known as list cloning. The slice operation is used to clone a list.
Lookup: A dictionary operation that takes a key and finds the corresponding value.
Mappings: A collections of objects that store objects by key instead of by relative position.
Method: A function that is called on an object using dot notation.
Mutable data value: Data that can be modified.
Nested Dictionary: A dictionary inside another dictionary.
Nested List: Nested list means a list within another list.
Nested tuple: Tuple inside another tuple.
Packing a tuple: Creating a tuple from a set of values is called packing.
Sequence: An ordered set of values in which each value is identified by an integer index.
Slice: A part of a string obtained by specifying a range of indices.
Traversing a string: Accessing each character in the string, one at a time.
Tuple: An immutable data structure that stores related items together.
Unpacking a tuple: Creating individual values from a tuple is known as unpacking.
Whitespace: Characters that move the cursor without printing visible characters.

Chapter Highlights

- The Python string data type is a sequence made up of one or more individual characters, where a character could be a letter, a digit, whitespace or any other symbol.
- The in operator checks if one character or string is contained in another string.
- The whitespace characters, exclamation mark and any other symbol (like ?, <, >,*, @, #, $, %, etc.) that form a part of the string would be assigned its own index number.
- Concatenate means to join together and append means to add something at the end.
- A raw string literal, which is prefixed by an 'r', passes all the characters as it.
- Python strings are immutable, which means that once created, they cannot be changed.
- The number and type of values in the tuple should match the number and type of format sequences or conversion specifications in the string, otherwise an error is returned.
- Strings are an example of Python objects.
- in and not in operators can be used with strings to determine whether a string is present in another string. Therefore, the in and not in operator are also known as membership operators.
- The string module consists of a number of useful constants, classes and functions. These functions are used to manipulate strings.

* List is a versatile data type available in Python, in which elements are written as a list of comma-separated values (items) between square brackets.
* Like strings, lists can also be sliced and concatenated.
* Once created, one or more elements of a list can be easily updated by giving the slice on the left-hand side of the assignment operator.
* We can append new values in the list and remove existing value(s) from the list using the append() method and del statement, respectively.
* To insert items from another list at a particular location, we can use the slice operation. This would create a nested list that is, list within another list.
* Lists behave in the similar way as strings when operators like + (concatenation) and * (repetition) are used.
* A tuple is an immutable object. This means that while you can change the value of one or more elements in a list, you cannot change the values in a tuple.
* Tuples use parentheses to define its elements whereas lists use square brackets.
* Any set of comma-separated, values written without an identifying symbol like brackets or parentheses, etc., is treated as a tuple by default.
* We can use the eval() function to input a tuple.
* The tuple() function is used to create a tuple with the specified sequence.
* When accessing a tuple, if the index is out of the range of legal indices of the tuple, then Python raises an IndexError.
* Since tuple is an immutable data structure, you cannot delete value(s) from it.
* Two or more tuples can be joined using the + operator. The + operator requires that both the operands must be of tuple types.
* `zip` is a built-in function that takes two or more sequences and 'zips' them into a list of tuples.
* Python has a built-in function `sorted()`, which takes any sequence as a parameter and returns a new list with the same elements but in a different order.
* While keys in the dictionary must be unique and be of any immutable data type (like strings, numbers, or tuples), there is no stringent requirement for uniqueness and type of values.
* Dictionaries are not sequences, rather they are mappings.
* To create a dictionary with one or more key-value pairs, the dict() function.
* To access values in a dictionary, square brackets are used along with the key to obtain its value.
* If an item with a key, which is not specified in the dictionary is accessed, a KeyError is generated.
* One or more items in a dictionary can be deleted using the del keyword.
* The clear() method does not delete the dictionary, it just deletes all the elements inside the dictionary.
* The pop() method removes an item from the dictionary and returns its value. If the specified key is not present in the dictionary, then the default value is returned.
* Keys must have unique values. Keys should not be duplicated in a dictionary.
* The keys() method of dictionary returns a list of all the keys used in the dictionary, in an arbitrary order. Use the sorted() function to sort the keys.
* The key-value pairs can be specified as a list or as a tuple.
* The copy() method of dictionary returns a shallow copy of the dictionary i.e; the dictionary returned will not be a duplicate copy of the original dictionary but will have the same reference.

Review Questions

1. With the help of an example, explain how we can create string variables in Python.
2. With the help of an explanation, how we can concatenate a string and a floating-point data.
3. Python strings are immutable. Comment on this statement.
4. Write a short note on format operator.
5. What will happen when the strip() is used with a string argument?
6. Explain the use of format() with the help of an example.
7. What is slice operation? Explain with an example.
8. With the help of an example explain the significance of membership operators.
9. Differentiate between the following.
   a. a method and a function
   b. find() and index()
   c. find() and rfind()
   d. captalise() and upper()
10. Name the function to do the following operations:
    a. Returns a string with the original string centred to a total of width columns.
    b. Checks if string ends with suffix; returns true if so and false otherwise
    c. Returns true if string has at least 1 character and every character is either a number or an alphabet and false otherwise.
    d. Returns true if string has at least 1 character and every character is a lower case alphabet and false otherwise.
    e. Removes all trailing whitespace in string.
    f. Returns the highest alphabetical character (having highest ASCII value) from the string str.
    g. Toggles the case of every character
    h. Returns a list of substrings separated by the specified delimiter.
    i. The function joins a list of strings using the delimiter with which the function is invoked.
    j. Returns a list of the lines in the string.
11. If str = 'Welcome to the world of Python Programming', answer the following,
    a. Write an instruction to print the tenth character of the string.
    b. Write an instruction that prints the index of the first occurrence of the letter 'o' in the string.
12. What is a list?
13. How can we define a list in Python?
14. With the help of an example demonstrate how lists can be sliced to access its values?
15. Explain the syntax of the slice operation.
16. What is the role of del statement with list variables?
17. Differentiate between shallow copy and deep copy of an object in Python.
18. Differentiate the use of del statement and remove() function?
19. What is a nested list? How can we make one in Python?
20. Differentiate between list cloning and list aliasing.

21. Differentiate between pop() and remove() methods of list objects.
22. Explain the purpose of the following functions:
    a. sorted() b. list()
    c. any() d. sum()
    e. min()
23. Name the function or the operator that can be used for the following tasks:
    a. Returns length of list
    b. Repeat elements in the list
    c. Joins two lists
    d. Checks if the value is present in the list
    e. Returns maximum value in the list
24. Name the methods that can be used in the following situations:
    a. Appends an element to the list.
    b. Counts the number of times an element appears in the list
    c. Returns the lowest index of obj in the list.
25. Explain the purpose of the following methods in Python:
    a. insert()
    b. reverse()
    c. extend()
26. Given a list, l= [1,2,3,4,5], write instructions for the following tasks,
    a. Set the third element to 100
    b. Insert 200 at the second index
    c. Append 300 to the list
    d. Remove the fourth element from the list
    e. Sort the list
    f. Reverse the list
27. Given a list L = [1,2,3,4,[5,6,7,8],9,10], write expressions that will print the values:
    a. [5,6,7,8]
    b. [6,7]
    c. [2,3,4]
    d. [1,3,[5,6,7,8], 10]
28. With the help of an example, explain the significance of + and * operators when used with tuples.
29. Can we change the value of one or more elements in a tuple? Justify your answer.
30. How is a tuple different from a list?
31. Can we add or delete values from a tuple?
32. What are nested tuples?
33. Explain different ways of defining a tuple?
34. How will you join two tuples?
35. With the help of an example differentiate between packing and unpacking a tuple.
36. Why do we use the index() function?
37. Demonstrate the use of membership operators on a tuple.
38. Explain the use of zip() function.
39. Differentiate between sort() and sorted().

40. List some advantages of using tuple over lists.
41. What is a dictionary?
42. How is a dictionary different from a list?
43. Discuss at least two ways in which you can create a dictionary.
44. Can lists be used as keys? Justify your answer.
45. How is the zip() function used to create a dictionary?
46. How will you add key-value pairs in a dictionary?
47. How will you modify key-value pairs in a dictionary?
48. Differentiate between the del statement and clear() method.
49. When will we use the pop() method?
50. List some restrictions which you will keep in mind when creating a dictionary.
51. Draw a comparison between a list and a dictionary.

Programming Exercise

1. Modify the `find_ch` function so that it starts finding the character from the specified position in the string.
2. Write a program to calculate the length of a string.
3. Write a program to count the number of vowels and consonants present in a user-inputted string.
4. Write a program to count the number of lower case and uppercase characters present in a user-inputted string.
5. Write a program to count the number digits, spaces and alphabets present in a user-inputted string.
6. Write a Python program to get a string made of the first 2 and the last 2 chars from a given a string. If the string length is less than 2, return instead the empty string.
7. Write a Python program to get a string from a given string where all occurrences of its first char have been changed to '$', except the first char itself.
8. Write a Python program to get a single string from two given strings, separated by a space and swap the first two characters of each string.
9. Program to copy a string.
10. Write a Python program to add `'ing'` at the end of a given string (length should be at least 3). If the given string is already ends with `'ing'` then add `'ly'` instead. If the string length of the given string is less than 3, leave it unchanged.
11. Write a program to find the first appearance of the substring 'not' and 'poor' from a given string, if 'bad' follows the 'poor', replace the whole 'not'...'poor' substring with 'good'. Return the resulting string.
12. Write a function that takes a list of words and returns the length of the longest one.
13. Write a program to remove the nth index character from a non-empty string.
14. Write a program to change a given string to a new string where the first and last chars have been exchanged.
15. Write a program to remove the characters that have odd index values of a given string.
16. Write a program to count the occurrences of each word in a given sentence.

17. Write a program that accepts a comma separated sequence of words as input and prints the unique words in sorted form (alphanumerically).
18. Write a function to insert a string in the middle of a string.
19. Write a function to get a string made of 4 copies of the last two characters of a specified string (length must be at least 2).
20. Write a function to get a string made of its first three characters of a specified string. If the length of the string is less than 3 then return the original string.
21. Write a function to get the first half of a specified string of even length.
22. Write a function to reverses a string if its length is a multiple of 4.
23. Write a function to convert a given string to all uppercase if it contains at least 2 uppercase characters in the first 4 characters.
24. Write a program to sort a string lexicographically.
25. Write a program to remove newline characters from text.
26. Write a program to check whether a string starts with specified characters.
27. Write a program to remove existing indentation from all of the lines in a given text.
28. Write a program to add a prefix text to all of the lines in a string.
29. Write a program to set the indentation of the first line.
30. Write a program to print floating numbers up to 2 decimal places.
31. Write a program to print floating numbers up to 2 decimal places with sign.
32. Write a program to print floating numbers with no decimal places.
33. Write a program to print integers with zeros on the left of specified width.
34. Write a program to print integers with '*' on the right of specified width.
35. Write a program to display a number with comma separator.
36. Write a program to format a number with percentage.
37. Write a program to display a number in left, right and centre aligned of width 10.
    Write a program to reverse words in a string.
38. Write a program to strip a set of characters from a string.
39. Write a program to create a mirror of the given string. For example, `"abc" = "abccba"`.
40. Write a program that removes all the occurrences of a specified character from a given string.
41. Write a program to check whether a string is palindrome or not.
42. Write a program to remove all the occurrences of a given word from the string.
43. Write a program to concatenate two strings in a third string. Do not use + operator.
44. Write a program to append a string to another string. Do not use += operator
45. Write a program to swap two strings.
46. Write a program to insert a string in another string.
47. Write a program to delete a string from another string.
48. Write a program to replace a string with another string. Do not use the `replace()`
49. Write a program that removes leading and trailing spaces from a string.
50. Write a program to read a name and then display it in abbreviated form, like Janak Raj Thareja should be displayed as JRT.
51. Write a program to read a name and then display it in abbreviated form, like Janak Raj Thareja should be displayed as J.R. Thareja.
52. Write a program to count the number of characters, words and lines in the given text.

53. Write a program to count the number of digits, upper case characters, lower case characters and special characters in a given string.
54. Write a program to extract the first n characters of a string.
55. Write a program to copy n characters of a string from the mth position in another string. Do not use the slice operation.
56. Write a program to delete the last character of a string.
57. Write a program to delete the first character of a string.
58. Write a program to encrypt a string using Substitution Cipher.
59. Write a program that encrypts a string using multiplicative cipher. Generate the key randomly.
60. Write the command to print "hello world" as "Hello world".
61. Write the command to print "hello world" as "Hello World"
62. Write the command to print "hElLo WoRlD" as "HeLlO wOrLd"
63. Write the command to print "hello world" as "Hello Friends"
64. Write a program that prompts the user to enter a 10-digit mobile number. Display the number by putting a '-' after area code and next three digits. (like `123-456-7890`).
65. Write a program that prompts the user to enter five words. If the length of any word is less than 8 or if the word does not contain any digit then prompt the user to enter that word again.
66. Write a program that creates a list of numbers in the series 2n-1. Display only the even indexed values in this list.
67. Write a program that prints the elements along with their indices from the start and end of the list.
68. Write a program that reads two lists. Make another list of all those elements in the first list that are also present in the second list.
69. Write a program that creates a list ['a','bb','ccc','dddd',....]
70. Write a program that forms a list of numbers in the series
    a. 2/9, –5/13, 8/17,… b. x,–x2/2!, x3/3!, –x4/4!, x5/5!,….
71. Make a list of five random numbers. Write instructions to sum the elements and find mean of the elements.
72. Write a program that adds corresponding elements of two lists.
73. Make a list of first ten letters of the alphabet, then using the slice operation do the following operations
    a. Print the first three letters from the list.
    b. Print any three letters from the middle
    c. Print the letters from any particular index to the end of the list
74. Write a program that prints the maximum value of the second half of the list.
75. Write a program that finds the sum of all the numbers using a while loop.
76. Write a program that finds sum of all even numbers in a list.
77. Write a program that reverses a list using a loop.
78. Write a program to find whether a particular element is present in the list using a loop.
79. Write a program that prompts user to enter an alphabet. Print all the words in the list that starts with that alphabet.
80. Write a program that prompts a number from user and adds it in a list. If the value entered by user is greater than 100, then add "EXCESS" in the list

81. Write a program that counts the number of times a value appears in the list. Use a loop to do the same.
82. Write a program to insert a value in a list at the specified location using while loop.
83. Write a program that creates a list of numbers from 1-50 that are either divisible by 3 or divisible by 6.
84. Write a program to create a list of numbers in the range 1 to 20. Then, delete all the numbers from the list that are divisible by 3.
85. Write a program to randomly select an item from a list.
86. Write a program to print the string "HELLOWORLD" as

```
H       E
 L     L
  O   W
   R L
    D
```

87. Write a program that creates a list ['a', 'b', 'c'], then create a tuple from that list. Now, do the opposite. That is create the tuple ('a', 'b', 'c'), and then create a list from it.
88. Create a tuple that has just one element which in turn may have three elements 'a', 'b' and 'c'. Print the length of this tuple.
89. Write a program that has a predefined list. Create a copy of this list in such a way that only those values that are in valid_tuple are added in the new list.
90. Create a nested tuple that has marks of at least 5 students obtained in three subjects. Now, perform the following operations on it.
    a. Display the marks of the fourth student.
    b. Display the marks obtained by second student in the first subject.
    c. Total marks obtained by each student
    d. Average (or mean) marks obtained by each student
    e. Using the average marks obtained by each student, calculate the average marks obtained by all the students (finding the mean of means)
    f. For each student display the maximum and minimum marks obtained.
91. Write a program that concatenates the first tuple at the end of the second tuple.
92. Write a program that creates the following tuples.
    a. Squares of first 10 natural numbers
    b. Cube of first 10 odd numbers
    c. First 10 multiples of 7
    d. –5,–3,–1,1,3
93. Write a program that creates a tuple of at least 10 pair of values. Count the number of pairs having both values odd.
94. Write a program that has two tuples. Check if the first tuple is a super-set of the second tuple.
95. Create a dictionary of products purchased and their `MRPs`. Calculate the bill and display to the customer.
96. Find `fib(n)` using dictionaries.
97. Write a program that prompts user to enter a string and returns in alphabetical order, a letter and its frequency of occurrence in the string. (Ignore Case)
98. Write a program to implement sparse matrix using a dictionary.

99. Write a program that has a dictionary of your friend's name (as keys) and their birthdays. Print the items in the dictionary in a sorted order. Prompt the user to enter a name and check if it is present in the dictionary. If the name does not exist, then ask the user to enter `DOB`. Add the details in the dictionary.
100. Write a program that displays a menu and its price. Take the order from the customer. Check if the ordered product is in the menu. In case it is not there, the customer should be asked to reorder and if it is present then product should be added in the bill.
101. Write a program that prints the maximum and minimum value in a dictionary.
102. Write a program to remove duplicates from Dictionary.
103. Write a program to check whether a dictionary has some key-value pairs stored in it or not.
104. Write a program that displays information about an employee. Use nested dictionary to do the task.
105. Write a program that prints keys with same values in the dictionary.
106. Write a program that prints keys with different values in the dictionary.
107. Write a program that accepts two dictionaries. Print all the keys that are present in both the dictionaries.
108. Create a dictionary which has name of the student as key and his total marks as value. Now, perform the following operations on this dictionary.
    a. Display the marks obtained by a particular student.
    b. Display the names of all the students who scored 90 and above.
    c. Display all key-value pairs sorted by keys.
    d. Display all key-value pairs sorted by marks.
    e. Create a list of all students.
    f. Create another list having marks obtained by the students.
109. Create a dictionary storing names of months as keys and the number of days as values.
110. Create a dictionary using nested tuple.

Fill in the Blanks

1. String is a sequence made up of one or more ________.
2. A multiple-line text within quotes must have a __________ at the end of each line.
3. Individual characters in a string are accessed using the ________ operator.
4. _____________ error is generated when index out of bounds is accessed.
5. __________ means to join together.
6. The _______ function is used to convert values of any other type into string type.
7. The ______ returns the memory address of that object.
8. Conversion specifications start with a ___ operator.
9. A method is invoked or called on an _______.
10. __________ function checks if string ends with suffix.
11. __________ function toggles the case of every character.
12. The _______ returns a list of the lines in the string.

13. Omitting both ends in the slice operation means selecting the ________.
14. If we access the string from the first character then we use a _____ based index but when doing it backward the index starts with ____.
15. ______ function returns the ASCII code of the character.
16. ____ and _____ operators are known as membership operators.
17. ________ function is used to know the details of a particular item.
18. _________ function displays the methods in a module.
19. ___________ defines a particular way of storing and organising data in a computer
20. When using slice operation, __________ is generated if the index is outside the list
21. [10,20] < [20,10] will return _______
22. `insert()`, `remove()` and `sort()` returns _____
23. The `sort()` method uses ________ values to sort the values in the list.
24. ___________ help programmers to create lists in a concise way.
25. ___________ is used to print both index as well as an item in the list.
26. Any argument that starts with a _____ is known as ______ and specifies a variable length argument.
27. Fill in the blanks to create a list and print its second element.

```
List = ___10, 20, 30, 40]
print(list[___])
```

28. Fill in the blanks to create a list, reassign its third element and print the list.

```
List = [1,2,3,4,5__
List[__] = 30
print(__)
```

29. Fill in the blanks to print "Hello" if the list contains 'H':

```
Letters = ['W', 'G', 'H']
__ 'H'__ Letters:
   print("______")
```

30. Fill in the blanks to add 'G' to the end of the list and print the list's length.

```
Letters._____('G')
print(______)
```

31. Fill in the blanks to print the letters in the list.

```
Letters = ['H', 'E', 'L', 'L','O']
___ i __Letters__
print(i)
```

32. Fill in the blanks to print the second element of the list, if it contains odd number of elements.

```
List =[10, 20, 30, 40, 50]
If ___(list)%2__0__
   print(List[__])
```

33. Fill in the banks to print the first two elements of the list:

```
List = [1,2,3,4,5,6]
print(list[0_])
```

34. Fill in the blanks to remove all items from the list that are greater than 55 from the list.

```
List = [10,20,50,80,30,100,70]
print(list(____(lambda x:x__55,____)))
```

35.
```
List = [15,20,25,30, 35, 40]
print(list(__(____ x: x%__!=0, List)))
```

36. The range of index values for a list of 10 elements will be ____

37. _______ use parentheses to define its elements.

38. _______ function takes two or more sequences and 'zips' them into a list of tuples.

39. To add a single element in the set use the _____ method and to add multiple elements in the set, use the ________ method.

40. The _______ function to create a tuple with the specified sequence.

41. The entire tuple can be deleted by using the _______ statement.

42. If tup = ("abc", "def", "ghi", "jkl"), tup[-1] will print _______

43. print(len(((('a',1,'bcd',3.0),'e',4.5),'fgh',(99,1.0)))) will give output ___.

44. We can access an individual element of a tuple by using its _______.

45. _______ are used to return more than one value from a function.

46. The ______ method returns the number of elements with a specific value in a tuple.

47. Fill in the blanks to print "Hi", if the key 90 is present in the dictionary named "Dict".

    if ___ __ ___ print("Hi")

48. Fill in the blanks to create a list, dictionary and tuple:

    List=__"abc", "def"_
    Dict=__1:"abc", 2:"def"__
    Tup=__"abc","def"__

49. __________ is a collection of objects that store objects by key instead of by relative position.

50. The ______ function can be used to create a dictionary with one or more key-value pairs.

51. One or more items in a dictionary can be deleted using the _____ keyword.

52. The ______ method of dictionary returns a list of all the keys used in the dictionary in an arbitrary order.

53. The ______ method of dictionary returns a shallow copy of the dictionary.

54. The ________ function returns a string representation of the dictionary.

55. The _______ function returns the value for the key passed as argument.

56. Dictionary is also known as a ________ table.

State True or False

1. Character in a string could a letter, digit, whitespace or any other symbol.
2. Python treats strings as contiguous series of characters delimited by single or double quotes but not triple quotes.
3. Python has a built-in string class as well as a string module that has many methods.
4. Index can either be an integer or an expression that evaluates to a floating-point number.
5. In a string, all whitespace characters are also assigned an index value.
6. Raw strings do not process escape sequences.
7. 'r' is used as a prefix for Unicode strings.
8. We cannot delete or remove characters from a string.
9. The % operator takes a format string on the right and the corresponding values in a tuple on the left.
10. Conversion specifications start with a % operator and can appear anywhere within the string.
11. The number and type of values in the tuple should match the number and type of format sequences or conversion specifications in the string.
12. The - after each % in the conversion string indicates right justification.
13. You can access a string using negative indexes.
14. odr() function returns character represented by an ASCII number.
15. A string is a substring of itself.
16. Strings are compared based on ASCII values of their characters.
17. The index value starts from zero.
18. List is an immutable data structure.
19. Once created, one or more elements of a list can be easily updated
20. It is possible to edit, add and delete elements from a list.
21. Slice operation can be used to insert items from another list or sequence at a particular location.
22. The slice operation is used to clone a list.
23. We cannot insert a list into another list.
24. When a list is assigned to another using the assignment operator, then a new copy of list is made.
25. Items in a list can be deleted by assigning an empty list to a slice of elements
26. If you specify a non-integer number as the index, then `IndexError` will be generated
27. Python sorts the original list with the help of sorted() function.
28. You cannot perform operations like concatenation, repetition, etc., on tuples
29. It is possible to specify a list within a tuple.
30. If a sequence is specified without parenthesis, it is treated to be a list by default.
31. Lists are faster than tuples

32. A tuple can be sliced
33. Once created, one or more elements of a tuple can be easily updated
34. It is possible to edit, add and delete elements from a tuple.
35. Tuples can store information that belongs to different data types.
36. Numbers or any other type values cannot be added to a tuple.
37. max() and min() functions can be used on a tuple if the values in it are of different data types.
38. In the zip() function, if the two sequences have different length then the result has the length of the longer one.
39. Tuples cannot be divided or subtracted.
40. Keys in the dictionary must be of any mutable data type
41. Tuples can be used as key for a dictionary but lists cannot be used as keys.
42. Values in a dictionary must be unique.
43. Slicing and concatenation operations are not possible on dictionaries.
44. Dictionary keys are case insensitive.
45. Dictionaries are sequences.
46. To remove an entire dictionary from the memory, we can use the clear() method.
47. pop() method randomly pops and returns an item from the dictionary.
48. Keys of a dictionary can be sorted using the sorted().
49. The key-value pairs can be specified as a list or as a tuple.

Give the Output

1.
```
s = "Welcome"
print(s[1:3])
```
2.
```
s = "Welcome"
print(s[ : 6])
```
3.
```
s = "Welcome"
print(s[4 : ])
```
4.
```
s = "Welcome"
print(s[1:-1])
```
5.
```
str = "Welcome"
print("come" in str)
```
6.
```
str = "Welcome"
print("come" not in str)
```
7. `"free" == "freedom"`
8. `print("12" + "34")`
9. `"man" != "men"`
10. `>>> 3*"PYTHON"`
11.
```
str = "Welcome to Python"
print(str.isalnum())
```
12. `"Hello".isalpha()`

13. `"14-10-2106".isdigit()`
14. `print("hello".islower())`
15. `"\t".isspace()`
16. ```
    str = "Hello"
    print(str.startswith("he"))
    ```
17. ```
    str = "Hello, welcome to the world of Python"
    print(str.find("o"))
    ```
18. ```
    str = "Hello, welcome to the world of Python"
    print(str.find("if"))
    ```
19. ```
    str = "Hello, welcome to the world of Python"
    print(str.rfind("of"))
    ```
20. ```
    str = "Hello, welcome to the world of Python"
    print(str.count("o"))
    ```
21. `"us" not in "success"`
22. `"mi" in "ours"`
23. ```
    for i in 'Python':
        print(2 * i, end=" ")
    ```
24. `string.find("abcdabcdabcd", "cd", 3)`
25. `string.find("abcdabcdabcdabcdabcd", "cd", 7, 13)`
26. ```
    a = 10
    b = 20
    print("3**4 = %d and %d * %d = %f" % (3**4, a, b, a * b))
    ```
27. ```
    print("%d %f %s" % (7, 15, 28))
    print("%-.2f" % 369)
    print("%-10.2f%-10.2f" % (91, 23.456))
    print("%5.2f %5.2f $%5.2f" % (9, 1.2, 55.78))
    ```
28. ```
    str1 = 'Welcome!'
    str2 = 'to Python'
    str3 = str1[:2] + str2[len(str2) - 2:]
    print(str3)
    ```
29. `print("She sells sea shells on the sea shore.".find("sea", 3, -6))`
30. `len("She sells sea shells on the sea shore.")`
31. ```
    str = "Welcome to the world of Python"
    print(str[:10].find("t"))
    ```
32. ```
    30. str = "Welcome to the world of Python"
    start = 3
    end = 10
    print(str[start:end])
    ```
33. ```
    str = "Hello"
    print(str.startswith('h'))
    print(str.lower().startswith('h'))
    ```
34. `'In %d years I have saved %g %s.' % (3, 4.5, 'lakh rupees')`

35. `', '.join(['Sun', 'Stars', 'Planets'])`
36. `' '.join(['Welcome', 'to', 'the', 'world', 'of', 'Python!'])`
37. `'Hello'.join(['Welcome', 'to', 'the', 'world', 'of', 'Python!'])`
38. `"Good morning students".split()`
39. `'WelcomeHellotoHellothe HelloworldHelloofHelloPython!'.split('Hello')`
40. `print("One"+"Two"*2)`
41.
```
>>> s = 'abcdefghijkl'
>>> print(s[-100:-5],s[-100:5])
```
42.
```
s1 = "HELLO"
s2 = s1 + s1[-1]
print(s2)
print(s1[:-1])
print(s1[-1:])
```
43.
```
str = "xyz"
while(len(str)<=4):
        if(str[-1] == 'z'):
            str = str[0:3]+'c'
        elif 'a' in str:
            str = str[0] + 'bb'
        elif 'x' not in str:
            str = '1'+str[1:]+'z'
        else:
            str = str+'*'
print(str)
```
44.
```
str = "helloworldofpython"
print(str[10],str[11:30])
```
45.
```
str1 = '''PYTHON
PRO'''
str2 = '''PYTHON\
PRO'''
print(len(str1)>len(str2))
```
46. `str1= 'PYTHON'; str1[-4]`
47.
```
colors = ['red', 'blue', 'green']
print(colors[2])
print(len(colors))
```
48.
```
list = ['abc', 'def', 'ghi', 'jkl']
print(list[1:-1])
list[0:2] = 'xyz'
print(list)
```
49.
```
list = ['abc', 'def', 'ghi', 'jkl', [1,2,3,4,5]]
print(list[4][2])
```

50.
```
list = ['p','r','o','g','r','a','m','m','i','n','g']
print(list[2:5])
print(list[:-5])
print(list[5:])
print(list[:])
```
51.
```
even = [2,4,6]
print(even + [10, 12, 14])
print(even*2)
even.insert(1,0)
print(even)
del even[2]
print(even)
```
52.
```
list = ['p','r','o','g','r','a','m']
list.remove('p')
print(list)
print(list.pop(1))
print(list)
print(list.pop())
print(list)
```
53.
```
list = [9,4,3,8,0,2,3,6]
print(list.index(3))
print(list.count(8))
list.sort()
print(list)
list.reverse()
print(list)
print(0 in list)
```
54.
```
list = [2 ** x for x in range(5)]
print(list)
```
55.
```
countries = ['India', 'Sri Lanka',
  'New Zealand', 'Japan', 'Russia']
for index, country in enumerate (countries):
    print("The country, " + country + ", is at position " + str(index) +
".")
```
56.
```
list = [(1, 2), [3, 4], '56', 78, 9.0]
print(list[0], type(list[0]))
print(list[2:3], type(list[0:1]))
print(list[2], type(list[2]))
```
57.
```
words = 'Welcome to the world of Programming'.split()
msg = [[word.upper(), word.lower(), len(word)] for word in words]
```

```
for i in msg:
   print(i)
```

58.
```
item = [x+y for x in 'cup' for y in 'pen']
print(item)
```

59.
```
print([x+y for x in 'cup' for y in 'pen' if x != 't' and y != 'o' ])
```

60.
```
list =[ [1,2]*3 ] *4
print(list)
```

61.
```
list = [10, 20, 30, 40, 50, 60, 70, 80, 90]
print(list[-4:-1])
print(list[-1:-4])
print(list[-5:])
print(list[-6:-2:2])
print(list[::-1])
```

62.
```
list = [[10, 20, [30, 40, [50, 60]]]]
print(list[0])
print(list[0][2])
print(list[0][2][2])
print(list[0][0])
print(list[0][2][1])
print(list[0][2][2][0])
```

63.
```
List = [100, 90, 80, 70, 60, 50]
List[2] = List[1] - 20
if 30 in List:
   print(List[3])
else:
   print(List[4])
```

64.
```
List = list(range(2, 20, 3))
print(List[5])
```

65.
```
List = [-5, -3, 0, 3, 6]
print([x*2 for x in List])
print([x for x in List if x >= 0])
```

66.
```
print([(x, x*2) for x in range(5)])
```

67.
```
List = [[1,2,3], [4,5,6], [7,8,9]]
print([val for x in List for val in x])
```

68.
```
DC = [-100, 0, 32, 40, 100]
DF = map(lambda temp: (9.0/5)*temp + 32, DC)
print(DF)
```

69.
```
List = [1,2,3,4,5,6,7,8,9,10]
print(list(filter(lambda x: x % 4 == 0, List)))
print(list( map(lambda x: x * 2 + 5, List))
print(reduce(lambda x, y: x + y, List))
```

70.
```
List = [-10,20,-30,40,-50]
if all([abs(i)<30 for i in List]):
    print("Hi")
else:
    print("Bye")
```
71.
```
def add_two(x):
    return x+2
List = [10,20,30,40,50]
result = list(map(add_two,List))
print(result)
```
72.
```
List = [13,26,39,52,64]
print(list(filter(lambda x:x%2==1,List)))
```
73.
```
str = "abcdefghijklmno"
for i in range(0, len(str), 2):
    print(str[i], end = ' ')
```
74.
```
print [ord(ch) for ch in 'PYTHON']
>>> eval("10 ** 2")
100
```
75.
```
>>> eval("'hello' + 'py'")
```
76.
```
l1 = [1,2,3]
l2 = ['a','b','c']
l3 = [1.2,3.4,5.6]
l4 = l1 + l2 + l3
print(l4)
```
77.
```
print([1,2,8,9] < [1,2,8,9,10])
```
78.
```
l = [1,2,3,4,5,6,7,8,9,10]
print(l[-1])
print(l[l[0]])
print(l[l[-8]])
print(l[l[l[0]+1]]+2)
```
79.
```
msg = ["PYTHON","is","a",["simple","iterpreted","OOP"],"language"]
print(msg[2:4])
print(msg[2:4][1][2])
print(msg[2:4][1][2][1])
print("im" in msg[2:4][1][2][1])
print(msg[2:4][1][1][3:])
print(msg[1]+msg[4])
```
80.
```
>>> [1,2,3] +[1,2,3] == [1,2,3]*2
```
81.
```
l = [1,2,3]
l * 3 == [l,l,l]
```

82.
```
msg = ["PYTHON","is","a",["simple","interpreted","OOP"],"language"]
print(msg[::2])
print('n' in msg[4])
print(msg[2] in msg[4])
```
83.
```
l = [1,2,3]
print((l + [4,5,6])[3])
```
84.
```
[1,2] == [1,2]
```
85.
```
[1,2] is [1,2]
```
86.
```
L = [1,2,3,4,5,6,7,8,9,10,11,12,
13,14]
print(L[::-1])
print(L[-1:-2:-3])
```
87.
```
for i in [1,2,3]:
    for j in [4,5,6]:
        print(i,j, end = "    ")
```
88.
```
count = 0
for i in range(5):
    for j in range(10):
        count = count + 1
print(count)
```
89.
```
list = [55, 66, 77, 88, 99]
print("random.choice to select a random element from a list - ", random.
choice(list))
```
90.
```
import random
city_list = ['New York', 'Los Angeles', 'Chicago', 'Houston',
'Philadelphia']
print("Select random element from list - ", random.choice(city_list))
```
91.
```
tup1 = (1,2,3)
tup2 = (1.0,2.0,3.0)
print(tup1 == tup2)
```
92.
```
from math import pi
[str(round(pi, val)) for val in range(1, 5)]
```
93.
```
Tup = ("abc", "def")
(key, value) = Tup
print(key, value)
```
94.
```
Tup = (1,2,3)
Add_Tup = Tup + Tup
print(Add_Tup)
Mul_Tup = Tup * 3
print(Mul_Tup)
```

95.
```
msg = "HelloWorld"
pairs = []
for i in range(1, len(msg), 2):
    first = msg[i - 1]
    second = msg[i]
    pairs.append((first, second))
for item in pairs:
    print(item)
```

96.
```
Tup  = (1, 'abc')
List = [1, 'abc']
print(Tup == List)
print(Tup == tuple(List))
print(list(Tup) == List)
print((1, 2) + (3, 4))
```

97.
```
list = ['Good', 'Morning']
y, x = list
print(x, y)
```

98.
```
A = ('Chinu', 30, 'Female')
B = ('Varun', 32, 'Male')
for i in [A, B]:
    print('%s is a %d year old %s' %i)
```

99.
```
Tup = ('Good',)
for i in range(4):
    Tup = (Tup,)
    print(Tup)
```

100.
```
Tup1='a','bcd',12.34
Tup2=Tup1,(5,6,7,8)
print(Tup2)
```

101.
```
Tup = (1, 2, [3, 4])
Tup[2][0] = 5
print(Tup)
```

102.
```
Tup = ("Good Morning")
print(Tup.index('M'), end = ' ')
print(Tup.index('n', 5))
print(Tup.index('r',4,8))
```

103.
```
t = (1,2,3,'a')
l = list(t)
 l
```

104.
```
tup = (1,2,3,4,5,6,7,8,9)
print(tup[3:5]*3)
```

105.
```
tup = (10,7,8,9,6,3,4,5,0,1,2)
print(tup[0])
print(tup[tup[3]])
print(tup[-4])
print(tup[tup[-2]])
print(tup[tup[tup[7]]-4])
print(tup[10*2-15+3])
```

106.
```
t = (1,2,3)
a,b,c = (x,y,z) = t
print(a,b,c)
print(x,y,z)
```

107.
```
t=('a')
print(type(t))
t=('a',)
print(type(t))
```

108.
```
t = (1,2,3)
tup = ('GO',) + t
print(tup)
```

109.
```
t1 = (1,2,3)
t2 = (4,5)
print(t1 + t2)
20.
t1 = (1,2,3)
t2 = t1 * (3)
print(t2)
```

110.
```
t1 = (1,2,3)
t2 = ('1','2')
print(t1 + t2)
```

111.
```
t = (78,98,80,76,53,54,78,98,87,74)
print(t[3:])
print(t[:6])
print(t[-4:])
print(t[-4:4])
print(t[:])
(76, 53, 54, 78, 98, 87, 74)
(78, 98, 80, 76, 53, 54)
(78, 98, 87, 74)
()
(78, 98, 80, 76, 53, 54, 78, 98, 87, 74)
```

```
['programming', 'is']
False
('but', 'fun')
False
```

112.
```
t =("Python","Programming","is","fun")
(a,b,c,d) = t
print(t[0][0] + t[1][1]+t[1])
```

113.
```
t = ('a',('b',('c',('d',))))
print(len(t))
print(t[1][0])
print('c' in t)
```

114.
```
t = (1,2,(3,4),5,(6,(7,8),9))
print(len(t))
print(t[3]+10)
print(t[t[1]])
print(t[t[1]][1]*10)
```

115.
```
t = ((1,2),)*7
print(t)
print(len(t[3:8]))
```

116.
```
tup = ("abc","def")
x,y = tup
print x, y
```

117.
```
students = ("Bhavya", "Era", "Falguni","Huma")
index = students.index("Falguni")
print("Falguni is present at location : ", index)
index = students.index("Isha")
print("Isha is present at location : ", index)
Falguni is present at location :  2
Traceback (most recent call last):
  File "C:\Python27\Try.py", line 4, in <module>
    index = students.index("Isha")
ValueError: tuple.index(x): x not in tuple
```

118.
```
Dict = {"India":"New Delhi", "Nepal":"Kathmandu", "USA":"Washington DC"}
del Dict["Nepal"]
for key,val in Dict.items():
    print(key,val)
```

119.
```
Dict = {"India":"New Delhi", "Nepal":"Kathmandu", "USA":"Washington DC"}
print(Dict.get("Russia"))
print(Dict.get("Pakistan", "No Idea"))
```

120.
```
Studs = {'Mitanshi', 'Harshita', 'Pritika'}
Toppers = {}.fromkeys(Studs, 0)
print(Toppers)
```

```
Toppers['Mitanshi'] = 97
Toppers['Harshita'] = 92
Toppers['Pritika'] = 89
Toppers.setdefault('Nisha', -1)
print(Toppers)
```

121.
```
Toppers = {}
Toppers['Mitanshi'] = 97
Toppers['Harshita'] = 92
Toppers['Pritika'] = 89
print('Harshita got ' + str(Toppers.get('Harshita')) + ' marks.')
```

122.
```
rec = {'Name': {'First': 'Chaitanya', 'Last': 'Raj'},
                'Marks': [80, 76, 84],
                'Course': 'BTech'}
print(rec['Name'])
print(rec['Name']['Last'])
print(rec['Marks'])
rec['Marks'].append(72)
print(rec)
```

123.
```
Dict = {"Amna":4,"Brij":2,"Chaitanya":5,"Divyanka":3}
s = 0
for v in Dict.values():
    s = s + v
print(s)
```

124.
```
Dict = {"Amna":4,"Brij":2,"Chaitanya":5,"Divyanka":3}
n = ''
for i in Dict:
    if n < i:
        n = i
print(n)
```

125.
```
Dict = {"Amna":4,"Brij":2,"Chaitanya":5,"Divyanka":3}
n = 'Chaitanya'
v = 10
if n in Dict:
    Dict[n] = v
print(Dict)
```

126.
```
Dict = {'a':1, 'b':2, ('c','d'):3}
print(Dict)
{'a': 1, 'b': 2, ('c', 'd'): 3}
```

127.
```
Dict = {'a':1, 'b':2, 'c':3,'d':4}
v = Dict['c']
if v in Dict:
    print("FOUND")
else:
    print("NOT FOUND")
```

128.
```
Dict = {'a':1, 'b':2, 'c':3,'d':4}
k = ''
for i in Dict:
    if i > k:
        k = i
        v = Dict[i]
print(k,v)
List = list(Dict.items())
List.sort()
print(List)
```

129.
```
Dict = {'a':1, 'b':2, 'c':3,'d':4, 'e':[5,6,7,8]}
print(Dict)
```

130.
```
Dict = {10:"TEN","HUNDRED":100,(1,2):("ONE","TWO")}
print(Dict)
```

131.
```
List = [10,10,10,20,30,30,20,40,40,40]
counts= {}
L= []
for i in List:
    if i not in L:
        L.append(i)
        counts[i] = 1
    else:
        counts[i] += counts[i]
print(counts)
```

132.
```
List = [10,10,10,20,30,30,20,40,40,40]
counts = {}
for i in List:
    if i in counts:
        counts[i] += 1
    else:
        counts[i] = 1
print(counts)
```

133.
```
Dict = {}
Dict[1] = 1
Dict['1'] = 2
Dict[1] += 1
sum = 0
for i in Dict:
    sum += Dict[i]
print(sum)
```

Find Out the Error, If Any

1. ```
   str = "Hello world"
   str[6] = 'W'
   print(str)
   ```
2. `"%s %s %s %s" % ('Welcome', 'to', 'Python')`
3. `"%s %s %s" % ('East', 'West', 'North', 'South')`
4. `"%d %f %f" % (10, 20, 'Hello')`
5. ```
   str = 'abcdefgh'
   str[5] = 'a'
   print(str)
   str = 'Python'
   print(str)
   ```
6. ```
   str = "Hello World"
   del str[2]
   print(str)
   ```
7. `print("Hello World" + 10)`
8. `print("Hello" * "World")`
9. ```
   list = ['abc', 'def', 'ghi', 'jkl']
   print list[2.0]
   ```
10. ```
    even = [2,4,6]
    del even
    print(even)
    ```
11. ```
    list = [(1, 2), [3, 4], '56', 78, 9.0]
    list.remove('abc')
    ```
12. ```
    msg = "Hello"
    msg.append("World")
    print(msg)
    ```
13. `[1,2,3] + 2`
14. ```
    L = [1,2,3,4]
    L.remove(7)
    ```
15. ```
    [1,2,3] * 3.0
    tup = ("abc", "def", "ghi", "jkl")
    tup.append("mno")
    ```
16. ```
    Tup1 = (9,8,7,6,5)
    Tup2 = (1,2,3,4,5)
    print(Tup1 - Tup2)
    ```
17. `tup.remove("abc")`
18. ```
    Tup = ('abc', 'def', 'ghi','jkl')
    Tup[2] = 'xyz'
    ```
    ```

19.
```
x, y = 10, 20, 30
```
20.
```
x = {1, 2, 3, 4, 5}
x.add([6,7,8])
print(x)
```
21.
```
Dict = {[02,89, 85]:"PCM"}
print(Dict)
```
22.
```
tup1 = (1,2,3)
tup2 = tup1 + (2)
print(tup2)
```
23.
```
tup = (23,12.56,90,[34,56])
print("Largest Value = ",max(tup))
```
24.
```
(a,b,c,d) = (10,20,30)
```
25.
```
t = (1,2,3,4,5)
print(t[10])
```
26.
```
26.t1 = (1,2,3)
t2 = (1,2)
print(t2-t1)
```
27.
```
t1 = (1,2,3)
t2 =  t1 *(4,)
print(t2)
```
28.
```
t = (1,)*3
t[0] = 2
print(t)
```
29.
```
Tup = (1,2,3,4.0,"abc")
print(min(Tup))
```
30.
```
Dict = {"India":"New Delhi", "Nepal":"Kathmandu"}
print(Dict["USA"])
```
31.
```
Dict = {}
print(Dict[0])
```
32.
```
Dict = {'a':1, 'b':2, ['c','d']:[3,4]}
print(Dict)
```
33.
```
msg = "How are you doing?"
counts = {}
for c in msg:
    counts[c] = counts[c] + 1
print(counts)
```
34.
```
Dict = {}
Dict[(1,2,3)] = 10
Dict[[3,2,1]] = 20
print(DIct)
```
35.
```
Dict = {'a':1,'b':2,'c':3,'d':4}
print(Dict['a','b'])
```

CHAPTER 3

Functions and Modules

In the previous chapters, we have learnt the basics of Programming. To understand the usability of the programs better, we should have a clear concept of the same. Let us consider a scenario – Suppose you are handling a huge project. Being the Project Manager, would you hand over the entire responsibility to one or divide the same into pieces and allocate accordingly?

Of course, you will divide and allocate. Same is the case with programs. Instead of writing the entire code in one place, we must break the program in different functions or modules. Individual modules should then be coded individually. Whenever their functionality is required, they can just be called. In a program, you can call a function any number of times depending on the requirements.

3.1 Function

A function is a block of organised and reusable program code that performs a single, specific and well-defined task. Consider Figure 3.1, which explains how a function func1() is called to perform a well-defined task. As soon as func1() is called, the program control is passed to the first statement in the function. All the statements in the function are executed, and then the program control is passed to the statement following the one that called the function.

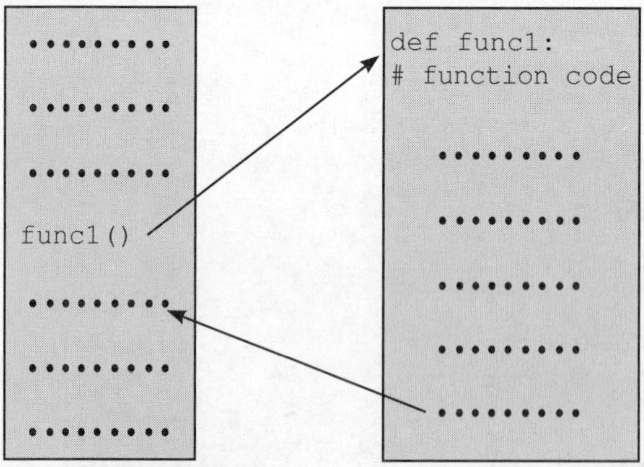

Figure 3.1 Calling Function func1()

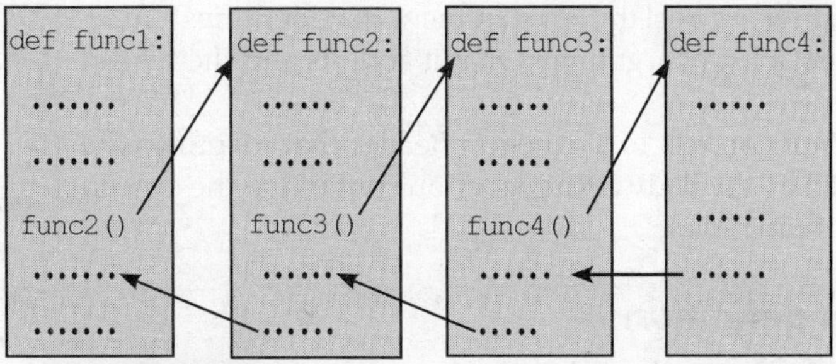

Figure 3.2 Function(s) Calling Another Function

In Figure 3.2, we see that func1() calls another function named func2(). Therefore, func1() is known as the *calling function* and func2() is known as the **called function**. The moment the compiler encounters a function call, instead of executing the next statement in the calling function, the control jumps to the statements that are a part of the called function. After the called function is executed, the control is returned back to the calling program.

It is not necessary that the func1() can call only one function, it can call as many functions as it wants and as many times as it wants as shown in Figure 3.3 where function func1() is called twice from the calling function. For example, a function call placed within for loop or while loop may call the same function multiple times until the condition holds true.

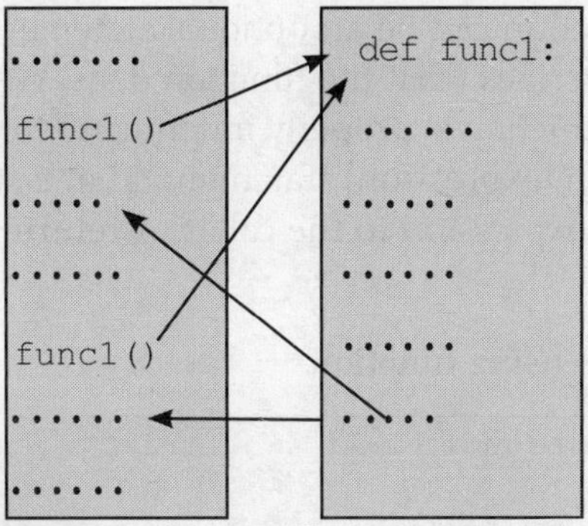

Figure 3.3 Function Calling Another Function Twice

3.2 Function declaration and function definition

We may declare a function that does not take any inputs at all, or a function that does not return any value at all. Before using a function, we must declare that function and also define it. Let us learn some important terminologies that we will be using while using functions.

- A function, *f* that uses another function *g*, is known as the *calling function* and *g* is known as the *called function*.
- The inputs that the function takes are known as *arguments/parameters*.
- When a called function returns some result back to the calling function, it is said to *return* that result.
- The calling function may or may not pass *parameters* to the called function. If the called function accepts arguments, the calling function will pass parameters, else not.

- *Function declaration* is a declaration statement that identifies a function with its name, a list of arguments that it accepts and the type of data it returns.
- *Function definition* consists of a function header that identifies the function, followed by the body of the function containing the executable code for that function

> Function naming follows the same rules of writing identifiers in Python

3.3 Function definition

Users can write their own functions. Such functions are called user-defined functions. Such functions are created by users in their programs using the def keyword.

As a Python programmer, you can write any number of functions in your program. However, to define a function, you must keep the following points in mind.

- Function blocks starts with the keyword **def**.
- The keyword is followed by the function name and parentheses (( )). The function name is used to uniquely identify the function.
- After the parentheses a colon (:) is placed.
- Parameters or arguments that the function accept are placed within parentheses. Through these parameters, values are passed to the function. They are optional. In case no values are to be passed, nothing is placed within the parenthesis.
- The first statement of a function can be an optional statement – the documentation string of the function or *docstring* describes what the function does. We will discuss later in the book
- The code block within the function is properly indented to form the block code.
- A function may have a return [expression] statement. That is, the return statement is optional. If it exits, it passes back an expression to the caller. A return statement with no arguments is the same as return none.

Program that adds two numbers using function

```
def add(x,y):    # function to add two numbers
        return x+y
a = 20
b = 10
print(add(a,b))
OUTPUT
10
```

> The words before parentheses specifies the function name, and the comma-separated values inside the parentheses are function arguments

When a function is defined, space is allocated for that function in the memory. A function definition comprises of two parts:

- Function header
- Function body

The syntax of a function definition can be given as: **Function Header**

```
def function_name(variable1, variable2,..)
    documentation string    Function Body
    statement block
    return [expression]
```

Example 3.1: To write a function that displays a string repeatedly

```
def func():
        for i in range(4):
                print("Hello World")
func()    #function call
OUTPUT
Hello World
Hello World
Hello World
Hello World
```

In the above code, name of the function is func. It takes no arguments, and prints "Hello World" four times. The function is first defined before being called. The statements in the function are executed only when the function is called.

3.4 Function call

Defining a function means specifying its name, parameters that are expected and the set of instructions. Once the basic structure of a function is finalized, it can be executed by calling it.

> The parameter list in the function definition as well as function declaration must match with each other

The function call statement invokes the function. When a function is invoked, the program control jumps to the called function to execute the statements that are a part of that function. Once the called function is executed, the program control passes back to the calling function.

The syntax of calling a function that does not accept parameter is simply name of the function followed by parenthesis, which is given as,

```
function_name()
```

Function call statement has the following syntax when it accepts parameters.

```
function_name(variable1, variable2, ...)
```

When the function is called, the interpreter checks that the correct number and type of arguments are used in the function call. It also checks the type of the returned value (if it returns a value to the calling function).

3.5 Function parameters

A function can take parameters which are nothing but some values that are passed to it so that the function can manipulate them to produce the desired result. These parameters are normal variables with a small difference that the values of these variables are defined (initialized) when we call the function and are then passed to the function.

Parameters are specified within the pair of parentheses in the function definition and are separated by commas.

Key points to remember while calling the function

- Function name and the number and type of arguments in the function call must be same as that given in the function definition.

- If by mistake the parameters passed to a function are more than that it is specified to accept, then an error would be returned.

Example 3.2: Program to demonstrate the mismatch between function parameters and arguments

```
def func(i, j):
        print("Hello World", i, j)
func(5)
OUTPUT
TypeError: func() takes exactly 2 arguments (1 given)
```

The indented statements form body of the function

- If by mistake the parameters passed to a function are less than that it is specified to accept, then an error would be returned.

Program to demonstrate the mismatch between function parameters and arguments

```
def func(i):
        print("Hello World", i)
func(5, 5)
OUTPUT
TypeError: func() takes exactly 1 argument (2 given)
```

- Names of variables in function call and header of function definition may vary.

Program to demonstrate mismatch of name of function parameters and arguments

```
def func(i):    # function definition header accepts a variable with name
i
print("Hello World", i)
j = 10
func(j)         # Function is called using variable j
OUTPUT
Hello World 10
```

- If the data type of the argument passed does not matches with that expected in function then an error is generated.

Program to demonstrate mismatch between data types of function parameters and arguments

```
def func(i):
    print("Hello World" + i)
func(5)
OUTPUT
TypeError: cannot concatenate 'str' and 'int' objects
```

- Arguments may be passed in the form of expressions to the called function. In such a case, arguments are first evaluated and converted to the type of formal parameter, and then the body of the function gets executed.

Program to demonstrate that the arguments may be passed in the form of expressions to the called function.

```
def func(i):
        print("Hello World", i)
func(5+2*3)
OUTPUT
Hello World 11
```

Before calling a function, you must define it

- The parameter list must be separated with commas.
- If the function returns a value, then it may be assigned to some variable in the calling program. For example,

```
variable_name = function_name(variable1, variable2, ...);
```

Let us now try a program using function.

Program to add two integers using function that accepts two arguments

```
def total(a,b):          # function accepting parameters
    result = a+b
    print("Sum of ", a, " and ", b, " = ", result)
a = int(input("Enter the first number : "))
b = int(input("Enter the second number : "))
total(a,b) #function call with two arguments
OUTPUT
Enter the first number : 10
Enter the second number : 20
Sum of 10 and 20 = 30
```

It is a logic error if the arguments in the fuction call are placed in a wrong order

In the total(), we have declared a variable result just like any other variable. Variables declared within a function are called local variables. We will read more about it in the next section.

3.6 Parameter passing mutable/immutable properties

Python uses a mechanism, known as 'Call-by-Object', or 'Call by Object Reference' or 'Call by Sharing'.

When immutable arguments like integers, strings or tuples are passed to a function, the parameters are passed using call-by-value technique. The object reference is passed to the function parameters. Since they are immutable, their value(s) cannot be changed in the function.

When we pass mutable objects as arguments to the function, even they are passed by object reference. However, their value(s) can be changed within the function. For example, when a list is passed to a function, its individual elements can be changed. Moreover, if we assign a new list to same name of the list, the old list will not be affected at all. The list remains unchanged in caller function's scope.

In Figure 3.4, we have an integer variable x. When this parameter is passed to a function, a reference to x is used as long as the parameter is not changed. The moment an attempt is made to change the value of x, Python creates a separate local variable so that the caller function's variable is not changed.

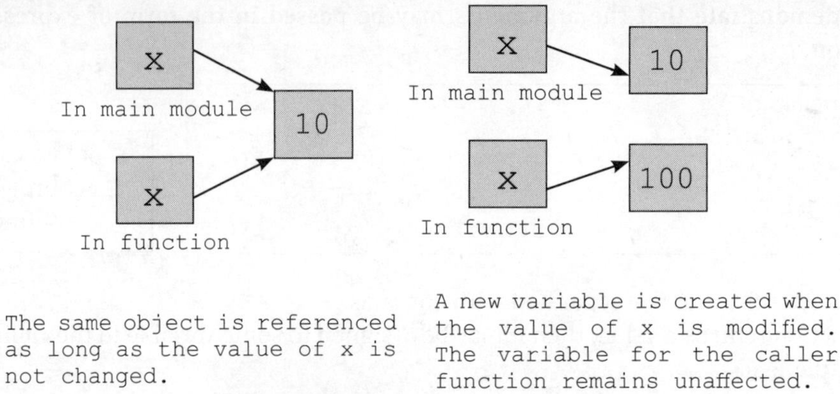

Figure 3.4 Function Parameters

```
def func(x):
    print(" In Func, before modification, ID of x =
",id(x), " and value of x = ",x)
    x = 100
    print(" In Func, after modification, ID of x =
",id(x), " and value of x = ",x)
x = 10
print(" In main module, before calling function,
ID of x = ",id(x), " and value of x = ",x)
func(x)
print(" In main module, after calling function, ID
of x = ",id(x), " and value of x = ",x)
OUTPUT
 In main module, before calling function, ID of x
=  1687091264  and value of x =  10
 In Func, before modification, ID of x =  1687091264
and value of x =  10
 In Func, after modification, ID of x =  1687092704
and value of x =  100
 In main module, after calling function, ID of x
=  1687091264  and value of x =  10
```

> List of variables used in fuction call is known as actual parameter list. The actual parameter list may be variable names, expresstions or constants

In the above example, id() function is used that takes an object as a parameter and returns the 'identity' of the object. This identity is a unique integer, which remains constant for this object during its lifetime.

The value and identity of x is printed at different locations to verify whether x is pointing to the same object or a different object. In the main module, the value and identity of x remain same before as well as after calling the function.

In the called function, the value and identity of x remain same as long as value of x is not changed. When the value of x is modified, a new variable with name x, but a different id is created, which is local to the function and the copy of in the main module is not affected by this change.

In programming languages like C, C++ and Java, we have call-by-value and call-by-reference techniques of passing arguments to a function. But in Python, we still have the same techniques but applicable in a different way. Python initially behaves like call-by-reference, but as soon as we change the value of a variable, Python 'switches' to call-by-value.

> You can call a function from another function or directly from the Python prompt

3.7 The return statement

In all our functions written above, nowhere have we used the return statement. But you will be surprised to know that every function has an implicit return statement as the last instruction in the function body. This implicit return statement returns nothing to its caller, so it is said to return NONE where NONE means nothing. But you can change this default behaviour by explicitly using the return statement to return some value back to the caller. The syntax of return statement is,

> A function may or may not return a value. A return statement with no arguments is the same as return None

return [expression]

The expression is written in brackets because it is optional. If the expression is present, it is evaluated and the resultant value is returned to the calling function. However, if no expression is specified, then the function will return **None**.

The return statement is used for two things.

- Return a value to the caller
- To end and exit a function and go back to its caller

It should be noted that in the output, None is returned from the function. The return value may or may not be assigned to another variable in the caller.

Example: Program to write a function without a return statement and try to print its return value. As mentioned earlier, such a function should return None.

```
def display(str):
  print(str)
# assigning return value to another variable
x = display("Hello World")
print(x)
# print return value without assigning it to another variable
print(display("Hello Again"))
```

OUTPUT

```
Hello World
None
Hello Again
None
```

Example: To write another function, which returns an integer to the caller.

```
def cube(x):
    return (x*x*x)
num = 10
result = cube(num)
print('Cube of ', num, ' = ',
result)
OUTPUT
Cube of 10 = 1000
```

Key points to remember

- The return statement must appear within the function
- Once you return a value from a function, it immediately exits that function. Therefore, any code written after the return statement is never executed.

```
Example: Program to demonstrate flow of
control after the return statement
def display():
    print("In Function")
    print("About to execute return
    statement")
    return
    print("This line will never be
    displayed")
display()
print("Back to the caller")
OUTPUT
In Function
About to execute return statement
Back to the caller
```

3.8 Types of function parameters

We have already discussed the technique to define and call a function. In this section, we will go a step forward and learn some more ways of defining a function. All these features make Python a wonderful language. Some of these features include: Required arguments, keyword arguments, default arguments, and variable-length arguments.

3.8.1 Required arguments

We have already been using this type of formal arguments. In required arguments, the arguments are passed to a function in correct positional order. Also, the number of arguments in the function call should exactly match with the number of arguments specified in the function definition.

Look at three different versions of display() given below and observe the output. The function displays the string only when number and type of arguments in the function call matches with that specified in the function definition, otherwise a type error is returned.

```
def display():
    print "Hello"
display("Hi")
OUTPUT
TypeError: display()
takes no arguments
(1 given)
```

```
def display(str):
    print str
display()
OUTPUT
TypeError: display()
takes exactly 1
argument (0 given)
```

```
def display(str):
    print str
str ="Hello"
display(str)
OUTPUT
Hello
```

3.8.2 Keyword arguments

When we call a function with some values, the values are assigned to the arguments based on their position. Python also allow functions to be called using keyword arguments in which the order (or position) of the arguments can be changed. The values are not assigned to arguments according to their position but based on their name (or keyword).

Having a required argument after keyword arguments will cause error

Keyword arguments when used in function calls helps the function to identify the arguments by the parameter name. This is especially beneficial in two cases.

- First, if you skip arguments
- Second, if in the function call, you change the order of parameters, that is, in any order different from that specified in the function definition.

In both the cases mentioned above, Python interpreter uses keywords provided in the function call to match the values with parameters.

Program to demonstrate keyword arguments

```
def display(str, int_x, float_y):
   print("The string is : ",str)
   print("The integer value is : ", int_x)
   print("The floating point value is : ", float_y)
display(float_y = 56789.045, str = "Hello", int_x = 1234)
OUTPUT
The string is:  Hello
The integer value is:  1234
The floating point value is:  56789.045
```

Consider another program for keyword arguments in which during function call we use assignment operator to assign values to function parameters using other variables (instead of values).

```
def display(name, age, salary):
    print("Name : ", name)
    print("Age : ", age)
    print("Salary : ", salary)
n = "Aadi"
a = 35
s = 123456
display(salary = s, name = n, age = a)
OUTPUT
Name :  Aadi
Age :  35
Salary :  123456
```

Key points to remember

- All the keyword arguments passed should match one of the arguments accepted by the function
- The order of keyword arguments is not important
- In no case, an argument should receive a value more than once.

Keyword arguments makes the program code easier to read and understand

3.8.3 Default arguments

Python allow users to specify function arguments that can have default values. This means that a function can be called with fewer arguments than it is defined to have. That is, if the function accepts three parameters, but function call provides only two arguments, then the third parameter will be assigned the default (already specified) value.

The default value to an argument is provided by using the assignment operator (=). Users can specify a default value for one or more arguments.

Program that uses default arguments.

```
def display(name, course = "BTech"):
    print("Name : " + name)
    print("Course : ", course)
display(course = "BCA", name = "Arav")
# Keyword Arguments
display(name = "Reyansh")
# Default Argument for course
OUTPUT
Name : Arav
Course :  BCA
Name : Reyansh
Course :  BTech
```

A default argument assumes a default value if a value is not provided in the function call for that argument

In the above code, the parameter name does not have a default value and is therefore mandatory. That is, you must specify a value for this parameter during the function call. But, parameter, course has already been given a default value, so it is optional. If a value is provided, it will overwrite the default value, and in case a value is not specified during function call, the one provided in the function definition as the default value will be used.

Key points to remember

- You can specify any number of default arguments in your function.
- If you have default arguments, then they must be written after the non-default arguments. This means that non-default arguments cannot follow default arguments. Therefore, the line of code given below will produce an error.

Program to demonstrate default arguments

```
def display(name, course = "BTech", marks):
# error
    print("Name : " + name)
    print("Course : ", course)
    print("Marks : ", marks)
display(name = "Reyansh", 90)
SyntaxError: non-default argument follows default
argument
```

All the arguments to the right of the default argument must also have default values

3.8.4 Variable-length arguments

In some situations, it is not known in advance how many arguments will be passed to a function. In such cases, Python allows programmers to make function calls with arbitrary (or any) number of arguments.

When we use arbitrary arguments or variable length arguments, then the function definition use an asterisk (*) before the parameter name. Syntax for a function using variable arguments can be given as,

```
def functionname([arg1, arg2,.... ] *var_args_tuple ):
    function statements
    return [expression]
```

Program to demonstrate the use of variable length arguments

```
def func(name, *fav_subjects):
     print("\n", name, " likes to read ")
     for subject in fav_subjects:
          print(subject)
func("Goransh", "Mathematics", "Android Programming")
func("Richa", "C", "Data Structures", "Design and
Analysis of Algorithms")
func("Krish")
OUTPUT
Goransh likes to read Mathematics Android Programming
Richa likes to read C Data Structures Design and
Analysis of Algorithms
Krish likes to read
```

A positional argument is assigned based on its position in the argument list but a keyword argument is assigned based on parameter name

In the above program, in the function definition, we have two parameters – name and variable length parameter fav_subjects. The function is called three times with 3, 4 and 1 parameter(s), respectively. The first value is assigned to name, and the other values are assigned to parameter fav_subjects. Everyone can have any number of favorite subjects, and some can even have none. So when the third call is made, fav_subjects has no value, and hence, the for loop will not execute as there is no subject available in fav_subjects.

Key points to remember

- The arbitrary number of arguments passed to the function basically forms a tuple before being passed into the function.
- Inside the called function, **for** loop is used to access the arguments.
- The variable sized arguments if present in the function definition should be last in the list of formal parameters.
- Any formal parameters written after the variable sized arguments must be keyword-only arguments.

A function cannot be used on the right side of an assignment statement. Therefore writing, total (a, b) = s; is invalid

3.9 Passing strings, lists, tuples, dictionaries to functions

We have already seen functions accepting strings as arguments. In this section, we will see how other objects like lists, tuples and dictionaries can be passed as arguments and manipulated within the function.

Program to access a tuple in a function that is passed to it as an argument.

```
def Func(Tup):
    for i in Tup:
        print(i, end = ' ')
Tup = (1,2,3,4,5)
Func(Tup)
OUTPUT
1 2 3 4 5
```

We have studied that when pass an argument by prefixing it with a *, it means that argument is variable in size. Such arguments are passed using a tuple.

Program to demonstrate variable-length arguments using tuple. The function adds the values it receives as arguments.

```
def sum(*args):
    '''Return the sum of each argument'''
    total = 0
    for i in args:
        total += i
    return total
tot = sum(1,2,3,4,5,6,7,8,9,10)
print("Sum of 1,2,3,4,5,6,7,8,9,10 = ", tot)
tot = sum(1,2,3,4,5)
print("Sum of 1,2,3,4,5 = ", tot)
OUTPUT
Sum of 1,2,3,4,5,6,7,8,9,10 =  55
Sum of 1,2,3,4,5 =  15
```

Passing dictionary as an argument

Python allow users to pass a dictionary as an argument to a function just as a normal variable is passed like other variables are passed.

```
# A function that takes dictionary as an argument
def func(Dict):
    for key in Dict:
        print("Dict[",key,"] = ", Dict[key])
Dict = {'NAME':'Priya', 'MARKS': 92, 'GRADE':'A+'}
func(Dict)
OUTPUT
Dict[ NAME ] =  Priya
Dict[ MARKS ] =  92
Dict[ GRADE ] =  A+
```

We can even pass a dictionary as kwargs where 'kwargs' means keyword arguments. Such arguments are even more useful when the user does not have a clue about the number of arguments. Therefore, the dictionary argument is passed by prefixing '**' it to the argument.

 # Program to demonstrate passing dictionary as keyword arguments

```
def Func(**name):
    print (name["fname"]+" "+name["mname"]+" "+name["lname"])
# passing dictionary key-value pair as arguments
Func(fname = "Lal", mname ="Bahadur", lname ="Shastri")
OUTPUT
Lal Bahadur Shastri
```

Apart from dictionary, we can also pass other values to the function as illustrated in the program given below.

 # Program to demonstrate passing dictionary as keyword arguments

```
def Func(marks, avg, **name):
    print (name["fname"]+" "+name["mname"]+" "+name["lname"] + " Got Marks
= "+ str(marks) + " And Average = " + str(avg))
# passing dictionary key-value pair as arguments
Func(87,85.2, fname = "Parth", mname ="M", lname ="Patel")
OUTPUT
Parth M Patel Got Marks = 87 And Average = 85.2
```

3.10 Modules

In the previous section, we have seen that functions help us to reuse a particular piece of code. Modules go a step ahead. It allows you to reuse one or more functions in your programs even in the programs in which those functions have not been defined.

> Modules are pre-written pieces of code that are used to perform common tasks like generating random numbers, performing mathematical operations, etc.

Putting simply, module is a file with a .py extension that has definitions of all functions and variables that you would like to use even in other programs. The program in which you want to use functions or variables defined in module will simply import that particular module (or .py file).

The basic way to use a module is to add import module name as the first line of your program and then writing module name.var to access functions and values with the name var in the module. Let us first use the standard library modules.

Program to print the PATH variable

```
import sys
print("\n PYTHONPATH = \n", sys.path)
OUTPUT
PYTHONPATH =
    ['C:\\Users\\Reema\\AppData\\Local\\Programs\\Python\\Python38-32\\
Lib\\idlelib',
    'C:\\Users\\Reema\\AppData\\Local\\Programs\\Python\\Python38-32\\
python38.zip',
    'C:\\Users\\Reema\\AppData\\Local\\Programs\\Python\\Python38-32\\DLLs'
    'C:\\Users\\Reema\\AppData\\Local\\Programs\\Python\\Python38-32\\lib'
    'C:\\Users\\Reema\\AppData\\Local\\Programs\\Python\\Python38-32',
    'C:\\Users\\Reema\\AppData\\Local\\Programs\\Python\\Python38-32\\
lib\\site-packages']
```

In the above code, we *import* the sys module (short form of system) using the import statement to use its functionality related to the Python interpreter and its environment.

When the import sys statement is executed, Python looks for the sys.py module in one of the directories listed in its sys.path variable. If the file is found, then the statements in the module are executed.

The sys module provides functions and variables used to manipulate different parts of the Python runtime environment.

3.10.1 Module loading and execution

A module imported in a program must be located and loaded into memory before it can be used. Python first searches for the modules in the current working directory. If the module is not found there, it then looks for the module in the directories specified in the PYTHONPATH environment variable. If the module is still not found or if the PYTHONPATH variable is not defined, then a Python installation-specific path (like C:\Python27\Lib) is searched. If the module is not located even there, then an error ImportError exception is generated.

Till now, we have saved our modules in the same directory as that of the program importing it. But, if you want the module to be available to other programs as well, then the module should be either saved in directory specified in the PYTHONPATH, or stored in the Python installation Lib directory.

Once a module is located, it is loaded in memory. A compiled version of the module with file extension .pyc is generated. Next time when the module is imported, this .pyc file is loaded, rather than the .py file, to save the time of recompiling. A new compiled version of a module is again produced whenever the compiled version is out of date (based on the dates when the .pyc file was created/modified). Even the programmer can force the Python shell to reload and recompile the .py file to generate a new .pyc file by using the reload() function.

3.10.2 The from...import statement

A module may contain definition for many variables and functions. When you import a module, you can use any variable or function defined in that module. But if you want to use only selected variables or functions, then you can use the from...import statement. For example, in the above program, you are using only the path variable in the sys module, so you could have better written from sys import path.

Example 3.3: Program that uses the from...import statement

```
from math import pi
print("PI = ", + pi)
OUTPUT
3.141592653589793
```

To import more than one item from a module, use a comma separated list. For example, to import the value of PI and sqrt() from the math module, you can write

```
from math import pi, sqrt
```

However, to import all the identifiers defined in the sys module, you can use the from sys import * statement. However, you should avoid using the import * statement as it confuses variables in your code with variables in the external module.

> Import * statement import all names except those beginning with an underscore (_)

You can also import a module with a different name using the **as** keyword. This is particularly more important when a module either has a long or confusing name.

For example,

```
from math import sqrt as square_root
......
print(square_root(81))
```

Python also allows you to pass command line arguments to your program. This can be done using the sys module. The argv variable in this modules keeps a track of command line arguments passed to the .py script as shown below.

```
import sys
print(sys.argv)
```

To execute this program code, go to Command Prompt (in Windows), write

```
C:\Python34> python main.py Hello World. You will get the output as,
['main.py', 'Hello', 'World']
```

Finally, you can use sys.exit([*arg*]) to exit from Python. arg is an optional argument, which can either be an integer giving the exit status or another type of object. If it is an integer, zero signifies successful termination, and any nonzero value indicates an error or abnormal termination of the program. Most systems require the value of arg to be in the range 0-127 and therefore produces undefined results otherwise. If another type of object is passed, None is same as passing zero, and any other object results in an exit code of 1. Generally, sys.exit("Error Message") is a quick way to exit a program when an error occurs.

Program to demonstrate sys.exit

```
import sys
print("HELLO WORLD")
sys.exit(0)
OUTPUT
HELLO WORLD
```

3.10.3 Name of module

Every module has a name. You can find the name of a module by using the __name__ attribute of the module.

Program to print the name of the module in which your statements is written

```
print("Hello")
print("Name of this module is : ", __name__)
OUTPUT
Hello
Name of this module is :  __main__
```

Observe the output and always remember that for every standalone program written by the user, the name of the module is __main__.

3.10.4 Making your own modules

You can easily create as many modules as you want. In fact, you have already been doing that. Every Python program is a module, that is, every file that you save as .py extension is a module. The code given below illustrates this concept.

First write these lines in a file and save the file as MyModule.py

```
def display():          # function definition
    print("Hello")
    print("Name of called module is : ", __name__)

str = "Welcome to the world of Python !!!      #variable definition
```

Then, open another file and write the lines of code given below.

```
import MyModule
print("MyModule str = ", MyModule.str)  # using variable defined in MyModule
MyModule.display()                      # using function defined in MyModule
print("Name of calling module is : ", __name__)
```

When you run this code, you will get the following output

```
MyModule str =  Welcome to the world of Python !!!
Hello
Name of called module is :  MyModule
Name of calling module is :  __main__
```

Note that we have been using the dot operator to access members (variables or functions) of the module. Assuming that MyModule had many other variables or functions definition, we could have specifically imported just str and display() by writing the import statement as

```
from MyModule import str, display
```

> Modules should be placed in the same directory as that of the program in which it is imported. It can also be stored in one of the directories listed in sys.path

3.10.5 Python - math module

Python has a standard library that has many important and useful built-in functions (like print(), ord(), int(), etc). Besides these built-in functions, the library also has various modules that have functionalities for specified actions.

Some of the most popular mathematical functions are defined in the math module. These include trigonometric functions, representation functions, logarithmic functions, angle conversion functions, etc. In addition, two mathematical constants – PI and Epsilon – are also defined in this module. Let us print the two values. Remember that, before using the math module, we must first import it by writing **import math**. Then, the specific function can be used by writing, **math.function_name**.

```
# Program to print the value
of PI and e
import math
print("PI = ", math.pi)
print("Epsilon = ", math.e)
OUTPUT
PI = 3.141592653589793
Epsilon = 2.718281828459045
```

Functions like sin, cos, tan, etc that need an angle accept the values in radians as an argument. In case you want to specify angle in degrees, then the math.degree() function must be used. Table 1 lists some commonly used built-in function in the math module.

Table 1: || Built-in Functions in math Module

Function	Description	Example
ceil(x)	Returns the smallest integer greater than or equal to x.	import math print(math.ceil(1.2345)) OUTPUT 2
fabs(x)	Returns the absolute value of x	import math print(math.fabs(-5.6)) OUTPUT 5.6
factorial(x)	Returns the factorial of x	import math print(math.factorial(6)) OUTPUT 720
floor(x)	Returns the largest integer less than or equal to x	import math print(math.floor(-5.6)) OUTPUT -6
fmod(x, y)	Returns the remainder when x is divided by y	import math print(math.fmod(-100,6)) OUTPUT -4.0
modf(x)	Returns the fractional and integer parts of x	import math print(math.modf(-123.456)) OUTPUT (-0.45600000000000307, -123.0)
trunc(x)	Returns the truncated integer value of x	import math print(math.trunc(-123.456)) OUTPUT -123
exp(x)	Returns e**x	import math print(math.exp(10)) OUTPUT 22026.465794806718
log2(x)	Returns the base-2 logarithm of x	import math print(math.log2(1024)) OUTPUT 10.0
log10(x)	Returns the base-10 logarithm of x	import math print(math.log10(1000)) OUTPUT 3.0
pow(x, y)	Returns x raised to the power y	import math print(math.pow(10,4)) OUTPUT 10000.0

Table 1: || *(Continued)*

Function	Description	Example

`sqrt(x)`	Returns the square root of x	`import math`
		`print(math.sqrt(10000))`
		`OUTPUT`
		`100.0`

`cos(x)`	Returns the cosine of x	`import math`
		`print(math.cos(90))`
		`OUTPUT`
		`-0.4480736161291701`

`sin(x)`	Returns the sine of x	`import math`
		`print(math.sin(90))`
		`OUTPUT`
		`0.8939966636005579`

`tan(x)`	Returns the tangent of x	`import math`
		`print(math.tan(90))`
		`OUTPUT`
		`-1.995200412208242`

Key Terms

Arguments/parameters: The inputs that the function takes.
Function: A piece of code that perform a well-defined task.
Function declaration: A declaration statement that identifies a function with its name, a list of arguments that it accepts and the type of data it returns.
Global variables: Variables which are defined in the main body of the program file. They are visible throughout the program file.
Lifetime of the variable: Duration for which the variable exists is called its *lifetime*.
Module: A file with a .py extension that has definitions of all functions and variables that you would like to use even in other programs.
Package: A hierarchical file directory structure that has modules and other packages within it.
Recursive function: A function that calls itself to solve a smaller version of its task until a final call is made, which does not require a call to itself.
Scope of the variable: Part of the program in which a variable is accessible is called its *scope*.

Chapter Highlights

- ✶ Understanding, coding and testing multiple separate functions are far easier than doing the same for one huge function.
- ✶ Large programs usually follow the DRY principle, that is, Don't Repeat Yourself principle. Once a function is written it can be called multiple times wherever its functionality is required.
- ✶ A bad repetitive code abides by the WET principle, i.e, While Everything Twice, or We Enjoy Typing.
- ✶ A function, *f* that uses another function *g*, is known as the *calling function* and *g* is known as the *called function*.
- ✶ When a called function returns some result back to the calling function, it is said to *return* that result.

* Defining a function means specifying its name, parameters that are expected and the set of instructions. Once the structure of a function is finalized, it can be executed by calling it.
* In nested functions, the inner function can access variables defined in both outer as well as inner function, but the outer function can access variables defined only in the outer function.
* Once you return a value from a function, it immediately exits that function. Therefore, any code written after the return statement is never executed.
* Keyword arguments when used in function calls help the function to identify the arguments by the parameter name.
* When number of arguments passed to a function is not known in advance then use arbitrary (or any) number of arguments in function header.
* Docstrings (documentation strings) serve the same purpose as that of comments, as they are designed to explain code.

Review Questions

1. Define function and give its advantages.
2. Can a function call another function? Justify your answer with the help of an example.
3. What do you understand by the term arguments? How do we pass them to a function?
4. What are user-defined functions? With the help of an example illustrate how you can have such functions in your program.
5. The return statement is optional. Justify this statement with the help of an example.
6. Define a function that calculates the sum of all numbers from 0 to its argument.
7. Arguments may be passed in the form of expressions to the called function. Justify this testament with the help of an example.
8. Explain the use of return statement.
9. Explain the utility of keyword arguments.
10. What are modules? How do you use them in your programs?
11. Write short notes on
    a. Keyword arguments
    b. Default arguments
    c. Variable sized arguments

Programming Exercise

1. Write a program that finds greater of three given numbers using functions. Pass the numbers as arguments.
2. Write a program that prints the time taken to execute a program in Python.
3. Write a function that returns the absolute value of a number.
4. Write a function is_prime() that returns a 1 if the argument passed to it is a prime a number and a 0 otherwise.
5. Write a function that accepts an integer between 1 and 12 to represent the month number and displays the corresponding month of the year (For example, if month = 1, then display JANUARY).
6. Write a function is_a leap_year, which takes the year as its argument and checks whether the year is a leap year or not and then displays an appropriate message on the screen.

7. Write a program to swap two variables that are defined as global variables.
8. Write a menu-driven program to add, subtract, multiply and divide two integers using functions.
9. Write a program using function that calculates the hypotenuse of a right-angled triangle.
10. Write a function that accepts a number n as input and returns the average of numbers from 1 to n.
11. Write a program to calculate the area of a triangle using function.
12. Write a program using function to calculate x to the power of y, where y be either negative or positive. Pass dictionary as an argument to the function.
13. Write a program using function to calculate compound interest given the principal, rate of interest and number of years.
14. Write a function that converts temperature given in Celsius into Fahrenheit.
15. Write a function to draw the following pattern on the screen

```
********
!     !
!     !
!     !
********
```

16. Write a function called printStatus that is passed status code 'S', 'M', 'D' or 'U' and returns the string 'Separated', 'Married', 'Divorced' or 'Unmarried', respectively. In case an inappropriate letter is passed, print an appropriate message. Also include a docstring with your function.
17. Write a function that accepts three integers and returns True if any of the integers is 0, otherwise it returns False
18. Write a function that accepts two positive numbers n and m where m<=n, and returns numbers between 1 and n that are divisible by m.
19. Write a function that displays "Hello name", for any given name passed to it.
20. Write a program to print the prime factors of a number.
21. Write a program that prompts user to enter 10 numbers. Find the smallest and the second smallest number entered by the user.

Fill in the Blanks

1. In range(0, 100, 5) name of the function is ________ and it has ______ arguments
2. ______ keyword allows you to have user defined functions in your program.
3. ________ error is caused by importing an unknown module.
4. _________ consists of a function header followed by function.
5. User-defined functions are created by using the ______ keyword.
6. The ___________ is used to uniquely identify the function.
7. _________ describe what the function does.
8. Fill in the blanks to define a function named display.

   __ display()__
   print("Hello World")
9. After the called function is executed, the control is returned back to the_________.
10. A return statement with no arguments is the same as return______.
11. Before calling a function, you must _______ it.

12. ________ variable can be accessed from the point of its definition until the end of the function in which it is defined.
13. To define a variable defined inside a function as global, ________ statement is used.
14. Every function has an implicit ______ statement as the last instruction in the function body.
15. Any formal parameters written after the variable sized arguments must be ________ arguments.
16. ________ are not declared as other functions using the *def* keyword.
17. This docstring specified can be accessed through the ______ attribute of the function.
18. You can find the name of a module by using the ______ attribute of the module.
19. ______ is a built-in function that lists the identifiers defined in a module.
20. Every package in Python is a directory, which must have a special file called______.
21. Packages have an attribute ______which is initialized with a list having the name of the directory holding the __init__.py file.
22. Fill in the blanks to define a function that takes two arguments and prints their sum

```
___ mult(x,y)__
print(x*__)
```

23. Fill in the blanks to define a function that prints 'Positive', if its parameter is greater than 0 and "Negative" otherwise.

```
___ pos_neg(x):
    if x>0:
        ____ "Positive"
    ___
        print("Negative")
```

24. Fill in the blanks to define a function that compares the lengths of its arguments and returns the longest one.

```
def max_len(x, y):
    if len(x)>=__(y):
        ___x
    else:
        ____y
```

25. Fill in the blanks to pass the function cube as an argument to the function "test":

```
___ cube(x):
return x*x*x
def do(func,x)__
  print(func(x))
do(_____, 2)
```

26. To import the sqrt and cos function from the math module, write ______________.
27. Trying to import a module that is not available results in ________.
28. Python's preinstalled modules forms the ______________.
29. The _________ command is used to force the reloading of a given module.

State True or False

1. Docstring can contain multiple lines of text.
2. Every function can be written more or less independently of the others.
3. When a function call is encountered, the control jumps to the calling function.
4. A function can call only one function.

5. Code reuse is one of the most prominent reasons to use functions.
6. Large programs usually follow the WET principle.
7. We can have a function that does not take any inputs at all.
8. The calling function may or may not pass *parameters* to the called function.
9. The return statement is optional.
10. Python does not allow you to assign the function name to a variable.
11. Names of variables in function call and header of function definition may vary.
12. Arguments may be passed in the form of expressions to the called function.
13. You can have a variable with the same name as that of a global variable in the program.
14. You should make extensive use of global variables and global statements.
15. The return statement can be used outside of a function definition.
16. Any code written after the return statement is never executed.
17. The order of keyword arguments is not important.
18. Default arguments should always be written after the non-default arguments.
19. You can specify only one default argument in your function.
20. The variable sized arguments if present in the function definition should be first in the list of formal parameters.
21. A function cannot be used on the left side of an assignment statement.
22. It is mandatory to place all import statements at the beginning of a module.
23. With the "import *moduleName*" statement, any item from the imported module must be prefixed with the module name.
24. All Python Standard Library modules must be imported before any programmer-defined modules.
25. If a particular module is imported more than once in a Python program, the interpreter will load the module only once.
26. A function can be called from anywhere within a program.
27. A statement can call more than one function.
28. Function calls may contain arguments that are function calls.
29. All functions that return a value must accept at least one parameter.

Give the Output

1.
```
num = 10
def show():
        var = 20
        print("In Function var is - ", num)

show()
print("Outside function, var is - ", num)
```

2.
```
def f():
    s = "Hello World!"
    print(s)

s = "Welcome to Python Programming"
f()
print(s)
```

3.
```
def f():
        global var
        print(varr)
        var = 10
        print(var)
var = 100
f()
```
4.
```
def display (str):
    print(str+"!")
display ("Hello World")
```
5.
```
def sqr(x):
    print(x*x)
sqr(10)
```
6.
```
def mul_twice(x,y):
    print(x*y)
    print(x*y)
mul_twice(5, 10)
```
7.
```
def func():
    global x
    print "x =", x
    x = 100
    print('x is now = ', x)

x = 10
func()
print('x =', x)
```
8.
```
def func1():
    var = 3
    func2(var)

def func2(var):
    print(var)

func1()
```
9.
```
def func(x):
    print 'x = ', x
    x = 100
    print('In Function, x after modification = ', x)

x = 50
func(x)
print('Outside Function, x = ', x)
```
10.
```
def display( str ):
   print(str)
   return;

display("Hello World !!")
display("Welcome to Python Programming")
```
11.
```
def sum( num1, num2 ):
   total = num1 + num2
```

```
    print("Inside function, Total = ", total)
    return total;

total = sum( 10, 20 )
print("Outside the function, Total = ", total)
```

12.
```
def min(x,y):
if x<y:
return x
else:
return y
print(min(4, 7))
```

13.
```
def add(x, y):
    sum = x + y
    return sum
     print("This won't be printed")
print(add(10,20))
```

14.
```
def display(str):
    "This prints a passed string into this function"
    Print(str)
    return;

display(str = "Welcome")
```

15.
```
def say(message, repeat_it = 2):
     print(message * repeat_it)
say('Hello')
say('Hello', 5)
```

16.
```
def func(x, y = 100, z = 1000):
     print('x = ', x, ' y = ', y, 'and z = ', z)

func(5, 15, 25)
func(35, z = 55)
func(y = 70, x = 200)
```

17.
```
def greet(*names):
     for name in names:
         print("Hello",name)
greet("Aryan","Nikita","Cahitanya")
```

18.
```
def func( arg1, *var):
"This prints arbitrary arguments"
print(arg1)
for i in var:
      print(i)
return;

func("Score is : ", 10, 20, 30)
func( "\n Average Score = ", 20)
```

19.
```
expo_3 = lambda x: x ** 3
print(expo_3(5))
```

20.
```
add_five = lambda n: n + 5
mult_add_five = lambda n: add_five(n * 10)
print(mult_add_five(9))
```

21.
```
def func():
    """Do nothing.

     Nothing doing.
     """
    pass

print(func.__doc__)
```
22.
```
def C_to_F(c):
    return c * 9/5 + 32

print C_to_F(37)
```
23.
```
def pow(x, y=3):
    r = 1
    for i in range(y):
        r = r * x
        return r
print(pow(5))
print(pow(2, 5))
```
24.
```
def display(name, deptt, sal):
    print("Name: ", name)
    print("Department: ", deptt)
    print("Salary: ", sal)
display(sal = 100000, name="Tavisha", deptt = "IT")
display(deptt = "HR", name="Dev", sal = 50000)
```
25.
```
def display(mesg):
        return mesg + "!"
print_str = display
str  = print_str("Hello")
print(str)
```
26.
```
from random import randint as r
for i in range(10):
        value = r(1,100)
        print(value)
```
27.
```
def is_even(x):
    if x==0:
        return True
    else:
        return is_odd(x-1)

def is_odd(x):
    return not is_even(x)

print(is_even(22))
```
28.
```
def display(x):
    for i in range(x):
        print(i)
        return
display(5)
```

Find Out the Error, If Any

1. ```
def func():
        print("Hello World")
```
2. ```
var1 = "Good"
def show():
        var2 = "Morning"
        print(var1)
        print(var2)
show()
print(var1)
print(var2)
```
3. ```
def f():
        print var
        var = 10
        print(var)
var = 100
f()
```
4. ```
def f():
    var = 100
    print(var)
    f()
    print(var)
```
5. ```
def func(var):
        var+=1
        var *= 2
        print(var)
func(9)
print(var)
```
6. ```
def func1():
    var = 3
    func2()

def func2():
    print(var)

func1()
```
7. ```
def display(x,y):
   print (x+y)
display(10)
```
8. ```
def func(a, b):
   print(a)
   print(b)
func (b=10, 20)
```

9.
```
def func1():
    print "func1()"
func1()
func2()
def func2():
    print "func2()"
```

10.
```
import math as m
print(math.sqrt(25))
```
a. Error
b. 25
c. 5
d. 625

11.
```
def factorial(x):
return x*factorial(x-1)
print(factorial(6))
```

12.
```
def sum_to(x):
return x+sum_to(x-1)
print(sum_to(5))
```

CHAPTER

4 Data Handling Using Numpy

Data is a collection of facts that is processed to obtain information. These data can be anything including numbers, words, measurements, observations, etc. In this chapter, our focus will therefore be on understanding the importance of data and learn how these data can be structured and analyzed to derive useful information in Python using the Numpy module.

4.1 Data and Its Purpose

Data can exist in different forms–numbers or text on paper or in computer. Irrespective of the industry, collection, and analysis of data has changed the way we do things today. For example, data are analyzed to study symptoms and appropriate treatment for a disease; increase the revenue of a company; generated targeted ads; etc.

Data help companies to make better decisions. These days, every business generate a lot of data. Any business with a website and that has social media presence, or is involved in any kind of electronic payments collects data about customers, user demographics, and more. Businesses can harness these data to make decisions about:

- Finding new customers
- Increasing customer retention
- Improving customer service
- Better managing marketing efforts
- Tracking social media interaction
- Predicting sales trends

Figure 4.1 Data for analyzing market trends and making strategic decisions

Thus, data help business leaders make smarter decisions about where to take their companies.

Thus, it is not wrong to say that data are the new oil. Every industry today can survive only by capturing, storing, and analyzing data for various needs. Data is also used for weather forecasting, studying protein structures in biology or designing a marketing campaign. For all these fields, a multidisciplinary approach using mathematical models, statistics, graphs, databases, and the business or scientific logic behind the data analysis is required (see Figure 4.1).

Python caters to all these diverse needs of data science. It has numerous libraries and built in features to provide functionalities for Data science. A code written in Python executes faster than other similar languages used for data analysis like R and MATLAB.

Datasets associated with this chapter can be accessed using the QR code provided on the back cover of the book.

Python supports handling and manipulating large volume of data through transformation, slicing, dicing, and visualization techniques. Moreover, it has packages that can directly use the code from other languages like Java or C. This helps in optimizing performance of the code by incorporating existing code written in other languages to achieve better results.

4.2 Introduction – Importance of Data

"Data is the new oil." Today, data is everywhere in every field. With 2.5 quintillion bytes of data being generated every day, businesses rely on data analytics for some useful insights. These insights guide marketing campaigns, strategy designing, product launches, and experimentation for better results. Around 80% of businesses boosted revenues with real-time data analytics.

To analyze large amounts of data, we must learn ways to handle and store it properly, without any error. However, before working on data, we must first know the type of that data so that it can be processed accurately to get the desired results.

Broadly speaking, there are two types of data–Qualitative and Quantitative data, which are further classified into four categories: Nominal data, Ordinal data, Discrete data, and Continuous data.

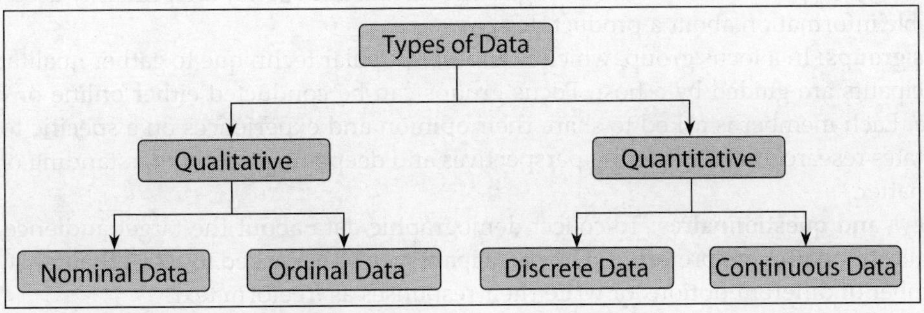

Qualitative or Categorical Data

Qualitative or categorical data cannot be measured or counted in the form of numbers. This data is sorted by category, not by number; hence, the name. Categorical or qualitative data usually consists of audio, images, symbols, or text. For example, the name, gender, designation, language(s) known, favorite holiday destination, opinion on something, etc. of a customer is qualitative data.

This type of data talks about the perception of people and helps the market researcher to know more about customers' tastes. Product design to business strategy, all are framed using the results of analyzing the crucial qualitative data available to the business.

Qualitative data can be further classified into two categories:

Nominal Data: Nominal data labels variables without any order or quantitative value. The word "nominal" has been derived from the Latin word "nomen," meaning "name." We cannot apply any numerical operation on nominal data values.

They cannot even be sorted in any meaningful order as their values are distributed into distinct categories. Examples of nominal data include,

- Color of hair (Blonde, Red, Brown, Black, etc.)
- Marital status (Single, Widowed, Married)

- Nationality (Indian, German, American)
- Gender (Male, Female, Others)
- Eye color (Black, Brown, etc.)

Ordinal Data: Unlike nominal data, ordinal data have natural ordering, as the values indicate some kind of order by their position on the scale. Businesses collect ordinal data when they ask the customer to rate their product/service. We can think of ordinal data as something in between qualitative and quantitative data. Though we can have some ordering, any arithmetical operation cannot be performed on it. Examples of ordinal data include,

- Grades obtained by a student in the exam (A, B, C, D, etc.)
- Rank obtained by candidates in an entrance exam (First, Second, Third, etc.)
- Economic status (High, Medium, and Low)
- Education level (Higher, Secondary, Primary)

Qualitative Data Collection Methods

- **Interviews:** An interview is the most common way to elicit qualitative data. It involves personal interaction either in real life or virtually with a participant. Such an interaction helps to explore attitudes and opinions of individuals regarding certain issue. They are primarily used to collect valuable information about a product design.
- **Focus groups:** In a focus group, which is another popular technique to gather qualitative data, participants are guided by a host. Focus groups can be conducted either online or in offline mode. Each member is asked to share their opinion and experiences on a specific topic. This facilitates researchers in gathering perspectives and deepening their understanding of the subject matter.
- **Surveys and questionnaires:** To collect demographic data about the target audience, surveys and questionnaires are preferred. The participants are either asked to select their answers from a number of different options or write their responses as freeform text.
- **Observations:** One of the popularly used techniques to collect qualitative data is actively engaging with people. The analysts observe the participants "naturally" and draw conclusions based on their analysis. For example, researchers may analyze product reviews written on social media posts.

Difference between Nominal and Ordinal Data

Nominal Data	Ordinal Data
Cannot be quantified	Have some kind of sequential order by their position on the scale
Purely qualitative data or categorical data	"in between" qualitative data and quantitative data
Do not have any quantitative value, neither can we perform any arithmetical operation	Numbers can be assigned to ordinal data but no arithmetical operation can be performed
Two categorical values cannot be compared with each other	Can be compared
Examples: Eye color, housing style, religion, ethnicity, etc.	**Examples:** Opinion on something (Strongly Agree, Agree, Disagree, Strongly Disagree, Cannot say) etc.

Qualitative data analysis examines non-numerical or categorical data to identify patterns, themes, and meanings. Commonly used methods for analyzing qualitative data include,

Thematic Analysis: In this type of analysis, recurring themes or patterns are identified in qualitative data by categorizing and coding the data.

Content Analysis: In this type of analysis, textual data is systematically analyzed by categorizing and coding it to identify patterns and concepts.

Narrative Analysis: This type of analysis, examines stories or narratives to understand experiences, perspectives, and meanings.

Grounded Theory: The analysis systematically analyzes qualitative data to develop theories or frameworks.

Quantitative Data

As the name suggests, quantitative data can be expressed in the form of numbers. It is countable and thus, we can answer the questions like "how much," "how many," and "how often." Any sort of mathematical operations as well as statistical data analysis can be easily performed on such data. For this reason, quantitative data is also known as numerical data. For example, the price of a product, memory capacity of a computer, the height or weight of a person, time, marks obtained in a test, temperature, etc., are quantitative data.

We can even plot quantitative data using a variety of graphs like bar graphs, histograms, scatter plots, boxplots, pie charts, line graphs, etc.

> Data analysis methodologies refer to the techniques used to analyze and interpret data. These techniques vary depending on the type of data being analyzed and the research objectives.

Quantitative Data is Further Classified as

Discrete Data: Discrete data consists of integers or whole numbers. For example, the total number of students in a class, the total number of students present in a class, the cost of a laptop, the number of employees in a company, the number of players who participated in a competition, and the days in a week are discrete data. Since this data has numbers, it is countable and has finite values. Their subdivision is not possible. We can easily plot discrete data using a bar graph, number line, or frequency table.

Continuous Data: Continuous data are available as fractional numbers. For example, the version of an Android phone, the height of a person, the length of an object, etc., are continuous data. Continuous values can be divided into smaller levels. A continuous variable can take any value within a range.

Difference between Discrete and Continuous Data

Discrete Data	Continuous Data
Discrete data are countable and finite. Discrete values are whole numbers or integers.	Continuous data are measurable. They are usually available as fractional numbers.
Discrete data are usually plotted using bar graphs.	Continuous data are usually plotted using a histogram.
The values cannot be divided into subdivisions into smaller pieces.	The values can be divided into subdivisions into smaller pieces.

(Continued)

Discrete Data	Continuous Data
Discrete data have gaps between the values.	Continuous data do not have any gap between them.
Examples: Total number of students in a class, number of days in a week, size of a shoe, etc.	**Example:** Temperature of room, the weight of a person, length of an object, etc.

Quantitative Data Collection Methods

We can collect quantitative data for research using the following techniques.

Surveys: The most common way to collect quantitative data is through surveys. It involves questioning a large group of people. The same set of closed-ended questions is shared with all the participants. An unclear and incomplete questionnaire can result in distorted research outcomes.

Polls: Like surveys, polls are created to collect quantitative data from a number of people. We can easily view and analyze how many people responded with each answer.

Experiments: An experiment is another commonly used technique to gather quantitative data. In an experiment, there are two groups–a control group and an experimental group. The experiment is controlled, and the conditions can be manipulated to analyze results.

Analytics tools: Data analysts and data scientists use specific data analytic tools to collect quantitative data from various sources. For example, Google Analytics collects data in real time that allows analysts to view important metrics for websites, including traffic, number of page views, and average session length.

Environmental sensors: A sensor is a device that detects changes in the surrounding environment and shares the changing values with another electronic device (like a computer). These values are usually numbers, providing a continuous stream of quantitative data.

Manipulation of pre-existing quantitative data: Researchers and analysts can generate new quantitative data by applying statistical analyses or calculations on existing data. For example, if you have the data about the sales price and all the costs involved, you can easily derive the profit margin.

> Quantitative data is structured and accountable that can be easily organized, arranged, and made searchable.

Analyzing Quantitative Data

Quantitative data can be analyzed using the following methods.

Descriptive Statistics: A data set is summarized using mean, median, mode, standard deviation, and percentages.

Inferential Statistics: Conclusions about a population are drawn from the sample data using hypothesis testing, t-tests, and regression analysis.

Data Mining: Algorithms and statistical techniques are used to identify patterns and correlations in the datasets.

Experimental Design: Causal relationships between variables are determined using controlled experiments.

The choice of methodology to be used depends on the particular research question to be addressed, research objectives, type of data, and the set of available resources. Usually, a combination of data analysis techniques is employed to comprehensively understand the data and draw meaningful conclusions from it.

Advantages of Quantitative Data

- Quantitative data can be easily and quickly collected.
- Conclusions can be easily drawn from quantitative data.
- A variety of statistical tests based on the data can be applied.
- Data can be easily interpreted and presented.
- Quantitative data can be easily replicated.

Disadvantages of Quantitative Data

- Quantitative data does not always reveal the full story.
- Research conducted on quantitative data may ignore broader themes and relationships.
- It consists of just numbers, thereby missing to capture crucial textual, audio, and other information.

Key Differences between Quantitative and Qualitative Data

Once we have a good idea about quantitative as well as qualitative data, let us quickly look at some points of differentiation between the two.

Qualitative Data	Quantitative Data
Qualitative data is collected through interviews, participant observation, and focus on a group.	Quantitative data is collected using questionnaires, surveys, and structural observations.
Data format is usually textual. It may also include audio or video recordings and notes.	Data format is usually numerical.
It answers the questions "why" and "how."	It answers the questions "how much" and "how many."
The data is analyzed by segregating it into different categories.	The data is analyzed using statistical techniques.
Qualitative data are subjective and can be further open for interpretation.	Quantitative data are fixed and universal.
Usually represented as Pie charts, frequency tables.	Usually represented as bar charts, histograms, scatter plots.
It facilitates developing a better understanding of human and social sciences including human behavior and personalities better.	It generates numerical data by using statistical and mathematical techniques.
Qualitative data is collected using open-ended questions.	Quantitative data is collected using multiple choice questions.
Qualitative research needs only a few respondents.	Quantitative research requires many respondents.
Research using qualitative data is holistic in nature.	Research using quantitative research is particularistic in nature.
Qualitative data develops the initial understanding of data and discovers various ideas.	Quantitative data recommends a final course of action after examining the cause and effect between the variables.

Advantages of Qualitative Data

- Qualitative data offers rich, in-depth insights to explore data in a given context.
- Qualitative data is best used for exploratory analysis.
- Qualitative data research can be used as a predictive element for continuous data.

Disadvantages of Qualitative Data

- It does not include numerical data that is statistically significant to capture.
- Missing of key numerical values may result in misleading conclusions.

> It is difficult to conduct a successful data analysis without qualitative and quantitative data. They complement each other.

When Should I Use Qualitative or Quantitative Data?

It is always best to include a combination of quantitative and qualitative data for analysis. However, to understand which data is better suited to which type of research, we need to keep the following points in mind.

- To get an understanding about a concept, experience, or opinions, prefer using qualitative data.
- To confirm or test a theory or hypothesis, prefer using quantitative data.
- For doing core research, a mixed-methods approach to data collection is used.

4.3 Structured, Semi-Structured, and Unstructured Data

Massive amount of data available today can be categorized into three groups–Structured data, Semi-structured data, and Unstructured data.

Structured data: Structured data, also referred to as quantitative data, is that data which can be used for effective analysis. It is stored in a database and has a well-defined structure and format. However, the downside of structured data is that it lacks flexibility in data storage and analysis techniques. There is a fixed format, and storage and retrieval is limited to a pre-defined format. *Example*: SQL tables.

Semi-structured data: Semi-structured data is not stored in a database. So, analyzing such data is not that easier. However, after processing this data, it can be stored in a database to make it convenient for further usage. *Example*: XML data.

Unstructured data: Unstructured data also referred to as qualitative data is not available in a pre-defined format. This data cannot be stored in a database. For example, data stored in Word processing applications (like MS Word), PDF files, social media posts, presentations, chats, IoT sensor data, satellite imagery, audio and video files, text messages, and locations are all important sources of unstructured data. Though this type of data has the freedom to be stored in different formats, it is however difficult to analyze. Special expertise and tools are required for data storage and retrieval for analysis.

Table 1 summarizes the difference between structured and unstructured data.

Table 1: || Comparison between Structured and Unstructured Data

Properties	Structured Data	Unstructured Data
Characteristics	Predefined format	Raw/native format
Ease of Searching	Easy and straight-forward	Difficult
Data Types	Defined data types	Many varied data types
Storage	Relational databases	Cannot be stored in relational databases
Flexibility	Not flexible; schema-dependent	Flexible; not schema-dependent
Availability	Approx. 20% of data	Approx. 80% of data
Examples	Excel, Google Sheets, SQL, customer data, phone records, transaction history	Text data, social media comments, phone calls transcriptions, various logs files, images, audio, video

4.4 Data Processing

Data processing is the process of converting raw data into meaningful information. This information may help to resolve a problem or improve an existing scenario. Data processing follows a cycle, where inputs are fed to a computer to generate some quality output (refer Figure 4.2). The output is usually expressed in appropriate forms like diagrams, reports, graphics, text, or a combination of all these.

Stages of the Data Processing Cycle can be Explained as Given Below.

Step I: Data *Collection:* This stage is very sensitive to the success of data processing activities as the quality of data collected will have an immense effect on the output. The data collection process must be well-defined and accurate. An effective collection process can only ensure that subsequent decisions based on the findings are valid.

Step 2: Data *Preparation* involves manipulation of data into a format suitable for further analysis and processing. Raw data cannot be processed as it is. For better accuracy, it has to be first prepared. The collected data may have missing or incorrect values. All these discrepancies must be removed during the data preparation stage.

Step 3: Data *Input* is the activity in which verified data is coded or converted into machine-readable form so that it can be processed using a computer software. Data can be entered using a keyboard, scanner, or from an existing data source. Data input is a time-consuming process that needs to be done accurately in the specified format. If there is even a single error during input, then the result will be adversely affected–garbage in, garbage out.

Step 4: Data *Processing* is done to apply different techniques for technical manipulations using any algorithm (like Machine Learning and Artificial Intelligence) to generate an output or interpretation about the data. The time taken for processing data depends on the complexity of the data.

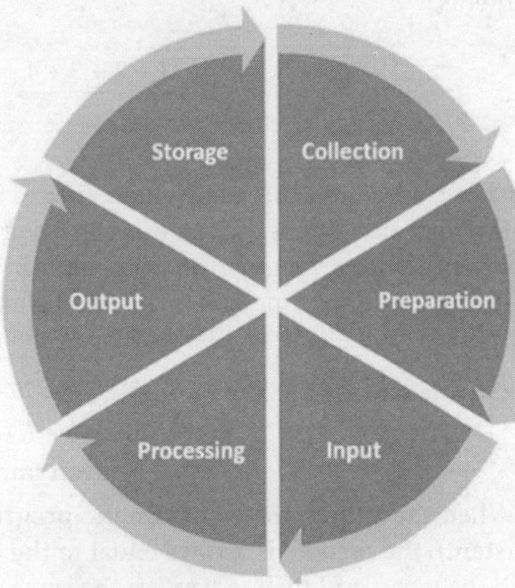

Figure 4.2 Data Processing Cycle

Step 5: *Output* and interpretation is the stage where processed information is displayed to the user. Output can be presented in various formats like graphical reports, audio, video, or in textual format. This output conveys meaningful information that will guide future decisions taken by the company.

Step 6: *Storage* is the last stage in the data processing cycle, where the data is preserved for future use.

Thus, we see that the **Data Processing Cycle** includes a series of steps that are performed to extract useful information from raw data. Every step must be carried out in the specified order. Partial output from one stage is passed as an input for the next stage. Failure in any one stage will not give the expected output.

All the above-mentioned activities are cyclic in nature as the output and storage stage may result in repeating the data collection stage leading to another cycle of data processing.

4.5 Descriptive Statistics

Descriptive statistics are evaluated to summarize and organize data for better understandability. As the name suggests, descriptive statistics, describe data, but they do not make inferences from the sample to the whole population. There are two types of descriptive statistics–Measures of central tendency and Measures of variability (spread).

4.5.1 Measure of Central Tendency

Central tendency indicates that there is one number that best summarizes the entire set of measurements. This number is "central" to the set.

Mean/Average: Mean or Average is a central tendency of the data. So, in other words, it is a number around which a whole data is spread out. It is that single number which can estimate the value of whole data set. Mean is calculated by dividing the sum of all elements by the number of elements.

$$X = \frac{1+2+3+4+5+6+7+8+9+10}{10} = 5.5$$

Median: Median is the value which divides the data into two equal parts. The number of elements on the right side of it is the same as the number of elements on the left side of the median. Median is obtained after arranging the data either in the **ascending or descending order**.

To make it simple, median is the middle term, if the number of elements is odd. In the case of an even number of elements, the median is the average of the middle two terms.

Median = 11 + 23 + 35 + 49 + 50 + 77 + 18 + 96 + 10 = 50 (odd number of elements)
Median = 11 + 23 + 35 + 49 + 50 + 62 + 77 + 18 + 96 + 10 = (50 + 62)/2 = 112/2 = 56 (even number of elements)

When the values are in arithmetic progression (difference between the consecutive terms is constant), the median is always equal to the mean. For example, in the data set 1, 3, 5, 7, 9, 11, 13, both the mean and the median are the same.

Mode: Mode is the term appearing maximum times in the data set. This means that the mode has the highest frequency of occurrence in the data set.

Mode = 11, 23, 39, 35, 41, 50, 41, 23, 39, 77, 23 = 23 because it is occurring thrice in the data.

Remember that,

- In some data sets, there can be no mode at all, as all the values appear same number of times.
- If two values appeared the same maximum number of times, then the data set is said to be **bimodal**.
- If three values appeared the same maximum number of times, then the data set is said to be **tri-modal**. Similarly, for n values appearing most frequently, the data set is said to be **multimodal**.

4.5.2 Measure of Spread/Dispersion

Measure of Spread refers to the idea of variability within your data.

Standard deviation: Standard deviation measures the average distance between each value and the mean. This gives a clarity about how the data is spread out from the mean. A low standard deviation indicates that the values are closer to the mean of the data set, while a high standard deviation means that the data values are spread out over a wider range of values.

Standard Deviation is calculated as,

$$\textbf{S.D.} = \sqrt{\frac{1}{n}\sum_{i=0}^{n}(x-\mu)^2}$$

where μ is mean of a population.

For example, consider the data set given below.

12, 7, 8, 11, 5, 4, 10, 9, 6, 9, 4, 9, 2, 5, 4, 9, 3, 7, 4, 12

Mean of the values = sum of all values/number of values = 7

For each number: subtract the mean and square the result.

This is the part of the formula that says: $(x_i - \mu)^2$

$x_1 = 12, x_2 = 7, x_3 = 8$, etc.

For each value, subtract the mean and square the result, as shown below.

$(12 - 7)^2 = (5)^2 = 25$ $(7 - 7)^2 = (0)^2 = 0$ $(8 - 7)^2 = (1)^2 = 1$

$(11 - 7)^2 = (4)^2 = 16$ $(5 - 7)^2 = (-2)^2 = 4$ $(4 - 7)^2 = (-3)^2 = 9$

$(10 - 7)^2 = (3)^2 = 9$ $(9 - 7)^2 = (2)^2 = 4$ $(6 - 7)^2 = (-1)^2 = 1$

$(9 - 7)^2 = (2)^2 = 4$ ... etc ...

Now, find the mean of those squared differences. For this, add up all the values then divide by the number of values. In our data set, the mean of squared differences = 178.

Finally, divide this mean by the number of values and find its squared root. So,

Mean of squared differences = (1/20) × 178 = 8.9

Standard Deviation, σ = √(8.9) = 2.983

Variance: Variance is calculated as the square of the average distance between each quantity and the mean. This means that the variance is the square of standard deviation.

$$\text{Variance} = (\text{S.D.})^2$$

Range: Range is calculated as the difference between the lowest and highest value.

Range = 11, 23, 39, 35, 41, 50, 41, 23, 39, 77, 23 = 77 – 11 = 66

Business Analytics

Business analytics is an important tool for interpreting large amounts of data collected and organized by the organization. Such an interpretation of data, helps the organization to

- ❑ understand customer behavior,
- ❑ analyze the performance of business processes, and
- ❑ transform the data points into actionable insights resulting in smarter decisions and better business outcomes.

Business analytics forms the foundation of designing and building a data warehouse/business intelligence (BI) architecture.

Though there are four types of business analytics, Python programming helps to do three of them.

Descriptive Analytics: Such an analysis is performed by data analytics to understand what has happened and evaluate the trends over time. With Python, we can study the data in detail, visualize the results, and create observations that could help in defining the next course of action.

Descriptive analytics is usually performed using exploratory data analysis. For example, analyzing the total units of Product A sold and the profit made in the last financial year. Even a non-data analyst can easily interpret the data by looking at the visual graphs and the results of descriptive analysis. In such a case, the person just has to identify the metrics to be measured, collect that data, and analyze it. Descriptive analytics converts the stream of business facts into actionable information. For example,

- ❑ Annual revenue reports
- ❑ Survey response summaries
- ❑ Yearly sales reports

The main limitation of descriptive analytics is that it can only analyze data from past events. It cannot reveal information about *how* or *why* those trends occurred. It just gives an insight as to how to approach the future. Almost all management reporting, such as sales, marketing, operations, and finance, uses descriptive analytics as a type of post-mortem analysis.

Descriptive models quantify relationships in data that help to classify customers based on their product preferences and life stage and identify relationships between customers or products. However, unlike predictive models, descriptive models do not rank-order customers by their likelihood of taking a particular action.

Descriptive modeling tools are usually used to develop further models that can make predictions. For example, descriptive analytics can analyze the historical electricity usage data to help plan power needs and guide electric companies to set optimal prices.

Diagnostic analytics: Diagnostic analytics helps to explain why things happened the way they did. It is more complex than descriptive analytics as it focuses on *why* it happened rather than *what* had happened. Such an analysis is often used to identify trends or patterns in the past and the reasons for their occurrence. It is a logical step after descriptive analytics, as it helps to develop better strategies without much trial and error.

Diagnostic analytics facilitates businesses in duplicating good outcomes and avoiding negative ones. Companies use diagnostic analysis for multiple reasons including,

- Why did sales decline this year?
- Why did the product register more sales than expected?
- Why did more customers search for a similar product last month?

The limitation of diagnostic analytics is that it does not provide actionable observations about the future. Though, a good understanding of relationships and sequences may be enough for some businesses, it does not provide vital answers.

Predictive Analytics: Predictive analytics helps to prepare for the future by showing a window to possible events. Python programming language is the most popularly used programming language that help users create machine learning models for data classification, data clustering, regression analysis, and more.

Predictive analytics tells us what will happen. This can be done by building predictive models. For example, predicting the total sales units of Product A and the profit that can be earned in the future.

A business can set realistic goals and avoid risks if it appropriately uses data to list the likely outcomes. Predictive analytics keeps all the employees aligned on the same strategic vision. For example,

- E-commerce businesses analyze customers' browsing and purchasing history to recommend products.
- Financial organizations use customers' data to predict how likely a customer is to pay their credit card bill on time.
- Marketing teams analyze data to calculate the probability that new customers will respond favorably to a given campaign or product offering.

In business, predictive models analyze patterns in historical and transactional data to identify risks and opportunities. Moreover, an organization offering multiple products use predictive analytics to understand customers' spending, usage, and other behavior for efficient cross sales, or selling additional products to current customers. This in turn results in higher profits as well as stronger customer relationships.

The main problem with predictive analytics is that its insights are limited to the data. This means that, smaller or incomplete data sets may not generate predictions as accurate as those obtained after analyzing a larger data set.

> Obtaining valuable business intelligence (BI) from predictive analytics requires "sufficient" data. However, the meaning of "sufficient" depends on the industry, business, audience, and specific use case.

Another problem with predictive analytics is that even the best algorithms with the biggest data sets may fail to take into account some important intangible or distinctly human factors. For example, a sudden economic shift or even a change in the weather can affect spending, but a predictive analytics model may not consider these factors.

Prescriptive Analytics: Also known as decision science, prescriptive analysis helps to anticipate what, when, and why certain outcomes will happen. It also helps in deciding what to do with that information. Python programming offers functionality required for creating prescriptive analytics tools like deep learning, which uses artificial neural networks to enhance outcomes.

In simpler terms, prescriptive analysis explains how to make something happen. This can be done by deriving key insights and hidden patterns from the data. For example, finding ways to improve sales (in units) and profit (in Rupees) of Product A.

Prescriptive analytics is the most advanced analytics as it provides actionable insights instead of raw data. This analysis helps to determine what *should* happen, not just what *could* happen. Thus, prescriptive analytics helps not only to get insights into future outcomes, but also to understand why they will happen. Such an analysis can be used to predict the effect of future decisions, including the ripple effects those decisions can have on the business.

Prescriptive analytics is a complex process that includes multiple variables and tools based on machine learning, and big data. So, businesses need proper data infrastructures to exploit data. For example,

- The insurance industry calculates client risk to determine what plans and rates an account should be offered.
- Companies analyze data like customer surveys and market research to determine features that are most desirable for customers so that they can be included in a new product.
- Healthcare companies analyze patient's data to assess the risk for developing specific health problems in the future and targeting treatment decisions to minimize them.

Prescriptive analytics goes beyond predicting future outcomes by also suggesting actions that can be taken. It offers the implications of each decision option to the decision makers. For this, it combines data, business rules, and mathematical models. The data inputs to prescriptive analytics may come from multiple sources, internal data (available within the organization) as well as external (for example, data available on social media, newspapers, etc.).

Moreover, the data used for analysis may be structured or unstructured. While structured data includes numerical and categorical data, unstructured data, on the other hand, includes data such as text, images, audio, and video data, including big data.

As the name suggests, business rules define the business process and are in line with business constraints, preferences, policies, best practices, and boundaries. Mathematical models are based on techniques from applied statistics, machine learning, operational research, and natural language processing.

> Prescriptive analytics can suggest decision options on how to take advantage of a future opportunity or mitigate a future risk and illustrate the implication of each decision option.

However, prescriptive analytics is dependent on the availability of a large amount of data which may not be always available. Moreover, machine learning algorithms may not consider important external variables. For example, in our case, the healthcare industries may not consider data of external factors, such as economic data, population demographic trends, and population health trends, to accurately plan for future investments–the trade-offs between expanding an existing facility versus building a new one.

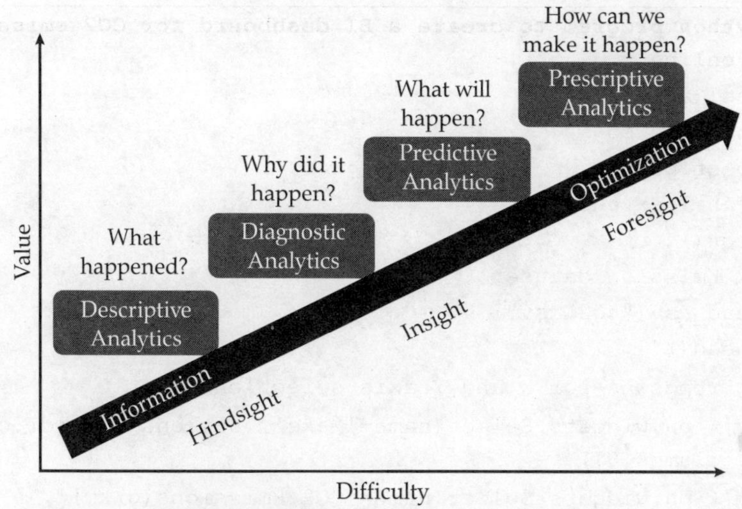

Figure 4.3 **Types of Data Analytics**

Leading Trends in Python Development for Business Analytics

The field of business analytics is evolving at a very rapid pace. The new-age analytics solutions are using techniques like AI/ML, Neural networks, etc. Some of them are discussed below.

Artificial Intelligence and Machine Learning: The AI/ML techniques have proved very beneficial to business analytics. AI/ML-based business analytics helps organizations to use algorithms to identify trends and derive useful insights from complex datasets across different sources.

The techniques not only facilitate diving deep into the data but also help to correlate simultaneous anomalies that reveal critical insight into business operations. Business analytics systems powered by AI and ML technologies autonomously learns and adapts to changing data. With this, behavioral patterns can be interpreted for more precision in detecting anomalies and deviations.

Big Data: Big data analysis means processing large amounts of data. Such an analysis is used for revealing trends about the market, customers, social media, healthcare, and more. With the massive digitization, huge amounts of user data can be used for better purposes. Big data for business analysis facilitates better decision-making, as the best information is now available to businesses to gain useful insights that would help them to expand their reach.

Neural Networks: Artificial neural networks are based on how the human brain processes information. Neural networks use the computing power of a large number of interconnected computers to process information quickly and automatically. This helps the system to perform new tasks by making accurate decisions.

Neural network models mimic customer behavior, purchase, and renewals; segment customers based on their credit line usage, loan advising, real estate appraisal, and more.

Deep Learning: Deep learning, a subset of ML, has algorithms that help in performing nonlinear data processing for fast and accurate analysis of complex data. Deep learning algorithms can be written in Python programming language to process large amounts of data. Developing virtual assistants, chatbots, and computer vision systems has been widely applied in the healthcare industry, entertainment applications, etc.

Write a Python program to create a BI dashboard for CO2 emission dataset available online.

```
import panel as pn
import pandas as pd
import hvplot.pandas
# Enable Panel extensions
pn.extension()
# Load CO2 Emission dataset
df = pd.read_csv("co2.csv")
df1 = df.head()
# Widget: Dropdowns for X and Y axis selection
x_selector = pn.widgets.Select(name='Make', options=list(df.columns),
value=df1.columns[0])
y_selector = pn.widgets.Select(name='CO2 Emissions(g/km)',
options=list(df.columns), value=df1.columns[11])
# Function to create plot
def create_plot(x, y):
    return df1.hvplot.scatter(x=x, y=y, size=80, alpha=0.6,
legend='top_right')
# Reactive plot based on widget selection
@pn.depends(x_selector.param.value, y_selector.param.value)
def update_plot(x, y):
    return create_plot(x, y)
# Layout with widgets and plot
layout = pn.Column(
    pn.Row(pn.Spacer(width=50), x_selector, y_selector),
    update_plot
)
# Serve the Panel app
layout.servable()
```

To run this application, the steps are given below.

Step I: Make sure that the required modules like Panel, hvPlot, and Pandas are installed. For example, we can install hvPlot using the following command:

pip install panel hvplot

Step 2: Save the Python script as try.py (or any other name).

Step 3: Run the script using Panel's built-in server. For this, type the following command in the Windows cmd.

panel serve try.py –show

But before running this command, make sure that your current working directory is the directory in which try.py is saved.

The – show flag automatically opens the app in the web browser.

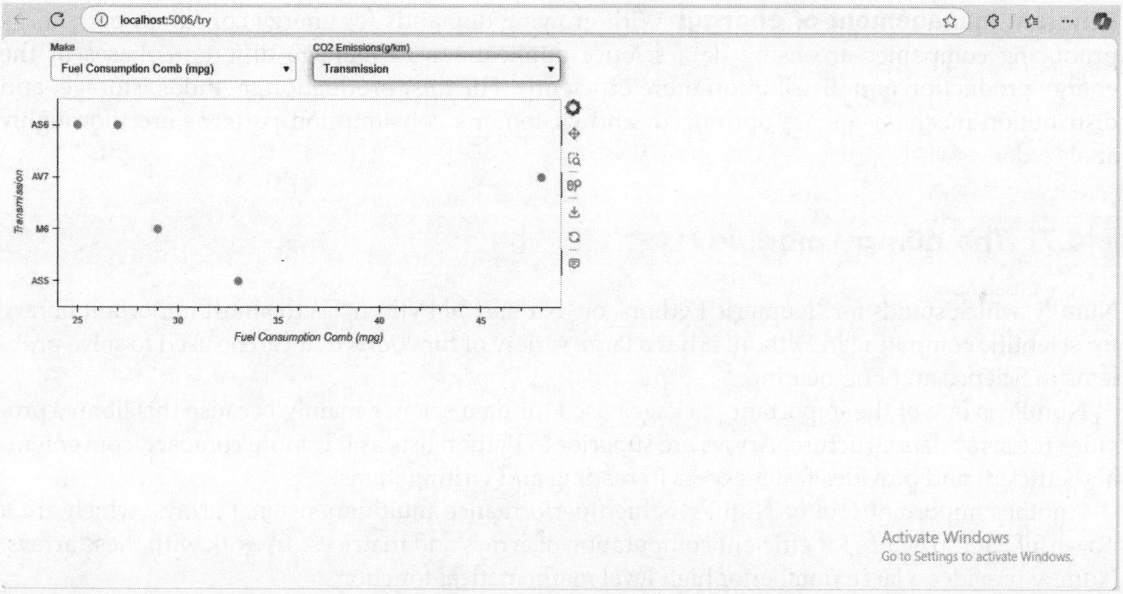

4.6 Data science and its applications

Data science is the process of deriving knowledge and insights from a huge and diverse set of data through organizing, processing, and analyzing the data. It applies techniques from multiple disciplines including mathematical and statistical modelling, extracting data, and applying data visualization techniques. Some popular applications of data science include:

Recommendation systems: With extensively growing numbers of online shoppers, companies are keeping a track of shopping preferences of every individual buyer. Recommendation systems are thus created to generate models for predicting buyers so that the website can display more of those products that fall in-line with what the user usually prefers to buy.

Financial risk management: Banking and other financial institutions use data science applications to uncover any financial risk involved before issuing a loan. This is done by analyzing a customer's past spending habits, past defaults, other financial commitments, and many socio-economic indicators. All these data are often present in different sources, probably in different formats. So, once these data are collected, cleaned, and organized, it is extensively used to gain insight into customers profile, thereby minimizing loss for the financial organization by avoiding bad debt.

Improvement in health care services: The health care industry collates a variety of data including financial data, patient information, medicines being given, surgeries undergone, and legal rules. All these data are analyzed in a coordinated way to get insights into data that would result in saving time, effort, and money of health care provider as well as receiver while remaining legally compliant.

Computer vision: The advancement in recognizing an image by a computer involves processing large sets of image data from multiple objects of same category. For example, face recognition. These data sets are modelled, and algorithms are created to apply the model to newer images to get a satisfactory result. Processing of these huge data sets and creation of models need various tools used in data science.

Efficient management of energy: With growing demands for energy consumption, energy producing companies are using data science applications to manage different phases of the energy production and distribution more efficiently. For this, production methods, storage, and distribution mechanisms are optimized, and customer's consumption patterns are thoroughly analyzed.

4.7 The numpy module

NumPy, which stands for "Numeric Python" or "Numerical Python," is the most important library for scientific computing in Python. It has a large variety of functions that can be used to solve problems in Science and Engineering.

NumPy is one of the important packages used for data science mainly because this library provides the array data structure. Arrays are superior to Python lists as it is more compact, convenient, and efficient and provides faster access in reading and writing items.

Another important tool of NumPy is high-performance multidimensional arrays, which are a powerful data structure for efficient computation of arrays and matrices. To work with these arrays, NumPy provides a large number of high-level mathematical functions.

NumPy module contains a rich collection of essential functions that support computations on multidimensional arrays. When using NumPy, you must remember the following points.

- To use this module, we must first import it by writing, **import numpy as np**.
- NumPy is mainly used for creating **homogeneous** multidimensional arrays. Homogeneous means elements of same data type.
- In NumPy, dimensions are called **axes**.
- Number of axes is called the **rank**.

4.8 Creating numpy arrays

There are several ways to create an array in NumPy like np.array, np.zeros, no.ones, etc. Each of them provides some flexibility.

np.array: np.array is a function that allow users to create an array of elements supplied as an argument. Numpy array() function takes a list of elements as argument and returns a one-dimensional array.

```
import numpy as np
a = np.array([1,2,3])
b = np.array((5,6,7))
print(a)
print(b)
OUTPUT
[1 2 3]
[5 6 7]
```

Here, a is an array of a list of integers. b is an array of a tuple of integers. Likewise, we can have array of elements that belong to other data types

np.arange: Numpy arange() function takes **start**, **end** of a range and the **interval** as arguments and returns a one-dimensional array with evenly spaced elements from the interval specified by the value of start and stop in the gap of step. The syntax is:

```
numpy.arange([start, ]stop, [step, ], dtype=None)
import numpy as np
a = np.arange(5,50,5)
print(a)
OUTPUT
[5 10 15 20 25 30 35 40 45]
```

Here, a is a one-dimensional array with elements from 5 to 50 in steps of 5.

np.linspace: Numpy linspace() functions takes **start**, **end**, and the **number of elements** to be created as arguments and returns a one-dimensional array that has evenly spaced numbers over the specified interval. It is similar to arrange() function, but it uses the number instead of the step as an interval. The syntax of linespace() function is,

numpy.linspace(start, stop, num, endpoint=True, retstep=False, dtype=None)

Here, num specifies number of values to generate.

```
import numpy as np
a = np.linspace(1,2/3,4)
print(a)
OUTPUT
[1. 0.91666667 0.83333333  0.75]
```

Create numPy array from list: A Python list having elements enclosed between square brackets can be converted into a NumPy array by using the array() method of the NumPy module. This is shown in the codes given below.

Create numPy array from tuple: The same array() method of the numpy module can be used to create a NumPy array from a tuple. Recall that a tuple contains a number of elements enclosed in round brackets. The code given below demonstrates creation of such an array.

```
# Creating NumPy Array From List
Import numpy as np
L = [1,2,3,4,5,6,7,8,9,10]
arr = np.array(L)
print("NUMPY ARRAY CREATED FROM LIST IS:
      ",arr)
OUTPUT
NUMPY ARRAY CREATED FROM LIST IS:
  [1 2 3 4 5 6 7 8 9 10]
```

```
# Creating NumPy Array From Tuple
import numpy as np
Tup = (1,2,3,4,5,6,7,8,9,10)
arr = np.array(Tup)
print("NUMPY ARRAY CREATED FROM TUPLE IS:
      ",arr)
OUTPUT
NUMPY ARRAY CREATED FROM TUPLE IS:
  [1 2 3 4 5 6 7 8 9 10]
```

Other miscellaneous functions: NumPy also allow users to create "empty" arrays that are placeholders for values and can be filled up later. Apart from empty arrays, we can create arrays and initialize them with ones or zeros or create arrays that get filled up with evenly spaced values, constant, or random values. All these functions are given in Table 2.

Table 2: || Functions for Creating Numpy Arrays

Function	Description	Example	Remarks

`np.ones`	Creates a matrix of specified data type and shape (or size) filled with ones.	`import numpy as np`
		`a = np.ones((4,5), dtype=np.int16)`
		`print(a)`
		OUTPUT
		`[[1 1 1 1 1]`
		`[1 1 1 1 1]`
		`[1 1 1 1 1]`
		`[1 1 1 1 1]]`
			a is a two- dimensional array with 4 rows and 5 columns. All elements in this array are 1.

`np.zeros`	Creates a matrix of specified data type and shape (or size) filled with ones.	`import numpy as np`
		`a = np.zeros((4,5), dtype=np.int16)`
		`print(a)`
		OUTPUT
		`[[0 0 0 0 0]`
		`[0 0 0 0 0]`
		`[0 0 0 0 0]`
		`[0 0 0 0 0]]`
			a is a two- dimensional array with 4 rows and 5 columns. All elements in this array are 0.

`np.full`	Returns a new array with the specified size and type. It also fills the array with specified value.	`import numpy as np`
		`a = np.full((3,2), 2.3)`
		`print(a)`
		OUTPUT
		`[[2.3 2.3]`
		`[2.3 2.3]`
		`[2.3 2.3]]`
			a is a two- dimensional array with 3 rows and 2 columns. All elements in this array have value 2.3.

`np.random.rand`	Creates an array of specified shape and fills it with random values.	`import numpy as np`
		`a = np.random.rand(3,2)`
		`print(a)`
		OUTPUT
		`[[0.46632055 0.19445536]`
		`[0.93474084 0.70868838]`
		`[0.18377336 0.55481711]]`
			A is a two dimensional array with 3 rows and 2 columns. to specify a 3D array, we could have given three values within the function.

`np.empty`	Return a new array of given shape and type, filled with random values.	`import numpy as np`
		`a = np.empty((3,2))`
		`print(a)`
		OUTPUT
		`[[ 4.35009137e-313 0.00000000e+000]`
		`[ 2.71827661e-311 4.46033568e-313]`
		`[-1.68577438e-037 2.12510837e-311]]`
			A is a 2-dimenional array with three rows and 2 columns filled with random values.

Points to Remember:

- Functions like np.ones(), np.zeroes(), np.random.random(), np.empty(), and np.full() take the shape of the array to be created as an argument.
- We can specify the data type of the array to be created in the np.ones() and np.zeroes() function.
- The np.full() function has to specify the constant value that has to be inserted into the array.
- np.linespace() and np.arrange() functions are used to create arrays of evenly spaced values. While np.linespace() function specifies the step value, np.arrange() function on the other hand, specifies number of samples in the array.
- We can also create an identitiy matrix (matrix is another name of 2D array) using np.eye() and np.identity() functions. An identity matrix is a square matrix of which all elements in the principal diagonal are ones, and all other elements are zeros. When a matrix is multiplied with an identity matrix, the given matrix is left unchanged.

4.9 Array attributes

Some of the important attributes of a NumPy array are:

> The head() and tail() methods are used to view a small sample of a Series or the DataFrame object.

Ndim: displays the dimension of the array

Shape: returns a tuple of integers indicating the size of the array

Size: returns the total number of elements in the NumPy array

Dtype: returns the type of elements in the array, i.e., int64, character

Itemsize: returns the size in bytes of each item

Reshape: Reshapes the NumPy array

```
import numpy as np
a = np.empty((5,3))
print("The Array is : \n",a)
print("Number of Dimensions in a : ",np.ndim(a))
print("Shape of a : ",np.shape(a))
OUTPUT
The Array is :
 [[6.23042070e-307 3.56043053e-307 1.60219306e-306]
 [2.44763557e-307 1.69119330e-306 1.33514617e-307]
 [3.56043053e-307 1.37961641e-306 8.06613040e-308]
 [1.24610383e-306 1.69118108e-306 8.06632139e-308]
 [1.20160711e-306 1.69119330e-306 1.39234638e+188]]
Number of Dimensions in a :  2
Shape of a :  (5, 3)
```

head(n): Returns the first n rows. If the value of n is not specified, then by default, first 5 rows will be displayed.

tail(n): Returns the last n rows. If the value of n is not specified, then by default, first 5 rows will be displayed.

```
import numpy as np

import pandas as pd

# Create a series with 10 random numbers

S = pd.Series(np.random.randn(10))

print("The original series is: ")

print(S)

print ("The first four rows of the data series: ")

print(S.head(4))

print ("The last four rows of the data series: ")

print(S.tail(4))
```

```
OUTPUT
The original series is :
0 0.867655
1 0.989083
2 0.460942
3 0.612183
4 -1.084612
5 0.959498
6 0.110584
7 -0.881249
8 2.333609
9 1.372371
dtype: float64
The first four rows of the data series :
0 0.867655
1 0.989083
2 0.460942
3 0.612183
dtype: float64
The last four rows of the data series :
6 0.110584
7 -0.881249
8 2.333609
9 1.372371
dtype: float64
```

4.10 Converting 2D numpy array into 1D array

There are three ways in which a 2D Numpy array can be converted into a 1D array–np.flatten(), np.ravel(), and np.reshape(). These techniques are discussed below.

4.10.1 np.flatten()

The np.flatten() function returns a copy of an array collapsed into one dimension as shown in Figure 4.4. The function takes a parameter order. Syntax of this function can be given as,

```
ndarray.flatten(order)
```

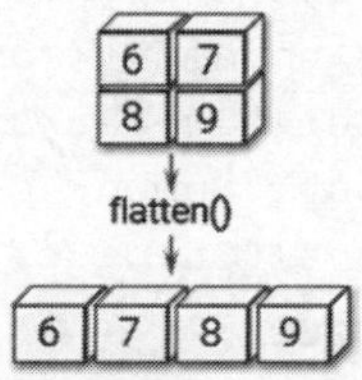

Figure 4.4 Flattening Array

where order is an optional argument that can take values 'C', 'K', 'F'.

order = 'C' means that the array gets flattened in row-major order.

order = 'F' means that the array gets flattened in column-major order.

order = 'K' flattens the array in same order in which the elements occurred in the memory. By default, this parameter is set to 'C'.

```
import numpy as np
TwoD_arr = np.array([[1,2,3],[4,5,6],[7,8,9]])
print("2D Array is : ", str(TwoD_arr))
OneD_arr = TwoD_arr.flatten()
print("1D Array is : ", OneD_arr)
OUTPUT
2D Array is :  [[1 2 3]
 [4 5 6]
 [7 8 9]]
1D Array is :  [1 2 3 4 5 6 7 8 9]
```

4.10.2 np.ravel()

numpy.ravel() is a method in the NumPy module, which changes a 2D array or a multidimensional array into a contiguous flattened 1D array, as shown in Figure 4.5. The returned array has the same data type as the source array or input array. The function makes a copy only if needed. The returned array will have the same type as that of the input array. The syntax of np.ravel() function can be given as,

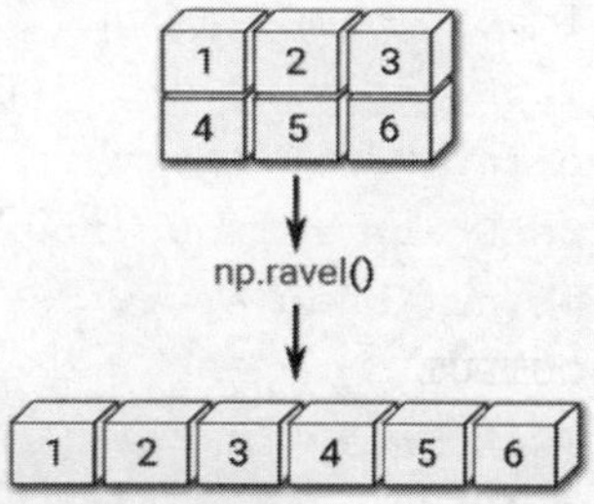

Figure 4.5 Flattening Array using np.ravel() method

numpy.ravel(a, order)

where,

a is the input array that has to be converted into a contiguous flattened array.

Order can take values 'C', 'K', or 'F'. 'C' specifies row major. 'F' denotes column major, and 'K' means flatten the array in the order in which the elements occur in the memory.

In the code given below, we have used the ravel() method without any arguments and called the method using the two dimensional array object.

```
import numpy as np
TwoD_arr = np.array([[1,2,3],[4,5,6],[7,8,9]])
print("TwoD Array is : ", str(TwoD_arr))
OneD_arr = TwoD_arr.ravel()
print("OneD Array is : ", OneD_arr)
OUTPUT
TwoD Array is :  [[1 2 3]
 [4 5 6]
 [7 8 9]]
OneD Array is :  [1 2 3 4 5 6 7 8 9]
```

4.10.3 np.reshape()

The reshape() method of the NumPy module is used to give a new shape to an array without changing its data. Syntax of this function can be given as,

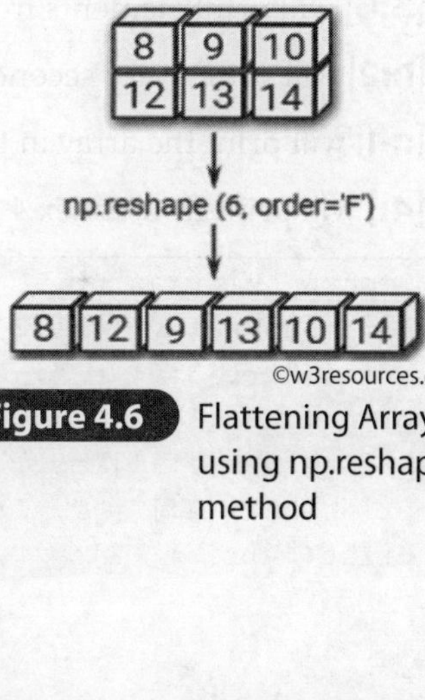

Figure 4.6 Flattening Array using np.reshape() method

numpy.reshape(a, newshape, order='C')

where,

a is array to be reshaped.

newshape should be compatible with the original shape. If an integer, then the result will be a 1-D array of that length (refer Figure 4.6). If one shape dimension is –1, then the value depends on the length of the array and remaining dimensions.

Order can take values 'C', 'F', and 'K'.

The code given below reshapes a 2D array into a 1D array.

```
import numpy as np
TwoD_arr = np.array([[1,2,3],[4,5,6],[7,8,9]])
print("TwoD Array is : ", str(TwoD_arr))
OneD_arr = TwoD_arr.reshape([1,9])
print("OneD Array is : ", OneD_arr)
OUTPUT
TwoD Array is :  [[1 2 3]
 [4 5 6]
 [7 8 9]]
OneD Array is :  [[1 2 3 4 5 6 7 8 9]]
```

Alternatively, we could have also passed -1 as value in the reshape() method to convert a 2D array into 1D array by writing,

```
OneD_arr = TwoD_arr.reshape(-1)
```

4.11 Array slicing: Accessing subarrays

Slicing an array is important when we have to analyze some array elements in other operations. These operations are very similar to how we performed on Python lists.

We use square brackets to access individual array elements. The same brackets can also be used to access subarrays with the *slice* notation, marked by the colon (:) character. Do you recall that the slicing syntax to access a slice of an array x is:

x[start:stop:step]

If any of these values are not specified, then default values are, start = 0, stop = size of dimension, step = 1. The step value can also be negative. In this case, the default values for start and stop are swapped. It helps in reversing the array. Let us see some examples to understand how slicing operation works.

Arr[3:6] will print elements from index 3 to 6. Index in an array starts from 0.

Arr[1::2] will print every second element from index items 1 to the end.

Arr[::-1] will print the array in the reverse order

Arr[4:] will print from index 4 to the end.

```
import numpy as np
Arr = np.array([0,1,2,3,4,5,6,7,8,9,10])
print("Arr[3:6] = ", Arr[3:6])
print("Arr[1::2] = ", Arr[1::2])
print("Arr[::-1] = ", Arr[::-1])
print("Arr[4:] = ", Arr[4:])
print("Arr[5::-2] = ", Arr[5::-2])
```

```
OUTPUT
Arr[3:6] =  [3 4 5]
Arr[1::2] =  [1 3 5 7 9]
Arr[::-1] =  [10  9  8  7  6  5  4  3  2  1  0]
Arr[4:] =  [4  5  6  7  8  9 10]
Arr[5::-2] =  [5 3 1]
```

4.11.1 Subarrays as no-copy views

Note that when we create array slices, *views* from the array are returned rather than *copies* of the array data. This is in fact the main difference between a Python List and a Numpy Array. A list produces slices that are copies. The code given below clarifies this concept.

```
import numpy as np

TwoD_arr = np.array([[1,2,3,4],[5,6,7,8],[9,4,5,1]])

print("ORIGINAL 2D ARRAY IS: \n",TwoD_arr)

sub_arr = TwoD_arr[:2, :2]

print("SLICED ARRAY IS: \n",sub_arr)

# change a value in the sliced array

sub_arr[1,1]= 1000

print("SLICED ARRAY AFTER MODIFICATION IS: \n",sub_arr)

print("ORIGINAL 2D ARRAY AFTER MODIFICATION IS: \n",TwoD_arr)
```

```
OUTPUT
ORIGINAL 2D ARRAY IS:
[[1 2 3 4]
[5 6 7 8]
[9 4 5 1]]
SLICED ARRAY IS:
[[1 2]
[5 6]]
SLICED ARRAY AFTER
MODIFICATION IS:
[[1 2]
[ 5 1000]]
ORIGINAL 2D ARRAY AFTER
MODIFICATION IS:
[[ 1 2 3 4]
[5 1000 7 8]
[9 4 5 1]]
```

Note that this feature of Numpy array is very important, especially when we have to access large datasets. We can simply access and process pieces of these datasets without copying the entire dataset.

4.11.2 Creating copies of arrays

Although creating a view is a very important feature of Numpy array, at times a need may arise to create a copy of the data within an array or a subarray. In such a situation, we must use the copy() method.

```
import numpy as np

TwoD_arr = np.array([[1,2,3,4],[5,6,7,8],[9,4,5,1]])

print("ORIGINAL 2D ARRAY IS: \n",TwoD_arr)

sub_arr = TwoD_arr[:2, :2].copy()

print("SLICED ARRAY IS: \n",sub_arr)
```

```
OUTPUT
ORIGINAL 2D ARRAY IS:
[[1 2 3 4]
[5 6 7 8]
[9 4 5 1]]
SLICED ARRAY IS:
[[1 2]
[5 6]]
SLICED ARRAY AFTER MODIFICATION IS:
[[1 2]
[5 1000]]
```

```
# change a value in the sliced array

sub_arr[1,1]= 1000

print("SLICED ARRAY AFTER MODIFICATION IS: \n",sub_arr)

print("ORIGINAL 2D ARRAY AFTER MODIFICATION IS: \n", TwoD_arr)
```

```
ORIGINAL 2D ARRAY AFTER MODIFICATION IS:
[[1 2 3 4]
[5 6 7 8]
[9 4 5 1]]
```

4.12 Reshaping of arrays

As discussed earlier, shape of an array is the number of elements in each dimension. Reshaping an array means changing the shape of an array. This can be done by adding or removing dimensions or changing the number of elements in each dimension. In Python, any array can be reshaped using the reshape() method.

> Trying to convert a 1D array with 8 elements to a 2D arry with 3 elements in each dimension will raise an error.

Can we reshape into any shape? Yes, we can reshape an array into any shape as long as number of elements in both the original as well as reshaped array is same. This means that we can reshape an 8 elements 1D array into a 2D array with 4 elements in 2 rows or 2 elements in 4 rows. But it cannot be reshaped into a 2D array with 3 elements in 3 rows as a 3 × 3 2D array will have 3 × 3 = 9 elements.

Let us now put the numbers 1 through 9 in a two-dimensional 3 × 3 array, we can write

```
import numpy as np

TwoD_arr = np.arange(1, 10).reshape((3, 3))

print("TWO DIMENSIONAL ARRAY IS: \n",
TwoD_arr)
```

OUTPUT

```
TWO DIMENSIONAL ARRAY IS:
[[1 2 3]
[4 5 6]
[7 8 9]]
```

In the above code, size of the initial array must match the size of the reshaped array. Usually, the reshape() method uses a no-copy view of the initial array, but this is not always the case (when dealing with noncontiguous memory buffers).

The reshape() method can also be used for converting a one-dimensional array into a two-dimensional row or column matrix as shown below.

```
import numpy as np

OneD_arr = np.array([1,2,3,4,5,6])

print("ORIGINAL 1-D ARRAY: \n",OneD_arr)

arr = OneD_arr.reshape((2, 3))

print("2-D ARRAY WITH 2 ROWS AND 3 COLUMNS: \n",arr)

arr = OneD_arr.reshape((3, 2))

print("2-D ARRAY WITH 3 ROWS AND 2 COLUMNS: \n",arr)
```

OUTPUT

```
ORIGINAL 1-D ARRAY
[1 2 3 4 5 6]
2-D ARRAY WITH 2 ROWS AND 3 COLUMNS:
[[1 2 3]
[4 5 6]]
2-D ARRAY WITH 3 ROWS AND 2 COLUMNS:
[[1 2]
[3 4]
[5 6]]
```

4.12.1 Unknown dimension

NumPy also allow users to specify one "unknown" dimension while reshaping an array. This means that you do not have to specify an exact number for one of the dimensions in the reshape method. Ydou can simply pass -1 as value for any one dimension and let NumPy calculate its correct value for you.

For example, in the code given below, we have specified -1 for number of rows. NumPy has itself calculated it to be 3 so as to accommodate all 8 elements and thus, given the desired output.

```
import numpy as np
a= np.array([400,200,350,550,500, 800, 200, 700, 1000, 2000, 300,400])
arr = a.reshape(2,-1,2)
print("3D Array is :\n",arr)
OUTPUT
3D Array is :
 [[[ 400  200]
  [ 350  550]
  [ 500  800]]
 [[ 200  700]
  [1000 2000]
  [ 300  400]]]
```

However, note that we cannot pass -1 more than one dimension.

4.12.2 Reshaping versus resizing arrays

When operating with arrays that do not have same dimensions, we can resize one of them. The np.resize() function returns a new array with specified shape (passed as argument to this function).

If we pass original array along with the new dimensions, and the new array is larger than the original one; the new array is filled with copies of the original array that are repeated as many times as is needed.

```
# Resizing Array

import numpy as np

arr = np.array([[1,2,3],[4,5,6],[7,8,9]])

print("ORIGINAL ARRAY :\n",arr)

arr1 = np.resize(arr,(4,4))

print("RESIZED ARRAY :\n", arr1)
```

```
OUTPUT
ORIGINAL ARRAY:
[[1 2 3]
[4 5 6]
[7 8 9]]
RESIZED ARRAY:
[[1 2 3 4]
[5 6 7 8]
[9 1 2 3]
[4 5 6 7]]
```

Besides resizing, we can also reshape the array. Reshaping means giving a new shape to an array without changing its data. When an array is reshaped, the total size of the new array is unchanged.

For example, a 4 × 3 array has 12 elements, while reshaping the total number of elements will still remain 12.

```
NumPy allow users to ask for more information about the modules, functions or
classes. For example, lookfor() function is used to do a keyword search on
docstrings. Similarly, the info() function is used to get quick explanations
and code examples of functions, classes, or modules. The instructions using
these functions are given below.
# Look up info on 'mean' with 'np.lookfor()'
print(np.lookfor("mean"))
# Get info on data types with 'np.info()'
np.info(np.ndarray.dtype)
```

4.13 Array concatenation (joining) and splitting

We can combine multiple arrays into a single array and also split a single array into multiple arrays.

4.13.1 Joining arrays

Two arrays can be joined or concatenated in NumPy using methods like np.concatenate(), np.hstack(), and np.vstack(). In this section, we will discuss all of these methods.

np.concatenate() method takes a tuple or list of arrays to be concatenated as its first argument. We can concatenate two or more arrays together using this method.

However, remember that while concatenating two arrays, the number of dimensions needs to be the same. This means that only a 1D array can be concatenated to another 1D array.

```
# Concatenating two arrays
import numpy as np
arr1 = np.array([1,2,3,4])
arr2 = np.array([5,6,7])
arr3 = np.concatenate([arr1,arr2])
print("THE CONCATENATED ARRAY IS: ", arr3)
OUTPUT
THE CONCATENATED ARRAY IS: [1 2 3 4 5 6 7]
```

```
# Concatenating three 1D arrays
import numpy as np
arr1 = np.array([1,2,3,4])
arr2 = np.array([5,6,7])
arr3 = np.array([8,9])
arr4 = np.concatenate ([arr1,arr2,arr3])
print("THE CONCATENATED ARRAY IS: ", arr4)
OUTPUT
THE CONCATENATED ARRAY IS: [1 2 3 4 5 6 7 8 9]
```

```
# Concatenating two 2D arrays rowwise
import numpy as np
arr1 = np.array([[1,2,3],[4,5,6]])
arr2 = np.array([[7,8,9],[1,3,5]])
```

```
# Concatenating two 2D arrays columnwise
import numpy as np
arr1 = np.array([[1,2,3],[4,5,6]])
arr2 = np.array([[7,8,9],[1,3,5]])
```

```
arr3 = np.concatenate([arr1,arr2])
print("THE CONCATENATED ARRAY IS: \n", arr3)
OUTPUT
THE CONCATENATED ARRAY IS :
[[1 2 3]
[4 5 6]
[7 8 9]
[1 3 5]]
```

```
arr3 = np.concatenate([arr1,arr2],axis=1)
print("THE CONCATENATED ARRAY IS: \n", arr3)
OUTPUT
THE CONCATENATED ARRAY IS :
[[1 2 3 7 8 9]
[4 5 6 1 3 5]]
```

np.vstack() and np.hstack(): When the two arrays to be concatenated are of different dimensions, then it is better to use the np.vstack() method (vertical stack) or the np.hstack() method (horizontal stack). The use of these two dimensions are illustrate in the code given below. In fact, there is another method- np.dstack() that will stack arrays along the third axis.

```
# Concatenating using vstack()
import numpy as np
arr1 = np.array([1,2,3])
arr2 = np.array([[4,5,6],[7,8,9]])
arr3 = np.vstack([arr1,arr2])
print("THE CONCATENATED ARRAY IS: \n", arr3)
OUTPUT
THE CONCATENATED ARRAY IS:
[[1 2 3]
[4 5 6]
[7 8 9]]
```

```
# Concatenating using hstack()
import numpy as np
arr1 = np.array([[1,2],[3,4]])
arr2 = np.array([[4,5,6],[7,8,9]])
arr3 = np.hstack([arr1,arr2])
print("THE CONCATENATED ARRAY IS: \n", arr3)
OUTPUT
THE CONCATENATED ARRAY IS:
[[1 2 4 5 6]
[3 4 7 8 9]]
```

Note that while using the np.hstack() function, the number of dimensions is the same and that the number of rows in both arrays is the same. This means that when we stack arrays with shapes (2,3) and (2,4), then the resultant array has a shape of (2,4). The two arrays must have same number of rows. Similarly, the number of columns must match while using the vstack() method.

4.13.2 Appending arrays

Two arrays can be appended in such a way that values from the second array are glued to the end of the first array. The NumPy np.append() function does the work of appending two arrays. The syntax of this function can be given as,

numpy.append(arr, values, axis=None)

where,

arr is an array-like object or a NumPy array. The values are appended to a copy of this array.

values are array-like objects, and it is appended to the end of the "arr" elements.

axis specifies the axis along which values are appended. If no value is specified, the arrays are flattened.

```
# Appending a 1-D array

import numpy as np

arr1 = np.array([1,2,3,4,5])

arr2 = np.array([6,7,8,9])

print("APPENDED ARRAY IS :\n")

arr3 = np.append(arr1, arr2)

print(arr3)

OUTPUT

APPENDED ARRAY IS:

[1 2 3 4 5 6 7 8 9]
```

```
# Appending 2-D array

import numpy as np

arr1 = np.array([[1,2,3],[4,5,6],[7,8,9]])
arr2 = np.array([[0,1,2],[3,4,5],[6,7,8]])

print("APPENDED ARRAY IS :\n")
arr3 = np.append(arr1,arr2,axis=1)

print(arr3)

OUTPUT

APPENDED ARRAY IS:

[[1 2 3 0 1 2]
[4 5 6 3 4 5]

[7 8 9 6 7 8]]
```

Note that hen appending 2-D arrays, we have appended as an extra column by specifying axis = 1. If axis = 0, then the array is appended as rows.

4.13.3 Splitting of arrays

The opposite of concatenation is splitting. An array can be split using np.split(), np.hsplit(), or the np.vsplit() methods. For each of these, we can pass a list of indices giving the split points:

Create a two-dimensional 4 × 4 array using np.arrange() method. Split the array vertically as well horizontally into two halves.

```
# vsplit()

import numpy as np

arr = np.arange(16).reshape((4,4))

print("TWO DIMENSIONAL ARRAY IS: \n", arr)

upper, lower = np.vsplit(arr, [2])

print("THE UPPER HALF OF THE ARRAY IS: \n",upper)

print("THE LOWER HALF OF THE ARRAY IS: \n",lower)

OUTPUT

TWO DIMENSIONAL ARRAY IS:

[[0 1 2 3]

[4 5 6 7]
```

```
# hsplit()

import numpy as np

arr = np.arange(16).reshape((4,4))

print("TWO DIMENSIONAL ARRAY IS: \n", arr)

left, right = np.hsplit(arr, [2])

print("THE LEFT HALF OF THE ARRAY IS: \n",left)

print("THE RIGHT HALF OF THE ARRAY IS: \n",right)

OUTPUT

TWO DIMENSIONAL ARRAY IS:

[[0 1 2 3]
[4 5 6 7]

[8 9 10 11]

[12 13 14 15]]
```

```
[8 9 10 11]
[12 13 14 15]]
```

```
THE LEFT HALF OF THE ARRAY IS :
[[0 1]
[4 5]
[8 9]
[12 13]]
THE RIGHT HALF OF THE ARRAY IS :
[[2 3]
[6 7]
[10 11]
[14 15]]
```

4.14 How numpy broadcasting works

Broadcasting concept is also applicable to numpy arrays. This happens when arithmetic operations are performed on arrays of different shapes. For example, when an array that is larger in size is operated with an array of smaller size, the smaller array is repeated multiple times to perform an operation (such as a sum, multiplication, etc.) on the larger array. Here, we need to apply broadcasting mechanism.

However, there are some rules that we need to follow to use broadcasting with arrays. First, we must make sure that the broadcasting is successful and that the dimensions of the two arrays are compatible. Two dimensions are compatible when they are equal. Also, two dimensions are compatible when one of them is 1. If the dimensions of two arrays are not compatible, then ValueError will be returned.

```
import numpy as np
# Initialize 'x'
x = np.ones((4,3))
# Check shape of 'x'
print("Dimensions of x : ",x.shape)
# Initialize 'y'
y = np.random.random((4,3))
# Check shape of 'y'
print("Dimensons of y:", y.shape)
# Add 'x' and 'y'
print(x + y)
OUTPUT
Dimensions of x: (4, 3)
Dimensions of y: (4, 3)
[[1.2388898 1.61297487 1.16992323]
[1.33369933 1.12230165 1.10217694]
[1.07697973 1.14186119 1.36611884]
[1.00416233 1.5186616 1.3807092]]
```

```
import numpy as np
# Initialize 'x'
x = np.ones((4,3))
# Check shape of 'x'
print("Dimensions of x : ",x.shape)
# Initialize 'y'
y = np.random.random((4,1))
# Check shape of 'y'
print("Dimensons of y:", y.shape)
# Add 'x' and 'y'
print(x + y)
OUTPUT
Dimensions of x: (4, 3)
Dimensions of y: (4, 1)
[[1.51196632 1.51196632 1.51196632]
[1.75200391 1.75200391 1.75200391]
[1.96067045 1.96067045 1.96067045]
[1.07990718 1.07990718 1.07990718]]
```

Note that when two arrays are operated that have not same but compatible dimensions then, the size of the resulting array is the maximum size along each dimension of the input arrays. This means that if we subtract two arrays x and y with dimensions (4,3) and (1,3), respectively, the resultant array will have dimensions (4,4).

```
import numpy as np
# Initialize 'x'
x = np.ones((3,4))
# Initialize 'y'
y = np.arange(2,3,4)
# Subtract 'x' and 'y'
print(x - y)
OUTPUT
[[-1.-1.-1.-1.]
[-1.-1.-1.-1.]
[-1.-1.-1.-1.]]
```

```
import numpy as np
# Initialize 'x'
x = np.ones((3,4))
# Initialize 'y'
y = np.arange(2,1,4)
# Subtract 'x' and 'y'
print(x - y)
OUTPUT
ValueError
```

Last, but not the least, the arrays can only be broadcasted together if they are compatible in all dimensions. Consider the example which illustrates this concept.

Note that two arrays are compatible even when one of them is equal to 1. When one array has size 1, and the other array has a size greater than 1 then, the first array behaves as if it were copied along that dimension. However, the shape of the resulting array will always be the maximum size along each dimension of the two arrays.

4.15 Performing mathematical operations on numpy arrays

Like data of any other type, we can even perform mathematical operations like +, -,*, /or % to add, subtract, multiply, divide, or calculate the remainder of two (or more) arrays. Besides these mathematical operators, NumPy also has functions like np.add(), np.subtract(),np.multiply(), np.divide(), and np.remainder() to do the same task.

Table 3: || Aggregate Functions 1

a.sum()	Array-wise sum
a.min()	Array-wise minimum value
b.max(axis=0)	Maximum value of an array row
b.cumsum(axis=1)	Cumulative sum of the elements
a.mean()	Mean
b.median()	Median
a.corrcoef()	Correlation coefficient
np.std(b)	Standard deviation

NumPy also has functions to calculate exponentiation–np.exp(), square root- np.sqrt(), natural logarithm- np.log(), sines or cosines with np.sin() and np.cos(). Other aggregate functions that works with arrays are given in Table 3.

For comparing two array elements, we have the ==, > and < operators. To check for equality between two arrays, we can also use np.array.equal() function. In addition to comparing, logical operations on arrays can be performed with np.logical_or(), np.logical_not(), and np.logical_and() functions. Recall that AND returns 1, if both elements are same, OR returns 1 if either or both of them are same and NOT negates the input value to give the output.

```
import numpy as np
arr = np.array([1,2,3,4,5,6,7,8,9,10])
print(arr[arr>5])
print(arr[(arr>6) | (arr%2==0)])
OUTPUT
[6 7 8 9 10]
[2 4 6 7 8 9 10]
```

Instead of specifying the normal integer index of the element to be accessed, we can specify Boolean indexing to select those values from the array that fulfils a certain condition. To formulate this condition, we can also use logical operators | (OR) and & (AND) as shown in the code.

4.16 Transposing arrays

Transposing an array means switching its dimensions. An array with 3 rows and 4 columns will now have 4 rows and 3 columns after being transposed.

There are two NumPy functions for transposing an array- T() and np.transpose(). Note that there will be no effect of transpose() function on a 1-D array.

```
# Transposing a 1-D array
import numpy as np
arr = np.array([1,2,3,4])
print("ORIGINAL ARRAY :\n",arr)
print("TRANSPOSED ARRAY IS :\n",arr.T)
OUTPUT
ORIGINAL ARRAY:
[1 2 3 4]
TRANSPOSED ARRAY IS:
[1 2 3 4]
```

```
# Transposing a 2-D array
import numpy as np
arr = np.array(
[[1,2,3,4],
 [5,6,7,8],
 [9,0,1,2],
 [3,4,5,6]])
print("ORIGINAL ARRAY:\n",arr)
print("TRANSPOSED ARRAY IS :\n", np.transpose(arr))
OUTPUT
ORIGINAL ARRAY:
[[1 2 3 4]
[5 6 7 8]
[9 0 1 2]
[3 4 5 6]]
TRANSPOSED ARRAY IS:
[[1 5 9 3]
[2 6 0 4]
[3 7 1 5]
[4 8 2 6]]
```

4.17 Inserting and deleting array elements

We can also insert or delete elements from an existing array. In NumPy, the insert() method is sued to insert an element or column. The difference between the insert() and the append() method is that we can specify at which index to add the element(s) when using the insert() method. But, the append() method always adds a value to the end of the array.

The insert() function inserts values in the input array along the given axis and before the given index. If the axis is not mentioned, the input array is flattened. The syntax of the insert() function is,

numpy.insert(arr, obj, values, axis)

Where,

arr is the Input array

obj specifies the index before which insertion is to be made

values is the array of values to be inserted

axis denotes the axis along which values have to be inserted.

```
# Inserting Values in Array
import numpy as np
arr = np.array([1,2,3,4,5])
print("ORIGINAL ARRAY IS :\n",arr)
arr = np.insert(arr, 2, 10)
print("ARRAY AFTER INSERTING VALUE IS :\n",arr)
OUTPUT
ORIGINAL ARRAY IS:
[1 2 3 4 5]
ARRAY AFTER INSERTING VALUE IS:
[1 2 10 3 4 5]
```

4.17.1 Deleting values from an array

The NumPy np.delete() function is used to delete one or more elements from an array. It returns a new array with the specified subarray deleted from the input array. The syntax of np.delete() function can be given as,

numpy.delete(arr, obj, axis)

Where,

arr is the input array

obj specifies can be a slice, an integer or array of integers, indicating the subarray to be deleted from the input array.

axis is the axis along values have to be deleted from the given subarray. If axis is not specified, then arr is flattened.

```
import numpy as np
arr = np.arange(10)
print("ORIGINAL ARRAY IS: ", arr)
print("Shape: ", arr.shape)
# deletion from 1D array
arr1 = np.delete(arr, 5)
print("Array after deleting 5: ", arr1)
print("Shape: ", arr1.shape)
arr1 = np.delete(arr, [6,7])
print("Array after deleting 6 and 7 is: ", arr1)
print("Shape: ", arr.shape)
```

```
OUTPUT
ORIGINAL ARRAY IS: [0 1 2 3 4 5 6 7 8 9]
Shape: (10,)
Array after deleting 5: [0 1 2 3 4 6 7 8 9]
Shape: (9,)
Array after deleting 6 and 7 is: [0 1 2 3 4 5 8 9]
Shape: (10,)
```

4.17.2 Check if numpy array is empty

The size() method, which returns the total number of elements in the array, can be used to check if an array has values or is empty. This is illustrated in the code given below.

```
import numpy as np
arr = np.ones(10)
if(arr.size == 0):
    print("The given Array is empty")
else:
    print("The array = ", arr)
OUTPUT
The array =  [1. 1. 1. 1. 1. 1. 1. 1. 1. 1.]
```

In the above code, since there were elements in the array, the array was printed. Otherwise a message stating that the array is empty would have been displayed.

Note that the size() method is also used to find the length of the array. The code given below prints the length of the 2D array.

```
import numpy as np
arr = np.arange(12).reshape(3,4)
print("THE ARRAY IS: ", arr)
print("LENGTH OF THE ARRAY IS :", arr.size)
OUTPUT
THE ARRAY IS:  [[ 0  1  2  3]
 [ 4  5  6  7]
 [ 8  9 10 11]]
LENGTH OF THE ARRAY IS : 12
```

4.18 Find the index of a value

The where() method of NumPy module is used to find the index of value in an array. The code given below demonstrates the use of this method.

```
import numpy as np
arr = np.arange(10)
print("THE ARRAY IS: ", arr)
index = np.where(arr==6)
print("THE INDEX OF VALUE 6 is: ", index[0])
OUTPUT
THE ARRAY IS:  [0 1 2 3 4 5 6 7 8 9]
THE INDEX OF VALUE 6 is:  [6]
```

Note that we have printed only index[0]. This is because the where() method will also return the datatype. Index[0] will just print the location of the value and not its data type.

4.19 Sorting a numpy array

A NumPy array can be sorted using the sort() method of the NumPy module. The syntax of the sort() function can be given as,

numpy.sort(array, axis=-1, kind='quicksort', order=None)

where,

array is the numpy array that has to be sorted

axis is the axis along which the array will be sorted. Default value is -1, i.e., the last axis

kind specifies the type of sorting algorithm to be used. Values can be "mergesort," "heapsort," "stable," and "quicksort"

order can be a single column name or list of column names along which sorting needs to be done.

The code given below demonstrates the application of the sort() method.

```
import numpy as np
arr = np.array([4,0,9,1,6,8,2,3,7,5])
print("ORIGINAL ARRAY IS : ", arr)
arr.sort()
print("SORTED ARRAY IS : ", arr)
OUTPUT
ORIGINAL ARRAY IS :  [4 0 9 1 6 8 2 3 7 5]
SORTED ARRAY IS :  [0 1 2 3 4 5 6 7 8 9]
```

4.20 Normalize array

Normalizing an array is the process of bringing the array values to some defined range. For example, we can normalize an array so that its values vary from -1 to 1. The formula for normalization is as follows:

x = (x – xmin) / (xmax – xmin)

The code given below illustrates normalizing a NumPy array.

```
import numpy
arr = numpy.array([450,620,390,530,250,320,410])
arr_max = arr.max()
arr_min = arr.min()
arr = (arr - arr_min)/(arr_max - arr_min)
print("After normalization array is : ",arr)
OUTPUT
After normalization array is :  [0.54054054 1.         0.37837838 0.75675676
0.         0.18918919 0.43243243]
```

4.21 Array subsets

We can create one or more subsets of a NumPy array. These subsets will also be NumPy array objects. However, while doing this, make sure that the returned objects are copies.

Creating such subsets from an existing NumPy array is based on several criteria. For example, we can create a subset of array that has only diagonal elements from the original array. Or, we can create a subset having a dimension omitted if there is only one element in that dimension. The subset can also be created based on Boolean conditions for each of the indices or based on an array of indices.

The NumPy module provides several methods that allow users to create arrays containing a subset of elements from an existing array objects. These methods can create subsets depending on user specified criteria. Some of these methods are compress(), diagonal(), squeeze(), and take(). All these methods are discussed in this section.

4.21.1 Subset an array based on a boolean condition:

The compress() method of the NumPy module can be used to specify a Boolean expression for each element in the array. The result of this Boolean expression will indicate the presence or the absence of that element in the new array. Note that this Boolean expression for each element is specified as a flat 1D array.

```
import numpy as np
arr3D = np.arange(36).reshape(3,4,3)
print("3D ARRAY IS : \n", arr3D)
newarr = arr3D.compress([1,1,1])
print("FIRST THREE ELEMENTS OF 3D ARRAY : ", newarr)
newarr = arr3D.compress([0,0,1,1,1])
print("THIRD FOURTH AND FIFTH ELEMENTS OF 3D ARRAY : ", newarr)
OUTPUT
3D ARRAY IS :
 [[[ 0  1  2]
  [ 3  4  5]
  [ 6  7  8]
  [ 9 10 11]]
```

```
 [[12 13 14]
  [15 16 17]
  [18 19 20]
  [21 22 23]]

 [[24 25 26]
  [27 28 29]
  [30 31 32]
  [33 34 35]]]
FIRST THREE ELEMENTS OF 3D ARRAY :  [0 1 2]
THIRD FOURTH AND FIFTH ELEMENTS OF 3D ARRAY :  [2 3 4]
```

4.21.2 Remove a redundant dimension from an array object

If an array needs to be reduced of a dimension, then it is possible only when there is one element in that dimension. To reduce dimension of an array, the squeeze() method of the NumPy module is used as shown in the code given below.

```
import numpy as np
arr2D = np.array([[1,2,3]])
print("2D ARRAY IS : ",arr2D)
squeezed_arr = arr2D.squeeze()
print("ARRAY AFTER REDUCING DIMENSION IS : ",squeezed_arr)
OUTPUT
2D ARRAY IS :  [[1 2 3]]
ARRAY AFTER REDUCING DIMENSION IS :  [1 2 3]
```

4.21.3 Retrieve diagonals from an array

The diagonal() of the NumPy module is used to retrieve diagonals of multidimensional arrays and matrixes.

```
import numpy as np
arr3D = np.arange(27).reshape(3,3,3)
print("3D ARRAY IS : \n", arr3D)
print("DIAGONAL ELEMENTS FOR AXIS1 = 1 AND AXIS2 = 2 ARE : ")
print(arr3D.diagonal(axis1=1,axis2=2))
OUTPUT
3D ARRAY IS :
 [[[ 0  1  2]
  [ 3  4  5]
  [ 6  7  8]]
 [[ 9 10 11]
  [12 13 14]
  [15 16 17]]
 [[18 19 20]
  [21 22 23]
  [24 25 26]]]
```

```
DIAGONAL ELEMENTS FOR AXIS1 = 1 AND AXIS2 = 2 ARE :
[[ 0  4  8]
 [ 9 13 17]
 [18 22 26]]
```

4.21.4 Sub-setting numPy arrays using indexing

Till now, we have been using regular indexing to create subsets of a 2D array. The indexes before the comma refer to the rows, while those after the comma refer to the columns. Note that in the code given below, the : is used for slicing, and here it tells Python to include all rows.

```
import numpy as np
arr = np.arange(12).reshape(4,3)
print("TWO DIMENSIONAL ARRAY IS :\n", arr)
print("VALUES IN FIRST COLUMN ARE : ", arr[:,0])
OUTPUT
TWO DIMENSIONAL ARRAY IS :
 [[ 0  1  2]
 [ 3  4  5]
 [ 6  7  8]
 [ 9 10 11]]
VALUES IN FIRST COLUMN ARE :  [0 3 6 9]
```

4.21.5 Indexing using index arrays

NumPy also allows users to do indexing by using an array as an index. When we do this, a copy of the original array is returned. Apart from arrays, Numpy arrays can be indexed with any other sequence except tuples. Before we get into this, do not forget the index of the first element is 0 and that of the last element is –1.

```
import numpy as np
# Create a sequence of integers from 10 to 1 with a step of -2
arr = np.arange(20,1,-2)
print("ARRAY IS : ",arr)
#Creating an index array
arr_index = [4,-5,9,1,-7]
newarr = arr[arr_index]
print("ELEMENTS AT INDEX 4,-5,9,1 and -7 IN THE ARRAY ARE : ",newarr)
OUTPUT
ARRAY IS :  [20 18 16 14 12 10  8  6  4  2]
ELEMENTS AT INDEX 4,-5,9,1 and -7 IN THE ARRAY ARE :  [12 10  2 18 14]
```

We can also slice a NumPy array by specifying the values for start : stop : step. This will create a shallow copy or a view of the original array.

```
import numpy as np
# Create a sequence of integers from 10 to 1 with a step of -2
arr = np.arange(50,1,-3)
print("ARRAY IS : ",arr)
print("ARRAY FROM 10th ELEMENT ONWARDS : ",arr[10:])
print("ELEMENTS FROM 12th POSITION FROM THE END TILL 15th POSITION FROM
THE BEGINNING : ",arr[-12:15:1])
OUTPUT
ARRAY IS :  [50 47 44 41 38 35 32 29 26 23 20 17 14 11  8  5  2]
ARRAY FROM 10th ELEMENT ONWARDS :  [20 17 14 11  8  5  2]
ELEMENTS FROM 12th POSITION FROM THE END TILL 15th POSITION FROM THE
BEGINNING :  [35 32 29 26 23 20 17 14 11  8]
```

We can also use Ellipsis along with basic slicing. Ellipsis (...) selects elements of the same length as obtained from the dimensions of the array. Therefore, when indexing a 2D array arr by writing, arr[...,1] is same as writing arr[::1].

4.21.6 Purely integer indexing in 2D arrays

When integers are used for indexing a 2D array, each element of first dimension is paired with the element of the second dimension. For example, in the code given below, the pairing goes as (0,2), (1,1), (2,0). This will select second element of first 1D array, first element of second 1D array and first element of third 1D array, respectively.

```
import numpy as np
a = np.array([[1,2,3],[4,5,6],[7,8,9]])
print(a[[0 ,1 ,2 ],[2 ,1 ,0]])
OUTPUT
[3 5 7]
```

4.21.7 Boolean indexing

We can specify indexing with boolean expression as the index. Elements satisfying the Boolean expression are returned. Such an indexing is used for filtering the desired values.

```
import numpy as np
arr = np.arange(2,50,2)
print(arr[arr<25])
OUTPUT
[ 2  4  6  8 10 12 14 16 18 20 22 24]
```

```
Write a Python program to insert elements in row as well as in a column
of a 2D array.
import numpy as np
arr = np.arange(12).reshape(4,3)
print("\n\n2D arr : \n", arr)
print("Shape : ", arr.shape)
arr = np.insert(arr, 1, 5, axis = 1)
```

```
print("\nArray after insertion : \n", arr)
print("Shape : ", arr.shape)
arr = np.insert(arr, 2, 6, axis = 0)
print("\nArray after insertion : \n", arr)
print("Shape : ", arr.shape)
OUTPUT
2D arr :
 [[ 0  1  2]
 [ 3  4  5]
 [ 6  7  8]
 [ 9 10 11]]
Shape :  (4, 3)
Array after insertion :
 [[ 0  5  1  2]
 [ 3  5  4  5]
 [ 6  5  7  8]
 [ 9  5 10 11]]
Shape :  (4, 4)
Array after insertion :
 [[ 0  5  1  2]
 [ 3  5  4  5]
 [ 6  6  6  6]
 [ 6  5  7  8]
 [ 9  5 10 11]]
Shape :  (5, 4)
Write a Python program to insert elements in row as well as in a column of
a 2D array at multiple insertion points.
import numpy as np
arr = np.arange(12).reshape(4,3)
# 7 will be inserted just before 1 and 5 in the array
arr = np.insert(arr, (1,5),7)
print("\n Array after inserting at two points :\n", arr)
print("Shape : ", arr.shape)
arr = np.arange(12).reshape(4,3)
# 8 will be inserted before the first and second column in the array
arr = np.insert(arr, (1,2),8, axis = 1)
print("\nArray after inserting at two points : \n", arr)
print("Shape : ", arr.shape)
OUTPUT
 Array after inserting at two points :
 [ 0  7  1  2  3  4  7  5  6  7  8  9 10 11]
Shape :  (14,)
Array after inserting at at two points :
 [[ 0  8  1  8  2]
 [ 3  8  4  8  5]
 [ 6  8  7  8  8]
 [ 9  8 10  8 11]]
```

```
Shape :  (4, 5)
Write a Python program to delete a row as well as a column from a 2D array.
import numpy as np
arr = np.arange(16).reshape(4,4)
print("ORIGINAL ARRAY IS : \n",arr)
print("Shape : ", arr.shape)
arr1 = np.delete(arr, 1, 0)
print("ARRAY AFTER DELETING FIRST ROW :\n",arr1)
print("Shape : ", arr1.shape)
arr1 = np.delete(arr, 2, axis = 1)
print("ARRAY AFTER DELETING SECOND COLUMN :\n",arr1)
print("Shape : ", arr1.shape)
```

OUTPUT

```
ORIGINAL ARRAY IS :
 [[ 0  1  2  3]
 [ 4  5  6  7]
 [ 8  9 10 11]
 [12 13 14 15]]
Shape :  (4, 4)
ARRAY AFTER DELETING FIRST ROW :
 [[ 0  1  2  3]
 [ 8  9 10 11]
 [12 13 14 15]]
Shape :  (3, 4)
ARRAY AFTER DELETING SECOND COLUMN :
 [[ 0  1  3]
 [ 4  5  7]
 [ 8  9 11]
 [12 13 15]]
Shape :  (4, 3)
Write a program that masks multiple elements in a 1D array using a mask
array.
import numpy as np
arr = np.arange(10)
print("ORIGINAL ARRAY IS : ", arr)
mask = np.ones(len(arr), dtype=bool)
# Masking elements at locations 1,3 and 5 from the array
mask[[1,3,5]] = False
print("\nMask set as : ", mask)
arr1 = arr[mask]
print("\n ARRAY AFTER MASKING ELEMENTS : ", arr1)
```

OUTPUT

```
ORIGINAL ARRAY IS :  [0 1 2 3 4 5 6 7 8 9]
Mask set as :  [ True False  True False  True False  True  True  True  True]
ARRAY AFTER MASKING ELEMENTS :  [0 2 4 6 7 8 9]
```

Write a program to create a 2D array and demonstrate deleting multiple rows and columns from it.

```
import numpy as np
arr = np.arange(25).reshape(5,5)
print("ORIGINAL ARRAY IS : \n",arr)
print("Shape : ", arr.shape)
arr1 = np.delete(arr,[2,3], axis= 0)
print("ARRAY AFTER DELETING SECOND AND THIRD ROWS IS :\n", arr1)
arr1 = np.delete(arr,[1,3], axis= 1)
print("ARRAY AFTER DELETING SECOND AND FOURTH COLUMNS IS :\n", arr1)
```

OUTPUT

```
ORIGINAL ARRAY IS :
 [[ 0  1  2  3  4]
 [ 5  6  7  8  9]
 [10 11 12 13 14]
 [15 16 17 18 19]
 [20 21 22 23 24]]
Shape :  (5, 5)
ARRAY AFTER DELETING SECOND AND THIRD ROWS IS :
 [[ 0  1  2  3  4]
 [ 5  6  7  8  9]
 [20 21 22 23 24]]
ARRAY AFTER DELETING SECOND AND FOURTH COLUMNS IS :
 [[ 0  2  4]
 [ 5  7  9]
 [10 12 14]
 [15 17 19]
 [20 22 24]]
```

The tolist() method which converts the array to a list.

Write a program that converts a NumPy array into a list in Python.

```
import numpy as np
arr = np.arange(10)
print("LIST OBTAINED FROM ARRAY IS : ",arr.tolist())
```

OUTPUT

```
LIST OBTAINED FROM ARRAY IS :  [0, 1, 2, 3, 4, 5, 6, 7, 8, 9]
```

Write a program to sort a NumPy array in descending order.

```
import numpy as np
arr = np.array([4,0,9,1,6,8,2,3,7,5])
print("ORIGINAL ARRAY IS : ", arr)
# Get a sorted copy of numpy array (Descending Order)
arr = np.sort(arr)[::-1]
print("SORTED ARRAY IS : ", arr)
```

OUTPUT

```
ORIGINAL ARRAY IS :  [4 0 9 1 6 8 2 3 7 5]
SORTED ARRAY IS :  [9 8 7 6 5 4 3 2 1 0]
```

```
Write a program that sorts rows of a 2D NumPy array in descending order.
Also sort its columns in ascending order.
import numpy as np
arr = np.array([[4,8,1],[6,3,9],[5,0,2],[4,8,1]])
print("ORIGINAL ARRAY IS : \n", arr)
# Sort the contents of each column in ascending order
arr = np.sort(arr,axis=0)
print("ARRAY WITH EACH COLUMN SORTED IS : \n", arr)
# Sort the contents of each row in descending order
arr = np.sort(arr,axis=1)[::-1]
print("ARRAY WITH EACH ROW SORTED IN DESCENDING IS : \n", arr)
OUTPUT
ORIGINAL ARRAY IS :
 [[4 8 1]
 [6 3 9]
 [5 0 2]
 [4 8 1]]
ARRAY WITH EACH COLUMN SORTED IS :
 [[4 0 1]
 [4 3 1]
 [5 8 2]
 [6 8 9]]
ARRAY WITH EACH ROW SORTED IN DESCENDING IS :
 [[6 8 9]
 [2 5 8]
 [1 3 4]
 [0 1 4]]
Write a program that converts a 1D array into a 3D array.
import numpy as np
a= np.array([400,200,350,550,500, 800, 200, 700, 1000, 2000, 300,400])
arr = a.reshape(2,3,2)
print("3D Array is :\n",arr)
OUTPUT
3D Array is :
 [[[ 400  200]
  [ 350  550]
  [ 500  800]]
 [[ 200  700]
  [1000 2000]
  [ 300  400]]]
Write a program that prints the diagonal as well as lower diagonal and
upper diagonal elements of a 2D array.
import numpy as np
arr = np.array([[5,2,8],[4,1,9],[2,7,6]])
print("TWO DIMENSIONAL ARRAY IS :\n", arr)
print("DIAGONAL WITH OFFSET 0 IS : ", arr.diagonal(0))
```

```
print("DIAGONAL WITH OFFSET -1 (LOWER DIAGONAL) IS : ", arr.diagonal(-1))
print("DIAGONAL WITH OFFSET 1 (UPPER DIAGONAL) IS : ", arr.diagonal(1))
```

OUTPUT

```
TWO DIMENSIONAL ARRAY IS :
 [[5 2 8]
 [4 1 9]
 [2 7 6]]
DIAGONAL WITH OFFSET 0 IS :  [5 1 6]
DIAGONAL WITH OFFSET -1 (LOWER DIAGONAL) IS :  [4 7]
DIAGONAL WITH OFFSET 1 (UPPER DIAGONAL) IS :  [2 9]
```

Write a program that prints the square of even numbers in the array

```
import numpy as np
arr = np.arange(10)
print(arr[arr%2==0]**2)
```

OUTPUT

```
[ 0  4 16 36 64]
```

Write a program that sums the rows of a 2D array and prints the rows whose sum is a multiple of 10.

```
import numpy as np
arr = np.array([[7,3],[13,6],[16,14]])
sumrow = arr.sum(-1) # -1 indicates sum the elements of a row
print(arr[sumrow%10==0])
```

OUTPUT

```
[[ 7  3]
 [16 14]]
```

Business Scenario: Data Analysis for Sales Performance

A retail company analyzes its past year sales data to understand trends, customer buying behavior, and seasonal effects. The company uses NumPy module in Python to analyze sales data that is given as an array with 12 values that represents total sales for a given month. The array is:

```
import numpy as np
# Sales data for each month in lakhs of rupees
sales_data = np.array([120, 135, 125, 150, 160, 155, 170, 180, 190, 210, 220, 240])
```

The business analyst is supposed to present a report on the following parameters.

1. **average sales** per month
2. the **month with the highest sales**
3. determine whether the sales have **increased or decreased** over the year
4. the **standard deviation** of monthly sales to understand variability
5. analyzing a **seasonal trend** in sales (high sales in specific months)

Solution:

1. The average sales per month is calculated using np.mean().
   average_sales = np.mean(sales_data)
   print("Average sales per month = Rs. : ", average_sales")
2. The month with the highest sales can be found using np.argmax() to locate the index of the highest value in the array.
   highest_sales_month = np.argmax(sales_data)
   print("Month with the highest sales: ", highest_sales_month + 1)
3. To analyze the trend, the difference between the first and last month's sales is calculated.
   first_month_sales = sales_data[0]
   last_month_sales = sales_data[-1]
   trend = "increase" if last_month_sales > first_month_sales else "decrease"
   print("Sales trend: ",trend)
4. To calculate the standard deviation, use np.std().
   sales_std_dev = np.std(sales_data)
   print("Standard deviation of sales: Rs. ", sales_std_dev)
5. To analyze seasonality, we look for patterns in the sales data. There is a **seasonal trend**, with sales peaking in the final quarter (October to December). This may be because of festivals and end-of-year discounts.

Business Scenario: Customer Retention Analysis

A subscription-based service company analyzes customer retention data to learn how many customers are renewing their subscriptions each month. The company has the following data for customer renewals over a 6-month period that is analyzed using NumPy in Python.

```
import numpy as np
# Number of customer renewals over the last 6 months
renewals_data = np.array([150, 165, 170, 160, 180, 200])
```

What instructions can be performed to answer the following queries?

1. The **total number of renewals** over the 6-month period.
2. The **percentage change** in renewals from one month to the next.
3. The **month with the largest increase** in renewals.
4. The **mean and median** of the renewals.
5. The **cumulative renewals** over the 6–month period (running total).

Solution:

1. total_renewals = np.sum(renewals_data)
   print("Total renewals over 6 months: ", total_renewals)
2. The percentage change can be calculated by finding the difference between consecutive months and dividing by the previous month's value, then multiplying by 100.
   percentage_change = np.diff(renewals_data) / renewals_data[:-1] * 100
   print("Percentage change in renewals: ", percentage_change)

The percentage change in renewals can be observed as,

a. From Month 1 to Month 2: **10%**

b. From Month 2 to Month 3: **3.03%**

c. From Month 3 to Month 4: **–5.88%**

d. From Month 4 to Month 5: **12.5%**

e. From Month 5 to Month 6: **11.11%**

3. To find the largest increase, first compute the percentage change, then find the maximum change.

largest_increase_index = np.argmax(percentage_change)

print("The month with the largest increase is Month ", largest_increase_index + 2)

4. The mean and median can be calculated using np.mean() and np.median().

mean_renewals = np.mean(renewals_data)

median_renewals = np.median(renewals_data)

print("Mean number of renewals: ", mean_renewals)

print("Median number of renewals: "median_renewals)

5. The cumulative renewals can be found using np.cumsum(), which computes the running total.

cumulative_renewals = np.cumsum(renewals_data)

print("Cumulative renewals month-by-month: ", cumulative_renewals)

Therefore, remember that

- It is always best to include a combination of quantitative and qualitative data for analysis.
- In some data sets, there can be no mode at all, as all values appear the same number of times. If two values appeared the same maximum number of times, then the data set is said to be bimodal. If three values appeared the same maximum number of times, then the data set is said to be trimodal. Similarly, for *n* values appearing most frequently, the data set is said to be multimodal.
- Diagnostic analytics helps to explain why things happened the way they did. It is more complex than descriptive analytics as it focuses on *why* it happened rather than *what* had happened.

Key Terms

Array: A collection of elements having the same data type. These elements are stored in consecutive memory locations and are referenced by an index.

Array: A collection of similar data elements (of the same data type) that are stored in consecutive memory locations and are referenced by an index (also known as the subscript).

Axes: In NumPy, dimensions are called axes.

Axes: In NumPy, dimensions of the array are called axes.

Data: *A collection of facts that are processed to obtained information. These data can be anything including numbers, words, measurements, observations, etc*

Data analysis methodologies: Techniques used to analyze and interpret data. These techniques vary depending on the type of data being analyzed and the research objectives.

Data processing: The process of converting raw data to meaningful information. This information may help to resolve a problem or improve an existing scenario.

Descriptive Analytics: Data analytics performed to understand what has happened and evaluate the trends over time.
Identity matrix: A square matrix of which all elements in the principal diagonal are ones, and all other elements are zeros.
Lists: Simple built-in data structures in Python, which can be easily used as a container to hold data of different data types like integer, float, and object.
Matrix: A two-dimensional array specified using two subscripts where one subscript denotes row and the other denotes column.
Multi-Dimensional Array: An array of arrays.
Normalizing an array: The process of bringing the array values to some defined range.
NumPy: An open source module of Python, which provides fast mathematical computation on arrays and matrices.
Rank: Number of axes in the a NumPy array is called the rank.
Rank: Number of axes is called the rank.
Reshaping an array: Changing the shape of an array. This can be done by adding or removing dimensions or changing the number of elements in each dimension
Standard deviation: A measure of the dispersion of data from its average.
Subscript: An ordinal number indicating the position of the element counting from the beginning of the array.
Two-Dimensional Array: An array of one-dimensional array. Every element in a 2-D array is specified using two subscripts where one subscript denotes row and the other denotes column.

Chapter Highlights

* Structured data **also referred to as quantitative data** is that data which can be used for effective analysis. It is stored in a database and has well-defined structure and format.
* Unstructured data, **also referred to as qualitative data**, are not available in a predefined format.
* Descriptive statistics are evaluated to summarize and organize data for better understandability.
* In a row major order, elements of the first row are stored before the elements of the second and third row. In a column major order, the elements of the first column are stored before the elements of the second and third column.
* np.arrange()returns an array with evenly spaced elements from the interval specified by the value of start and stop in the gap of step.
* Importing a module means loading it in memory for using its functionalities.
* A CSV file is a type of plain text file that uses specific structuring to arrange tabular data. The format used for data interchange by a CSV file is compact, simple, and general. This feature facilitates websites and its users to export tabular data from the website into a CSV file.
* NumPy which stands for "Numeric Python" or "Numerical Python" is the most important library for scientific computing in Python.
* Arrays are superior to Python lists as it is more compact, convenient, and efficient and provides faster access in reading and writing items.
* Numpy arange() function takes start, end of a range and the interval as arguments and returns a one-dimensional array with evenly spaced elements from the interval specified by the value of start and stop in the gap of step.
* Numpy linspace() functions takes start, end and the number of elements to be created as arguments and returns a one-dimensional array that has evenly spaced numbers over the specified interval.

* Subscript indicates an ordinal number of the element counting from the beginning of the array.
* When we create array slices, *views* from the array are returned rather than *copies* of the array data.
* When operating with arrays that do not have same dimensions, we can resize one of them. The np.resize() function returns a new array with specified shape.
* We can combine multiple arrays into a single array, and also split a single array into multiple arrays.
* When two arrays are operated that have not same but compatible dimensions then, the size of the resulting array is the maximum size along each dimension of the input arrays.
* Instead of specifying the normal integer index of the element to be accessed, we can specify Boolean indexing to select those values from the array that fulfil a certain condition.
* Transposing an array means switching its dimensions. An array with 3 rows and 4 columns will now have 4 rows and 3 columns after being transposed.
* To export a NumPy array to a CSV file, the savetxt() method of the NumPy module can be used.
* We can create one or more subsets of a NumPy array. These subsets will also be NumPy array objects.
* The compress() method of the NumPy module can be used to specify a Boolean expression for each element in the array. The result of this Boolean expression will indicate the presence or the absence of that element in the new array.
* If an array needs to be reduced of a dimension, then it is possible only when there is one element in that dimension. To reduce dimension of an array, the squeeze() method of the NumPy module is used
* NumPy also allow users to do indexing by using an array as an index. When we do this, a copy of the original array is returned.
* Ellipsis (...) selects elements of the same length as obtained from the dimensions of the array.

Review Questions

1. Define data and state its importance.
2. Differentiate between structured and unstructured data.
3. What is data processing? Explain the set of activities involved to process data.
4. With the help of an example explain the difference between bimodal, trimodal, and multimodal.
5. Why do we calculate descriptive statistics? Explain with the help of relevant examples.
6. What is NumPy?
7. Which one will you prefer and why, a Python List or a NumPy array?
8. What is an array? How does it store data elements?
9. List different methods that can be used to create arrays in NumPy.
10. With the help of an example explain the difference between np.arange() and np.linspace().
11. Explain different methods that convert a 2D array into a 1D array.
12. Why do we slice an array? How can it be done?
13. What happens when we supply a negative value for the step argument when slicing an array?

14. Which elements will be printed when the following slicing operations are performed?
    a. Arr[2:5]   b. Arr[3::3]
    c. Arr[::-2]   d. Arr[2:]
15. Explain the significance of copy() method when slicing an array.
16. What do you understand by reshaping an array? Is there any restriction to be considered while doing so?
17. Is it possible to convert a 1D array into a 2D array using the reshape() method?
18. Differentiate between reshape() and resize() with the help of a relevant example.
19. Compare different methods of joining two or more arrays.
20. What do you mean by Boolean indexing?
21. Differentiate between insert() and delete() methods to add an element in an existing array.
22. What do you understand by normalizing an array? How is it done?
23. With the help of an example explain the utility of compress() method.
24. How can we reduce a dimension of an array? Illustrate with an example.
25. What is covariance? Explain its significance.
26. How is correlation coefficient a better measure than covariance?
27. How will you interpret the meaning of correlation coefficient?
28. What is linear regression? Why do we perform regression analysis?
29. Write instructions for:
    a. Create an array of ones
    b. Create an array of zeros
    c. Create an array with random values
    d. Create an empty array
    e. Create a full array
    f. Create an array of evenly-spaced values
    g. print the number of 'my_array''s elements
    h. Print the length of one array element in bytes
    i. Print the total consumed bytes by 'my_array''s elements
    j. Select the element at row 1 column 2
    k. Select items at index 0 and 1
    l. Select items at row 0 and 1, column 1
    m. Select items at row 1 of a 3D array
    n. Delete the value at index 1
30. Identify the significance of the following instructions.
    a. np.linspace(0,2,9)
    b. print(len(my_array))
    c. my_array.astype(float)
    d. print(my_array[1])
    e. print(my_3d_array[bigger_than_3])
    f. np.insert(arr, 1, 5)
    g. x_new = np.arange(5).reshape((-1, 1))
31. Compare different data structures in Python.

32. What do you understand by a CSV file? With the help of an example demonstrate how will you read and write data to such a file.
33. Differentiate between the following:
    a. quantitative and qualitative data
    b. nominal and ordinal data
    c. discrete and continuous data
    d. structured and unstructured data
34. How is qualitative data analyzed?
35. Define data processing and explain the stages in data processing.
36. Write a short note on different types of business analytics.

Programming Exercise

1. Create a Python list that stores temperature of 10 consecutive days measured in degree Celsius. Convert this list into a NumPy array.
2. Create a NumPy array containing multiples of 3 in the range 1 to 100.
3. Create a NumPy array containing 10 evenly spaced values from 100 to 105.
4. Create a 4x3 NumPy array filled with value 3.9.
5. Create a 5x5 NumPy array filled with random values.
6. Create a two-dimensional array and print its attributes.
7. Create an array of students enrolled in Arts, Dance, and Music activities. Form a single array containing a list of all the students.
8. Create an array storing marks obtained by 5 students in 4 different subjects.
    a. Find the highest marks obtained in each subject.
    b. Print the minimum marks obtained by each student.
    c. Insert marks of one more student in this array.
    d. Insert marks of one more subject in the array.
    e. Delete a specific row from this array.
    f. Delete a user specified column from this array.
9. Create a 3D array and print elements at even column and odd row index.
10. Write a program that prints the first column elements of a 2D array.
11. Write a program that creates an array from a tuple and vice versa.
12. Create a program that converts a 1D array into 3D array and vice versa.
13. Write a program that prints the cube of odd numbers in the array
14. Write a program that sums the columns of a 2D array and prints the columns whose sum is divisible by 5.
15. Write a program that prints the sum of columns of a 3D array.
16. Convert a 1D array with 12 elements into a 2-D array. The outermost dimension will have 4 arrays, each with 3 elements.
17. Create a 3D array with only one 2D array as its element. Reduce dimension of this array and print the resultant array.

Fill in the Blanks

1. SQL table is an example of _________ data.
2. ________ is a collection of facts that is processed to obtained information.
3. ___________ is the process of converting raw data to meaningful information.
4. _________ are evaluated to summarize and organize data for better understandability.
5. _______ specifies the value appearing maximum time in data set.
6. _______ module provides fast mathematical computation on arrays and matrices.
7. The elements of the array are stored in consecutive memory locations and are referenced by an _______.
8. _________ is an array of one-dimensional array. Ans. Two-dimensional array
9. Every element in a ________ is specified using two subscripts.
10. In a ________ representation of a 2D array, element (1,0) is followed by element (1,1).
11. Before using a module, we must first _________ it.
12. ________ creates a matrix of specified data type and shape (or size) filled with ones.
13. ________ returns an array with evenly spaced elements from the interval specified by the value of start and stop in the gap of step.
14. _______ displays the dimension of the NumPy array.
15. ________ a module means loading it in memory for using its functionalities.
16. The _____ function is used to check whether all elements are True.
17. The ______ method is used to return value associated with a specified label.
18. If we compare numpy objects of different length then objects can be _______.
19. The elements of the array are referenced by an ________.
20. Number of axes is called the ______.
21. _______ function takes start, end and the number of elements to be created as arguments and returns a one-dimensional array that has evenly spaced numbers over the specified interval.
22. ________ creates a matrix filled with ones.
23. _______ attribute returns a tuple of integers indicating the size of the array.
24. The ________ function displays first 5 rows of the data.
25. When we create array slices, _____ from the array.
26. ________ *method is used to create a copy of NumPy array data.*
27. If the dimensions of two arrays are not compatible, then ________ will be returned.
28. The arrays can only be broadcast together if they are ________ in all dimensions.
29. _______ an array means switching its dimensions.
30. The _______ of the NumPy module is used to retrieve diagonals of multidimensional arrays.
31. Numpy arrays can be indexed with any other sequence except _______.

32. _______ selects elements of the same length as obtained from the dimensions of the array.
33. Mode = 'w' indicates that the file is being opened for _______ data.
34. ___________ data cannot be measured or counted in the form of numbers.
35. _______ data cannot even be sorted in any meaningful order.
36. ______ analysis identifies recurring themes or patterns in qualitative data.
37. _______ data are countable and finite.
38. Hypothesis testing, t-tests, and regression analysis fall under the category of _______ statistics.
39. To confirm or test a theory or hypothesis, prefer using _______ data.
40. ______ is the number around which a whole data is spread out.
41. _______ measures the average distance between each value and the mean.
42. ______ is calculated as the difference between lowest and highest value.
43. _______ analytics focuses on why it happened.
44. _______ analytics is the most advanced analytics as it provides actionable insights.

State True or False

1. Array indexes are written in round brackets.
2. Array elements are placed in consecutive memory locations.
3. Measure of Spread refers to the idea of variability within your data.
4. An mXn matrix has m columns and n rows.
5. NumPy is mainly used for creating heterogeneous multidimensional arrays.
6. Shape returns a tuple of integers indicating the size of the array.
7. Python list is more powerful than NumPy array.
8. A list is a collection of elements having the same data type.
9. The elements of the array are stored in consecutive memory locations.
10. Data elements of a 2D array are not stored consecutively in memory.
11. np.empty() return a new array of given shape and type, filled with random values.
12. Default value of size = 0.
13. While slicing an array, the value of step cannot be negative.
14. A list produces slices that are views of data.
15. We can convert a 1D array into a 2D array using the reshape() method.
16. The size() method is also used to find the length of the array.
17. Array subsets are themselves NumPy array objects.
18. When arrays are used for indexing NumPy arrays, a view of the original array is returned.
19. The not in operator returns True if the index is present and False otherwise.

20. The isnull() function returns False if a particular value is null and True otherwise.
21. NaN is equal to NaN.
22. Quantitative data talks about the perception of people about a product.
23. We cannot apply any numerical operation on nominal data values.
24. Mean, median, mode, standard deviation, and percentages are examples of inferential statistics.
25. It is always best to include a combination of quantitative and qualitative data for analysis.
26. In some data sets, there can be no mode at all as all values appear the same number of times.
27. _______ analysis is performed by data analytics to understand what has happened and evaluate the trends over time.
28. Descriptive analytics tells us what will happen.

Give the Output

1.
```
import numpy as np
a = np.arange(5, 14, 2)
print(a)
```
2.
```
import numpy as np
a = np.linspace(5, 25, 4)
print(a)
```
3.
```
x = np.arange(10)
x
array([0, 1, 2, 3, 4, 5, 6, 7, 8, 9])
x[:5]
x[5:]
x[4:7]
x[::2]
x[1::2]
```
4.
```
x = np.array([1, 2, 3])
x.reshape((1, 3))
x[np.newaxis, :]
x.reshape((3, 1))
x[:, np.newaxis]
```
5.
```
z = [99, 99, 99]
print(np.concatenate([x, y, z]))
```
6.
```
grid = np.array([[1, 2, 3],
                 [4, 5, 6]])
np.concatenate([grid, grid])
np.concatenate([grid, grid], axis=1)
```

7.
```
x = np.array([1, 2, 3])
grid = np.array([[9, 8, 7],
                 [6, 5, 4]])
np.vstack([x, grid])
y = np.array([[99], [99]])
np.hstack([grid, y])
```
8.
```
x = [1, 2, 3, 99, 99, 3, 2, 1]
x1, x2, x3 = np.split(x, [3, 5])
print(x1, x2, x3)
```
9.
```
import numpy as np
x = np.ones((4,3))
print("Dimensions of x : ",x.shape)
y = np.random.random((1,3))
print("DImensons of y  : ", y.shape)
print(x + y)
```
10.
```
import numpy as np
arr  = np.array(
[[1,2,3,4],
   [5,6,7,8],
   [9,0,1,2],
   [3,4,5,6]])
print("Elements at (1,0), (0,1), (1,2) and (0,0) \n")
print(arr[[1, 0, 1, 0],[0, 1, 2, 0]])
```
11.
```
import numpy
a = numpy.array([1, 2, 3, 4, 5])
b = numpy.array([10, 20, 30, 40, 50])
newArray = numpy.append(a, b)
print("The new array = ", newArray)
```
12.
```
import numpy as np
a = np.array([[1,2],[3,4],[5,6]])
print( np.insert(a,3,[11,12]) )
print( np.insert(a,1,[11],axis = 0) )
print( np.insert(a,1,11,axis = 1))
```
13.
```
import numpy as np
arr = np.arange(6).reshape(2, 3)
print("1D arr : \n", arr)
print("Shape : ", arr.shape)
a = np.insert(arr, (2, 4), 9)
print("\nInsertion at two points : ", a)
print("Shape : ", a.shape)
```
14.
```
arr = np.arange(12).reshape(3, 4)
print("\n\n2D arr : \n", arr)
print("Shape : ", arr.shape)
a = np.insert(arr, (0, 3), 66, axis = 1)
```

```
print("\nInsertion at two points : \n", a)
print("Shape : ", a.shape)
```

15.
```
import numpy as np
a = np.arange(12).reshape(3,4)
print(a)
print(np.delete(a,5) )
print(np.delete(a,1,axis = 1))
```

16.
```
a = np.array([1,2,3,4,5,6,7,8,9,10])
print(np.delete(a, np.s_[::2]))
```

17.
```
arr = np.arange(12).reshape(3, 4)
print("arr : \n", arr)
print("Shape : ", arr.shape)
```

18.
```
a = np.delete(arr, 1, 0)
print("Shape : ", a.shape)
a = np.delete(arr, 1, 1)
print("Shape : ", a.shape)
```

19.
```
import numpy
a = numpy.array([1, 2, 3])
newArray = numpy.delete(a, 1, axis = 0)
print(newArray)
```

20.
```
import numpy
a = numpy.array([[1, 2, 3], [4, 5, 6], [10, 20, 30]])
newArray = numpy.delete(a, 1, axis = 0)
print(newArray)
```

21.
```
import numpy as np
arr = np.array([])
if(arr.size == 0):
    print("The given Array is empty")
else:
    print("The array = ", arr)
```

22.
```
import numpy
a = numpy.array([1, 2, 3, 4, 5, 6, 7, 8])
print("A subset of array a = ", a[2:5])
```

23.
```
import numpy
a = numpy.array([1, 2, 3, 4, 5, 6, 7, 8])
print("A subset of array a = ", a[-3:])
print(np.hsplit(my_stacked_array, 2))
print(np.vsplit(my_stacked_array, 2))
```

24.
```
import numpy as np
arr = np.array([1, 2, 3, 4, 5, 6, 7, 8])
newarr = arr.reshape(3, 3)
print(newarr)
```

25.
```
import numpy as np
arr = np.array([1, 2, 3, 4, 5, 6, 7, 8])
```

```
   newarr = arr.reshape(2, 2, -1)
   print(newarr)
26. import numpy as np
   arr = np.array([[1, 2, 3], [4, 5, 6]])
   newarr = arr.reshape(-1)
   print(newarr)
27. import numpy as np
   a = np.arange(10, 1, -2)
   newarr = a[np.array([3, 1, 2 ])]
   print("\n Elements at these indices are:\n",newarr)
28. import numpy as np
   x = np.array([1, 2, 3, 4, 5, 6, 7, 8, 9])
   arr = x[np.array([1, 3, -3])]
   print.("\n Elements are : \n",arr)
29. import numpy as np
   a = np.arange(20)
   print("\n a[-8:17:1]  = ",a[-8:17:1])
   print("\n a[10:]  = ",a[10:])
30. import numpy as np
   b = np.array([[[1, 2, 3],[4, 5, 6]],
                 [[7, 8, 9],[10, 11, 12]]])
    print(b[...,1]) # Equivalent to b[: ,: ,1 ]
31. import numpy as np
   a = np.array([10, 40, 80, 50, 100])
   print(a[a>50])
32. import numpy as np
   a = np.array([[1, 2], [3, 4]])
   print(a)
33. import numpy as np
   a = np.array([1, 2, 3,4,5], ndmin = 2)
   print(a)
34. import numpy as np
   a = np.array([1, 2, 3], dtype = complex)
   print(a)
```

Fill in the Blanks to Complete the Code

```
1. # Import 'numpy' as 'np'
   _________________
   # Make the array 'arr'
   arr = ________([[1,2,3,4], [5,6,7,8]], dtype=np.int64
   )
   # Print 'arr'
   print(_________)
```

2.
```
# Initialize 'x' with all ones
x = np.ones((3,4))
# Check shape of 'x'
print(_______)
# Initialize 'y' with random values
y = np.random.random((3,4))
# Check shape of 'y'
print(_______)
# Add 'x' and 'y'
Print(______)
```

3.
```
# Add 'x' and 'y'
_______________(x,y)
# Subtract 'x' and 'y'
_______________(x,y)
# Multiply 'x' and 'y'
_______________(x,y)
# Divide 'x' and 'y'
______________(x,y)
# Calculate the remainder of 'x' and 'y'
______________(x,y)
# 'a' AND 'b'
_____________(a, b)
# 'a' OR 'b'
_____________(a, b)
# 'a' NOT 'b'
_____________(a,b)
```

4.
```
# Append a 1D array to your 'arr'
new_arr = _________(arr, [7, 8, 9, 10])
# Print 'new_arr'
_________(new_arr)
```

5.
```
# Append an extra column to your 'arr'
new_arr = __________(arr, [[7], [8]], axis=1)
# Print 'new_arr'
_________(new_arr)
```

Find Out the Error, If Any

1.
```
import numpy as np
x = np.ones((3,4))
print(x.shape)
y = np.arange(1,4)
print(y.shape)
x - y
```

2.
```
import numpy as np
arr = np.array([1, 2, 3, 4, 5, 6, 7, 8])
newarr = arr.reshape(2, 2, -1)
print(newarr)
```

Exercise Question

A company sells three different products and analyzes the sales and customer satisfaction data over the past year to assess product performance and understand which product is most popular among customers. The company uses NumPy to analyze the data.

The sales and customer satisfaction data for the three products (Product A, Product B, and Product C) over 12 months are as follows:

import numpy as np

Sales data for the 3 products (in units sold) over 12 months

sales_data = np.array([[100, 150, 200], [120, 160, 180], [130, 170, 210], [140, 165, 190], [150, 180, 220], [160, 175, 200], [170, 160, 210], [180, 190, 250], [190, 200, 240], [200, 210, 230], [210, 220, 260], [220, 230, 270]])

Customer satisfaction data for the 3 products (on a scale of 1-10) over 12 months

satisfaction_data = np.array([[7.2, 8.5, 7.8], [7.5, 8.4, 8.0], [7.8, 8.6, 7.9], [7.3, 8.3, 7.7], [7.9, 8.7, 8.1], [8.0, 8.5, 7.6], [7.6, 8.1, 7.9], [8.2, 8.8, 8.3], [7.9, 8.6, 7.7], [8.1, 8.4, 8.2], [8.3, 8.9, 8.5], [8.5, 9.0, 8.7]])

The company wants to answer the following questions:

1. What is the total sales for each product over the year?
2. Which product had the highest average satisfaction rating across all months?
3. What is the percentage change in sales for each product from month 1 to month 12?
4. Which product has the highest correlation between sales and satisfaction?
5. Calculate the month-over-month change in satisfaction for each product. Which product has the most consistent satisfaction throughout the year?

CHAPTER

5 Python Pandas

Customer Lifetime Value (CLV) Prediction and Churn Analysis

Assume that you are a Data Analyst in an e-commerce company that has been assigned the task of improving customer retention and increase revenue by predicting Customer Lifetime Value (CLV) and analyzing the likelihood of customer churn. The company has historical transaction data and customer demographics. The dataset stored in a CSV file includes the following columns:

- Transaction ID
- Product ID
- Product Category
- Quantity Sold
- Price Per Unit
- Total Sales Value
- Date of Sale
- Region
- Customer ID
- Customer Age Group
- Customer Gender
- Customer First Purchase Date
- Your tasks are to:
  1. Identify customers who are at high risk of churn (i.e., those who have not purchased in the past 6 months).
  2. Segment the customers into low, medium, and high CLV groups for targeted marketing.

Pandas is an open-source Python library that has functions providing high-performance data manipulation and analysis. Prior to Pandas, Python had very little contribution toward data analysis. But with Pandas solved, Python can be used to load, prepare, manipulate, model, and analyze data.

Python with Pandas is used in a wide range of fields including academic and commercial domains such as finance, economics, statistics, analytics, etc. Some important features of Pandas include:

- Fast and efficient DataFrame object with default and customized indexing
- Ability to read data in objects from different file formats
- Managing missing data
- Reshaping and pivoting of date sets
- Label-based slicing, indexing, and sub-setting of large datasets
- Ease of inserting and deleting rows/columns in a data structure
- Support of aggregating and grouping data
- Functionality for high performance merging and joining of data
- Ability to deal with Time Series data

Datasets associated with this chapter can be accessed using the QR code provided on the back cover of the book.

5.1 Data frame

Pandas is the fundamental building block for doing practical, real-world data analysis in Python. It has become the most powerful and flexible open source data analysis/manipulation tool available in any language. The key component in Pandas is the Data Frame.

Typically, data science practitioners often need to perform various data engineering operations, such as aggregation, sorting, and filtering data. And data frame tends to be the best object for this purpose.

A Data frame is a two-dimensional data structure in which data are organized in a tabular fashion using rows and columns. Basic features of data frame can be given as,

- Columns of different data types
- Size is mutable
- Data frame has labelled axes for rows and columns
- Arithmetic operations can be performed on rows and columns

5.1.1 Creating a data frame

A pandas DataFrame can be created by using the pandas.DataFrame function. The syntax of this function can be given as,

pandas.DataFrame(data, index, columns, dtype, copy)

where,

data can be an ndarray, series, map, lists, dict, constants, or any other data frame.

index denotes the row labels for the resulting frame. It is optional argument. By default, if no index is passed, its value will be equal to np.arange(n).

column is used for specifying column labels. It is optional argument. By default, its value is np.arange(n), if no index is passed.

dtype specifies the data type of each column.

copy is used for copying of data, if the default is false.

Some examples of creating a data frame are given below.

```
# Creating Empty Data Frame
import numpy as np
import pandas as pd
import pandas as pd
df = pd.DataFrame()
print(df)
OUTPUT
Empty DataFrame
Columns: []
Index: []
```

```
# Creating a Data Frame from a List
import numpy as np
import pandas as pd
import pandas as pd
data = [1,2,3,4,5]
df = pd.DataFrame(data)
print(df)
OUTPUT
 0
0 1
1 2
2 3
3 4
4 5
```

```
# Creating Data From a List of Lists
import numpy as np
import pandas as pd
import pandas as pd
data = [1,['a',3],4,[5,'b'],7]
df = pd.DataFrame(data)
print(df)
OUTPUT
      0
0     1
1 [a,3]
2     4
3 [5,b]
4     7
```

5.1.2 Creating data frame from dictionary

We can also create a data frame from a dictionary of containing ndarrays or lists. But when doing so, remember that all the ndarrays must be of same length. Moreover, if an index is passed, then the length of the index should be equal to the length of the arrays. In case no index is passed, then by default, index will be range(n), where n is the array length.

Key points to remember

To access a column of this data frame, we just use the notation, *data_frame_object['column_name'].*

To add a column to the data frame, use the notation, *data_frame_object[key'] = value.*

To delete a column from the data frame, we can either use the del statement by writing *del data_frame_object['column-name']* or using the pop() method by writing *data_frame_object.pop('key').*

To access a particular row from the data frame using label or column name, we can use the loc() method. It is used by writing *data_frame_object.loc['row-name'].*

To access a particular row from the data frame, we can even pass an integer location to an **iloc** method by writing *data_frame_object.iloc[row-number].*

To access multiple rows from a data frame, use the selection operator (:) by writing *data_frame_object.iloc[starting-row-number : ending-row-number].*

To add new rows at the end of a data frame, use the append() function.

To delete or drop rows from a data frame, the drop() method is used. We can specify a row label or index in the drop() method. If label is duplicated, then multiple rows will be dropped.

Write a program that creates a data frame storing names and marks of students using list of lists. Give relevant names to the columns.

```
import numpy as np
import pandas as pd
import pandas as pd
data = [['Ananya',67],['Nayonika',76],['Paras',91]]
df = pd.DataFrame(data, columns = ['NAME','AGGREGATE'])
print(df)
```

OUTPUT

```
        NAME     AGGREGATE
0      Ananya       67
1     Nayonika      76
2       Paras       91
```

Write a program that creates a data frame from a dictionary of ndarrays and Lists.

```
import numpy as np
import pandas as pd
import pandas as pd
```

```
# data = {'Name':['Tom', 'Jack', 'Steve', 'Ricky'],'Age':[28,34,29,42]}
data = {'NAME' : ['Ananya','Shreya','Priya'],'MARKS':[98,76,45]}
df = pd.DataFrame(data)
print(df)
```

OUTPUT

```
     NAME     MARKS
0   Ananya     98
1   Shreya     76
2    Priya     45
```

Write a program that creates a data frame from a list of dictionary.

```
import numpy as np
import pandas as pd
data  =[{'Name':'Navya','Marks':90},{'Name':'Kian','Marks':88},{'Name':'Rama
ira'}]
df = pd.DataFrame(data, index = ['Stud 1','Stud 2','Stud 3'])
print(df)
```

OUTPUT

```
            Name       Marks
Stud 1     Navya        90.0
Stud 2      Kian        88.0
Stud 3    Ramaira        NaN
```

When we create a data frame from a list of dictionary, the dictionary keys are set as column names.

Write a program to create a data frame from a dictionary of Series

```
import numpy as np
import pandas as pd
data = {'Kiara' : pd.Series([89,90,78],index = ['M1', 'M2','M3']),
        'Meera' : pd.Series([85,87,88,92],index = ['M1', 'M2','M3','M4'])}
df = pd.DataFrame(data)
print(df)
```

OUTPUT

```
           Kiara      Meera
M1          89.0        85
M2          90.0        87
M3          78.0        88
M4           NaN        92
```

Write a program that selects a particular column from the above data frame. Also add a new column to it.

```
import numpy as np
import pandas as pd
data = {'Kiara' : pd.Series([89,90,78],index = ['M1', 'M2','M3']),
       'Meera' : pd.Series([85,87,88,92],index = ['M1', 'M2','M3','M4'])}
df = pd.DataFrame(data)
name= input("Enter the name of the student whose marks you want to see : ")
print(df[name])    # column selection
# adding a column
df['Shaina'] = pd.Series([98,79,90,85],index = ['M1', 'M2','M3','M4'])
print(df)
```

OUTPUT

```
Enter the name of the student whose marks you want to see : Kiara
M1          89.0
M2          90.0
M3          78.0
M4           NaN
Name:     Kiara,     dtype:     float64
           Kiara       Meera      Shaina
M1          89.0         85         98
M2          90.0         87         79
M3          78.0         88         90
M4           NaN         92         85
```

Write a program that demonstrates deleting columns from a data frame using the del statement and pop method.

```
import numpy as np
import pandas as pd
data = {'Kiara' : pd.Series([89,90,78],index = ['M1', 'M2','M3']),
       'Meera' : pd.Series([85,87,88,92],index = ['M1', 'M2','M3','M4']),
       'Shaina': pd.Series([98,79,90,85],index = ['M1', 'M2','M3','M4']),
       'Harman': pd.Series([48,52,67,71],index = ['M1', 'M2','M3','M4'])}
df = pd.DataFrame(data)
print(df)
```

```
# deleting a column
del df['Shaina']        # deleting using del statement
print(df)

# deleting another column
df.pop('Harman')        # deleting using pop method of data frame
print(df)
```

OUTPUT

```
        Kiara     Meera      Shaina      Harman
M1       89.0      85          98          48
M2       90.0      87          79          52
M3       78.0      88          90          67
M4        NaN      92          85          71
        Kiara      Meera     Harman
M1       89.0       85        48
M2       90.0       87        52
M3       78.0       88        67
M4        NaN       92        71
        Kiara      Meera
M1       89.0       85
M2       90.0       87
M3       78.0       88
M4        NaN       92
```

Write a program to select a row(s) from a data frame.

```
import numpy as np
import pandas as pd
data = {'Kiara' : pd.Series([89,90,78],index = ['M1', 'M2','M3']),
      'Meera' : pd.Series([85,87,88,92],index = ['M1', 'M2','M3','M4']),
      'Shaina': pd.Series([98,79,90,85],index = ['M1', 'M2','M3','M4']),
      'Harman': pd.Series([48,52,67,71],index = ['M1', 'M2','M3','M4'])}
df = pd.DataFrame(data)
print(df)
print("Marks obtained by students in second subject (M2) : ")
print(df.loc['M2'])
print(df.iloc[1])
```

```
print("Marks obtained by students in second subject (M2) and third subject (M3) : ")
print(df[1:3])
```

OUTPUT

```
        Kiara    Meera    Shaina    Harman
M1       89.0      85        98        48
M2       90.0      87        79        52
M3       78.0      88        90        67
M4        NaN      92        85        71
Marks obtained by students in second subject (M2) :
Kiara       90.0
Meera       87.0
Shaina      79.0
Harman      52.0
Name: M2, dtype: float64
Kiara       90.0
Meera       87.0
Shaina      79.0
Harman      52.0
Name: M2, dtype: float64
Marks obtained by students in second subject (M2) and third subject (M3) :
        Kiara    Meera    Shaina    Harman
M2       90.0      87        79        52
M3       78.0      88        90        67
```

Write a program to add new rows to the above data frame. Also demonstrate the procedure to delete row(s) with a specified label.

```
import numpy as np
import pandas as pd
df1 = pd.DataFrame([[89, 93], [67,76]], columns = ['Meera','Sheena'])
df2 = pd.DataFrame([[77, 84], [87, 92]], columns = ['Meera','Sheena'])
# Appending rows to a data frame
df1 = df1.append(df2)
print(df1)
```

```
# Deleting row(s) with specified label
df1 = df1.drop(1)
print('Data Frame after deleting row 1 : ')
print(df1)
OUTPUT
          Meera      Sheena
0          89         93
1          67         76
0          77         84
1          87         92
Data Frame after deleting row 1 :
          Meera      Sheena
0          89         93
0          77         84
```

5.2 Pandas dataframe functions and attributes

The *Pandas DataFrame* has a number of column helper functions, which can be used for extracting valuable information from the column. Some of these are:

Unique(): This method provides unique elements from a column by removing duplicates.

Mean(): Returns the mean value of all the items in the column.

```
# unique method
import numpy as np
import pandas as pd
data = {
'Name': ["Shrey", "Gini", "Chitra", "David",
"Meher", "Faizal", "Geet"],
'Age': [15,16,17,15,17,16,15],
'Interest': ["Sketching", "Outdoor Games", "Cooking",
"Surfing", "Reading", "Sketching", "Surfing"]
}
df = pd.DataFrame(data)
print(df.Age.unique())
OUTPUT
[15 16 17]
```

```
# mean method
import numpy as np
import pandas as pd
data = {
'Name': ["Shrey", "Gini", "Chitra", "David",
"Meher", "Faizal", "Geet"],
'Age': [15,16,17,15,17,16,15],
'Interest': ["Sketching", "Outdoor Games", "Cooking",
"Surfing", "Reading", "Sketching", "Surfing"]
}
df = pd.DataFrame(data)
print("MEAN AGE: %.2f"%df.Age.mean())
OUTPUT
MEAN AGE: 15.86
```

head(): Returns the first n rows. If n is not passed as an argument, then by default, first five rows are displayed.

tail(): Returns last n rows. If n is not passed as an argument, then by default last five rows are displayed.

Some important attributes are:

T: Returns the transpose of a data frame by interchanging rows and columns.

axes: Returns the list of row axis labels and column axis labels.

dtypes: Returns the data type of each column.

empty: Returns a Boolean value stating whether the data frame object is empty or not. A true value indicates that the object is empty.

ndim: Returns the number of dimensions of the data frame object.

shape: Returns a tuple representing the dimensionality of the DataFrame. Tuple (a,b), where a represents the number of rows and b represents the number of columns.

Size: Returns the number of elements in the DataFrame.

Values: Returns the data values stored in the data frame object as an NDarray.

```
Import numpy as np
Import pandas as pd
data = {'Name': ["Shrey", "Gini", "Chitra", "David",
"Meher", "Faizal", "Geet"],
'Age': [15,16,17,15,17,16,15),
'Interest': ["Sketching", "Outdoor Games", "Cooking",
"Surfing", "Reading", "Sketching", "Surfing"]}
print("The first two rows of the data frame : ")
print(df.head(2))
print ("The last two rows of the data series : ")
print(df.tail(2))
# Transposing Data Frame
df = df.T
print(df)
# Print Axes
print(df.axes)
# Print Data Type
print(df.dtypes)
# Check if data frame is empty
print ("Is the object empty?", df.empty)
# Number of dimensions in data frame
print ("Number of Dimensions: ", df.ndim)
# Shape of Data frame Object
print ("Shape of Data Frame object is: ", df.shape)
print ("Number of elements: ", df.size)
print ("Data Values in Data Frame are: ",df.values)
```

OUTPUT

```
The first two rows of the data frame :
  Name Age   Interest
0 Shrey 15 Sketching
1 Gini 16 Outdoor Games
The last two rows of the data series :
  Name Age Interest
5 Faizal 16 Sketching
6 Geet 15 Surfing
          0    1  2 ...  4    5    6
Name    Shrey  Gini  Chitra ...  Meher Faizal
Geet
Age     15      16   17 ...   17      16     15
Interest Sketching Outdoor Games Cooking ...
Reading Sketching Surfing
[3 rows x 7 columns]
[Index(['Name', 'Age', 'Interest'], dtype='object'),
Rangelndex(start=0, stop=7, step=1)]
0  object  1  object  2  object   3   object
4  object  5  object  6  object  dtype: object
Is the object empty? False
Number of Dimensions: 2
Shape of Data Frame object is: (3,7)
Number of elements: 21
Data Values in Data Frame are: [['Shrey' 'Gini' 'Chitra'
'David' 'Meher' 'Faizal' 'Geet'] [15 16 17 15 17 16 15]
['Sketching' 'Outdoor Games' 'Cooking' 'Surfing'
'Reading 'Sketching' 'Surfing']]
```

5.3 Pivoting data frame

The pivot() function is used to reshape a given DataFrame object organized by given index/column values. The syntax of pivot() function can be given as,

DataFrame.pivot (self, index=None, columns=None, values=None)

Where,

index is an optional argument, which specifies columns that will be used to make new frame's index. If no column is specified, existing index is used.

columns is used to specify columns that will be used to make new frame's columns.

values is an optional argument that specifies column(s) to be used for populating new frame's values. If nothing is specified, all remaining columns will be used, and the result will have hierarchically indexed columns.

The pivot() function returns a reshaped DataFrame. However, ValueError will be raised if there are any index, columns combinations having multiple values. In other words, ***ValueError is raised if there are any duplicate values in the data frame.***

```
PIVOTING DATA FRAME
import pandas as pd
# creating a dataframe
df = pd.DataFrame({'NAME': ['Gitisha', 'Sonakshi', 'Meena'],
   'DEGREE': ['Masters', 'Graduate', 'Graduate'],
   'AGE': [24, 26, 25]})
print("ORIGINAL DATA FRAME:")
print(df)
print("DATA FRAME AFTER USING ONLY AGE AS VALUE:")
df1 = df.pivot('NAME', 'DEGREE', 'AGE')
print(df1)
print("DATA FRAME AFTER USING AGE AND NAME AS VALUES:")
df1 = df.pivot(index = 'NAME', columns = 'DEGREE', values = ['AGE',
'NAME'])
print(df1)
```

```
OUTPUT
ORIGINAL DATA FRAME:
     NAME    DEGREE   AGE
0 Gitisha   Masters   24
1 Sonakshi  Graduate  26
2 Meena   Graduate  25
DATA FRAME AFTER USING ONLY AGE AS VALUE:
DEGREE  Graduate  Masters
NAME
Gitisha     NaN   24.0
Meena       25.0   NaN
Sonakshi    26.0   NaN
DATA FRAME AFTER USING AGE AND NAME AS VALUES:
     AGE      NAME
DEGREE Graduate Masters Graduate Masters
NAME
Gitisha    NaN    24   NaN    Gitisha
Meena      25     NaN  Meena      NaN
Sonakshi   26     NaN  Sonakshi  NaN
```

5.4 Sorting

To sort data means arranging data in a specific order. We can sort data either in ascending (small to big) order or descending order (big to small). Both numerical and textual data can be sorted in the specified order. Pandas **sort_values()** function sorts a data frame in ascending or descending order of passed column. The syntax of this function can be given as,

DataFrame.sort_values(by, axis=0, ascending=True, inplace=False, kind='quicksort', na_position='last')

where,

by specifies column(s) names by which the data frame has to be sorted.

axis specifies rows or columns. axis = 0 indicates "index" for rows and 1 for "columns" for column.

ascending is a Boolean value, which sorts data frame in an ascending order if true. By default, the values are sorted in the ascending order.

inplace is a Boolean value. If its value is true, then the changes are made in the data frame passed to the function.

kind accepts a string that chooses a particular algorithm to sort data frame. It can take the value "quicksort," "mergesort," or "heapsort." By default, mergesort is used.

na_position takes a string value, which can be either "last" or "first." It is used to set position of Null values. The default of this argument is "last."

Note that every parameter has some default values except the "by" parameter.

The function returns a sorted Data Frame with same dimensions as that of the original data frame.

```
# Sort by Brand in descending order
from pandas import DataFrame
Cars = {'Brand': ['Ecosport', 'Brezza', 'Nexon', 'Audi A5'],
    'Price': [963000,734000,695000,6751000],
    'Year': [2012,2016,2014,2017]
    }
df = DataFrame(Cars, columns= ['Brand', 'Price', 'Year'])
print("ORIGINAL DATA FRAME")
print(df)
# sort by Brand - descending order
df.sort_values(by=['Brand'], inplace=True, ascending=False)
print("SORTED DATA FRAME")
print (df)
```

OUTPUT

```
ORIGINAL DATA FRAME
Brand Price Year
0 Ecosport 963000 2012
1 Brezza 734000 2016
2 Nexon 695000 2014
3 Audi A5 6751000 2017
SORTED DATA FRAME
  Brand  Price Year
2 Nexon 695000 2014
0 Ecosport 963000 2012
1 Brezza 734000 2016
3 Audi A5 6751000 2017
```

We can sort a data frame not by one but by several columns together. For this, we can specify a list of columns as value in the by parameter as given below.

df.sort_values(by=['First Column','Second Column',...], inplace=True)

For example, we can sort by *both* the "Year" and the "Price." Here, Year will take priority over Price. We will sort by Year, and if two records have same value for Year, then, the one with lower price will be displayed first (provided sorting is done in the ascending order).

```
# Sort-multiple columns
from pandas import DataFrame
Cars = {'Brand': ['Ecosport','Brezza','Audi Q5','Audi A5'],
   'Price': [963000,734000,5026000,6751000],
   'Year': [2012,2016,2008,2017]
   }
df = DataFrame(Cars, columns= ['Brand', 'Price', 'Year'])
print("ORIGINAL DATA FRAME")
print(df)
# sort by Year and Price
df.sort_values(by=['Year','Price'], inplace=True)
print("SORTED DATA FRAME")
print(df)
```

```
OUTPUT
ORIGINAL DATA FRAME
 Brand Price Year
0 Ecosport 963000 2012
1 Brezza 734000 2016
2 Audi Q5 5026000 2008
3 Audi A5 6751000 2017
SORTED DATA FRAME
 Brand Price Year
2 Audi Q5 5026000 2008
0 Ecosport 963000 2012
1 Brezza 734000 2016
3 Audi A5 6751000 2017
```

5.4.1 Sorting by labels

We can even sort the data frame by using index. The **sort_index()** function sorts a data frame by its row index.

Basically, the term sort_index() is little misleading. Pandas DataFrame allows users to indicate which column acts as the *row index. If no* specific column is specified to be the row index, Pandas will create a zero-based row index by default. Once a column is specified as row index, the data frame can be sorted using the sort_index() function.

By default, sort_index() function sorts on row labels in ascending order. We can even use the axis argument and set it to 1 and specify the order of sorting. This will sort the data frame by column labels and not column values.

```
import pandas as pd
import numpy as np
unsorted_df =
pd.DataFrame(np.random.randn(5,2),index=[1,4,3,2,0],columns= ['Z','A'])
sorted_df=unsorted_df.sort_index(axis=1)
print(sorted_df)
```

```
OUTPUT
        A        Z
1 -0.280872 0.239151
4 -0.907434 0.023017
3 -0.402850 0.083142
2 0.551225 -0.645303
0 1.518120 -0.604385
```

Write a program that reads data from the given link into a data frame in Python. Demonstrate sorting of the data frame in different ways.

```
import pandas as pd
data_url = 'https://raw.githubusercontent.com/jvns/pandas-cookbook/master/
data/weather_2012.csv'
# read data from url as pandas dataframe
weather = pd.read_csv(data_url)
sort_by_weather = weather.sort_values('Weather')
print("SORTED DATA FRAME")
print(sort_by_weather.head(n=6))
```

```
# sort by weather in descending order
sort_by_weather_desc = weather.sort_values('Weather',ascending=False)
print("SORTED DATA FRAME INDESCENDING ORDER")
print(sort_by_weather_desc.head(n=6))
# Sort by Weather and Temp
sort_by_weather_temp = weather.sort_values(['Weather','Temp (C)'])
print("DATA FRAME SORTED BY WEATHER AND TEMP")
print(sort_by_weather_temp.head(n=6))
# Sort by Weather and Temp in different order
sort_by_weather_asc_temp_desc = weather.sort_values(['Weather','Temp (C)'],
ascending=[True, False])
print("DATA FRAME SORTED BY WEATHER AND TEMP IN DIFFERENT ORDERS")
print(sort_by_weather_asc_temp_desc.head(n=6))
# sort by putting missing values first
sort_na_first = weather.sort_values('Weather',na_position='first')
print("DATA FRAME SORTED BY PUTTING NAs FIRST")
print(sort_na_first.head(n=6))
# sort by index
weather.sort_index(inplace=True)
print(weather.head(n=6))
```

OUTPUT

```
SORTED DATA FRAME
               Date/Time  Temp (C)  ...  Stn Press (kPa)  Weather
7103  2012-10-22 23:00:00       6.4  ...           101.34    Clear
4203  2012-06-24 03:00:00      14.9  ...           101.02    Clear
4204  2012-06-24 04:00:00      14.4  ...           101.04    Clear
4205  2012-06-24 05:00:00      14.0  ...           101.04    Clear
4206  2012-06-24 06:00:00      17.8  ...           101.04    Clear
4207  2012-06-24 07:00:00      20.0  ...           101.03    Clear
[6 rows x 8 columns]
SORTED DATA FRAME INDESCENDING ORDER
               Date/Time  ...                               Weather
4757  2012-07-17 05:00:00  ...             Thunderstorms,Rain,Fog
4761  2012-07-17 09:00:00  ...  Thunderstorms,Rain Showers,Fog
4323  2012-06-29 03:00:00  ...  Thunderstorms,Rain Showers,Fog
5108  2012-07-31 20:00:00  ...  Thunderstorms,Rain Showers,Fog
3580  2012-05-29 04:00:00  ...      Thunderstorms,Rain Showers
```

```
4768  2012-07-17 16:00:00  ...      Thunderstorms,Rain Showers
[6 rows x 8 columns]
DATA FRAME SORTED BY WEATHER AND TEMP
               Date/Time  Temp (C)  ...  Stn Press (kPa)  Weather
344  2012-01-15 08:00:00     -23.3  ...           102.45    Clear
363  2012-01-16 03:00:00     -19.2  ...           103.07    Clear
365  2012-01-16 05:00:00     -19.1  ...           103.02    Clear
364  2012-01-16 04:00:00     -18.7  ...           103.05    Clear
366  2012-01-16 06:00:00     -18.7  ...           103.01    Clear
362  2012-01-16 02:00:00     -18.5  ...           103.08    Clear
[6 rows x 8 columns]
DATA FRAME SORTED BY WEATHER AND TEMP IN DIFFERENT ORDERS
                Date/Time  Temp (C)  ...  Stn Press (kPa)  Weather
5199  2012-08-04 15:00:00      32.8  ...           101.39    Clear
5200  2012-08-04 16:00:00      32.5  ...           101.34    Clear
5201  2012-08-04 17:00:00      32.5  ...           101.32    Clear
5198  2012-08-04 14:00:00      32.0  ...           101.48    Clear
4671  2012-07-13 15:00:00      31.9  ...           101.46    Clear
4118  2012-06-20 14:00:00      31.7  ...           100.83    Clear
[6 rows x 8 columns]
DATA FRAME SORTED BY PUTTING NAs FIRST
                Date/Time  Temp (C)  ...  Stn Press (kPa)  Weather
7103  2012-10-22 23:00:00       6.4  ...           101.34    Clear
4203  2012-06-24 03:00:00      14.9  ...           101.02    Clear
4204  2012-06-24 04:00:00      14.4  ...           101.04    Clear
4205  2012-06-24 05:00:00      14.0  ...           101.04    Clear
4206  2012-06-24 06:00:00      17.8  ...           101.04    Clear
4207  2012-06-24 07:00:00      20.0  ...           101.03    Clear
[6 rows x 8 columns]
             Date/Time  Temp (C)  ...  Stn Press (kPa)                Weather
0  2012-01-01 00:00:00      -1.8  ...           101.24                    Fog
1  2012-01-01 01:00:00      -1.8  ...           101.24                    Fog
2  2012-01-01 02:00:00      -1.8  ...           101.26  Freezing Drizzle,Fog
3  2012-01-01 03:00:00      -1.5  ...           101.27  Freezing Drizzle,Fog
4  2012-01-01 04:00:00      -1.5  ...           101.23                    Fog
5  2012-01-01 05:00:00      -1.4  ...           101.27                    Fog
[6 rows x 8 columns]
```

5.5 Missing data

Many a times, when collecting data from users, some entries are left blank. For example, many of us do not like to give our phone number, date of birth, father's name, annual income, etc. as we hardly know who will use our data in what way. However, data analysts and data scientists always face issues because of missing data. With missing data in the dataset, machine learning models predict data with lower accuracy. Therefore, handling missing values before application of any data analytics or machine learning technique is of utmost importance.

5.5.1 Missing data and operations with fill values

When working with series and DataFrame, we can use arithmetic functions to input a *fill_value* that can be used to substitute missing values. This is more important when we are adding two DataFrame objects. In such a case, if one of the data frame has a NaN at a particular location and a non-NaN value at the corresponding location in the other data frame, then it is better to replace NaN with 0.

```
import numpy as np

import pandas as pd

df = pd.DataFrame({'one': pd.Series([1,2,3],
   index=['a', 'b', 'c']),

   'two': pd.Series([4,5,6,7), index=['a', 'b', 'c',
     'd']),

   'three': pd.Series([8,9,10], index=['b', 'c',
     'd'])})

print("Data Frame 1 \n", df)

df2 = pd.DataFrame({'one': pd.Series([1,2,3],
  index=['a', 'c', 'd']),

   'two': pd.Series([4,6,7], index=['a', 'b', 'c']),

   'three': pd.Series([8,9,10], index=['a', 'b',
     'd'])})

print("Data Frame 2 \n", df)

print("Adding data frames with missing values")

print(df.add(df2))

print("Adding data frames with filled values")

print(df.add(df2, fill_value=0))
```

```
OUTPUT
Data Frame 1
  one two three
a 1.0 4 NaN
b 2.0 5 8.0
c 3.0 6 9.0
d NaN 7 10.0
Data Frame 2
  one two three
a 1.0 4 NaN
b 2.0 5 8.0
c 3.0 6 9.0
d NaN 7 10.0
Adding data frames with
missing values
  one two three
a 2.0 8.0 NaN
b NaN 11.0 17.0
c 5.0 13.0 NaN
d NaN NaN 20.0
Adding data frames with filled
values
  one two three
a 2.0 8.0 8.0
b 2.0 11.0 17.0
c 5.0 13.0 9.0
d 3.0 7.0 20.0
```

5.5.2 Replacing the missing values

We can fill missing values in a data frame by passing a value to the keyword `fill_value` argument of the reindex() function. This keyword replaces the NaN values.

```
# Adding New Indexes and Filling Missing Values
import pandas as pd
import numpy as np
cols =['C1','C2','C3','C4','C5']
index =['R1','R2','R3','R4','R5']
 # create a dataframe of random values of array
df = pd.DataFrame(np.random.rand(5,5),
      columns=cols, index=index)
print(df)
new_index =['R1', 'B', 'R3', 'D', 'R4']
print('Dataframe after reindexing rows:\n',
df.reindex(new_index,fill_value = 'KKK'))
         C1        C2        C3        C4        C5
R1 0.754298  0.677610  0.218998  0.364835  0.023662
R2 0.437800  0.587752  0.859596  0.247670  0.450628
R3 0.650649  0.877077  0.311036  0.550397  0.099493
R4 0.391660  0.018353  0.430367  0.449634  0.785371
R5 0.162567  0.019885  0.149455  0.461566  0.564482
Dataframe after reindexing rows:

         C1       C2        C3        C4        C5
R1 0.754298 0.67761  0.218998  0.364835  0.0236618
B   KKK      KKK   KKK   KKK    KKK
R3 0.650649  0.877077  0.311036  0.550397  0.0994928
D   KKK      KKK   KKK   KKK    KKK
R4 0.39166  0.0183535  0.430367  0.449634  0.785371
```

```
# Re-indexing columns and filling missing values
import pandas as pd
import numpy as np
cols =['C1','C2','C3','C4','C5']
index =['R1','R2','R3','R4','R5']
 # create a dataframe of random values of array
df = pd.DataFrame(np.random.rand(5,5),
      columns=cols, index=index)
print(df)
new_cols = ['A','C2','C3','B','C5']
print('Data frame after re-indexing rows:\n',
df.reindex(new_cols,axis=1,fill_value = 0.0))
         C1        C2        C3        C4        C5
R1 0.721655  0.994150  0.805925  0.305934  0.274084
R2 0.450128  0.812512  0.897468  0.920742  0.272612
R3 0.029670  0.496479  0.668620  0.688773  0.289656
R4 0.323558  0.429265  0.878404  0.045277  0.607734
R5 0.915661  0.568562  0.143303  0.033207  0.149640
Data frame after re-indexing rows:

      A       C2        C3     B       C5
R1 0.0  0.994150  0.805925  0.0  0.274084
R2 0.0  0.812512  0.897468  0.0  0.272612
R3 0.0  0.496479  0.668620  0.0  0.289656
R4 0.0  0.429265  0.878404  0.0  0.607734
R5 0.0  0.568562  0.143303  0.0  0.149640
```

5.5.3 Drop Missing Values

To exclude missing values, we can use the dropna function along with the axis argument. By default, axis=0, that is, along row. This means that if any value within a row is NA, then the whole row is excluded from analysis.

```
import pandas as pd
import numpy as np
df = pd.DataFrame(np.random.randn(5, 3), index=['a', 'c', 'e', 'f',
'h'],columns=['one', 'two', 'three'])
df = df.reindex(['a', 'b', 'c', 'd', 'e', 'f', 'g', 'h'])
print(df.dropna())
```

```
OUTPUT

        one       two     three

a -1.838383 -1.339424 -0.921113

c  1.118784 -0.194514  0.825073

e -1.472931  0.266379  2.254129

f -0.214746 -0.813053 -1.290501

h -1.480884  1.018973 -2.065045
```

5.5.4 Replace missing (or) generic values

Python allow programmers to replace a generic value or a missing value with some specific value. This can be done by replacing NA with a scalar value as we did in case of fillna() function.

```
import pandas as pd

import numpy as np

df = pd.DataFrame({'A':[10,20,30,40,50,7000], 'B':[8000,90,100,75,58,63]})

print( df.replace({7000:70,8000:80}))

OUTPUT

    A    B

0  10   80

1  20   90

2  30  100

3  40   75

4  50   58

5  70   63
```

5.6 Combining data frames

We can combine two similar datasets. This is especially important where values in one dataset are preferred over the other. This situation frequently occurs when one of the two data series representing a particular economic indicator is considered to be of "higher quality." However, the lower quality series may have more complete data coverage. So, we can combine two DataFrame objects where missing values in one DataFrame are conditionally filled with like-labelled values from the other DataFrame. The combine_first() function is used for implementing this operation.

```
import numpy as np

import pandas as pd

df1 = pd.DataFrame({'A': [1., np.nan, 3., 5., np.nan],

        'B': [np.nan, 2., 3., np.nan, 6.]})

df2 = pd.DataFrame({'A': [5., 2., 4., np.nan, 3., 7.],

          'B': [np.nan, np.nan, 3., 4., 6., 8.]})

print("DATA FRAME 1: ")

print(df1)

print("DATA FRAME 2: ")

print(df2)

print("COMBINING DATA FRAMES: ")

print(df1.combine_first(df2))
```

```
OUTPUT
DATA FRAME 1:
   A B
0 1.0 NaN
1 NaN 2.0
2 3.0 3.0
3 5.0 NaN
4 NaN 6.0
DATA FRAME 2:
   A B
0 5.0 NaN
1 2.0 NaN
2 4.0 3.0
3 NaN 4.0
4 3.0 6.0
5 7.0 8.0
COMBINING DATA FRAMES:
   A B
0 1.0 NaN
1 2.0 2.0
2 3.0 3.0
3 5.0 4.0
4 3.0 6.0
5 7.0 8.0
```

The combine_first() method used in the above code can be replaced with a more general DataFrame method combine(). The combine() is a method that takes another DataFrame and a combiner function as an argument to perform its intended task.

5.7 Descriptive statistics

Python supports a large number of methods for computing descriptive statistics and other related operations on Series and DataFrame objects. Aggregation functions like sum(), mean(), and quantile() produce a lower dimensional result. However, other functions like cumsum() and cumprod() produce an object of the same size.

All such methods have a skipna option specifying whether to exclude missing data or not. skipna is true by default. This means that by default, all NaN values are skipped or ignored.

Another important argument of descriptive functions is axis. Users can specify the axis by name or integer. The default value of axis is 0 indicating indexes or rows. If axis = 1, the descriptive function is applied on columns.

```
df = pd.DataFrame({'A': [1, 2, 3, 5, np.NaN],

     'B': [7, 8, np.NaN, 10,1],

     'C': [np.NaN, 4, 3, 2,0]})

print("DATA FRAME: ")

print(df)
```

```
DATA FRAME:
   A   B   C
0 1.0 7.0 NaN
1 2.0 8.0 4.0
2 3.0 NaN 3.0
3 5.0 10.0 2.0
4 NaN 1.0 0.0
COLUMN WISE MEAN:
A 2.75
B 6.50
C 2.25
dtype: float64
ROW WISE MEAN:
0  4.000000
```

```
print("COLUMN WISE MEAN: ")

print(df.mean(0))

print("ROW WISE MEAN: ")

print(df.mean(1))

print("COLUMN WISE MEAN CONSIDERING NA: ")

print(df.mean(0,skipna=False))

print("ROW WISE MEAN CONSIDERING NA: ")

print(df.mean(1,skipna=False))
```

```
1  4.666667
2  3.000000
3  5.666667
4  0.500000
dtype: float64
COLUMN WISE MEAN CONSIDERING NA:
A  NaN
B  NaN
C  NaN
dtype: float64
ROW WISE MEAN CONSIDERING NA:
0    NaN
1  4.666667
2    NaN
3  5.666667
4    NaN
dtype: float64
```

Function	Description
count	Number of non-NA observations
sum	Sum of values
mean	Mean of values
mad	Mean absolute deviation
median	Arithmetic median of values
min	Minimum
max	Maximum
mode	Mode
abs	Absolute value
prod	Product of values
std	Standard deviation
var	Unbiased variance
sem	Standard error of the mean
quantile	Sample quantile

We can use broadcasting to describe various statistical procedures, like standardization (rendering mean equal to zero and standard deviation equal to 1) by writing,

standardized = (df - df.mean()) / df.std()

Methods like cumsum() and cumprod() preserve the location of NaN values. It can be used as df.cumsum(). Other important commonly used functions are given in Table.

Note that like Data Frame, even NumPy methods like mean, std, and sum will exclude NAs on series input by default.

```
import numpy as np
import pandas as pd
df = pd.DataFrame({'A':[1, 2, 3, 5, np.NaN],
        'B': [7, 8, np.NaN, 10,1],
        'C': [np.NaN, 4, 3, 2,0]})
print("DATA FRAME: ")
print(df)
print("MEAN OF COLUMN B: ", np.mean (df['B']))
```

```
OUTPUT
DATA FRAME:
   A    B    C
0 1.0  7.0  NaN
1 2.0  8.0  4.0
2 3.0  NaN  3.0
3 5.0  10.0 2.0
4 NaN  1.0  0.0
MEAN OF COLUMN B: 6.5
```

We can even use the sum() function to count the number of nulls in each column by writing, df.isnull().sum().

Always remember that,

- Since DataFrame is a heterogeneous data structure, generic functions do not work with all functions.
- Functions like sum() and cumsum() work with both numeric and character or string data. Although practically we will never use character aggregations, these functions will not throw any exception if we try to do so.
- Functions like abs() and cumprod() throw exception when the DataFrame contains character or string data because such operations cannot be performed on nonnumerical data.

5.8 Summarizing or describing data

The describe() function computes a variety of summary statistics on a series or the columns of a DataFrame object. This function ignores NAs. This function gives the **mean, std**, and **IQR** values.

```
import numpy as np

import pandas as pd

df = pd.DataFrame({'A': [1, 2, 3, 5, np.NaN],

        'B': [7, 8, np.NaN, 10,1],

        'C': [np.NaN, 4, 3, 2,0)})

print("DESCRIBING DATAFRAME: ")

print(df.describe())

S = pd.Series(np.random.randn(1000))

S[::3] = np.nan

print("DESCRIBING DATAFRAME: ")

print(S.describe())
```

```
OUTPUT
DESCRIBING DATAFRAME:
       A    B    C
count 4.000000 4.000000 4.000000
mean 2.750000 6.500000 2.250000
std 1.707825 3.872983 1.707825
min 1.000000 1.000000 0.000000
25% 1.750000 5.500000 1.500000
50% 2.500000 7.500000 2.500000
75% 3.500000 8.500000 3.250000
max 5.000000 10.000000 4.000000
DESCRIBING SERIES:
count 666.000000
mean 0.038206
std 0.997166
min -3.006498
25% -0.657822
50% 0.013089
75% 0.753421
max 3.016491
dtype: float64
```

In the above code, we could have even selected specific percentiles to include in the output by writing, series.describe(percentiles=[.05, .25, .75, .95])

For a nonnumerical series object, describe() will give a simple summary of the number of unique values and most frequently occurring values.

On a mixed-type DataFrame object, describe() will restrict the summary to include only numerical columns. If there are no numerical values, only categorical columns are included as shown in the code given below.

However, we can also provide a list of type of objects that can be included in the include argument of the describe() function. We can even specify **include = all** to include every data type for calculating the summary. This can be done by writing, frame_object.describe(include='all'). The general syntax of specifying include argument is frame_object.describe(include=['object']). For example, writing df.describe(include=['number']).

```
import numpy as np

import pandas as pd

S=pd.Series(['P','Y','T','H','O','N',np.nan,'P','R','O','G','R','A',
  'M','M','I','N','G'])

print("DESCRIBING SERIES: ")

print(S.describe())

df = pd.DataFrame({'A': ['Python','Yes',np.nan,'Programming'], 'B':
  range(4)})

print("DESCRIBING DATA FRAME")

print(df.describe())

print("DESCRIBING DATA FRAME WITH include = all")

print(df.describe(include='all'))
```

```
OUTPUT
DESCRIBING SERIES:
count   17
unique   11
top      P
freq    2
dtype: object
DESCRIBING DATA FRAME
      B
count 4.000000
mean 1.500000
std 1.290994
min 0.000000
25% 0.750000
50% 1.500000
75% 2.250000
max 3.000000
DESCRIBING DATA FRAME WITH
include = all
         A     B
count   3 4.000000
unique   3   NaN
top  Python   NaN
freq    1    NaN
mean NaN 1.500000
std NaN 1.290994
min NaN 0.000000
25% NaN 0.750000
50% NaN 1.500000
75% NaN 2.250000
max NaN 3.000000
```

Note that the **"include"** argument of the describe() function is used to pass necessary information regarding what columns need to be considered for summarizing. The value of the include argument can be one of the following,

- **Object**–Summarizes string columns
- **number**–Summarizes numeric columns. This is also the default value of include.
- **all**–Summarizes all columns together (should not pass it as a list value)

5.8.1 Index of min/max values

The idxmin() and idxmax() functions can be used with series and DataFrame objects to compute the index labels with the minimum and maximum corresponding values.

```
# For single column data frame
import numpy as np
import pandas as pd
df = pd.Series(np.random.
  randn(5))
print("DATA FRAME : ")
print(df)
print("Index with minimum
  value :
",df.idxmin())
print("Index with maximum
  value: ",
df.idxmax())
```

OUTPUT

```
DATA FRAME:
0 -0.433586
1 -1.230765
2 -0.690756
3 0.123188
4 0.354238
dtype: float64
Index with minimum value: 1
Index with maximum value: 4
```

```
# For data frame having multiple rows
and columns
import numpy as np
import pandas as pd
df = pd.DataFrame(np.random.randn(5,3),
columns=['A','B','C'])
print("DATA FRAME: ")
print(df)
print("Index with minimum value (column
  wise): ")
print(df.idxmin (axis = 0))
print("Index with maximum value (row
  wise): ")
print(df.idxmax(axis = 1))
print("Index with minimum value in
  column B: ",
df['B'].idxmin())
print("Index with maximum value in
  column C:",
df['C'].idxmax())
```

OUTPUT

```
DATA FRAME:
     A        B        C
0 0.721215 -0.312569
2.053623
1 0.295069 -0.117734
1.348776
2 -0.528853 -0.034825
1.572288
3 0.613757 -0.448653 -
1.060948
4 1.124058 -0.927208
0.164340
Index with minimum value
(column wise):
A 2
B 4
C 3
dtype: int64
Index with maximum value
(row wise):
0 C
1 C
2 C
3 A
4 A
dtype: object
Index with minimum value in
column B: 4
Index with maximum value in
column C: 0
```

Key Points to Remember:

- When a particular value, which is either minimum or maximum, is repeated in a data frame or series object, then idxmin() and idxmax() functions return the index of the first occurrence of that value. Therefore,

  ```
  df = pd.DataFrame([1,2,3,3,1,1,3], columns=['A'], index=range(7))
  print(df['A'].idxmax())
  ```

  Will give an output 2, since 3 is the maximum value, which first occurs at index 2 in the data frame.
- idxmin and idxmax are called argmin and argmax in NumPy.

5.8.2 Value counts and mode() function

The value_counts() series method and top-level function compute a histogram of a 1D array of values. It can also be used as a function on regular arrays:

mode() function is used to get the most frequently occurring value(s) (or the mode) of the values in a series or DataFrame as shown in the code given below.

```
import numpy as np
import pandas as pd
df = pd.DataFrame({"A": np.random.randint
   (0, 7, size=10),
   "B": np.random.randint(-10, 15, size=10)})
print("DATA FRAME")
```

```
import numpy as np
import pandas as pd
data = np.random.randint(0, 7, size=20)
s = pd.Series(data)
print(s)
print("COUNTS OF VALUES : ")
print(s.value_counts())
print("MODE: ")
```

```
print(df)
print("MODE:")
print(df.mode())
OUTPUT
DATA FRAME
  A B
0 2 10
1 3 8
2 1 11
3 4 6
4 1 -5
5 2 1
6 1 5
7 0 2
8 5 6
9 2 10
MODE:
  A B
0 1 6
1 2 10
```

```
print(s.mode())
OUTPUT
0  3
1  4
2  2
3  4
4  1
5  0
6  3
7  3
8  2
9  4
10 5
11 4
12 6
13 0
14 0
15 1
16 5
17 6
18 5
19 3
dtype: int32
COUNTS OF VALUES:
4 4
3 4
5 3
0 3
6 2
2 2
1 2
dtype: int64
MODE:
0 3
1 4
dtype: int32
```

5.8.3 Other statistical functions

As discussed, statistical methods help in the understanding and analyzing the behavior of data. Some other very useful statistical functions include:

Percent_change: Series and Data Frames have the function pct_change() that compares every element with its prior element and computes the change percentage.

By default, the pct_change() operates on columns.to apply the function on rows, use axis=1() argument.

Covariance: Covariance is applied on series data to compute covariance between series objects. The cov method automatically excludes NA.

```
# Percent_change()
import pandas as pd
import numpy as np
s = pd.Series([1,2,3,4,5,4])
print(s.pct_change())
OUTPUT
0    NaN
1 1.000000
2 0.500000
3 0.333333
4 0.250000
5 -0.200000
```

Covariance method when applied on a DataFrame computes cov between all the columns.

Correlation: Correlation shows the linear relationship between any two array of values or series as wecall in pandas. There are multiple methods to compute the correlation like pearson (default), spearman, and kendall.

```
# cov() method
import pandas as pd
import numpy as np
s1 = pd.Series(np.random.
randn(10))
s2 = pd.Series(np.random.
randn(10))
print(s1.cov(s2))
OUTPUT
-0.18450525864415426
```

```
# Finding Correlation
import pandas as pd
import numpy as np
frame = pd.DataFrame(np.random.randn(10, 5), columns=['a', 'b', 'c', 'd', 'e'])
print(frame['a'].corr(frame['b']))
print(frame.corr())
OUTPUT
-0.7617698565607718
          a         b         c         d         e
a  1.000000 -0.761770  0.180424 -0.292428 -0.474428
b -0.761770  1.000000 -0.485660  0.442686  0.263709
c  0.180424 -0.485660  1.000000 -0.324710 -0.218734
d -0.292428  0.442686 -0.324710  1.000000  0.351329
e -0.474428  0.263709 -0.218734  0.351329  1.000000
```

5.8.4 Row-wise or column-wise application of functions

Any user-defined or library function can be applied to pandas objects either on an entire DataFrame or series, one or more rows, columns, or elements. The apply() function can be used for row-wise or column-wise application of a function on a pandas object. In this section, we will demonstrate the use of descriptive statistics using the apply() function with an optional axis argument.

```
import numpy as np

import pandas as pd

df = pd.DataFrame
    ({"A": np.random.randint(0, 7, size=7),

        "B": np.random.randint(-10, 15, size=7)})

print("DATA FRAME")

print(df)

print("APPLYING MEAN WITH DEFAULT AXIS")

print(df.apply(np.mean))

print("APPLYING MEAN WITH AXIS = 1")

print(df.apply(np.mean, axis = 1))
```

```
OUTPUT
DATA  FRAME
 A  B
0 4 14
1 6 3
2 3 8
3 1 10
4 4 -5
5 1 -10
6 3 2
APPLYING MEAN WITH DEFAULT AXIS
A 3.142857
B 3.142857
dtype: float64
APPLYING MEAN WITH AXIS = 1
0 9.0
1 4.5
2 5.5
3 5.5
4 -0.5
5 -4.5
6 2.5
dtype: float64
```

Like the mean() function, try the use of cumsum() and exp() functions both define in numpy. Remember that the apply() function also takes an argument raw, which is false by default. This argument is used to convert each row or column into a series before applying the function. When set to true, the passed function will instead receive an ndarray object.

5.8.5 Quantles

As we said earlier, Python is a great language for doing data analysis. We know that quantile plays a very important role in statistics when one deals with the normal distribution. **Quantile** is a measure of location and to evaluate it, Series.quartile(), Pandas **dataframe.quantile(),** and the numpy. quantile(arr, q, axis = None) function return values at the given quantile over requested axis. But before going into details of these functions, let us first understand the term quantile.

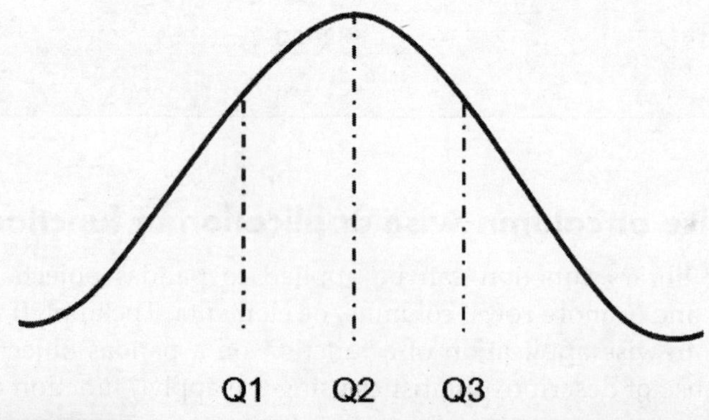

Figure 5.1 Plotting First, Second and Third Quantiles on a Curve

In the above Figure 5.1, we see that `Q2` is the `median` of the normally distributed data. `Q3 - Q2` represents the **interquantile range** of the given dataset.

Practically speaking, we often use the term percentages or percentiles. When we say that a student appeared in an exam along with 1000 others and scored 68% marks, then it is difficult to say how good or bad he performed in the exam and what is his rank overall. But, when we say that a student had 80 percentile, then it means 20% of the students have performed better than him and 80% scored less than him.

Thus, we see that percentiles make the data easy to read. pth percentile means that p percent of observations below it, (100 – p)% above it. Percentiles help us in getting an idea on outliers.

Quartiles: While percentiles divide the whole population into 100 groups, quartiles divide the population into 4 groups. Quartiles are values that break up the dataset into quarters:

p = 25: First quartile or lower quartile (LQ). The first quartile is the point below which a quarter of the data lie.

p = 50: Second quartile or median. The second quartile is the point below which half of the data lie. We already know this point by the name of median. It is also called the middle quartile.

p = 75: Third quartile or upper quartile (UQ). It is the point below which three-quarters of the data lie.

The describe() function computes the 1st, 2nd, and 3rd quartiles, but the quantile() function can be used to compute any kind of quantile–0.2, 0.4, 0.6, etc where 0.2 stands for the 20th percentile, 0.4 stands for the 40th percentile, so on and so forth.

Quantile indicates a point in distribution below which, a portion of the data lies. Basically, quantile is a generic term. The measures percentile, quintile, decile, and quartiles are all quantiles that divide a distribution into portions. For example,

Percentiles divide the distribution into hundredths.

Quintiles divide the distribution as parts of fifths.

Deciles divide the distribution into parts of tenths.

Quarters divide the distribution into quarters.

The syntax of the quantile() function can be given as,

Object_name.quantile(q, axis, numeric_only, interpolation)

Where,

q is float or array. Its default value is 0.5 (or 50% quantile). The value of q varies from 0 to 1. That is, 0 <= q <= 1.

axis indicates index or columns. Its value is 0 to specify index or row and 1 for columns. The default value of axis is 0.

numeric_only is a Boolean value. If false, the quantile of datetime and timedelta data will also be computed else not. Its default value is true.

interpolatoin can be "linear," "lower," "higher," "midpoint," "nearest." The default value is linear.

The function returns quantiles (Series or DataFrame). If q is an array, a DataFrame will be returned where the index is q. If q is a float, a series will be returned where the values are the quantiles. **The return value will depend on the value of q. The value of q can be as specified in table.**

Value of 'q'	Quantile
0.05	1st quintile
0.1	1st Decile/2nd quintile
0.2	2nd Decile/4th quintile
0.25	1st quarter/5th quintile/ 25th percentile
0.3	3rd Decile/6th quintile/ 30th percentile
0.4	4th Decile/8th quintile/ 40th percentile
0.5	1st half/2nd quarter/5th Decile/10th quintile/50th percentile
0.6	6th Decile/12th quintile/60th percentile
0.7	7th Decile/14th quintile/70th percentile
0.75	3rd quarter/15th quintile/ 75th percentile
0.9	9th Decile/18th quintile/90th percentile
1.0	10th Decile/20th quintile/100th percentile

```
import pandas as pd
# Creating the dataframe
df = pd.DataFrame({"A":[1, 2, 3, 4, 5],
                   "B":[6, 7, 8, 9, 10],
                   "C":[9, 8, 7, 6, 5],
                   "D":[1, 2, 6, 3, 4]})
print("Data Frame")
print(df)
print("0.2 Quantile Values of all columns")
print(df.quantile(.2, axis = 0))
print("0.1,0.25,0.5 and 0.75 Quantile Values of all columns")
print(df.quantile([.1, .25, .5, .75], axis = 0))
OUTPUT
ata Frame
   A   B  C  D
0  1   6  9  1
1  2   7  8  2
2  3   8  7  6
3  4   9  6  3
4  5  10  5  4
```

```
0.2 Quantile Values of all columns
A    1.8
B    6.8
C    5.8
D    1.8
Name: 0.2, dtype: float64
0.1,0.25,0.5 and 0.75 Quantile Values of all columns
        A    B    C    D
0.10  1.4  6.4  5.4  1.4
0.25  2.0  7.0  6.0  2.0
0.50  3.0  8.0  7.0  3.0
0.75  4.0  9.0  8.0  4.0
```

Demonstrate the use of numpy.quantile() function on a one-dimensional array.

```
# numpy.quantile() method
import numpy as np
arr = [45,59,65,75,55,90,87,71,67,49]
print("The array elements are : ", arr)
print("Q1 quantile of arr : ", np.quantile(arr, .25))
print("Q2 quantile of arr : ", np.quantile(arr, .50))
print("Q3 quantile of arr : ", np.quantile(arr, .75))
print("Q4 quantile of arr : ", np.quantile(arr, .1))
```

OUTPUT

```
The array elements are :  [45, 59, 65, 75, 55, 90, 87, 71, 67, 49]
Q1 quantile of arr :  56.0
Q2 quantile of arr :  66.0
Q3 quantile of arr :  74.0
Q4 quantile of arr :  48.6
```

Demonstrate the use of numpy.quantile() function on a two-dimensional array.

```
# numpy.quantile() method
```

```
import numpy as np
arr = [[12, 13, 27, 35, 44],
       [18, 9 , 27, 20, 15],
       [20, 3, 54, 41, 60, ]]
print("Array Elements are: : \n", arr)
# quantile of the flattened array
print("50th quantile of arr, axis = None : ", np.quantile(arr, .50))
print("0th quantile of arr, axis = None : ", np.quantile(arr, 0))
# quantile along the axis = 0
print("50th quantile of arr, axis = 0 : ", np.quantile(arr, .50, axis = 0))
print("0th quantile of arr, axis = 0 : ", np.quantile(arr, 0, axis = 0))
# quantile along the axis = 1
print("50th quantile of arr, axis = 1 : ", np.quantile(arr, .50, axis = 1))
print("0th quantile of arr, axis = 1 : ", np.quantile(arr, 0, axis = 1))
```

OUTPUT

```
Array Elements are: :
[[12, 13, 27, 35, 44], [18, 9, 27, 20, 15], [20, 3, 54, 41, 60]]
50th quantile of arr, axis = None :  20.0
0th quantile of arr, axis = None :  3
50th quantile of arr, axis = 0 :  [18.  9. 27. 35. 44.]
0th quantile of arr, axis = 0 :  [12  3 27 20 15]
50th quantile of arr, axis = 1 :  [27. 18. 41.]
0th quantile of arr, axis = 1 :  [12  9  3]
```

5.9 Function application

While coding, we often need to apply functions to Pandas objects. For this, Pandas provides pipe(), apply(), and applymap() methods to its users. The appropriate method to be used depends on whether the function expects to operate on an element, row, or column.

The **pipe()** method applies function on Table.
The **apply()** method applies function of a row or column.
The **applymap()** method applies function to each element in the Pandas object.

5.9.1 Table-wise function application: pipe()

pipe() function performs the operation for the entire data frame with the help of user defined or library function. In example given below, pipe() method is used to add 5 to the entire data frame.

```
# pipe() Method in Pandas
import pandas as pd
import numpy as np
import math
# user defined function
def add(num1,num2):
  return(num1+num2)
# Create a Dictionary of series
Test_marks = {'Marks_Maths':pd.Series([88,90,92,67,73,59]),
  'Marks_Science':pd.Series([65,67,78,77,89,90])}
df = pd.DataFrame(Test_marks)
print("ORIGINAL MARKS")
print(df)
print("MODIFIED MARKS")
print(df.pipe(add,5))
```

```
OUTPUT
ORIGINAL MARKS
    Marks_Maths   Marks_Science
0       88              65
1       90              67
2       92              78
3       67              77
4       73              89
5       59              90
MODIFIED MARKS
    Marks_Maths   Marks_Science
0       93              70
1       95              72
2       97              83
3       72              82
4       78              94
5       64              95
```

The pipe() method is also used for one more thing. Suppose you want to apply a function to a data frame or series, to then apply on other function, so on and so forth. In this scenario, one way would be to perform these operations in a "sandwich"-like fashion:

```
df = func3(func2(func1(df, arg1= 1), arg2= 2), arg3=3)
```

However, in this long statement, function calls have become fairly messy and error prone. So a better alternative is to use the pipe() method. Pipe can therefore be used for function chaining. With pipe(), the same series of function calls can be written as,

```
df.pipe(func1, arg1=1).
      pipe(func2, arg2=2).
      pipe(func3, arg3=3)
```

This way the code becomes cleaner and it is far easier to track the order in which the functions and its corresponding arguments are applied. For example, in the code given below, we use the pipe() method to add, divide, subtract, and multiply elements of a data frame.

```
import pandas as pd
# creating a dataframe
def adder(x,a):
  return(x+a)
def div(x,d):
  return(x/d)
def sub_mult(x,sub=2,mult=10):
  return((x-2)*10)
data = {'A': [10,20,30,40,50,60,70,80,90,100],
   'B': [15,25,35,45,55,65,75,85,95,105],
   'C': [12,22,32,42,52,62,72,82,92,102]
   }
df = pd.DataFrame(data, columns= ['A', 'B','C'])
print("ORIGINAL DATA FRAME")
print(df)
df = df.pipe(adder, a=5).pipe(div, d=20).
pipe(sub_mult, sub=2, mult=10)
print("MODIFIED DATA FRAME")
print(df)
```

OUTPUT

```
ORIGINAL DATA FRAME
   A   B   C
0 10   15  12
1 20   25  22
2 30   35  32
3 40   45  42
4 50   55  52
5 60   65  62
6 70   75  72
7 80   85  82
8 90   95  92
9 100 105 102
MODIFIED DATA FRAME
    A     B     C
0 -12.5 -10.0 -11.5
1 -7.5  -5.0  -6.5
2 -2.5   0.0  -1.5
3  2.5   5.0   3.5
4  7.5  10.0   8.5
5 12.5  15.0  13.5
6 17.5  20.0  18.5
7 22.5  25.0  23.5
8 27.5  30.0  28.5
9 32.5  35.0  33.5
```

5.9.2 Row- or column-wise function operations: apply()

We can apply any function to the axes of a DataFrame object or to a series object by using the apply() method. The apply() method takes an optional axis argument. If no value is specified, then by *default, the function will be applied column-wise, taking every column as an array.* In this way, the function passed in the apply() method is applied to all the values of the DataFrame or series.

```
# apply() Method in Pandas
import pandas as pd
import numpy as np
import math
# user defined function
def reduce(num):
  return(num-2)
# Create a Dictionary of series
```

OUTPUT

```
ORIGINAL MARKS
   Marks_Maths   Marks_Science
0     88              65
1     90              67
2     92              78
3     67              77
4     73              89
5     59              90
```

```
Test_marks = {'Marks_Maths':pd.Series([88,90,92,67,73,59]),
    'Marks_Science':pd.Series([65,67,78,77,89,90])}
df = pd.DataFrame(Test_marks)
print("ORIGINAL MARKS")
print(df)
print("MODIFIED MARKS")
print(df.apply(reduce))
```

```
MODIFIED MARKS
    Marks_Maths    Marks_Science
0   86             63
1   88             65
2   90             76
3   65             75
4   71             87
5   57             88
```

5.9.3 Element-wise function application: applymap()

To perform element-wise application of a function, the applymap() is used. The function performs the specified operation for all the elements in the dataframe. The applymap() method takes and returns a single value. Note that this method does not work on a series.

```
import pandas as pd
import numpy as np
import math
def abs(x):
    if x>0:
        return x
    else:
        return(-x)
S = pd.Series(10*np.random.randn(5))
print("ORIGINAL VALUES ARE : ")
print(S)
df = pd.DataFrame(S)
df = df.applymap(abs)
print("DATA FRAME WITH ABSOLUTE VALUES IS : ")
print(df)
OUTPUT
ORIGINAL VALUES ARE :
0    -2.817097
1     6.236797
```

```
2     -5.107213
3     14.181766
4     -4.375742
dtype: float64
DATA FRAME WITH ABSOLUTE VALUES:
           0
0   2.817097
1   6.236797
2   5.107213
3  14.181766
4   4.375742
```

5.10 Aggregation (group by)

Aggregation is the process of turning the values of a dataset (or a subset of it) into one single value. Pandas offers a couple of functions that provide sql-like aggregation functions. These functions can be applied when we group values of one or more columns. In this section, we will read about different ways in which we can perform grouping on Pandas objects.

5.10.1 Group by one column

Let us compute mean, min, and max values by group. For this, we will first use the groupby function and then pass the aggregation functions to the grouped object as a dictionary within the agg function.

First, we will group by Team with Pandas' group by function. After grouping, we can pass aggregation functions to the grouped object as a dictionary within the agg() function. This dictionary will specify the name of the column that is being used as a key for aggregation. We can apply either a single aggregation function or a list of aggregation functions.

```
import pandas as pd
data = {"Team":["Bhabha","Bhabha","Bhabha","Bhabha","Bhabha","Bhabha","Bhabha",
        "Aryabhatta","Aryabhatta","Aryabhatta","Aryabhatta","Aryabhatta","Aryabhatta",
          "Aryabhatta"],
     "Status":["Completed","Completed","Not Completed","Completed","Not Completed","Completed",
               "Not Completed","Completed","Completed","Not Completed","Not Completed",
                  "Completed","Not Completed","Completed"],
     "Score":[1,9,5,8,2,7,5,6,4,5,7,8,3,9]}
df = pd.DataFrame(data)
print(df)
# groupping by Team and calculating mean, min and max of Score for each Team
```

```
group1 = df.groupby('Team').agg({'Score':['mean','min','max']})
print(group1)
     Team       Status    Score
 0  Bhabha        Completed   1
 1  Bhabha        Completed   9
 2  Bhabha      Not Completed   5
 3  Bhabha        Completed   8
 4  Bhabha      Not Completed   2
 5  Bhabha        Completed   7
 6  Bhabha      Not Completed   5
 7  Aryabhatta    Completed   6
 8  Aryabhatta    Completed   4
 9  Aryabhatta  Not Completed   5
10  Aryabhatta  Not Completed   7
11  Aryabhatta    Completed   8
12  Aryabhatta  Not Completed 3
13  Aryabhatta    Completed 9
       Score
       mean min max
Team
Aryabhatta     6.000000    3    9
Bhabha         5.285714    1    9
```

In the above code, we have applied multiple aggregation functions to a single column. This is also known as a multiIndex. Observe that the grouping column is now the data frame's index.

5.10.2 Grouping by multiple columns

We can extend grouping further to work with multiple columns. Therefore, to apply aggregations to multiple columns, we can add additional key:value pairs to the dictionary. Instead of passing a single string value to the groupby() function, we will pass a list of column names.

```
import pandas as pd
data = {"Team":["Bhabha","Bhabha","Bhabha","Bhabha","Bhabha","Bhabha","Bhabha",
          "Aryabhatta","Aryabhatta","Aryabhatta","Aryabhatta","Aryabhatta",
             "Aryabhatta","Aryabhatta"],
      "Status":["Completed","Completed","Not Completed","Completed","Not Completed","Completed",
         "Not Completed",
"Completed","Completed","Not Completed","Not Completed","Completed","Not
   Completed","Completed"],
       "Score":[1,9,5,8,2,7,5,6,4,5,7,8,3,9]}
df = pd.DataFrame(data)
print(df)
group2 = df.groupby(['Team','Status']).agg({'Score':['mean','min','max']})
print(group2)


OUTPUT
Team    Status Score
0   Bhabha Completed     1
1   Bhabha Completed     9
2   Bhabha Not Completed   5
3   Bhabha Completed     8
4   Bhabha Not Completed   2
5   Bhabha Completed     7
6   Bhabha Not Completed   5
```

```
7 Aryabhatta Completed    6
8 Aryabhatta Completed    4
9 Aryabhatta Not Completed 5
10 Aryabhatta Not Completed 7
11 Aryabhatta Completed    8
12 Aryabhatta Not Completed 3
13 Aryabhatta Completed    9
             Score
             mean min max
Team     Status
Aryabhatta Completed   6.75 4 9
      Not Completed 5.00  3  7
Bhabha    Completed  6.25 1 9
      Not Completed 4.00 2 5
```

5.11 Transform function in Python

The transform() function returns a self-produced data frame with transformed values after applying the function specified in its parameter. The resultant data frame has the same length as that of the original data frame passed to it.

Transform functionality is extensively used for feature extraction. The term feature extraction means extracting new features from existing ones. The time taken by the transform() function for feature selection is comparatively less over a large data frame. It also gives a significant advantage over other techniques to do the same operation.

Pandas' pipeline feature allows you to string together Python functions in order to build a pipeline of data processing.

Pandas **DataFrame.transform()** function call func on self-producing a DataFrame with transformed values and that has the same axis length as self. This means that the transorm() function will make changes in the original data frame. After applying the changes, number of rows will still remain the same, only the number of columns may change. The syntax of this f DataFrame. transform(func, axis=0, *args, **kwargs)

Where,

func is the function to be used for transforming the data
axis is 0 or "index" and 1 or "columns." By default, it is 0.unction can be given as,

Rest of the two arguments we will not be using here. From the code given below, let us understand the use of transform() function.

```
# importing pandas as pd

import pandas as pd

# Creating the DataFrame

df = pd.DataFrame({"A":[12, 4, 5, None, 1],

                   "B":[7, 2, 54, 3, None],

                   "C":[20, 16, 11, 3, 8],

                   "D":[14, 3, None, 2, 6]})

# Set the index of the data frame

df.index = ['Row1', 'Row2', 'Row3', 'Row4', 'Row5']
```

```
# Print the DataFrame
print(df)
# add 10 to each element of the dataframe
result = df.transform(func = ['sqrt', 'exp'])
# Print the result
print(result)
OUTPUT
          A        B        C       D
Row1    12.0      7.0      20     14.0
Row2     4.0      2.0      16      3.0
Row3     5.0     54.0      11      NaN
Row4     NaN      3.0       3      2.0
Row5     1.0      NaN       8      6.0
             A                B  ...          C          D
          sqrt        exp     sqrt  ...        exp       sqrt          exp
Row1 3.464102 162754.791419 2.645751 ... 4.851652e+08 3.741657 1.202604e+06
Row2 2.000000    54.598150 1.414214  ... 8.886111e+06 1.732051 2.008554e+01
Row3  2.236068    148.413159 7.348469 ... 5.987414e+04     NaN           NaN
Row4   NaN      NaN  1.732051  ... 2.008554e+01  1.414214  7.389056e+00
Row5  1.000000   2.718282      NaN ... 2.980958e+03 2.449490  4.034288e+02
[5 rows x 8 columns]
```

Create a data frame containing 6 rows and 3 columns. Fill it with random values and use the pipe() method to scale the value of each element by 10.

```
import pandas as pd
import numpy as np
import math
# user defined function
def scale(num):
   return(num*10)
df = pd.DataFrame(6*np.random.randn(6,3),columns=['A','B','C'])
df = df.pipe(scale)
print(df)
```

OUTPUT

```
           A          B           C
0 -14.320374 -41.115159  -33.601141
1  21.659777  -1.906765   38.518445
2  -3.252923  45.891514 -103.855270
3   8.930942 -92.797391   22.087857
4 -68.109612 -64.390266  -32.272999
5  77.912319 -49.543111  -14.282236
```

Create a data frame containing 5 rows and 3 columns. Fill it with random values and use the apply() method to find the mean of values with axis = 1 (or row-wise)

```
import pandas as pd
import numpy as np
import math
df = pd.DataFrame(6*np.random.randn(5,3),columns=['A','B','C'])
df = df.apply(np.mean,axis = 1)
print(df)
```

OUTPUT

```
0    3.684398
1   -0.375202
2    2.525387
3   -3.749754
4   -3.679718
dtype: float64
```

Read the zoo.csv file and perform the following:

a. Number of the animals

b. sum of the values in the water_need column

c. Smallest value in the water_need column

d. Largest value in the water_need column

e. Mean value of water_need columns

```
f. Median value of water_need columns
g. Mean value of water_need column group by animal
import pandas as pd
import numpy as np
zoo = pd.read_csv('zoo.csv', delimiter = ',')
print("Data in zoo.csv :")
print(zoo)
num = zoo.animal.count()
print("Number of the animals : ",num)
sum = zoo.water_need.sum()
print("sum of the values in the water_need column = ", sum)
min = zoo.water_need.min()
print("Smallest value in the water_need column is : ", min)
max = zoo.water_need.max()
print("Largest value in the water_need column is : ", max)
mean = zoo.water_need.mean()
print("Mean value of water_need columns is : ", mean)
median_value = zoo.water_need.median()
print("Median value of water_need columns is : ", median_value)
animal_mean = zoo.groupby('animal').mean()[['water_need']]
print("Mean value of water_need column group by animal is : ", animal_mean)
OUTPUT
Data in zoo.csv :
         animal   uniq_id   water_need
0      elephant      1001          500
1      elephant      1002          600
2      elephant      1003          550
3         tiger      1004          300
4         tiger      1005          320
5         tiger      1006          330
```

To ignore missing values in a data frame use the drop.na() method of data frame by writing df.drop.na()

```
6          tiger      1007       290
7          tiger      1008       310
8          zebra      1009       200
9          zebra      1010       220
10         zebra      1011       240
11         zebra      1012       230
12         zebra      1013       220
13         zebra      1014       100
14         zebra      1015        80
15          lion      1016       420
16          lion      1017       600
17          lion      1018       500
18          lion      1019       390
19      kangaroo      1020       410
20      kangaroo      1021       430
21      kangaroo      1022       410
Number of the animals :  22
sum of the values in the water_need column =  7650
Smallest value in the water_need column is :  80
Largest value in the water_need column is :  600
Mean value of water_need columns is :  347.72727272727275
Median value of water_need columns is :  325.0
Mean value of water_need column group by animal is : water_need
animal
elephant  550.000000
kangaroo  416.666667
lion      477.500000
tiger     310.000000
zebra     184.285714
```

Create a data frame storing name, qualification, address and age of students. Find the sum of ages group by Qualification. Also compute the mean of ages in each group.

```
import pandas as pd
import numpy as np
data1 = {'Name':['Jia', 'Aman', 'Jia', 'Parul',
                'Garv', 'Aman', 'Parul', 'Priya'],
        'Age':[23, 22, 24, 32,
               22, 20, 23, 22],
        'Address':['Nagpur', 'Kanpur', 'Allahabad', 'Kannuaj',
                   'Jaunpur', 'Kanpur', 'Allahabad', 'Aligarh'],
        'Qualification':['MSc', 'MA', 'MCA', 'PhD',
                         'B.Tech', 'B.Com', 'MSc', 'MA']}
df = pd.DataFrame(data1)
print(df)
print(df.groupby(['Qualification']).sum() )
print(df.groupby(['Qualification'], sort = True).mean() )
```

OUTPUT

```
    Name  Age    Address  Qualification
0    Jia   23     Nagpur            MSc
1   Aman   22     Kanpur             MA
2    Jia   24  Allahabad            MCA
3  Parul   32    Kannuaj            PhD
4   Garv   22    Jaunpur         B.Tech
5   Aman   20     Kanpur          B.Com
6  Parul   23  Allahabad            MSc
7  Priya   22    Aligarh             MA
              Age
Qualification
B.Com          20
B.Tech         22
```

NaN stands for Not a Number

```
MA              44
MCA             24
MSc             46
PhD             32
               Age
Qualification
B.Com           20
B.Tech          22
MA              22
MCA             24
MSc             23
PhD             32
```

Write a program that creates a series of first 11 natural numbers. Use the transform() method to find the sqrt and exp of the values in the series.

```
import numpy as np
import pandas as pd
s = pd.Series(range(11))
print(s)
s = s.transform([np.sqrt, np.exp])
print(s)
```

OUTPUT

```
       sqrt          exp
0  0.000000     1.000000
1  1.000000     2.718282
2  1.414214     7.389056
3  1.732051    20.085537
4  2.000000    54.598150
5  2.236068   148.413159
6  2.449490   403.428793
7  2.645751  1096.633158
8  2.828427  2980.957987
```

```
9   3.000000   8103.083928
10  3.162278  22026.465795
```

Write a program to take an object and reindex its axes to be labelled as another object.

```
import pandas as pd
import numpy as np
df1 = pd.DataFrame(np.random.randn(5,3),columns=['C1','B','C3'])
df2 = pd.DataFrame(np.random.randn(4,3),columns=['C1','C2','C3'])
df1 = df1.reindex_like(df2)
print(df1)
```

OUTPUT

```
         C1  C2        C3
0 -0.453925 NaN -0.238405
1  0.081728 NaN -1.057288
2 -1.477602 NaN  1.072387
3  0.320976 NaN -0.169116
```

> Here, df1 is altered and reindexed like df2. The column names should be matched or else NAN will be added for the entire column label.

Write a program to take a data frame and reindex its axes to be labelled as another object. Also fill the NaN using any method of your choice.

```
import pandas as pd
import numpy as np
df1 = pd.DataFrame(np.random.randn(5,3),columns=['C1','C2','C3'])
df2 = pd.DataFrame(np.random.randn(3,3),columns=['C1','C2','C3'])
df2 = df2.reindex_like(df1,method='nearest')
print(df2)
```

OUTPUT

```
         C1         C2         C3
0  1.861295  -0.017680  -0.435243
1  0.460061  -1.404898   1.683461
2  0.739224   0.053781   1.556290
3  0.739224   0.053781   1.556290
4  0.739224   0.053781   1.556290
```

> The limit argument of the reindex() method specifies the maximum count of filling NaN values. For example, we can write, print df2.reindex_like(df1,method='ffill',limit=1)

5.12 Reindexing in Pandas dataframe

Reindexing in Pandas is used to change the index of rows and columns of a data frame. Indexes can be used to reference data structures like Pandas series or Pandas Data Frame. The code given here reindexes the columns and rows in a Pandas Data frame.

We can reindex a single row or multiple rows by using `reindex()` method. This method takes the new index as well as axis as argument and returns a reindexed data frame.

In the first code given below, we have reordered the rows using reindex(), and in the second code, we have created new indexes for the data frame. Note that default values in the new index that are not present in the data frame are assigned NaN.

```
# Reordering indexes
import pandas as pd
import numpy as np
cols =['C1','C2','C3','C4','C5']
index =['R1','R2','R3','R4','R5']
 # create a dataframe of random values of array
df = pd.DataFrame(np.random.rand(5,5),
       columns=cols, index=index)
print(df)
print('Data frame after re-indexing rows:\n',
df.reindex(['R3','R1','R2','R4','R5']))
```

```
         C1        C2        C3        C4        C5
R1 0.493102  0.811385  0.008166  0.299422  0.483170
R2 0.998660  0.631610  0.270461  0.457065  0.495796
R3 0.980782  0.734258  0.536033  0.522151  0.930235
R4 0.489830  0.665597  0.138179  0.111670  0.146060
R5 0.801327  0.138832  0.698386  0.935052  0.589710
Data frame after re-indexing rows:
         C1        C2        C3        C4        C5
R3 0.980782  0.734258  0.536033  0.522151  0.930235
R1 0.493102  0.811385  0.008166  0.299422  0.483170
R2 0.998660  0.631610  0.270461  0.457065  0.495796
R4 0.489830  0.665597  0.138179  0.111670  0.146060
R5 0.801327  0.138832  0.698386  0.935052  0.589710
```

```
# Adding New Indexes
import pandas as pd
import numpy as np
 cols =['C1','C2','C3','C4','C5']
index =['R1','R2','R3','R4','R5']
 # create a dataframe of random values of array
df = pd.DataFrame(np.random.rand(5,5),
       columns=cols, index=index)
print(df)
new_index =['R1','B','R3','D','R4']
print('Dataframe after reindexing rows:\n',
df.reindex(new_index))
```

```
         C1        C2        C3        C4        C5
R1 0.705821  0.974293  0.749270  0.340964  0.144562
R2 0.734417  0.001402  0.062133  0.607034  0.745289
R3 0.497827  0.422662  0.444784  0.361989  0.966052
R4 0.501082  0.604928  0.253406  0.930383  0.638558
R5 0.728509  0.401761  0.085836  0.993651  0.667026
Dataframe after reindexing rows:
         C1        C2        C3        C4        C5
R1 0.705821  0.974293  0.749270  0.340964  0.144562
B       NaN       NaN       NaN       NaN       NaN
R3 0.497827  0.422662  0.444784  0.361989  0.966052
D       NaN       NaN       NaN       NaN       NaN
R4 0.501082  0.604928  0.253406  0.930383  0.638558
```

```
# Re-indexing columns
import pandas as pd
import numpy as np
cols =['C1','C2','C3','C4','C5']
index =['R1','R2','R3','R4','R5']
 # create a dataframe of random values of array
df = pd.DataFrame(np.random.rand(5,5),
       columns=cols, index=index)
```

```
# Reindexing columns
import pandas as pd
import numpy as np
cols=['C1','C2','C3','C4','C5']
index =['R1','R2','R3','R4','R5']
 # create a dataframe of random values of array
df = pd.DataFrame(np.random.rand(5,5),
       columns=cols, index=index)
```

```
print(df)
print('Data frame after re-indexing rows:\n',
df.reindex(['C3', 'C1', 'C2', 'C4', 'C5'], axis=1))
         C1        C2        C3        C4        C5
R1 0.257785  0.667991  0.706676  0.233302  0.377173
R2 0.056890  0.597683  0.376673  0.139345  0.630611
R3 0.210198  0.795495  0.875716  0.613650  0.805473
R4 0.538860  0.279949  0.578101  0.202765  0.302528
R5 0.624405  0.208100  0.708359  0.679449  0.835302
Data frame after re-indexing rows:
         C3        C1        C2        C4        C5
R1 0.706676  0.257785  0.667991  0.233302  0.377173
R2 0.376673  0.056890  0.597683  0.139345  0.630611
R3 0.875716  0.210198  0.795495  0.613650  0.805473
R4 0.578101  0.538860  0.279949  0.202765  0.302528
R5 0.708359  0.624405  0.208100  0.679449  0.835302
```

```
print(df)
new_cols = ['A', 'C2', 'C3', 'B', 'C5']
print('Data frame after re-indexing rows:\n',
df.reindex(new_cols,axis=1))
         C1        C2        C3        C4        C5
R1 0.622108  0.388899  0.058391  0.170691  0.558634
R2 0.144692  0.867697  0.108545  0.908884  0.407697
R3 0.390215  0.689716  0.857022  0.422999  0.226193
R4 0.076215  0.761085  0.986030  0.521373  0.285629
R5 0.540212  0.550815  0.883104  0.176268  0.231696
Data frame after re-indexing rows:
     A        C2        C3    B        C5
R1 NaN  0.388899  0.058391  NaN  0.558634
R2 NaN  0.867697  0.108545  NaN  0.407697
R3 NaN  0.689716  0.857022  NaN  0.226193
R4 NaN  0.761085  0.986030  NaN  0.285629
R5 NaN  0.550815  0.883104  NaN  0.231696
```

Till now, we have reindexed the rows. We can also reindex columns using the *axis* keyword. A single column or multiple columns can be re indexed using `reindex()` method and specifying the `axis` we want to reindex. Default values in the new index that are not present in the dataframe are assigned NaN.

Note that the reindex() method also takes an optional parameter method, which specifies a filling method with values any of the given below.

- pad/ffill to fill values forward
- bfill/backfill to fill values backward
- nearest to fill from the nearest index values

```
Example: Filling Values Forward
import pandas as pd
import numpy as np
df = pd.DataFrame(np.random.randn(5, 3), index=['a', 'c', 'e', 'f',
'h'],columns=['one', 'two', 'three'])
df = df.reindex(['a', 'b', 'c', 'd', 'e', 'f', 'g', 'h'])
print df.fillna(method='pad')
OUTPUT
ORIGINAL DATA FRAME :
        one        two      three
a -1.151653   2.157601  -0.382743
b       NaN        NaN        NaN
c -1.974643   0.123408  -0.922009
```

```
d        NaN        NaN        NaN
e  0.397603   0.277598   0.779476
f  1.234860  -1.747849  -2.002897
g        NaN        NaN        NaN
h -0.930553   1.653887   0.973504
REINDEXED DATA FRAME :
        one        two      three
a -1.151653   2.157601  -0.382743
b -1.151653   2.157601  -0.382743
c -1.974643   0.123408  -0.922009
d -1.974643   0.123408  -0.922009
e  0.397603   0.277598   0.779476
f  1.234860  -1.747849  -2.002897
g  1.234860  -1.747849  -2.002897
h -0.930553   1.653887   0.973504
```

5.13 Altering column labels

Pandas allow users to alter the column labels in two ways–column method and rename method. In this section, we will discuss both of them.

Using the Columns Method: The simplest way to change labels of a data frame already created is to overwrite the column labels by calling the `columns` method on the data frame object and providing a new list of names to be specified. The code given below demonstrates the use of column() method to alter column labels.

```
import pandas as pd
df = pd.DataFrame([('The Jungle Book', 'Rudyard Kipling'),
   ('Malgudi Days','R.K.lyer Narayanaswami'),
   ('Godan','Prem Chand')])
print(df)
print('\n')
df.columns = ['title', 'author']
print(df)
```

```
                 0                        1
0 The Jungle Book          Rudyard Kipling
1 Malgudi Days      R.K.lyer Narayanaswami
2 Godan                         Prem Chand

             title                   author
0 The Jungle Book          Rudyard Kipling
1 Malgudi Days      R.K.lyer Narayanaswami
2 Godan                         Prem Chand
```

Using the Rename Method: The other technique for renaming column labels is to call the rename method on the data frame object. We can pass the list of new labels to the columns parameter of the rename method. That is, to rename the existing data frame rather than creating a copy, we must use the following sytax.

df.rename(columns={'oldName1': 'newName1', 'oldName2': 'newName2'}, inplace=True)

```
import pandas as pd
df = pd.DataFrame([('The Jungle Book','Rudyard Kipling'),
   ('Malgudi Days','R.K.lyer Narayanaswami'),
   ('Godan','Prem Chand')])
print(df)
print('\n')
df.rename(columns={0: 'TITLE',1:'AUTHOR'},inplace=True)
print(df)
```

```
                0                        1
0 The Jungle Book          Rudyard Kipling
1 Malgudi Days      R.K.lyer Narayanaswami
2 Godan                         Prem Chand

            TITLE                   AUTHOR
0 The Jungle Book          Rudyard Kipling
1 Malgudi Days      R.K.lyer Narayanaswami
2 Godan                         Prem Chand
```

Note that since the rename method *renames* existing labels, the data frame must have existing labels. This was not a necessity with columns method. Also, we have set inplace = TRUE. This is important when you have to update the existing data frame rather than returning a newly created data frame.

5.14 Data wrangling

Data wrangling is a process that involves processing of data so that it could be used for analysis or for preparing the data so that it can be used with another set of data. Data wrangling encompasses techniques like data merging, and concatenation.

5.14.1 Merging data

The merge() function is used to combine data on common columns or indices of a data frame. Syntax of merge() function can be given as,

pd.merge(left, right, how= "inner," on=None, left_on=None, right_on=None,left_index=False, right_index=False, sort=True)

To use merge(), we need to provide two required arguments–left DataFrame and the right DataFrame. Apart from these parameters, we can optionally also provide additional parameters including:

how, which specifies the kind of merge to make. Its default value is "inner" but other possible options include "outer," "left," and "right."

on, indicates columns or indices on which the join operation will be performed. By default, if left_index and right_index are false, then columns from the two DataFrames that share names will be used as join keys. If you use on, then the specified column or index must be present in both objects.

left_on and right_on, any of the two can be used to specify a column or index that is present only in the left or right data frames that are being merged. Both default to none.

left_index and right_index are set to true to use the index of the left or right data frame to be merged. By default, their value is false.

Suffixes is a tuple of strings to append to identical column names that are not merge keys. It is usually used to keep track of the origins of columns with the same name as shown in the below Figure 5.2.

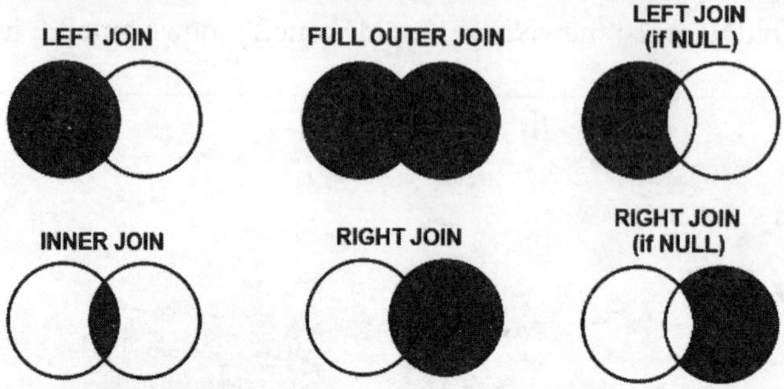

Figure 5.2 Merging Columns of Data Frame(s)

Example: Joining two data frames

```
# importing pandas module
import pandas as pd
 # Define a dictionary containing employee data
data1 = {'RollNo': ['01', '02', '03', '04'],
         'Name':['Jai', 'Princi', 'Gaurav', 'Anuj'],
         'Marks':[27, 24, 22, 32],}
 # Define a dictionary containing employee data
data2 = {'RollNo': ['01', '02', '03', '04'],
         'Course':['BCA', 'BTech', 'MCA', 'MTech'],
         'Fees':['128000', '140000', '85000', '160000']}
# Convert the dictionary into DataFrame
df = pd.DataFrame(data1)
# Convert the dictionary into DataFrame
df1 = pd.DataFrame(data2)
  print(df, "\n\n", df1)
# using .merge() function
res = pd.merge(df, df1, on='RollNo')
print(res)
```

OUTPUT

```
        RollNo      Name     Marks
0          01        Jai        27
1          02     Princi        24
```

```
2          03    Gaurav       22
3          04     Anuj        32
       RollNo    Course      Fees
0          01       BCA    128000
1          02     BTech    140000
2          03       MCA     85000
3          04     MTech    160000
       RollNo      Name     Marks    Course     Fees
0          01       Jai        27       BCA   128000
1          02    Princi        24     BTech   140000
2          03    Gaurav        22       MCA    85000
3          04      Anuj        32     MTech   160000
```

Example: Merging two data frames on two keys with how = "outer"

```
import pandas as pd
 # Define a dictionary containing employee data
data1 = {'RollNo': ['01', '02', '03', '04'],
         'AdmNo': ['101', '102', '103', '104'],
         'Name':['Jai', 'Princi', 'Gaurav', 'Anuj'],
        'Marks':[27, 24, 22, 32],}
 # Define a dictionary containing employee data
data2 = {'RollNo': ['01', '02', '03', '04'],
         'AdmNo': ['101', '102', '103', '104'],
         'Course':['BCA', 'BTech', 'MCA', 'MTech'],
        'Fees':['128000', '140000', '85000', '160000']}
# Convert the dictionary into DataFrame
df = pd.DataFrame(data1)
# Convert the dictionary into DataFrame
df1 = pd.DataFrame(data2)
print(df, "\n\n", df1)
# using .merge() function
res = pd.merge(df, df1, how = 'outer', on= ['RollNo','AdmNo'])
print(res)
```

```
OUTPUT
  RollNo AdmNo    Name  Marks
0     01   101     Jai     27
1     02   102  Princi     24
2     03   103  Gaurav     22
3     04   104    Anuj     32
  RollNo AdmNo Course    Fees
0     01   101    BCA  128000
1     02   102  BTech  140000
2     03   103    MCA   85000
3     04   104  MTech  160000
  RollNo AdmNo    Name  Marks Course    Fees
0     01   101     Jai     27    BCA  128000
1     02   102  Princi     24  BTech  140000
2     03   103  Gaurav     22    MCA   85000
3     04   104    Anuj     32  MTech  160000
```

5.14.2 Joining DataFrame

The join() function is used for combining the columns of two potentially differently indexed DataFrames into a single result DataFrame.

```
# importing pandas module
import pandas as pd
 # Define a dictionary containing employee data
data1 = {'Name':['Jai', 'Princi', 'Gaurav', 'Anuj','Mrinal'],
         'Marks':[27, 24, 22, 32,45]}
# Define a dictionary containing employee data
data2 = {'Course':['BCA', 'BTech', 'MCA', 'MTech'],
         'Fees':['128000', '140000', '85000', '160000']}
# Convert the dictionary into DataFrame
df = pd.DataFrame(data1)
# Convert the dictionary into DataFrame
df1 = pd.DataFrame(data2)
```

```
print(df, "\n\n", df1)
# using .join() function
res = df.join(df1)
print(res)
OUTPUT
          Name     Marks
0          Jai        27
1       Princi        24
2       Gaurav        22
3         Anuj        32
4       Mrinal        45
        Course      Fees
0          BCA    128000
1        BTech    140000
2          MCA     85000
3        MTech    160000
          Name     Marks      Course      Fees
0          Jai        27         BCA    128000
1       Princi        24       BTech    140000
2       Gaurav        22         MCA     85000
3         Anuj        32       MTech    160000
4       Mrinal        45         NaN       NaN
```

We can use the on argument in join() function. Value of on argument can be a single column or multiple column names. These column(s) specify that the passed DataFrame must be joined on that column in the DataFrame.

```
import pandas as pd
 # Define a dictionary containing employee data
data1 = {'RollNo': ['01', '02', '03', '04','05'],
         'Name':['Jai', 'Princi', 'Gaurav', 'Anuj','Mrinal'],
         'Marks':[27, 24, 22, 32,45]}
 # Define a dictionary containing employee data
data2 = {'Course':['BCA', 'BTech', 'MCA', 'MTech'],
         'Fees':['128000', '140000', '85000', '160000']}
```

```
# Convert the dictionary into DataFrame
df = pd.DataFrame(data1)
# Convert the dictionary into DataFrame
df1 = pd.DataFrame(data2, index = ['01','02','03','04'])
print(df, "\n\n", df1)
# using .join() function
res = df.join(df1,on='RollNo')
print(res)
```

OUTPUT

```
      RollNo    Name   Marks
0         01     Jai      27
1         02  Princi      24
2         03  Gaurav      22
3         04    Anuj      32
4         05  Mrinal      45
      Course    Fees
01       BCA  128000
02     BTech  140000
03       MCA   85000
04     MTech  160000
      RollNo    Name   Marks   Course    Fees
0         01     Jai      27      BCA  128000
1         02  Princi      24    BTech  140000
2         03  Gaurav      22      MCA   85000
3         04    Anuj      32    MTech  160000
4         05  Mrinal      45      NaN     NaN
```

5.14.3 Concatenating data frames

Pandas can concatenate two or more data frames using the concat() function. Syntax of this function can be given as,

pd.concat(objs,axis=0,join='outer',join_axes=None,ignore_index=False)

objs is a dataframe object.

axis can be either 0 or 1. It specifies the axis along which concatenation has to be done. By default, axis=0.

join can be either "inner" or "outer." By default, its value is "outer."

ignore_index is a Boolean value, which is by default, false. If true, index values are not used on the concatenation axis. The resulting axis will be labeled 0, ..., n - 1.

join_axes is the list of index objects.

Example: Concatenating Two Data Frames

```
# importing pandas module
import pandas as pd
 # Define a dictionary containing employee data
data1 = {'RollNo': ['01', '02', '03', '04'],
         'AdmNo': ['101', '102', '103', '104'],
         'Name':['Jai', 'Princi', 'Gaurav', 'Anuj'],
         'Marks':[27, 24, 22, 32],}
 # Define a dictionary containing employee data
data2 = {'RollNo': ['01', '02', '03', '04'],
         'AdmNo': ['101', '102', '103', '104'],
         'Course':['BCA', 'BTech', 'MCA', 'MTech'],
         'Fees':['128000', '140000', '85000', '160000']}
# Convert the dictionary into DataFrame
df = pd.DataFrame(data1)
# Convert the dictionary into DataFrame
df1 = pd.DataFrame(data2)
print(df, "\n\n", df1)
res = pd.concat([df, df1],keys= ['ONE','TWO'])
print(res)
           RollNo      AdmNo       Name      Marks
0              01        101        Jai         27
1              02        102     Princi         24
2              03        103     Gaurav         22
```

```
3          04        104        Anuj        32
      RollNo     AdmNo     Course        Fees
0          01        101         BCA    128000
1          02        102       BTech    140000
2          03        103         MCA     85000
3          04        104       MTech    160000
      RollNo     AdmNo       Name       Marks      Course       Fees
ONE 0      01        101         Jai       27.0        NaN        NaN
    1      02        102      Princi       24.0        NaN        NaN
    2      03        103      Gaurav       22.0        NaN        NaN
    3      04        104        Anuj       32.0        NaN        NaN
TWO 0      01        101         NaN        NaN        BCA     128000
    1      02        102         NaN        NaN      BTech     140000
    2      03        103         NaN        NaN        MCA      85000
```

In the above program, we have associated specific keys with data from each DataFrame using the **keys** argument. Note that the index of the resultant data frame is duplicated as each index is repeated. If the resultant object has to follow its own indexing, then we must set **ignore_index** to **true**.

Observe, the index changes completely and the keys are also overridden.

If two objects need to be added along **axis=1**, then the new columns will be appended.

5.14.4 Concatenating using append

The append() method, which is actually predated concat, concatenates two or more data frames along **axis=0**.

```
# importing pandas module
import pandas as pd
 # Define a dictionary containing employee data
data1 = {'RollNo': ['01', '02', '03', '04'],
         'AdmNo': ['101', '102', '103', '104'],
         'Name':['Jai', 'Princi', 'Gaurav', 'Anuj'],
         'Marks':[27, 24, 22, 32],}
 # Define a dictionary containing employee data
data2 = {'RollNo': ['01', '02', '03', '04'],
```

```
        'AdmNo': ['101', '102', '103', '104'],
        'Course':['BCA', 'BTech', 'MCA', 'MTech'],
        'Fees':['128000', '140000', '85000', '160000']}
# Convert the dictionary into DataFrame
df = pd.DataFrame(data1)
# Convert the dictionary into DataFrame
df1 = pd.DataFrame(data2)
print(df, "\n\n", df1)
res = df.append([df1, df, df1])
print(res)
```

OUTPUT

```
     RollNo    AdmNo     Name    Marks
0       01      101       Jai       27
1       02      102    Princi       24
2       03      103    Gaurav       22
3       04      104      Anuj       32
     RollNo    AdmNo    Course     Fees
0       01      101       BCA   128000
1       02      102     BTech   140000
2       03      103       MCA    85000
3       04      104     MTech   160000
     RollNo    AdmNo     Name    Marks    Course      Fees
0       01      101       Jai     27.0       NaN       NaN
1       02      102    Princi     24.0       NaN       NaN
2       03      103    Gaurav     22.0       NaN       NaN
3       04      104      Anuj     32.0       NaN       NaN
0       01      101       NaN      NaN       BCA    128000
1       02      102       NaN      NaN     BTech    140000
2       03      103       NaN      NaN       MCA     85000
3       04      104       NaN      NaN     MTech    160000
0       01      101       Jai     27.0       NaN       NaN
1       02      102    Princi     24.0       NaN       NaN
```

```
2        03    103    Gaurav    22.0      NaN      NaN
3        04    104      Anuj    32.0      NaN      NaN
0        01    101       NaN     NaN      BCA   128000
1        02    102       NaN     NaN    BTech   140000
2        03    103       NaN     NaN      MCA    85000
3        04    104       NaN     NaN    MTech   160000
```

5.15 Time series data structures

Pandas provide support to time series data structures to add more power to its functionality. While working with time series data, users can generate sequence of time and convert the time series to different frequencies.

In pandas, a single point in time is represented as a **Timestamp**. The to_datetime() function is used to create Timestamps from strings in a wide variety of date/time formats. Time-stamped data are the most basic type of timeseries data that associates values with points in time.

Example: Converting dates and times to Timestamps.

```
import pandas as pd
print(pd.to_datetime('2021-01-10 5:06 PM'))
print(pd.to_datetime('01/10/2021'))
```

OUTPUT

```
2021-01-10 17:06:00
2021-01-10 00:00:00
```

Programming Tip

Pandas Timestamp type uses DatetimeIndex as index structure.

Note that in the second string, date 01/10/2021 is treated to be in the format *month/day/year.* However, the parameter dayfirst can be set to TRUE to tell pandas to interpret the date as 10th January 2021.

```
import pandas as pd
d = pd.to_datetime('2021-01-10 5:06 PM')
print("DAY : ",d.day)
print("MONTH : ",d.month)
print("YEAR : ",d.year)
```

OUTPUT

```
DAY :  10
MONTH :  1
YEAR :  2021
```

To print the current date and time, we will use the now() function as illustrated below.

```
import pandas as pd

print(pd.datetime.now())

OUTPUT

2021-10-04 07:40:23.443217
```

Pandas also allow users to convert integer or float epoch times. The default unit for these is nanoseconds (as Timestamps are stored in that way). However, we can also store epochs in another unit, which can be specified.

> **Programming Tip**
>
> The to_datetime() function can parse a wide variety of formats. Passing a single date to pd.to_datetime() yields a Timestamp; passing a series of dates by default yields a DatetimeIndex.

```
import pandas as pd

print( pd.Timestamp(443217404,unit='s'))

OUTPUT

1984-01-17 19:56:44
```

We can also convert multiple strings in a list into datetime format as shown below. Note that here NaT means Not a Time (which equivalent to NaN- Not a Number).

```
import pandas as pd

d= pd.to_datetime(['2021/11/23', '2021.01.31', None])

print(d)

OUTPUT

DatetimeIndex(['2021-11-23', '2021-01-31', 'NaT'], dtype='datetime64 [ns]',
freq=None)
```

5.15.1 Native Python dates and times: datetime and dateutil

Python's basic objects for working with dates and times are available in the datetime module. Along with this module, the dateutil module can be used to perform some more useful functionalities on dates and times. For example, look at the codes given below.

```
from datetime import datetime

print(datetime(year=2021, month=4, day=26))

OUTPUT

2021-04-26 00:00:00
```

Parsing dates from a variety of string formats using the dateutil module.

```
from dateutil import parser

date = parser.parse("26th of April, 2021")

print(date)

print(date.strftime('%A'))          # print the day of the week

OUTPUT

2021-04-26 00:00:00

Monday
```

5.15.2 NumPy's datetime64

The weaknesses of Python's datetime format motivated NumPy to have another time series data type, the datetime64 (as dtype), which encodes dates as 64-bit integers to store arrays of dates very compactly. The code given below illustrates how we can use the Numpy to represent dates and times using the datetime64 type. After creating the date, vectorized operations can be performed on it.

```
import numpy as np

date = np.array('2021-04-26', dtype=np.datetime64)

print(date)

arr = date + np.arange(12)

print(arr)

OUTPUT

2021-04-26

['2021-04-26' '2021-04-27' '2021-04-28' '2021-04-29' '2021-04-30'

 '2021-05-01' '2021-05-02' '2021-05-03' '2021-05-04' '2021-05-05'

 '2021-05-06' '2021-05-07']
```

Programming Tip

The time zone is automatically set to the local time on the computer executing the code

5.15.3 Indexing by time

Pandas time series objects can be used to *index data by timestamps*. For example, we can construct a series object that has time indexed data. The major advantage of doing this is that it allows users use special date-only indexing operations, such as passing a year to obtain a slice of all data from that year:

```
import numpy as np
import pandas as pd
dates = pd.DatetimeIndex(['2020-07-04', '2021-08-04',
                          '2020-09-04', '2021-10-04'])
sales = pd.Series([2000, 2500, 4000, 8000], index = dates)
print(sales)
# slicing data of a particular year
print(sales['2021'])
OUTPUT
2020-07-04    2000
2021-08-04    2500
2020-09-04    4000
2021-10-04    8000
dtype: int64
2021-08-04    2500
2021-10-04    8000
dtype: int64
```

Points to remember,

- For *time periods,* Pandas provides the period type to encode a fixed-frequency interval based on numpy.datetime64 having PeriodIndex as the associated index structure.
- For *time deltas* or *durations,* Pandas provides the Timedelta type, which is more efficient replacement for Python's native datetime.timedelta type, and is based on numpy.timedelta64 with TimedeltaIndex as the associated index structure. *Time deltas* or *durations* reference an exact length of time (e.g., a duration of 18.48 seconds).
- *Time intervals* and *periods* reference a length of time between a particular beginning and end point. Periods usually reference a special case of time intervals in which each interval is of uniform length and does not overlap. For example, 24-hour-long periods comprise of days.
- Any DatetimeIndex can be converted to a PeriodIndex with the to_period() function with the addition of a frequency code. For example, "D" to indicate daily frequency, "M" for monthly, and "Y" for yearly.

```
import numpy as np
import pandas as pd
dates = pd.DatetimeIndex(['2020-07-04', '2021-08-04',
                          '2020-09-04', '2021-10-04'])
print(dates.to_period('Y'))
```

```
OUTPUT

PeriodIndex(['2020', '2021', '2020', '2021'], dtype='period[A-DEC]',
freq='A-DEC')
```

A TimedeltaIndex is created when a date is subtracted from another as shown below.

```
import numpy as np

import pandas as pd

dates = pd.DatetimeIndex(['2020-07-04', '2021-08-04',

                          '2020-09-04', '2021-10-04'])

print(dates - dates[0])

OUTPUT

TimedeltaIndex(['0 days', '396 days', '62 days', '457 days'],
dtype='timedelta64[ns]', freq=None)
```

5.15.4 Regular sequences: pd.date_range()

To create a sequence of regular dates, Pandas has the pd.date_range() function for timestamps, pd.period_range() function for periods, and the pd.timedelta_range() for time deltas. These range() functions turn a startpoint, endpoint, and optional stepsize into a sequence. Similarly, pd.date_range() function accepts a start date, an end date, and an optional frequency code to create a regular sequence of dates. By default, the frequency is one day. However, in the date range function, we can also specify a start and number of periods instead of specifying the endpoint.

Also, we can change the frequency from daily to weekly, hourly, quarterly, yearly, etc.

```
import pandas as pd

d = pd.date_range('2021-08-01', '2021-08-10')

print(d)

# specifying periods instead of endpoint

d = pd.date_range('2021-08-11', periods=8)

print(d)

# specifying frequency as weekly

d = pd.date_range('2021-08-21', periods=8, freq = 'w')

print(d)

OUTPUT

DatetimeIndex(['2021-08-01', '2021-08-02', '2021-08-03', '2021-08-04',

               '2021-08-05', '2021-08-06', '2021-08-07', '2021-08-08',
```

```
           '2021-08-09', '2021-08-10'],
           dtype='datetime64[ns]', freq='D')
DatetimeIndex(['2021-08-31', '2021-09-01', '2021-09-02', '2021-09-03',
               '2021-09-04', '2021-09-05', '2021-09-06', '2021-09-07'],
              dtype='datetime64[ns]', freq='D')
DatetimeIndex(['2021-08-01', '2021-08-02', '2021-08-03', '2021-08-04',
               '2021-08-05', '2021-08-06', '2021-08-07', '2021-08-08',
               '2021-08-09', '2021-08-10'],
              dtype='datetime64[ns]', freq='D')
DatetimeIndex(['2021-08-11', '2021-08-12', '2021-08-13', '2021-08-14',
               '2021-08-15', '2021-08-16', '2021-08-17', '2021-08-18'],
              dtype='datetime64[ns]', freq='D')
DatetimeIndex(['2021-08-22', '2021-08-29', '2021-09-05', '2021-09-12',
               '2021-09-19', '2021-09-26', '2021-10-03', '2021-10-10'],
              dtype='datetime64[ns]', freq='W-SUN')
```

Table 1 gives some values for freq parameter.

Table 1: || Values for `'freq'` parameter in `pd.date_range()` function

Code	Description	Code	Description	Code	Description	Code	Description
D	Calendar day	B	Business day	W	Weekly	M	Month end
BM	Business Month	Q	Quarter End	QB	Business Quarter End	A	Year end
H	Hours	BH	Business Hours	T	Minutes	S	Seconds
L	Milli Seconds	U	Micro Seconds	N	Nano Seconds	MS	Month Start
QS	Quarter Start	YS	Year Start	BAS	Business Year Start	BMS	Business Month Start

Additionally, we can change the month used to mark any quarterly or annual code by adding a three-letter month code as a suffix:

Q-JAN, BQ-FEB, QS-MAR, BQS-APR, etc.
A-JAN, BA-FEB, AS-MAR, BAS-APR, etc.

Similarly, the weekly frequency can be modified by adding a three-letter weekday code by writing, W-MON, W-WED, W-FRI, etc. for example, to change business day to Monday, we can write the following line of code.

```
import pandas as pd
from pandas.tseries.offsets import BDay
d = pd.date_range('2021-05-09', periods=10, freq=BDay())
print(d)
```

```
OUTPUT
DatetimeIndex(['2021-05-10', '2021-05-11', '2021-05-12', '2021-05-13',
               '2021-05-14', '2021-05-17', '2021-05-18', '2021-05-19',
               '2021-05-20', '2021-05-21'],
               dtype='datetime64[ns]', freq='B')
```

Business Scenario: Retail Sales Data Analysis

Assume that you are a Data Analyst for a retail company that analyses sales data to improve decision-making. The company has a dataset containing sales transactions for the past year stored in a CSV File. The dataset contains information such as:

- Transaction ID
- Product ID
- Product Category
- Quantity Sold
- Price Per Unit
- Total Sales Value
- Date of Sale
- Region
- Customer Age Group

Now, analyze the sales data to provide actionable insights for improving revenue, customer targeting, and product inventory decisions.

1. To load the dataset, write
   import pandas as pd
   df = pd.read_csv("sales_data.csv")
   print(df.head())
2. Calculate the total sales revenue for each product category.
   Group the data by product category and sum the total sales value.
   category_sales = df.groupby('Product Category')['Total Sales Value'].sum()
   print(category_sales)
3. To find the average quantity sold per transaction for each region. For this, we can group the data by region and calculate the mean of the Quantity Sold column.
   average_quantity_region = df.groupby('Region')['Quantity Sold'].mean()
   print(average_quantity_region)
4. Identify the product with the highest total sales value. For this, group by Product ID and sum the Total Sales Value, then find the product with the maximum sales value.
   product_sales = df.groupby('Product ID')['Total Sales Value'].sum()
   top_product = product_sales.idxmax()
   print("Product with the highest total sales value: ",top_product)
5. Find the total sales revenue by age group. For this, group by Customer Age Group and sum the Total Sales Value to get the total sales by age group.

```
age_group_sales = df.groupby('Customer Age Group')['Total Sales Value'].sum()
print(age_group_sales)
```

6. Display transactions where the total sales value is greater than 500. For this, create boolean indexing to filter the rows based on the condition.

```
high_sales = df[df['Total Sales Value'] > 500]
print(high_sales)
```

7. Identify if there is any relation between Quantity Sold and Total Sales Value. To check this, use the .corr() method that returns the correlation between two columns.

```
correlation = df['Quantity Sold'].corr(df['Total Sales Value'])
print("Correlation between Quantity Sold and Total Sales Value: ", correlation)
```

8. Find the total sales revenue for the entire dataset.

```
total_sales = df['Total Sales Value'].sum()
print(f"Total Sales Revenue: ${total_sales}")
```

9. Find the average sales price per unit for each product

```
average_price_per_product = df.groupby('Product ID')['Price Per Unit'].mean()
print(average_price_per_product)
```

Business Scenario: Customer Segmentation and Sales Forecasting

Assume that you are a Data Analyst for a retail chain that operates in multiple regions and sells a variety of products. You have been assigned the task to optimize marketing efforts by targeting high-value customers and identifying trends in product sales. The dataset includes sales transactions over the past 18 months and is stored in a CSV file.

- Transaction ID
- Product ID
- Product Category
- Quantity Sold
- Price Per Unit
- Total Sales Value
- Date of Sale
- Region
- Customer ID
- Customer Age Group
- Customer Gender

For marketing efforts, you have to segment customers into High, Medium, and Low spenders based on their total purchase value.

You also have to forecast the total sales for the next 3 months based on historical sales data, using a simple time series method.

1. To segment customers into High, Medium, and Low spenders, calculate the total sales value per customer and then use a threshold to categorize them into different segments.

```
# Calculate total sales value per customer
customer_sales = df.groupby('Customer ID')['Total Sales Value'].sum()
# Define thresholds for segmentation
high_spender_threshold = customer_sales.quantile(0.75)
low_spender_threshold = customer_sales.quantile(0.25)
# Segment customers
def categorize_spender(value):
    if value >= high_spender_threshold:
        return 'High'
    elif value <= low_spender_threshold:
        return 'Low'
    else:
        return 'Medium'
customer_sales_segment = customer_sales.apply(categorize_spender)
print(customer_sales_segment)
```

2. To forecast total sales for the next 3 months using time series analysis, aggregate the sales by month and then apply a simple moving average method or an exponential smoothing technique to forecast future sales. To compute moving average, write,

```
import pandas as pd
import numpy as np
import matplotlib.pyplot as plt
# Convert 'Date of Sale' to datetime format
df['Date of Sale'] = pd.to_datetime(df['Date of Sale'])
# Aggregate total sales by month
monthly_sales = df.groupby(df['Date of Sale'].dt.to_period('M'))['Total Sales Value'].sum()
# Moving Average to forecast next 3 months
moving_avg = monthly_sales.rolling(window=3).mean()
# Display forecasted values for next 3 months
forecasted_sales = moving_avg[-1]  # Take the most recent moving average value
print("Forecasted sales for the next 3 months: ", forecasted_sales[-3:].values)
```

3. **Identify which product category has the highest sales growth over the last 6 months.**

```
last_6_months = pd.to_datetime('today') - pd.DateOffset(months=6)
df_recent = df[df['Date of Sale'] >= last_6_months]
# Aggregate total sales by product category in the last 6 months
recent_sales = df_recent.groupby('Product Category')['Total Sales Value'].sum()
# Compare with sales from 6 months ago (create a reference period for comparison)
six_months_ago = pd.to_datetime('today') - pd.DateOffset(months=12)
df_old = df[df['Date of Sale'] >= six_months_ago]
old_sales = df_old.groupby('Product Category')['Total Sales Value'].sum()
# Calculate sales growth percentage for each category
```

```
sales_growth = (recent_sales - old_sales) / old_sales * 100
# Identify the product category with the highest sales growth
highest_growth_category = sales_growth.idxmax()
print("Product category with the highest sales growth: ", highest_growth_category)
```

4. Calculate the average sales value per transaction for each region. This is done by grouping the data by region and calculating the average of the Total Sales Value for each region.

```
average_sales_region = df.groupby('Region')['Total Sales Value'].mean()
print(average_sales_region)
```

Key Terms

Aggregation: The process of turning the values of a dataset (or a subset of it) into one single value.
Data frame: A two-dimensional data structure in which data are organized in a tabular fashion using rows and columns.
Multi-index: The process of applying multiple aggregation functions to a single column.
Quartiles: Values that break up the dataset into quarters.
Sorting: Arranging data in a specific order. We can sort data either in the ascending (small to big) order or descending order (big to small).

Chapter Highlights

- The pivot() function is used to reshape a given Data Frame object organized by given index / column values.
- While combining two similar DataFrame objects where one object has missing values, the values are conditionally filled with like-labeled values from the other DataFrame.
- Python supports a large number of methods for computing descriptive statistics and other related operations on series and DataFrame objects. Aggregation functions like sum(), mean(), and quantile() produce a lower-dimensional result. However, other functions like cumsum() and cumprod() produce an object of the same size.
- Users can specify the axis by name or integer. The default value of axis is 0 indicating indexes or rows. If axis = 1, the descriptive function is applied on columns.
- Data Frame even NumPy methods like mean, std, and sum, will exclude NAs on Series input by default.
- The describe() function computes a variety of summary statistics on a Series or the columns of a DataFrame object.
- The idxmin() and idxmax() functions can be used with Series and DataFrame objects to compute the index labels with the minimum and maximum corresponding values.
- The apply() function can be used for row-wise or column-wise application of a function on a pandas object.
- In statistics, a histogram represents distribution of numerical data in bins. The count of each bin is represented in the histogram. It's not that only numerical data can be represented, we can even categorize categorical or date data in different bins.
- pth percentile means that p percent of observations below it, (100 – p)% above it. Percentiles help us in getting an idea on outliers.

- Quantile() function returns quantiles as Series or DataFrame. If q is an array, a DataFrame will be returned where the index is q. If q is a float, a Series will be returned where the values are the quantiles. **The return value will depend on the value of q.**
- To compute Mean, Min, and Max values by Group, first use the groupby function and then pass the aggregation functions to the grouped object as a dictionary within the agg function.
- We perform grouping to work with multiple columns by adding additional key:value pairs to the dictionary.
- The transform() function returns a self-produced data frame with transformed values after applying the function specified in its parameter. The resultant data frame has the same length as that of the original data frame passed to it.
- Re-indexing in Pandas is used to change the index of rows and columns of a data frame.

Review Questions

1. What is a data frame? How is it created?
2. Explain the use and syntax of pivot() function.
3. Define sorting. How can we sort a data frame in pandas?
4. How can we fill missing values in a data frame or series object? Write a code to demonstrate how missing values can be filled while subtracting two data frame objects.
5. What is a histogram? How does it represent values?
6. What do you understand by the term quartiles?
7. With the help of an example explain the use of pipe() function.
8. What is re-indexing? How is it done?
9. What are the two ways of altering column labels in Pandas?
10. Identify the functions to be used for:
    a. providing unique elements from a column by removing duplicates.
    b. `returning` the mean value of all the items in the column.
    c. Returning the first n rows.
    d. Returning last n rows.
    e. Sorting a data frame by its row index.
    f. Combining two data frames
    g. Computing a histogram of a 1D array of values.
    h. Getting the most frequently occurring value(s) of the values in a series or DataFrame.
11. Identify the attributes of the data frame object.
    a. Returns the transpose of a data frame by interchanging rows and columns.
    b. Returns the list of row axis labels and column axis labels.
    c. Returns the data type of each column.
    d. Returns a Boolean value stating whether the data frame object is empty or not.
    e. Returns the number of dimensions of the data frame object.
    f. Returns a tuple representing the dimensionality of the DataFrame.
    g. Returns the number of elements in the DataFrame.
    h. Returns the data values stored in the data frame object as an NDarray.

12. Find error in the code given below.

```
importing pandas as pd
import pandas as pd
  # creating a dataframe
df = pd.DataFrame({'A': ['John', 'John', 'Mina'],
     'B': ['Masters', 'Masters', 'Graduate'],
     'C': [27, 23, 21]})
df.pivot('A', 'B', 'C')
```

13. What do you mean when we say the highest income value is 400,000 but 95th percentile is 20,000 only?

Explain the Instructions

a.
```
df.sort_values(by=['Year','Brand'], inplace=True)
```

b.
```
data.groupby(['C'])['A'].transform('mean')
```

c.
```
import numpy as np
unsorted_df = pd.DataFrame(np.random.randn(10,2),index=[1,4,6,2,3,5,9,8,0,7],
columns = ['col2','col1'])
sorted_df=unsorted_df.sort_index()
print(sorted_df)
```

d.
```
import pandas as pd
import numpy as np
unsorted_df = pd.DataFrame(np.random.randn(10,2),index=[1,4,6,2,3,5,9,8,0,7],
columns = ['col2','col1'])
sorted_df = unsorted_df.sort_index(ascending=False)
print(sorted_df)
```

e.
```
import pandas as pd
import numpy as np
unsorted_df = pd.DataFrame(np.random.randn(10,2),index=[1,4,6,2,3,5,9,8,0,7],
columns = ['col2','col1'])
sorted_df=unsorted_df.sort_index(axis=1)
print(sorted_df)
```

f.
```
import pandas as pd
import numpy as np
unsorted_df = pd.DataFrame({'col1':[2,1,1,1],'col2':[1,3,2,4]})
sorted_df = unsorted_df.sort_values(by='col1')
print(sorted_df)
```

g.
```
import pandas as pd
import numpy as np
unsorted_df = pd.DataFrame({'col1':[2,1,1,1],'col2':[1,3,2,4]})
sorted_df = unsorted_df.sort_values(by='col1' ,kind='mergesort')
print(sorted_df)
```

h.
```
Income_Data['capital-gain'].quantile([0, 0.1, 0.2, 0.3, 0.4, 0.5, 0.6, 0.7,
0.8, 0.9, 1])
bank=pd.read_csv("datasets\\Bank Marketing\\bank_market.csv",encoding =
"ISO-8859-1")
bank.shape
summary_bala=bank["balance"].describe()
bank['balance'].quantile([0, 0.1, 0.2, 0.3, 0.4, 0.5, 0.6, 0.7, 0.8, 0.9, 1])
summary_age=bank['age'].describe()
print(summary_age)
bank['age'].quantile([0, 0.1, 0.2, 0.3, 0.4, 0.5, 0.6, 0.7, 0.8, 0.9, 1])
```

i.
```
import pandas as pds
# Read a JSON file
scoreFile = "./scores.json";
dataFrame = pds.read_json(scoreFile);
scores = dataFrame["Score"];
print("Scores as loaded into the pandas.Series instance:");
print(scores);
print("First Quartile:%.2f"%scores.quantile(.25));
print("Second Quartile:%.2f"%scores.quantile(.5));
print("Third Quartile:%.2f"%scores.quantile(.75));
print("100th Percentile:%.2f"%scores.quantile(1));
print("1st Percentile:%.2f"%scores.quantile(.1));
```

j.
```
import pandas as pd
import numpy as np
df = pd.DataFrame(np.random.randn (5,3),columns=['col1','col2','col3'])
df.apply(np.mean,axis=1)
print(df.apply(np.mean)
```

k.
```
df.rename({'$a':'a', '$b':'b', '$c':'c', '$d':'d', '$e':'e'},
axis='columns')
or
df.rename({'$a':'a', '$b':'b', '$c':'c', '$d':'d', '$e':'e'}, axis=1)
```

Programming Exercise

1. Create a data frame storing student's Roll number, Name, Total Marks and Class. Sort the data frame using Name and Marks.
2. Use pivot operation to reshape the above data frame using Class.
3. Write a program to count the number of null values in a series object.
4. Create a data frame with three columns-Name, Age and Rating
   a. Find the sum of columns
   b. Find average age and rating
   c. Find the standard deviation
   d. Describe the data frame

5. Create a data frame with three columns and 5 rows of random values. Find the row-wise sum using the apply() funtion.
6. Create a data frame recording marks in Physics and Chemistry class tests. Find out at what point or below 100%(1), 95%(.95), and 50%(.5) of the scores are lying.
7. Consider the following data frame and illustrate application aggregate functions both row-wise and column-wise.

```
   A    B    C
0  1.0  2    3.0
1  4.0  5    6.0
2  7.0  8    9.0
3  NaN  NaN  NaN
```

8. Download phon.csv from http://python-ds.com/download-aggregation-csv-data and write code to find:
   a. How many rows are there in the dataset?
   b. What was the longest phone call / data entry?
   c. How many seconds of phone calls are recorded in total?
   d. Number of nonnull unique network entries.
   e. How many entries are there for each month?
   f. Get the first entry for each month
   g. Get the sum of the durations per month
   h. Get the number of dates/entries in each month
   i. Sum of durations, for calls only, to each network
   j. How many calls, sms, and data entries are in each month?
   k. How many calls, texts, and data are sent per month, split by network type?
9. Consider the table that describes a dataset about a department store. Write the code to know what is the mean purchase amount of each user. The desired output should be

User_ID	Product_ID	Purchase
1001	P1	100
1001	P2	200
1001	P3	300
1001	P4	500
1002	P2	200
1003	P3	400
1004	P1	200
1004	P2	300
1004	P3	400
1004	P4	500
1005	P1	100
1005	P2	200
1005	P3	300
1005	P4	400
1005	P5	500

User_ID	Product_ID	Purchase	User_Mean
1001	P1	100	275
1001	P2	200	275
1001	P3	300	275
1001	P4	500	275
1002	P2	200	200
1003	P3	400	400
1004	P1	200	350
1004	P2	300	350
1004	P3	400	350
1004	P4	500	350
1005	P1	100	300
1005	P2	200	300
1005	P3	300	300
1005	P4	400	300
1005	P5	500	300

10. Create a data frame with any values of your choice. Reindex the data frame rows and fill the missing values with value 100. Reindex the data frame columns and fill the missing values with value 25.
11. Download the gapminder data. Print the names of the columns. Rename the column labels using both the ways.
12. Create a data frame with columns country, year and reports. Demonstrate changing the rows and columns.
13. Create a data frame with a column Gender having values "m" and "f" and a column Height. Find average height of both males and females.
14. Create a data frame with name, age and marks.
    a. Group the data by a column and return the mean age per group
    b. Capitalizes all the column headers
    c. Create a pipeline that applies the mean_age_by_group function and then applies the uppercase column name function
15. Create a data frame containing 10 rows and 4 columns of random values.
    a. Use date values in gaps of 10 to specify the index of the data frame.
    b. Apply sum on the data frame
    c. Find mean of first column
    d. Find minimum values of last two columns
16. Download user_device and user_usage from GitHub and demonstrate the merge() operation on it.
17. Write a program that concatenates two data frames storing information about students along column axis and a continuous index.
18. Write a program to concatenate three data frames and append two data frames.

Fill in the Blanks

1. ______ denotes the row labels.
2. To delete a column from the data frame, we can either use the _____ statement or using the _____ method.
3. To access a particular row from the data frame using label or column name, we can use the _____method.
4. ________ function sorts a data frame in Ascending or Descending order of passed Column.
5. _______ option in aggregation functions specify whether to exclude missing data or not.
6. The default value of axis is _____ indicating ________.
7. The ______ method applies function on Table.
8. ___________ is the process of turning the values of a dataset (or a subset of it) into one single value.
9. The process of applying multiple aggregation functions to a single column is known as _________.
10. ________ property of data frame helps to skip missing values.
11. NaN stands for ________.
12. ________ is used to change the index of rows and columns of a data frame.

State True or False

1. A data frame has columns of different data types.
2. The drop() method cannot be used to delete rows from a data frame.
3. We can sort only numerical data and not textual data in pandas.
4. The sort_values() function returns a sorted Data Frame with same dimensions as that of the original data frame.
5. We can sort a data frame by several columns together.
6. Aggregation functions like sum(), mean(), and quantile() produce a higher-dimensional result.
7. If axis = 1, the descriptive function is applied on indexes or rows.
8. Data Frame even NumPy methods like mean, std, and sum, will exclude NAs on Series input by default.
9. On a mixed-type DataFrame object, describe() will restrict the summary to include only numerical columns.
10. The applymap() method applies function of a row or column.
11. We can group data by a single column only.
12. The transform() function produces a data frame with same length as that of the original data frame passed to it.
13. Covariance is applied on series data only.

Give the Output

1. ```
   import pandas as pd
   import numpy as np
   client_dictionary = {'name': ['Michael', 'Ana', 'Sean'],
   'country': ['UK', 'UK', 'USA'],
   'age': [10, 51, 13],
   'latest date active': ['07-05-2019', '23-12-2019', '03-04-2016']}
   df = pd.DataFrame(client_dictionary)
   df.head()
   df.sort_values(by='name')
   df.sort_values(by='name', ascending=False)
   df.sort_values(by='age')
   df['latest date active'] = df['latest date active'].astype('datetime64[ns]')
   df.sort_values(by='latest date active')
   df.sort_values(by=['country','name'])
   df.sort_values(by=['country','name'], inplace=True)
   ```
2. ```
   import pandas as pd
   import numpy as np
   unsorted_df = pd.DataFrame(np.random.randn(10,2),index=[1,4,6,2,
   3,5,9,8,0,7],columns = ['col2','col1'])
   sorted_df=unsorted_df.sort_index()
   print(sorted_df)
   ```
3. ```
   import pandas as pd
   import numpy as np
   import math
   # user defined function
   def scale(num):
      return(num*10)
   df = pd.Series([1,2,3,4,5,6,7,8,9,10])
   df = df.pipe(scale)
   print(df)
   ```
4. ```
   import pandas as pd
   import numpy as np
   import math
   # user defined function
   def scale(num):
      return(num*10)
   df = pd.DataFrame(6*np.random.randn(6,3),columns=['A','B','C'])
   df = df.apply(scale,axis=1)
   print(df)
   ```

5.
```
import pandas as pd
import numpy as np
def adder(ele1,ele2):
   return ele1+ele2
df = pd.DataFrame(np.random.randn(5,3),columns=['col1','col2','col3'])
df.pipe(adder,2)
print(df.apply(np.mean))
```

6.
```
import pandas as pd
import numpy as np
df = pd.DataFrame(np.random.randn(5,
3),columns=['col1','col2','col3'])
df.apply(np.mean)
print df.apply(np.mean)
```

7.
```
data = {"Team": ["Red Sox", "Red Sox", "Red Sox", "Red Sox", "Red Sox", "Red
Sox", "Yankees", "Yankees", "Yankees", "Yankees", "Yankees", "Yankees"],
 "Pos": ["Pitcher", "Pitcher", "Pitcher", "Not Pitcher", "Not Pitcher", "Not
Pitcher", "Pitcher", "Pitcher", "Pitcher", "Not Pitcher", "Not Pitcher",
"Not Pitcher"],
 "Age": [24, 28, 40, 22, 29, 33, 31, 26, 21, 36, 25, 31]}
df = pd.DataFrame(data)
grouped_single = df.groupby('Team').agg({'Age': ['mean', 'min', 'max']})
print(grouped_single)
grouped_single.columns = ['age_mean', 'age_min', 'age_max']
grouped_single = grouped_single.reset_index()
print(grouped_single)
grouped_multiple = df.groupby(['Team', 'Pos']).agg({'Age': ['mean', 'min',
'max']})
grouped_multiple.columns = ['age_mean', 'age_min', 'age_max']
grouped_multiple = grouped_multiple.reset_index()
print(grouped_multiple)
```

8.
```
import pandas as pd
import numpy as np
df = pd.DataFrame([[1, 2, 3],
                   [4, 5, 6],
                   [7, 8, 9],
     [np.nan, np.nan, np.nan]],
      columns=['A', 'B', 'C'])
print(df)
print(df.agg(['sum', 'min']))
print(df.agg({'A' : ['sum', 'min'], 'B' : ['min', 'max']}))
print(df.agg("mean", axis="columns"))
print(df.agg("mean", axis="rows"))
```

9.
```
import pandas as pd
import numpy as np
  column=['a','b','c','d','e']
index=['A','B','C','D','E']
df1 = pd.DataFrame(np.random.rand(5,5),
          columns=column, index=index)
  colum=['e','a','b','c','d']
print(df1.reindex(colum, axis='columns'))
```

10.
```
import pandas as pd
import numpy as np
column =['a', 'b', 'c', 'd', 'e']
index =['A', 'B', 'C', 'D', 'E']
   df1 = pd.DataFrame(np.random.rand(5, 5),
         columns = column, index = index)
  colum =['a', 'b', 'c', 'g', 'h']
  print(df1.reindex(colum, axis = 'columns', fill_value = 1.5))
print(df1)
print(df1.reindex(colum, axis = 'columns', fill_value ='data missing'))
print(df1)
```

11.
```
Import pandas as pd
    info1 =pd.DataFrame
       ({«A»:[1, 5, 3, 4, 2],
         «B»:[3, 2, 4, 3, 4],
         «C»:[2, 2, 7, 3, 4],
         «D»:[4, 3, 6, 12, 7]})
info.reindex(columns =["A", "B", "D", "E"])
info.reindex(columns = ["A", "B", "D", "E"], fill_value = 37)
```

12.
```
import pandas as pd
df = pd.DataFrame([[1,2,3,4,5],
[6,7,8,9,10],[11,12,13,14,15]],
index=range(3), columns=list('abcde'))
print(df)
df2 = df.rename({'a': 'X', 'b': 'Y'}, axis=1)  # new method
df2 = df.rename({'a': 'X', 'b': 'Y'}, axis='columns')
df2 = df.rename(columns={'a': 'X', 'b': 'Y'})  # old method
print(df2)
df.rename({'a': 'X', 'b': 'Y'}, axis=1, inplace=True)
print(df)
```

13.
```
import pandas as pd
import numpy as np
N=20
df = pd.DataFrame({
    'A': pd.date_range(start='2016-01-01',periods=N,freq='D'),
    'x': np.linspace (0,stop=N-1,num=N),
    'y': np.random.rand(N),
    'C': np.random.choice(['Low',
```

```
'Medium','High'],N).tolist(),
     'D': np.random.normal(100, 10, size=(N)).tolist()
  })
  df_reindexed = df.reindex(index=[0,2,5], columns=['A', 'C', 'B'])
  print(df_reindexed)
```

14.
```
import pandas as pd
import numpy as np
df1 = pd.DataFrame(np.random.randn(6,3),columns=['col1','col2','col3'])
print(df1)
print ("After renaming the rows and columns:")
print df1.rename(columns={'col1' : 'c1', 'col2' : 'c2'},
index = {0 : 'apple', 1 : 'banana', 2 : 'durian'})
```

15.
```
import pandas as pd
A = pd.DataFrame({
        'RollNo':[1,2,3,4,5],
        'Name': ['Alex', 'Amy', 'Allen', 'Alice', 'Ayoung'],
        'Subject':['S1','S2','S4','S6','S5']})
B = pd.DataFrame(
        {'RollNo':[1,2,3,4,5],
        'Name': ['Billy', 'Brian', 'Bran', 'Bryce', 'Betty'],
        'Subject':['S2','S4','S3','S6','S1']})
print(A)
print(B)
```

16.
```
import pandas as pd
A = pd.DataFrame({
    'Name': ['Amit', 'Ana', 'Alis', 'Aman', 'Aadi'],
    'subject_id':['S1','S2','S4',
'S6','S5'],
    'Marks_scored':[98,90,87,69,78]},
    index=[1,2,3,4,5])
B = pd.DataFrame({
    'Name': ['Brit', 'Brey', 'Bel', 'Ben', 'Bali'],
    'subject_id':['S2','S4','S3',
'S6','S5'],
    'Marks_scored':[89,80,79,97,88]},
    index=[1,2,3,4,5])
print(pd.concat([A,B]))
```

17.
```
import pandas as pd
import datetime
d = pd.to_datetime('7/8/2022', dayfirst=True)
print(d)
print(pd.period_range('2022-03', periods=8, freq='M'))
print(pd.timedelta_range(0, periods=9, freq="2H30T"))
```

CHAPTER

6 Plotting Graphs*

We study statistics to collect and organize data. These data must be properly organized and presented in such a way that it is easily and clearly interpreted. For this reason, we can either organize data in the form of tables or present it pictorially using bar charts, histograms, frequency plots, scatter plots, box plots, etc. Visualizing data through charts help users to easily understand and interpret even complex and/or large amount of data in one glance.

6.1 Importance of data visualization

Data visualization helps us to see how the data look like and the kind of correlation that exists between the attributes of data. It also helps us to understand how the features correspond to the output. As shown in figure, data visualization plots are of two types—univariate and multivariate.

A univariate plot helps us to visualize a single-variable and understand each attribute of our dataset independently.

While histograms, density plots, and box plots are used for drawing univariate plots, correlation plots, on the other hand, are used for multivariate plot.

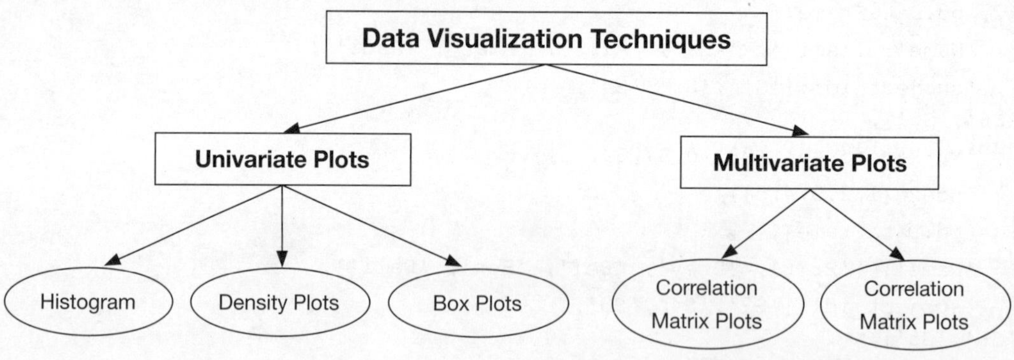

In this chapter, we will be using the pyplot module, which is in turn a sub-module of the matplotlib module. So before drawing charts, make sure you have installed the matplotlib module. Matplotlib is the most widely used scientific plotting library in Python. To install matplotlib, just use the pip command by writing pip install matplotlib.

*Note: The datasets and colored pictorial representation of graphs and charts from this chapter is available online. For more details, please refer to the back cover of the book.

The pyplot module provides an interface for graphing data. It contains over 100 functions and to use them you must import this module by writing, `import matplotlib.pyplot as plt` where, `plt` is the standard variable name used. This module allows users to,

- Create a plot
- Visualize data effectively
- Customizing plot with a focus on plot legends and text, titles, axes labels and plot layout.
- Save the plot for future use
- Show the plot
- Clear the plot area
- Close the plot

6.2 Bar chart

A bar chart or bar graph is a chart or graph that presents categorical data with rectangular bars. These bars can be drawn either vertically or horizontally. The height or length of the bars is proportional to the values they represent.

In a bar graph, while one axis of the chart shows the specific categories being compared, the other axis, on the other hand, represents a measured value. The main advantage of plotting a bar graph is that it depicts comparisons among discrete categories.

6.2.1 Drawing a bar graph in Python

The pyplot module in the Matplotlib provides the **bar()** function that can be used to plot a bar graph. The syntax of this function can be given as,

bar(x, height, width, bottom, align)

where,

x is a sequence of values representing the x coordinates of the bars.

height represents sequence of values representing the height(s) of the bars.

weight is an optional parameter that is either scalar or array-like. It represents the width(s) of the bars. By default, its value is 0.8.

bottom is an optional parameter that is either scalar or array-like. It denotes the Y coordinates of the bars. By default, it is none. It is used when plotting stacked bar graphs.

align can have values "center" or "edge." The default value is "center." "center" is used to center the base of the bar on the x positions. "edge" aligns the left edges of the bars with the x positions. To align the bars on the right edge, a negative width and align="edge" is used.

Other optional but useful parameters include.

color which is a scalar or array-like value indicating the colors of the bars.

edgecolor is a scalar or array-like value that specifies the colors of the edges of the bar.

linewidths is a scalar or array-like value denoting width of the bar edge(s). If its value is zero, then no edges will be drawn.

tick_label is a string or array-like value that specifies the labels of the ticks on the bars. By default, its value is none, and it uses default numeric labels.

The code given below plots a bar graph:

```
import numpy as np
import pandas as pd
from pandas import Series, DataFrame
import matplotlib.pyplot as plt
data = [27,45,36,18,72,81,108,19,9]
x = range(1,10)
plt.bar(x, data)
plt.show()
```

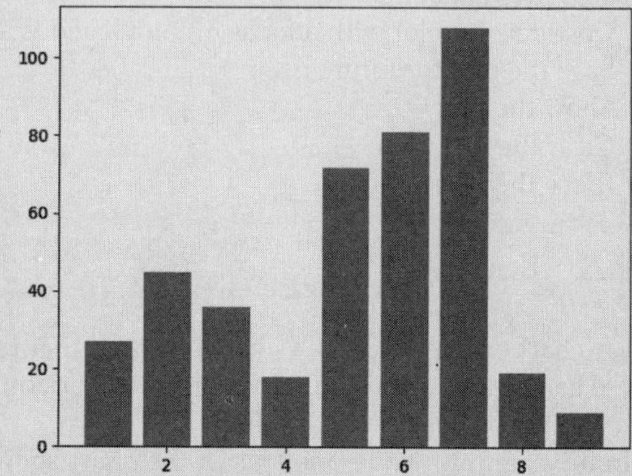

To draw a horizontal bar graph, the barh() function is used. The syntax of barh() function is

matplotlib.pyplot.barh(y, width, height=0.8, align="center")

The bars are positioned at y with the given alignment. Their dimensions are given by width and height.

Write a program that plots a bar graph depicting number of students who are interested in learning Mathematics, Computers, English, Accountancy and Economics.

```
import numpy as np
import pandas as pd
from pandas import Series, DataFrame
import matplotlib.pyplot as plt
fav_subjs = ['Mathematics',
'Computers', 'English',
'Accountancy', 'Economics']
counts = [10,40,35,29,20]
plt.bar(fav_subjs,counts)
plt.show()
```

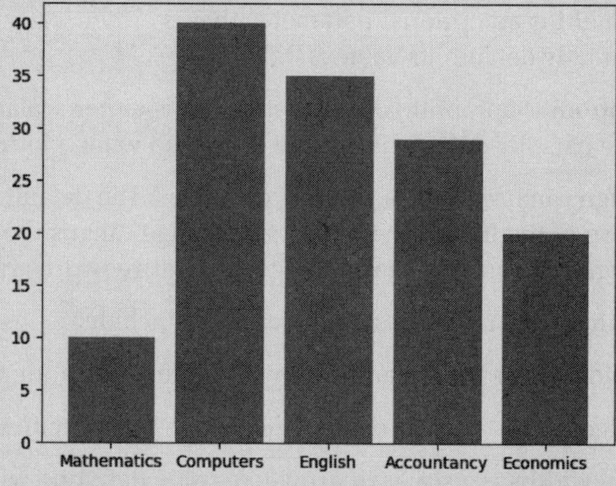

Write a program that draws horizontal bar graph depicting marks obtained by a student in different subjects.

The barh() function is used to plot a horizontal bar graph

```
import numpy as np

import matplotlib.pyplot as plt

subjects = ['Mathematics', 'Accounts', 'English', 'Computers', 'Economics']

y_pos = np.arange(len(subjects))

performance = [85,90,100,80,75]

plt.barh(y_pos, performance, align='center')

plt.yticks(y_pos, subjects)

# write some data on x-axis

plt.xlabel('Marks')

plt.title('Marks Obtained in Different Subjects')

plt.show()
```

> The xticks() function takes two parameters–index and lable. The function places the Labels on each tick that is generated due to index sequence.

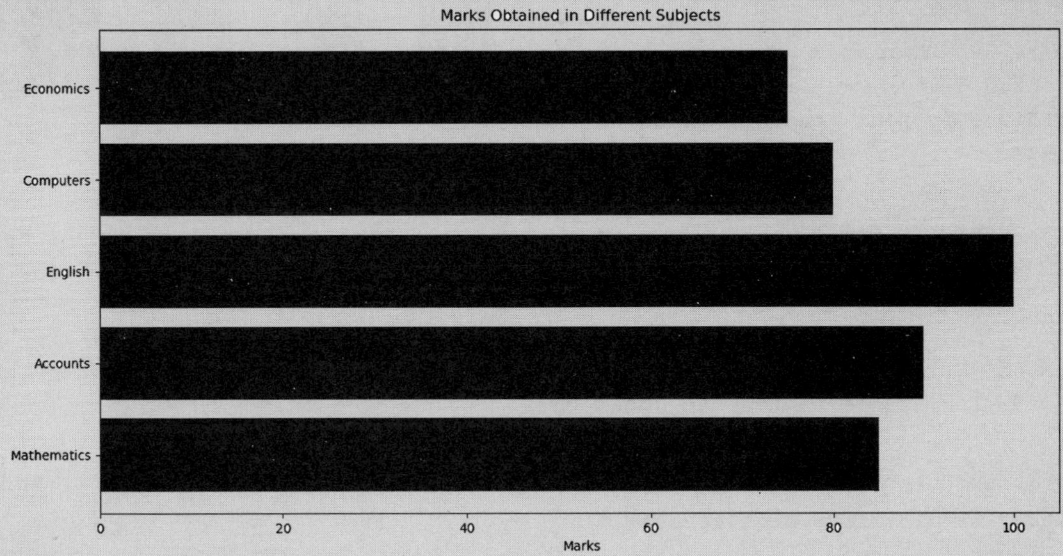

Write a program that plot marks obtained by two students in four subjects using bar graph.

Note that we can plot multiple bar charts by adjusting the thickness and the positions of the bars. In the code each bar has a thickness of 0.30 units. Each bar chart is shifted 0.30 units from the previous one.

```
import numpy as np
```

```
import matplotlib.pyplot as plt
marks_Jia = (83,79,80,83)
marks_Goransh = (95,84,89,99)

index = np.array([1,2,3,4])
width = 0.30
plt.bar(index, marks_Jia, width, label = 'Marks Obtained by Jia')
plt.bar(index + width, marks_Goransh, width, label = 'Marks Obtained by Goransh')
plt.ylabel('Marks')
plt.title('Comparing Marks of Jia and Goransh')

plt.xticks(index + width/2, ('Subject1','Subject2','Subject3', 'Subject4'))
plt.legend(loc='best')
plt.show()
```

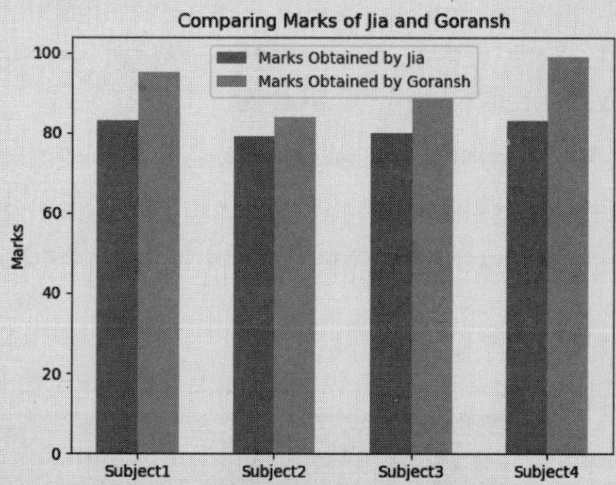

Write a program that creates a stacked bar graph depicting marks obtained by four students in three tests.

The stacked bar chart stacks bars that represent different groups on top of each other. The height of the resulting bar shows the combined result of the groups. The bar() function allow users to specify a starting value for a bar. Instead of running from zero to a value, it will go from the bottom to the value. In the code, the first call to pyplot.bar() plots the blue bars. The second call to pyplot.bar() plots the green bars, with the bottom of the blue bars being at the top of the green bars.

```
import numpy as np
import matplotlib.pyplot as plt
students = ['Reyansh', 'Tanvi', 'Parakh','Ziva']
Test1 = np.array([18,14,12,15])
Test2 = np.array([20,18,16,19])
Test3 = np.array([16,16,13,15])
index = students
plt.bar(index, Test1, width=0.5, label='Test1', color='red', bottom = Test2 + Test3)
```

```
plt.bar(index,  Test2,  width=0.5,
label='Test2', color='green', bot-
tom = Test3)

plt.bar(index,  Test3,  width=0.5,
label='Test3', color='blue')

plt.xticks(index, students)

plt.ylabel("Marks")

plt.xlabel("Students")

plt.legend(loc="upper right")

plt.title("Marks Obtained in Three
Tests")

plt.show()
```

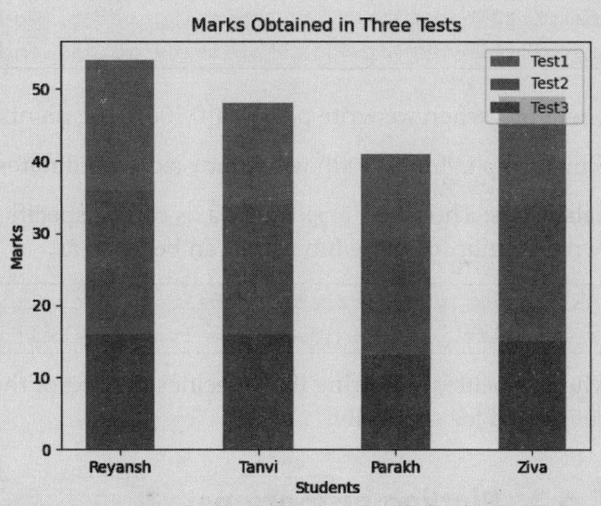

6.2.2 Some important miscellaneous functions

Saving Figure: After plotting the graph, the graph can be saved using the savefig() function of pyplot. The syntax of savefig() function is,

plt.savefig(fname, **kwargs),

where,

fname is name of the file. We can also specify the destination or path along with the name of the file.

The **kwargs** parameter is optional. It is used to change the orientation, format, facecolor, quality, dpi, etc.

Changing Font and Font Size: Font size of a plot can be changed with the help of rc() function. The rc() function is used to customize the rc settings. Syntax of this function can be given as,

matplotlib.pyplot.rc('fontname', **font)

or

matplotlib.pyplot.rc('font', size=sizeInt)

where font is a user-defined dictionary, that specifies the weight, font family, font size, etc. of the text.

Clear Plot: The clf() function of the pyplot clears the plot or the entire figure. Syntax of this function is,

matplotlib.pyplot.clf()

Note that the clf() function does not have any argument. Note that you can use plt.cla() to clear the axis and plt.close() to close a window that has popped up to show you your plot.

Axis Range: The range or limit of the x and y axis can be set by using the xlim() and ylim() functions of pyplot, respectively. The syntax for these functions can be given as,

```
matplotlib.pyplot.xlim([starting_point, ending_point])
matplotlib.pyplot.ylim([starting_point, ending_point])
```

Therefore, when we write plt.xlim([0,100]), the points in the x axis will start from 0 till 100.

Similarly, plt.ylim([0,100]) will limit y axis coordinates.

Label Axis: The labels for x and y axis can be specified using the xlabel() and ylabel() functions of pyplot. Syntax of these functions can be given as,

```
matplotlib.pyplot.xlabel(labeltext, labelfontdict, **kwargs)
matplotlib.pyplot.ylabel(labeltext, labelfontdict, **kwargs)
```

where, labeltext is a string that specifies the text of the label. Rest are optional parameters and can be ignored for simplicity.

6.3 Plotting histograms

Histogram is a graphical representation, which is quite similar to a bar graphs. Histogram is a great tool for assessing a probability distribution of a continuous variable that is easily understood by people looking at it.

Histogram plots the frequency distribution of numeric array by splitting it to small equal-sized bins. It is not only an excellent tool for visualizing and understanding the probabilistic distribution of numerical data bust also of image data.

To construct a histogram, we need to keep in mind three basic steps.

Step 1: Bin the range of values.

Step 2: Divide the entire range of values into a series of intervals.

Step 3: Count how many values fall into each interval.

Remember that the bins are usually specified as consecutive, nonoverlapping intervals of a variable.

To plot a histogram, the hist() function of matplotlib and pyplot module is used. The syntax of this function is,

plt.hist(data, bins = number of bins)

The function accepts the data and number of bins as arguments. Writing passing bins="auto" makes "ideal" number of bins width that generates the most faithful representation of data.

Besides these two parameters, few additional parameters can also be passed. These optional parameters are,

range which specifies the lower and upper range of the bins.

density is a Boolean value which if true, the first element of the return tuple will be the counts normalized to form a probability density

cumulative is a Boolean value. If true, a histogram is computed where each bin gives the counts in that bin plus all bins for smaller values.

histtype species the type of histogram to be drawn. Default value is "bar," which draws a traditional bar-type histogram. If multiple data are given, then the bars are arranged side by side. If histtype = "barstacked," a bar-type histogram where multiple data are stacked on top of each other is drawn.

However, if histtype = "step" an unfilled lineplot is drawn. histtype = "stepfilled" generates a lineplot that is by default filled.

The code given below draws a simple histogram of 100 random integer data values. A histogram uses its bin edges on the x-axis and the corresponding frequencies on the y-axis.

```
import numpy as np
import matplotlib.pyplot as plt
from random import seed
from random import randint
# seed random number generator
seed(1)
data = []
# generate some integers
for i in range(100):
   value = randint(0, 100)
      data.append(value)
print(data)
plt.hist(data, bins=25)
plt.show()
```

The seed() function of NumPy module is used to get the same set of random numbers each time the program is executed

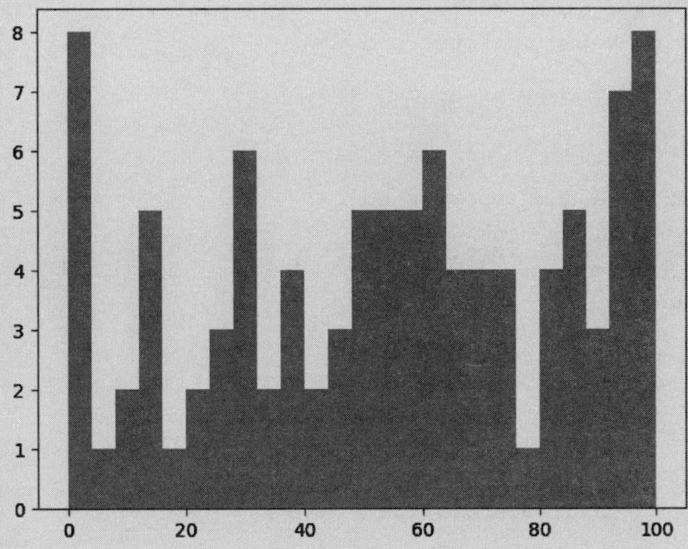

Additional way to determine the number of bins: In the above code, we have specified 25 bins. You can even choose any other number. However, we can also mathematically compute number of bins by using the following formula, **Range / (number of intervals)**

Where,

n = number of observations

Range = maximum value – minimum value

Number of intervals = $\sqrt{n}$

These formulas can then be used to create the frequency table followed by the histogram. For example, in the above code,

- n = number of observations = 100
- Range = maximum value – minimum value = 97 – 1 = 96

- Number of intervals = $\sqrt{n} = \sqrt{100} = 10$
- Number of bins = Range / (number of intervals) = 96/10 = 9.6 or 10

Now we can either specify bins = 10 or specify the bins. That is, either by writing,

plt.hist(data, bins=10) or

plt.hist(data, bins=[0,10,20,30,40,50,60,70,80,90,100])

Thus, we can now conclude the following characteristics of histograms:

- It provides us a count of the number of observations in each bin created for visualization.
- From the shape of the bin, we can find out the type of distribution (Gaussian, skewed, or exponential).
- Histograms help us to see possible outliers.

Draw a green-coloured histogram plotting 100 random integers with number of bins being optimum.

```
import numpy as np
import matplotlib.pyplot as plt
from random import seed
from random import randint
data = []
# generate some integers
for i in range(100):
    value = randint(0, 100)
    data.append(value)
print(data)
plt.hist(data, bins='auto',
color='green',alpha=0.7)
plt.xlabel('Value')
plt.ylabel('Frequency')
plt.title('Plotting Random
Integers')
plt.show()
```

bins='auto' chooses ideal number of bins

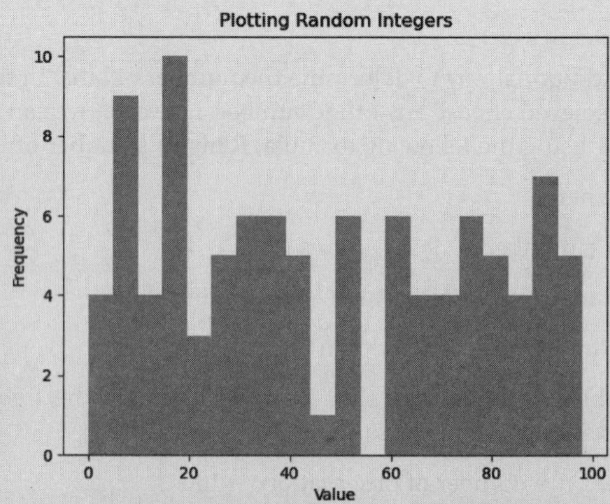

plot a yellow color histogram plotting number of times 1000 commute every year. Draw grid lines and place suitable labels.

```
import numpy as np
```

```
import matplotlib.pyplot as plt
from random import seed
from random import randint
import pandas as pd
# Generate data on commute times.
commutes = pd.Series(np.random.
rand(1000) * 100)
plt.hist(commutes, bins=20, rwidth=0.9,
color='yellow')
plt.title('Commute Times for 1,000
Commuters')
plt.xlabel('Counts')
plt.ylabel('Commute Time')
plt.grid(axis='y', alpha=0.75)
plt.show()
```

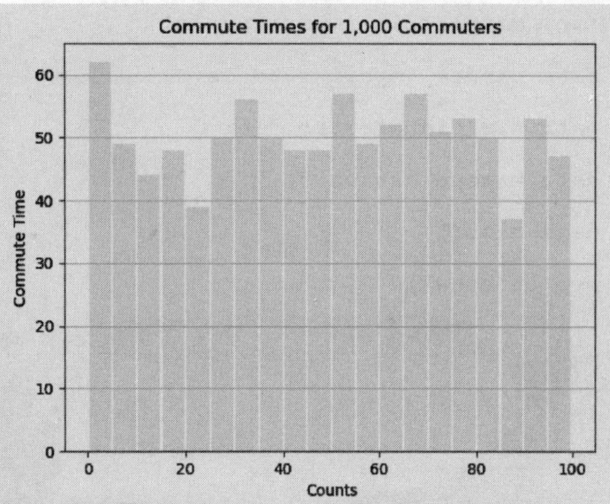

Write a program that plots a stacked histogram of five data sets.

```
import numpy as np
import matplotlib.pyplot as plt
from random import seed
from random import randint
import pandas as pd
x1 = np.random.normal(0, 10, 1000)
x2 = np.random.normal(4, 10, 1000)
x3 = np.random.normal(-2, 10, 1000)
x4 = np.random.normal(5, 10, 1000)
x5 = np.random.normal(-7, 10, 1000)
colors = ['red','green','blue','orange','olive']
plt.hist([x1,x2,x3,x4,x5],bins = 7, stacked=True, color = colors, alpha =
0.3)
plt.xlabel('Data Values')
plt.ylabel('Counts')
plt.show()
```

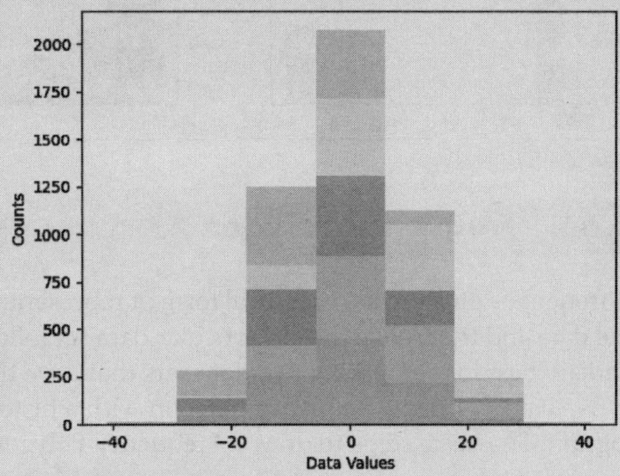

Download the diabetes dataset and draw a histogram to show relation between different variables.

```
from matplotlib import pyplot
from pandas import read_csv
path = r"diabetes.csv"
data = read_csv(path)
data.hist()
pyplot.show()
```

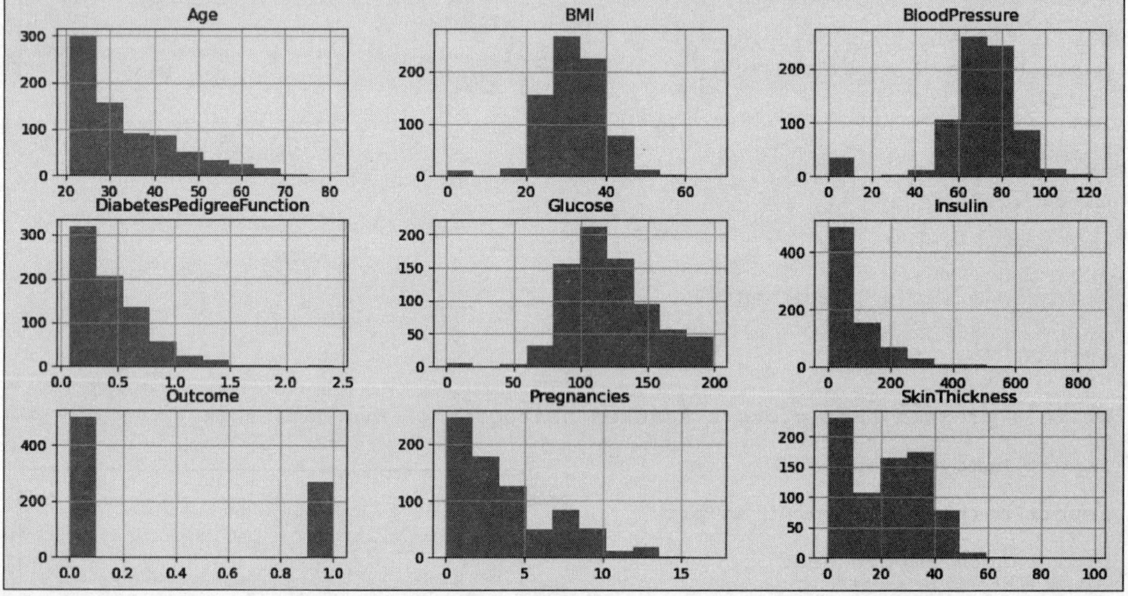

6.4 Frequency polygon

A frequency polygon is a graphical form of representation of data. It gives an idea about the shape of the data and the trends that a particular data set follows. It can be used to compare two sets of data and are best for comparing two data sets that have the same sample size.

We usually draw a frequency polygon with a histogram, but it can be drawn even without a histogram. The basic **steps to draw a Frequency Polygon include:**

Step 1: On the horizontal axis (X-axis), mark the class intervals. Frequency will be plotted on the vertical axis (Y-axis).

Step 2: Calculate the class_mark for each class interval by using the formula.

```
class_mark = (Upper limit + Lower limit)/2
```

Step 3: Mark all the class marks on the horizontal axis.

Step 4: Corresponding to each class mark, plot the frequency. The height always depicts the frequency. Note that the frequency is plotted against the class mark and not the upper or lower limit of any class.

Step 5: Join all the plotted points using a line segment. The curve obtained will be kinked. This resulting curve is called the frequency polygon.

The above steps are used to draw a frequency polygon without drawing a histogram. To draw a frequency polygon with a histogram, first draw rectangular bars against the given class intervals. Then, join the midpoints of the bars to obtain the frequency polygon.

Consider the data set and the corresponding frequency plot given below.

Test Scores	Frequency	Cumulative Frequency
49.5-59.5	5	5
59.5-69.5	10	15
69.5-79.5	30	45
79.5-89.5	40	85
89.5-99.5	15	100

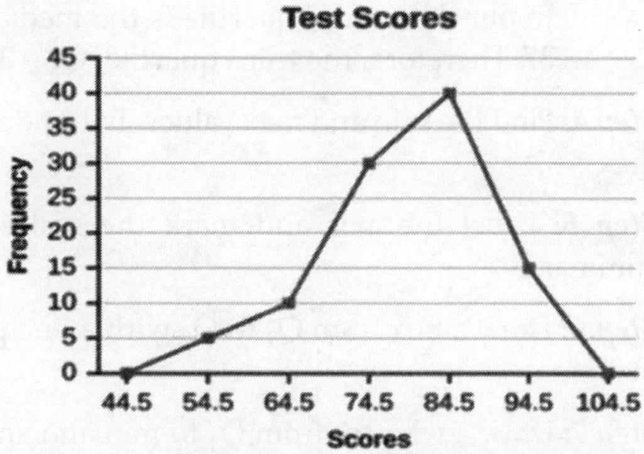

6.5 Box plot

A box plot or a whisker plot displays a summary of a set of data containing the minimum, first quartile, median, third quartile, and maximum. Recall that quartile is a measure of central tendency that divides a data set in to 4 parts.

In a box plot, we draw a box from the first quartile to the third quartile. A vertical line goes through the box at the median. The whiskers go from each quartile to the minimum or maximum.

The median (percentile 50%) is drawn with a red line. The box represents Q1 and Q3 (percentiles 25 and 75), and the whiskers give an idea of the range of the data. The position of the whiskers is set by default to 1.5 * IQR (IQR = Q3 - Q1) from the edges of the box. Outlier points are those past the end of the whiskers.

In a boxplot, the X-axis has the data for which the box plot has to be drawn, and the Y-axis denotes the frequency distribution.

6.5.1 Understanding a boxplot

A boxplot can be very useful when comparing the distribution of data across data sets. In such a case, different boxplots can be drawn for each data in the data set.

Example: Let's draw a boxplot of the following data which represent the ages of people working on a crucial project.

24, 27, 28, 28, 29, 33, 34, 34, 36, 37

Step 1: Sort the data. Our sample data is already sorted.

Step 2: Find the median. So, here median is (29 + 33) / 2 = 64 / 2 = 32.

Step 3: Find the quartiles.

The first quartile would be the median of the data points to the *left* of the median.

> Outlier values would be 1.5 times greater than the size of the spread of the middle data

In our data, first quartile is the median of 24, 27, 28, 28, 29. Therefore, the first quartile, Q_1 = 28.

The third quartile would be the median of the data points to the right of the median.

In our data, third quartile is the median of 33, 34, 34, 36, 37. Therefore, the third quartile, Q_3 = 34.

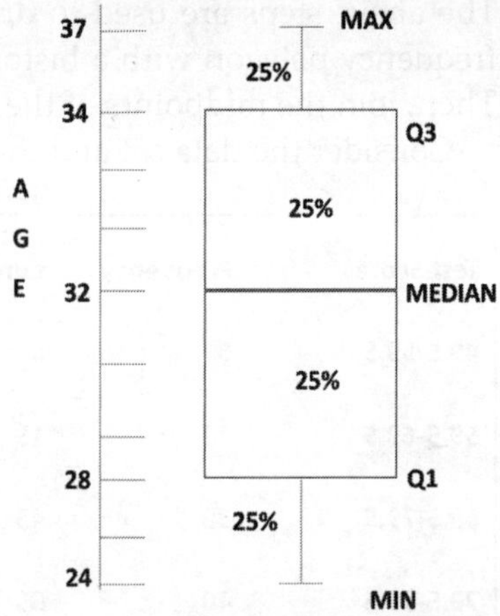

Step 4: Find the min and max values. In our data set, min = 24 and max = 37.

Step 5: Label the axis and mark the scales with five number summary.

Step 6: Draw a box from Q_1 to Q_3 with a line passing through the median.

Step 7: Draw a whisker from Q_1 to min and another whisker from Q_3 to the max.

Now, once our boxplot graph is ready, let's interpret the information presented by it. The boxplot says that 25% of the people working on the project are below the age of 25 and 75% are above the age of 28.

Correspondingly, 25% of the people are above the age of 34. Moreover, half of the people are below the age of 32.

> The span from first quartile to the third is called IQR (Inter Quartile Range)

6.5.2 Use of box plot graph

Box plots are very useful to identify the outliers. John Tukey has provided a precise definition for two types of outliers:

Outliers are either 3×*IQR* or more above the third quartile or 3×*IQR* or more below the first quartile.

Suspected outliers are slightly more central versions of outliers. They are either 1.5×*IQR* or more above the third quartile or 1.5×*IQR* or more below the first quartile.

If any outlier is present, then the inner fence on that side of the whisker is taken as 1.5×*IQR* from the quartile. All suspected outliers are displayed as unfilled circles and outliers are filled circles. From the figure, it is clear that the outer fence is 3×*IQR* from the quartile.

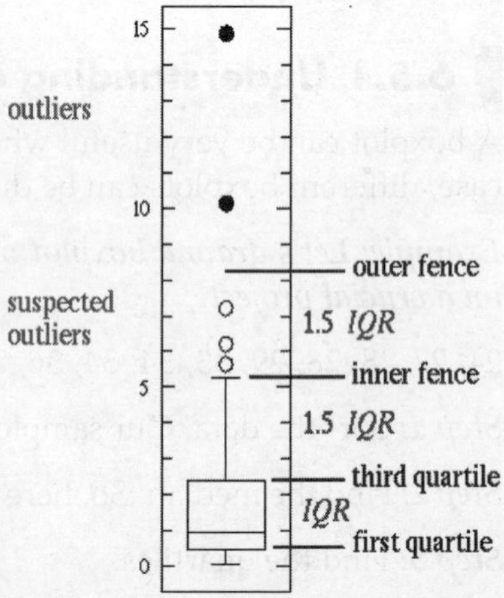

Usually, suspected outliers are not uncommon in large normally distributed datasets (for example, those having more than 100 data-points).. Outliers are expected in normally distributed datasets with more than about 10,000 data-points.

We should never treat the outliers as bad data points as many a times most useful information in the data set is depicted by them. They should never be discarded or removed from the dataset. Rather, they may deserve special consideration as they may be the key to the phenomenon under study or the result of human blunders.

All in all, a box plot can be used to make the following observations:

- Key values like the mean, median, minimum, maximum, 25th percentile etc.
- Outliers and suspected outliers if any.
- How tightly is the data grouped

6.5.3 Creating a Boxplot

The boxplot() function of the pyplot module is used to draw a boxplot. Syntax of this function can be given as,

boxplot(x, notch, vert, meanline, showmeans, showbox)

where,

x is the array or any other sequence of values. It forms the input data.

notch is a Boolean value. If notch = True, a notched boxplot will be drawn else a rectangular box plot is created.

vert is a Boolean value. its value is True by default. If False, a horizontal boxplot will be drawn.

meanline is a Boolean value. If both meanline and showmean are True then the mean will be rendered as line spanning full width of the box.

showbox is a Boolean value which displays the box on the boxplot. If False, the boxe will not be drawn.

showmeans shows the arithmetic means of the input data values.

To create a boxplot, we first need to generate some random data. In the code given below, we have used the numpy.random.normal() function that takes three arguments, mean, and standard deviation of the normal distribution, and the number of values to be generated.

```
import numpy as np
import matplotlib.pyplot as plt
from random import seed
from random import randint
import pandas as pd
x1 = np.random.normal(0, 10,
1000)
x2 = np.random.normal(4, 10,
1000)
x3 = np.random.normal(-2, 10,
1000)
x4 = np.random.normal(5, 10,
1000)
```

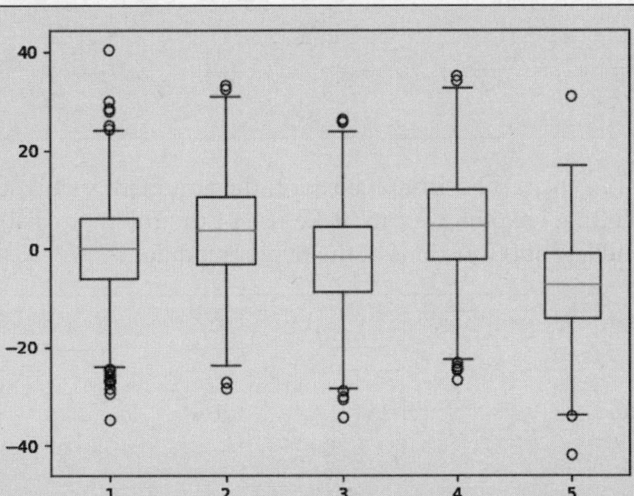

```
x5 = np.random.normal(-7, 10, 1000)
data=[x1,x2,x3,x4,x5]
plt.boxplot(data)
plt.show()
```

In the above code, we created five arrays to create a single data set data. Data are then used to plot the boxplots. To add labels to the boxplots, we can use the labels argument of the boxplot() function. We can even pass additional parameters in this function to color the boxplot. The argument **patch_artist=True** fills the boxplot with the default colour. To create notch of the boxplot, we set notch=**"True." The code given below uses all these parameters to draw the boxplot.**

```
import numpy as np
import matplotlib.pyplot as plt
from random import seed
from random import randint
import pandas as pd
x1 = np.random.normal(0, 10, 50)
x2 = np.random.normal(4, 10, 50)
x3 = np.random.normal(6, 10, 50)
x4 = np.random.normal(5, 10, 50)
x5 = np.random.normal(3, 10, 50)
data=[x1,x2,x3,x4,x5]
plt.boxplot(data,patch_artist=True, notch = True,
labels=['Group1','Group2','Group3','Group4','Group5'])
plt.show()
```

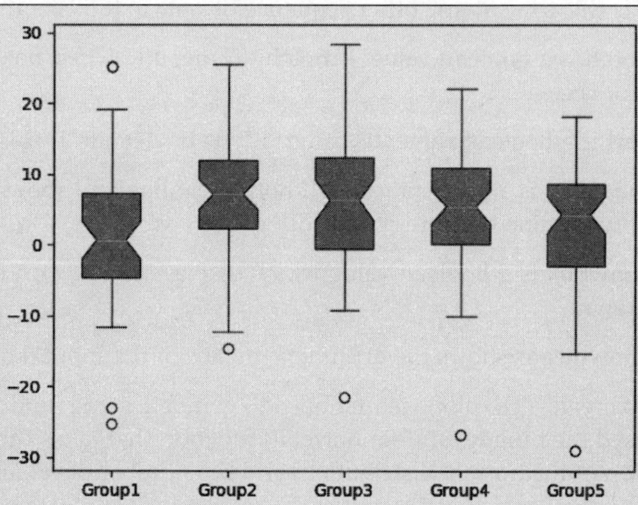

To create a horizontal boxplot, the argument vert is set to 0 by writing vert = 0. Note that while plotting boxplot, we can make use of the title(), xticks(), yticks(), xlabel(), ylabel(), xlim(), ylim(), and legend() functions of the pyplot module.

```
title() function adds title to the plot     legend() adds legend to the plot.
xticks() sets the xticks.                   yticks() sets the yticks.
xlim() sets x limit                         ylim() sets y limit
xlabel() sets x-axis label                  ylabel() sets y-axis label
```

Use diabetes dataset to draw box plot to depict relationship between different variables

```
from matplotlib import pyplot
```

```
from pandas import read_csv
path = r"diabetes.csv"
data = read_csv(path)
data.plot(kind='box', subplots=True, layout=(3,3), sharex=False)
pyplot.show()
```

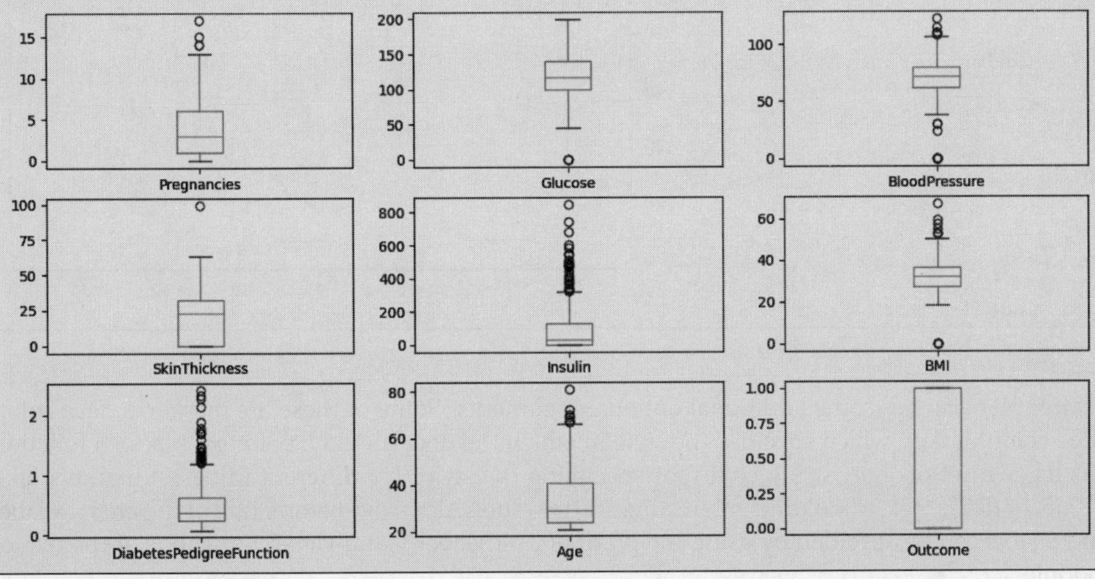

6.6 Scatter plot

A scatter plot is a chart that plots each value in the data set by a dot. A scatter plot is drawn using the scatter() function. This function has the capability to render a different size and/or color for each point.

Scatter plots show how much one variable is affected by another or the relationship between them with the help of dots in two dimensions. They are similar to line graphs as they use horizontal and vertical axes to plot data points.

Scatter plot is a type of plot that shows data as a collection of points. To draw a scatter plot, we need two arrays of the same length. The position of a point depends on its two-dimensional value, where each value is a position on either the X or Y axis. So, one of the arrays species values of the x-axis, and the other denotes the values of the y-axis.

Scatter plots are usually used to represent the correlation between two or more variables. It also helps us to identify outliers, if any. For example, the code given below draws a scatter plot to depict marks obtained by 15 students in a test.

```
import numpy as np
import matplotlib.pyplot as plt
from random import seed
from random import randint
```

```
# seed random number generator
seed(1)
x = []
y = []
# generate some integers
for i in range(20):
    value = randint(0, 100)
    x.append(value)
    value = randint(0, 100)
    y.append(value)
plt.scatter(x, y)
plt.show()
```

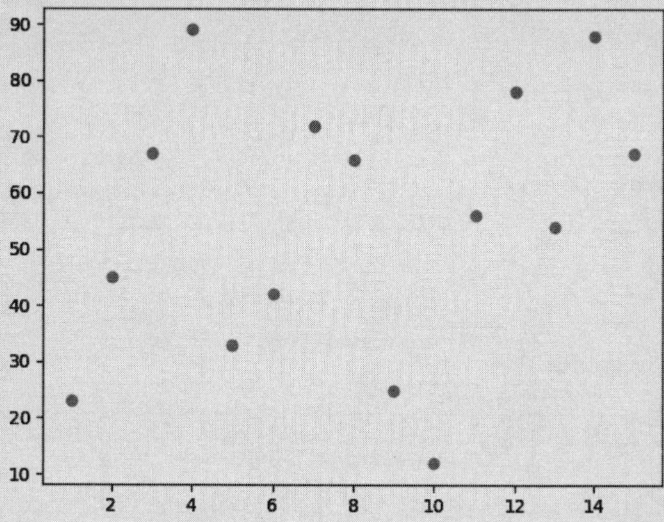

Scatter plot also has some additional optional arguments. Some of these are marker, s, face color, edge color Marker, which specifies the style in which the dots should be plotted. scatter() function has its own set of short string codes for specifying the style. Try different values of markets (like "^"; (5,1); (5,2); "+"; "o") to draw interesting scatter plots. As we did before, title of the chart, x label and y label can be specified by using the plt.title(), plt.xlabel(), and ylabel() methods of the pyplot module.

Scatter plots are used to plot data points on horizontal and vertical axis in the attempt to show how much one variable is affected by another. Each row in the data table is represented by a marker; the position depends on its values in the columns set on the X and Y axes. A third variable can be set to correspond to the color or size of the markers, thus adding yet another dimension to the plot.

Write a program that creates boxplots of class wise performance. Make use of additional optional parameters.

```
import numpy as np
import matplotlib.pyplot as plt
from random import seed
from random import randint
import pandas as pd
x1 = np.random.normal(3, 10, 50)
x2 = np.random.normal(4, 10, 50)
x3 = np.random.normal(6, 10, 50)
x4 = np.random.normal(5, 10, 50)
```

The alpha keyword is used to adjust the transparency level

```
x5 = np.random.normal(7, 10, 50)
data=[x1,x2,x3,x4,x5]
box = plt.boxplot(data,patch_
artist=True,notch = True, vert = True,
meanline=True,showbox = True,
showmeans=True, labels=['SecA','SecB',
'SecC','SecD','SecE'])
plt.title('CLASS PERFORMANCE')
plt.xlabel('CLASS XII')
plt.ylabel('MARKS')
```

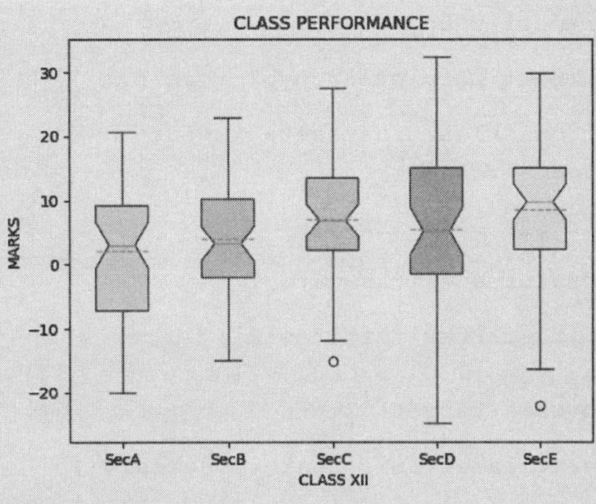


```
colors = ['cyan', 'lightblue', 'lightgreen', 'tan','yellow']
for patch, color in zip(box['boxes'], colors):
    patch.set_facecolor(color)
plt.show()
```

Write a program that draws a scatter plot to represent two data sets of 1000 values. The first array should the mean value 5.0 and standard deviation of 1.0. The second array should have mean 10.0 and a standard deviation of 2.0:

```
import numpy
import matplotlib.pyplot as plt
x = numpy.random.normal(5.0, 1.0, 1000)
y = numpy.random.normal(10.0, 2.0, 1000)
plt.scatter(x,y,color = 'red',edgecolor
= 'yellow',s=50, alpha = 0.7,marker =
'o')
plt.show()
```

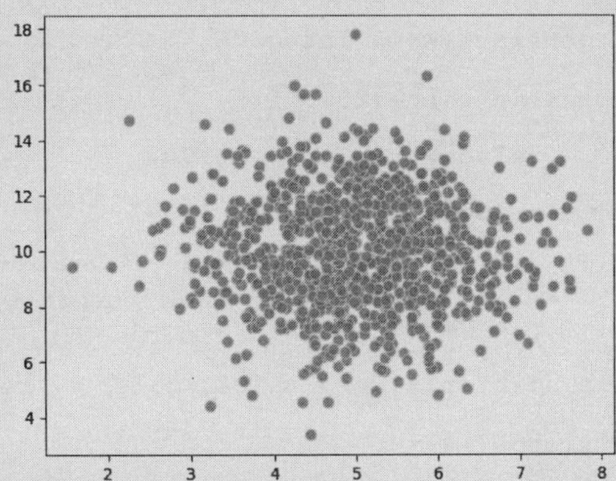

Read the iris dataset. Transpose the data and draw a scatter plot of first two columns. The (x, y) location of each point should correspond to the sepal length and width, relate the size of the point to the petal width, and the color to the particular species of flower.

For this, set the size of dots based on the third column and colour of the dots based on the column target.

```
import numpy
import matplotlib.pyplot as plt
from sklearn.datasets import
load_iris
iris = load_iris()
features = iris.data.T
plt.scatter(features[0], features[1],
alpha=0.2,s=100*features[3],
c=iris.target)
plt.xlabel(iris.feature_names[0])
plt.ylabel(iris.feature_names[1]);
plt.show()
```

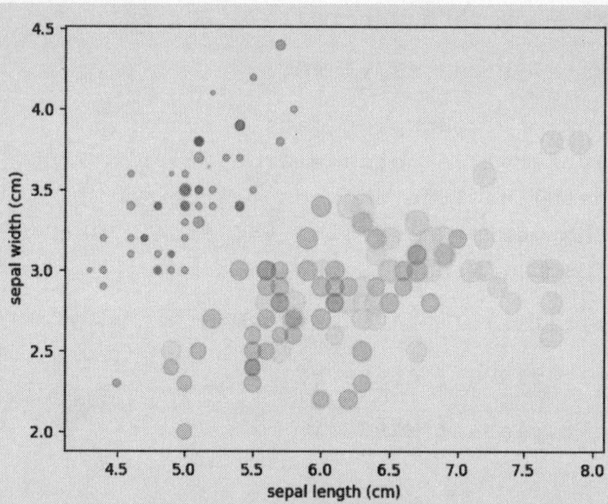

Write a program that plots a scatter plot using two data sets containing random integers.

```
import numpy as np
import matplotlib.pyplot as plt
from random import seed
from random import randint
# seed random number generator
seed(1)
x = []
y = []
# generate some integers
for i in range(20):
    value = randint(0, 100)
    x.append(value)
    value = randint(0, 100)
    y.append(value)
plt.scatter(x, y, s = 100, color = 'red', alpha = 0.2, marker = r'$\clubsuit$')
plt.show()
```

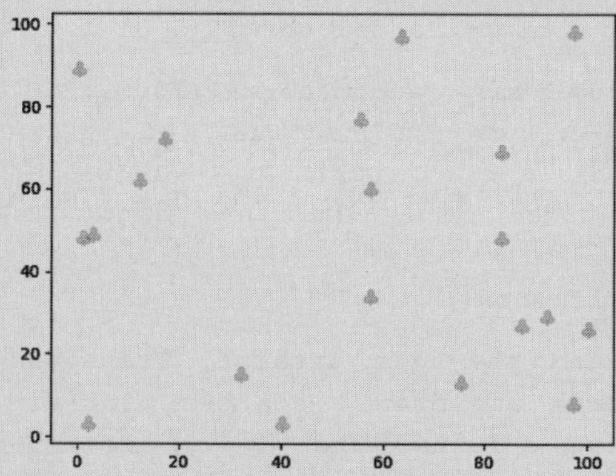

Write a Python program to draw a scatter plot comparing two subject marks of Mathematics and Science. Use marks of 10 students.

```
import matplotlib.pyplot as plt
import pandas as pd
math_marks = [88, 92, 80, 89, 100, 40, 60, 20, 80, 34]
science_marks = [95, 87, 75, 78, 98, 58, 72, 30, 70, 30]
marks_range = [10, 20, 30, 40, 50, 60, 70, 80, 90, 100]
plt.scatter(marks_range, math_marks, label='Marks in Maths', color='red',marker = (5,2))
plt.scatter(marks_range, science_marks, label='Marks in Science', color='olive', alpha = 0.2,marker = '^')
plt.title('Scatter Plot')
plt.xlabel('Marks Range')
plt.ylabel('Marks Scored')
plt.legend()
plt.show()
```

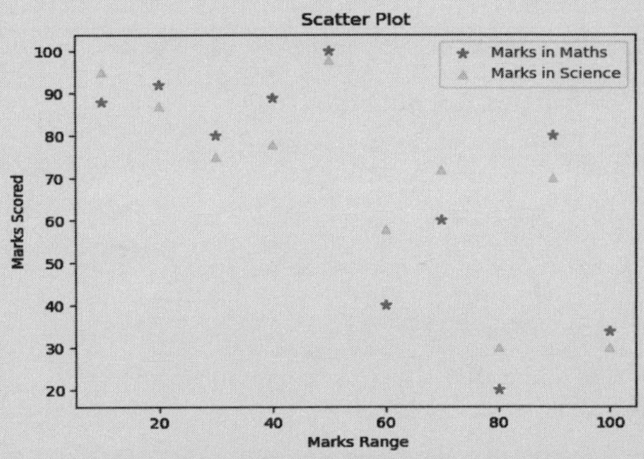

6.7 Correlation matrix plot

As stated in the beginning of the chapter, some data sets demand a thorough understanding of interaction between multiple attributes in the dataset through multivariate visualization. Also, in statistics, we have studied that correlation is used to find out relationship between two variables. Python allow users to go a step ahead and plot correlation matrix to represent, which variable is having a high or low correlation in respect to another variable.

A correlation coefficient is a number that indicates the strength of relationship between two variables. Although there are different types of correlation coefficients, the most commonly used is the Pearson's coefficient, which is denoted by the Greek letter ρ (rho). It is calculated by dividing the covariance between two variables by the product of the standard deviations of the two variables.

$$\rho(X,Y) = \frac{COV(X,Y)}{\sigma_X \sigma_Y}$$

Where, COV(X, Y) is the covariance between X and Y. Covariance is defined as the "expected value of the product of the deviations of X and Y from their respective means." That is,

$$COV(X, Y) = E[(X - \mu_X)(Y - \mu_Y)]$$

Therefore, Pearson's correlation can be given as,

$$\rho(X,Y) = \frac{E[(X - \mu_X)(Y - \mu_Y)]}{\sigma_X \sigma_Y}$$

The value of ρ varies from −1 to +1. If ρ = 1, then there is a strong positive relation between X and Y. Correspondingly, ρ = −1 indicates a strong negative relation between X and Y. A value equal to zero means no relationship between X and Y.

6.7.1 Calculating and plotting correlations

The corrcoef() function in the Numpy module returns a matrix of correlations of x with x, x with y, y with x and y with y.

```
from matplotlib import pyplot
from pandas import read_csv
import numpy as np
import matplotlib
import matplotlib.pyplot as plt
np.random.seed(1)
# 500 random integers between 0 and 100
x = np.random.randint(0, 100, 500)
# Positive Correlation with some noise
y = x + np.random.normal(0, 10, 500)
print(np.corrcoef(x, y))
plt.scatter(x, y)
plt.show()
```

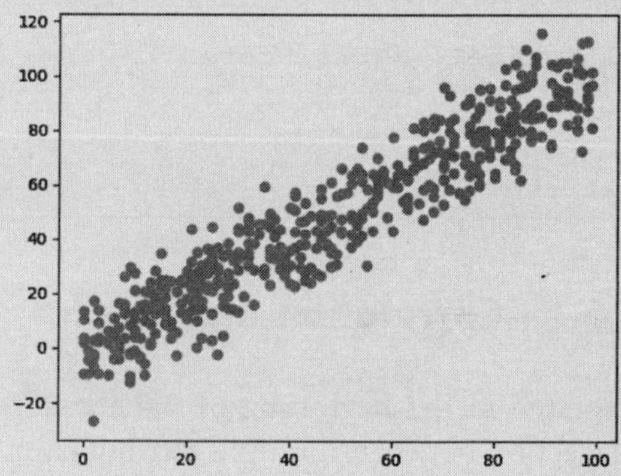

OUTPUT

```
[[1.         0.94463296]
 [0.94463296 1.        ]]
```

In the output, correlation 0.94463 indicates a strong positive correlation. This is also very clearly evident from the scatter plot. In the plot, y values increase with the increase in x values. So, a *large* value of one variable results in a *larger* value of the other variable and vice versa. Let us plot a scatter plot depicting a negative correlation and zero correlation.

Example: Graph showing a negative correlation between x and y values.

```
from matplotlib import pyplot
from pandas import read_csv
import numpy as np
import matplotlib
```

```
import matplotlib.pyplot as plt
np.random.seed(1)
# 500 random integers between 0
and 100
x = np.random.randint(0, 100, 500)
# Positive Correlation with some
noise
y = 100 - x + np.random.normal(0,
10, 500)
print(np.corrcoef(x, y))
plt.scatter(x, y)
plt.show()
OUTPUT
[[ 1.         -0.94246594]
 [-0.94246594  1.        ]]
```

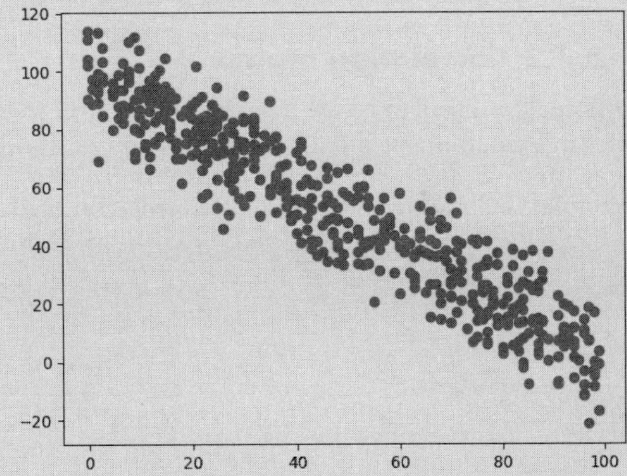

In the plot on the left, the y values tend to decrease as the x values increase. This shows strong negative correlation, which occurs when *large* values of a variable correspond to *small* values of the other and vice versa. Observe that the correlation coefficient between two variables is -0.9424.

Example: Graph showing no or weak correlation between two variables.

```
from matplotlib import pyplot
from pandas import read_csv
import numpy as np
import matplotlib
import matplotlib.pyplot as plt
np.random.seed(1)
# 500 random integers between 0 and 100
x = np.random.randint(0, 100, 500)
# Positive Correlation with some noise
y = np.random.normal(0, 10, 500)
print(np.corrcoef(x, y))
plt.scatter(x, y)
plt.show()
[[1.         0.02980859]
 [0.02980859  1.        ]]
```

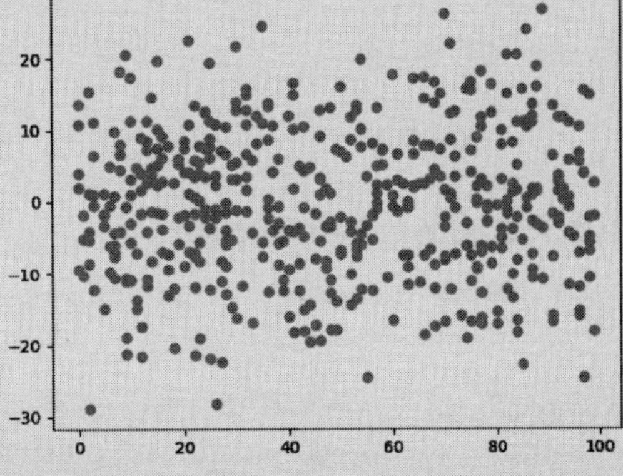

In the plot, there is absolutely not relation between the two variables. Even the correlation coefficient has a vale 0.029, which is a negligible amount.

6.7.2 Correlation matrix

Python allow users to create a correlation matrix to view the correlations between different variables in a dataframe using the corr() function as shown below.

Example: Generating and Plotting a Correlation Matrix

```
import pandas as pd
import numpy as np
from pandas.plotting import scatter_matrix
from matplotlib import pyplot as plt
df = pd.DataFrame({'Var_1': np.random.randint(0, 100, 500)})
df['Var_2'] = df['Var_1'] + np.random.normal(0, 20, 500) # positively
correlated with 'a'
df['Var_3'] = 100 - df['Var_1'] + np.random.
normal(0, 20, 500) # negatively correlated
with 'a'
df['Var_3'] = np.random.randint(0, 100,
500) # not correlated with 'a'
print(df.corr())
scatter_matrix(df, figsize=(6, 6))
plt.show()
```

OUTPUT

```
          Var_1      Var_2      Var_3
Var_1  1.000000   0.816443  -0.000331
Var_2  0.816443   1.000000  -0.004281
Var_3 -0.000331  -0.004281   1.000000
```

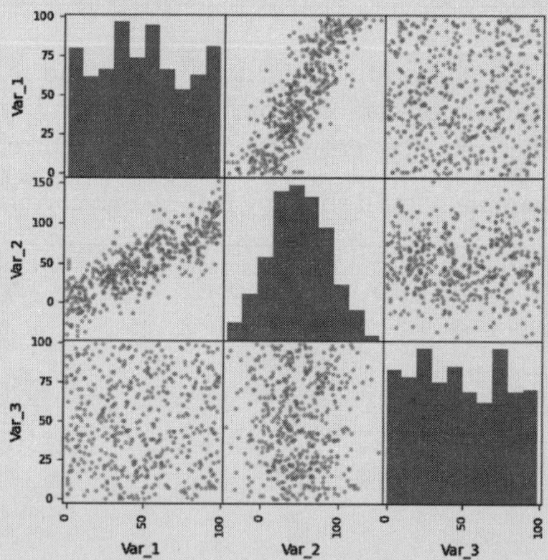

6.7.3 Correlation plot

Python also allow users to generate and plot correlation matrix for different variables in the data set. This can be done by using the corr() function on Pandas DataFrame and plotted with the help of pyplot.

Example: Plot the correlation matrix for the variables in diabetes.csv that can be downloaded from from https://www.kaggle.com/uciml/pima-indians-diabetes-database.

```
from matplotlib import pyplot
from pandas import read_csv
```

```
import numpy as np
path = r"diabetes.csv"
data = read_csv(path)
names = ['preg', 'plas', 'pres', 'skin', 'test', 'mass', 'pedi', 'age', 'class']
correlations = data.corr()
fig = pyplot.figure()
ax = fig.add_subplot(111)
cax = ax.matshow(correlations, vmin=
-1, vmax=1)
fig.colorbar(cax)
ticks = np.arange(0,9,1)
ax.set_xticks(ticks)
ax.set_yticks(ticks)
ax.set_xticklabels(names)
ax.set_yticklabels(names)
pyplot.show()
```

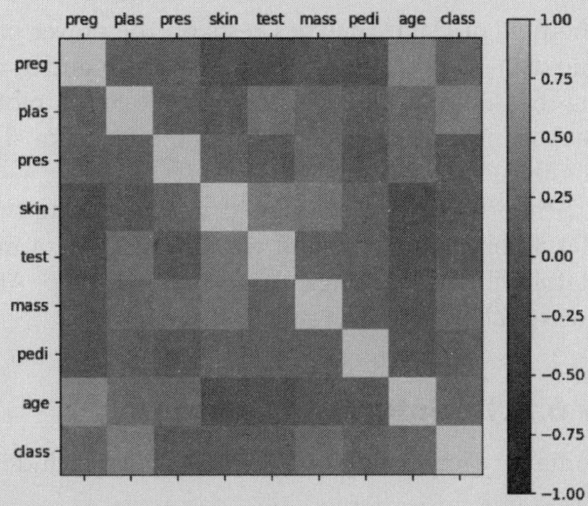

Plotting and styling a simple function

Let x be an array of numbers ranging from 1 to 10. Define y to be a function such that y = x2. Plot the points with a ">" mark and save it as a PDF file.

```
import numpy as np
import matplotlib.pyplot as plt
x = np.arange(0,10)
y = x ^ 2
#Labeling the Axes and Title
plt.title("Plotting x * x")
plt.xlabel("Time")
plt.ylabel("Distance")
# Formatting the line colors
plt.plot(x,y,'r')
# Formatting the line type
plt.plot(x,y,'>')
```

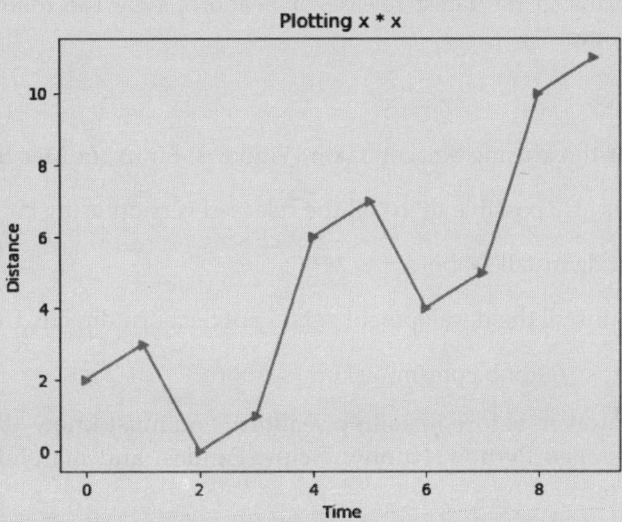

```
plt.show()
# save in pdf formats
plt.savefig('xsquare.pdf', format='pdf')
```

6.8 The Seaborn library

The field of Data Analytics rests on the power of visualizing results. The best way to get insights into data is to plot graphs that are easy to understand, explore, and grasp. Such data help in drawing the attention of key elements. While Matplotlib is a widely implemented 2D plotting library, Seaborn is built on top of Matplotlib to make simple things even more simpler and hard things possible.

Seaborn is mainly designed to resolve the two major problems faced by Matplotlib- default Matplotlib parameters and working with data frames. Since Seaborn compliments and extends Matplotlib, the learning curve is not that steep. Anyone who has worked with Matplotlib can easily learn Seaborn.

6.8.1 Features of Seaborn

Some very important features of Seaborn include:

- Built in themes for styling matplotlib graphics
- Visualize values of univariate and bivariate variables
- Visualize linear regression models
- Supports plotting of time series data
- Can work with NumPy and Pandas data structures

> Anaconda (from https://www.anaconda.com/ is a free Python distribution for SciPy stack. It is also available for Linux and Mac.

6.8.2 Installing Seaborn

To install the latest release of Seaborn, type the following command in Window's Command Prompt.

```
pip install seaborn
```

For those using Anaconda on Windows, Linux, or Mac using type,

It is also possible to install the released version using conda –

conda install seaborn

To install the development version of Seaborn directly from github, use the link given below.

https://github.com/mwaskom/seaborn"

However, before installing seaborn, you must know about some dependencies. You must have installed Python, NumPy, Scipy, Pandas, and matplotlib prior to using seaborn in its fullest extent.

It is interesting to know that Seaborn comes with a few important datasets in the library. When Seaborn is installed, these datasets also download automatically. Once these datasets are installed, they can be loaded by writing, load_dataset().

```
import pandas as pd
# Seaborn for plotting and styling
import seaborn as sb
df = sb.load_dataset('tips')
print(df.head(10))
OUTPUT
   total_bill   tip     sex smoker  day    time  size
0       16.99  1.01  Female     No  Sun  Dinner     2
1       10.34  1.66    Male     No  Sun  Dinner     3
2       21.01  3.50    Male     No  Sun  Dinner     3
3       23.68  3.31    Male     No  Sun  Dinner     2
4       24.59  3.61  Female     No  Sun  Dinner     4
5       25.29  4.71    Male     No  Sun  Dinner     4
6        8.77  2.00    Male     No  Sun  Dinner     2
7       26.88  3.12    Male     No  Sun  Dinner     4
8       15.04  1.96    Male     No  Sun  Dinner     2
9       14.78  3.23    Male     No  Sun  Dinner     2
```

To view all the available data sets in the Seaborn library, we can use the `get_dataset_names()` function as shown below.

```
import pandas as pd
# Seaborn for plotting and styling
import seaborn as sb
print(sb.get_dataset_names() )
OUTPUT
['anagrams', 'anscombe', 'attention', 'brain_networks', 'car_crashes', 'dia-
monds', 'dots', 'exercise', 'flights', 'fmri', 'gammas', 'geyser', 'iris',
'mpg', 'penguins', 'planets', 'tips', 'titanic']
```

Visualization is an art of representing data in effective and easiest possible way

6.8.3 Seaborn—figure aesthetic

To better visualize data, we can make the plots look attractive using by figure aesthetics. Aesthetics means a set of principles concerned with the nature and appreciation of beauty, especially in art.

Seaborn has a number of built-in themes and a high-level interface for customizing and controlling the look of Matplotlib figures.

Example: Plotting sine waves

```
import pandas as pd
# Seaborn for plotting and styling
import seaborn as sb
import seaborn as sb
import numpy as np
from matplotlib import pyplot as plt
def sinplot():
    x = np.linspace(0, 20, 50)
    for i in range(1, 5):
        plt.plot(x, np.sin(x + i * .5) * (7 - i))
sinplot()
plt.show()
```

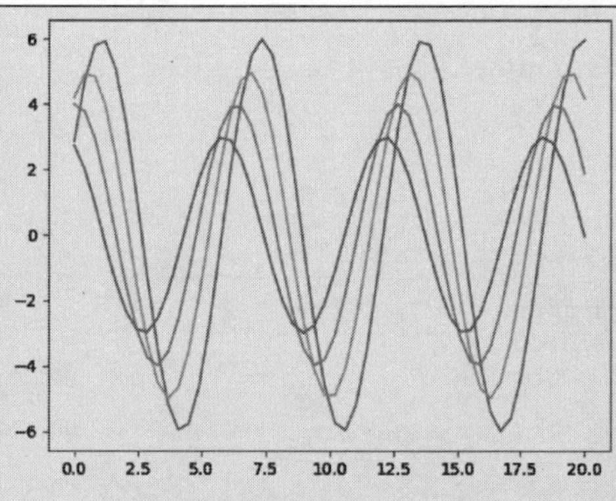

In the white and ticks themes, we can remove the top and right axis spines using the despine() function

To use the default Seaborn theme to plot the waves, use the function set() by writing sb.set() before calling the sinplot() function.

To set any other style, we can use the set_style() function. Five themes that are available with Seaborn are darkgrid, whitegrid, dark, white, and ticks. The default theme is white.

To scale the plot elements, we can use the set_context() function. Four preset templates for contexts, based on relative size are, paper, notebook, talk, and poster. The default context is notebook.

To customize the Seaborn styles, we can pass a dictionary of parameters to the set_style() function. Parameters available can be checked using axes_style() function by writing, print(sb.axes_style). Altering the values of any of the parameter(s) will change the plot style.

Parameters for set_style() viewed using axes_style()

```
'axes.axisbelow' : False   'axes.edgecolor' : 'white'   'axes.facecolor' : '#EAEAF2'
'axes.grid' : True        'axes.labelcolor' : '.15'    'axes.linewidth' : 0.0
'figure.facecolor' : 'white' ,'font.family' : [u'sans-serif'] 'grid.color' : 'white'
'grid.linestyle' : u'-'   'image.cmap' : u'Greys'      'legend.frameon' : False
'legend.numpoints' : 1    'legend.scatterpoints' : 1    lines.solid_capstyle' : u'round'
'text.color' : '.15'      'xtick.color' : '.15'         'xtick.direction' : u'out'
'xtick.major.size' : 0.0  'xtick.minor.size' : 0.0      'ytick.color' : '.15'
'ytick.direction' : u'out' 'ytick.major.size' : 0.0      'ytick.minor.size'  : 0.0
'font.sans-serif' : [u'Arial', u'Liberation Sans', u'Bitstream Vera Sans', u'sans-serif']
```

```
import pandas as pd
# Seaborn for plotting and styling
import seaborn as sb
import seaborn as sb
import numpy as np
from matplotlib import pyplot as plt
def sinplot():
   x = np.linspace(0, 20, 50)
   for i in range(1, 5):
      plt.plot(x, np.sin(x + i * .5) * (7 - i))
sb.set_style("darkgrid", {'text.color': '.25','axes.edgecolor':'green'})
sinplot()
sb.despine()
plt.show()
```

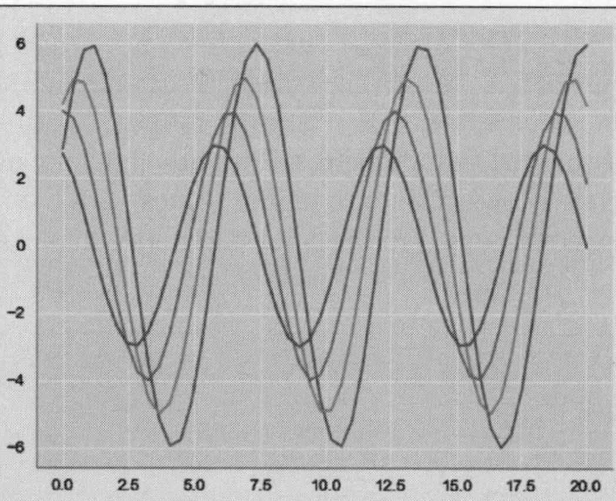

6.9 The color palette

While visualizing charts and graphics, colors always play a very crucial role. So, we must use good color scheme to make our plots eye catchy as well as easily understandable. The Seaborn library has a color pallete (a palette is a flat surface on which the user arranges and mixes paints).

To build a color palette, the color_palette() function is used. The function allows users to give colors to plots and add more aesthetic value to it. Syntax of this function can be given as,

seaborn.color_palette(palette = None, n_colors = None, desat = None)

where,

`n_colors` is the number of colors in the palette. By default the value of n_colors is 6 colors.

`desat` specifies the proportion to desaturate each color.

The `color_palette()` function returns a list of RGB tuples. Some readily available Seaborn palettes are deep, muted, bright, pastel, dark, and colorblind. Besides these options, users can themselves generate a new palette.

A color palette has different characteristics like qualitative, sequential, and diverging. Another function `seaborn.palplot()` plots the color palette as horizontal array.

Qualitative Color Palettes: These palettes are best suitable to plot the categorical data. The default color palette has 6 colors, but we can set the n_colors parameter to change this value. In the code given below, the `palplot()` is used to plot the array of colors horizontally.

```
from matplotlib import pyplot as plt
import seaborn as sb
current_palette = sb.color_palette()
```

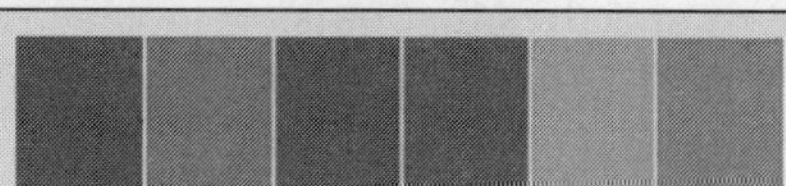

```
sb.palplot(current_palette)
plt.show()
```

Sequential Color Palettes: They are generally used to express the distribution of data ranging from relative lower values to higher values within a range. We can append an additional character 's' to the color passed to the color parameter to plot the Sequential plot.

```
from matplotlib import pyplot as plt
import seaborn as sb
current_palette = sb.color_palette()
sb.palplot(sb.color_palette("Reds"))
plt.show()
```

Diverging Color Palette: This palette has two different colors where each color represents variation in the value ranging from a common point in either direction. For example, when plotting the data ranging from -1 to 1, one color can take values from -1 to 0 and the other takes from 0 to +1.

```
from matplotlib import pyplot as plt
import seaborn as sb
current_palette = sb.color_palette()
sb.palplot(sb.color_palette("BrBG", 7))
plt.show()
```

6.9.1 Setting the default color palette

The function set_palette() is used to set the default color palette. We have read that there are 6 basic color palettes available to us. To set the color palette to pastel, we will write,

```
sb.set_palette("pastel")
```

6.10 Plotting univariate distribution

The distplot() function allows users to plot univariate distribution. The function can plot a histogram that fits the kernel density estimation of the data. Technically, the distplot() function is used to visualize the parametric distribution of a dataset. Its syntax can be given as,

```
seaborn.distplot()
```

where,

`data` is a Series, 1d array or a list object.

`bins` specifies hist bins.

`hist` is a Boolean value which can be either True or False.

`kde` is a Boolean value which can be either True or False.

6.10.1 Seaborn—Histogram and density plot

We have been drawing histograms from junior classes to represent the data distribution by forming bins along the range of the data. Bars are drawn to show the number of observations in each bin.

If kde is FALSE, then only the histogram is plotted

Along with the histogram, we can also plot kernel density estimation (kde) by setting its value to TRUE. KDE is used to estimate the probability density function of a continuous random variable for non-parametric analysis. A density plot is like a histogram but has a smooth curve drawn through the top of each bin. We can call such a histogram as an abstracted histogram.

Setting the hist parameter to False will plot only kernel density estimation curve.

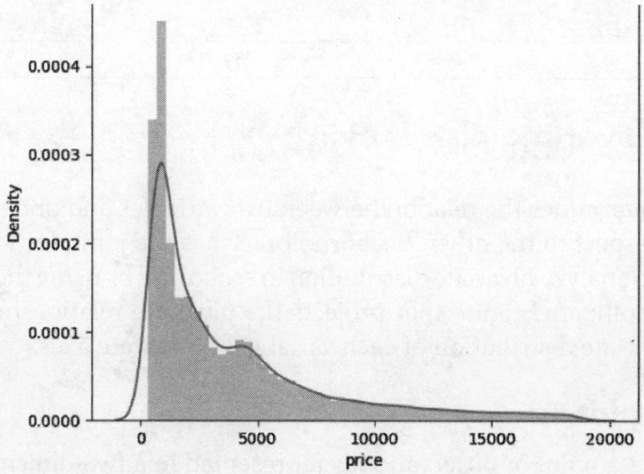


```
import pandas as pd
import seaborn as sb
from matplotlib import pyplot as plt
df = sb.load_dataset('diamonds')
sb.distplot(df['price'],kde = True)
plt.show()
```

Use the diabetes dataset to draw a density plot to depict the relation among variables.

```
from matplotlib import pyplot
from pandas import read_csv
path = r"diabetes.csv"
data = read_csv(path)
data.plot(kind='density', subplots=True, layout=(3,3), sharex=False)
pyplot.show()
```

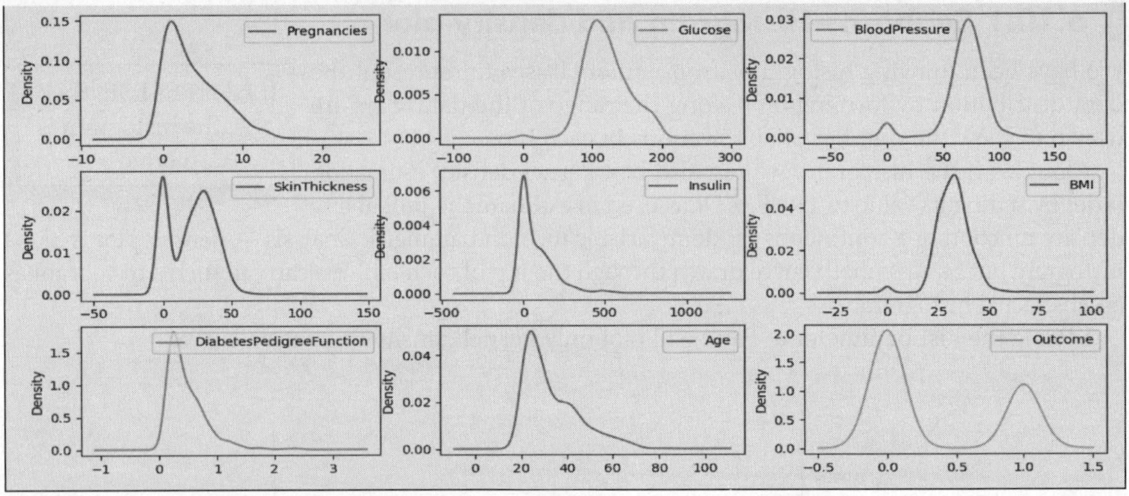

6.11 Plotting bivariate distribution

Bivariate distribution determines the relation between two variables and understand how one variable is behaving with respect to the other. Seaborn library has the jointplot() function, which provides the best features to analyze bivariate distribution in seaborn is by using the jointplot() function.

Jointplot creates a multipanel figure that projects the bivariate relationship between two variables and also the univariate distribution of each variable on separate axes.

6.11.1 Scatter plot

In a scatter plot, each data point or observation is represented in a two-dimensional plot along the x and y axis.

Example: Plotting with a scatter plot

```
import pandas as pd

import seaborn as sb

from matplotlib import pyplot as plt

df = sb.load_dataset('diamonds')

print(df.head())

sb.jointplot(x = 'carat',y = 'depth',data = df)

plt.show()
```

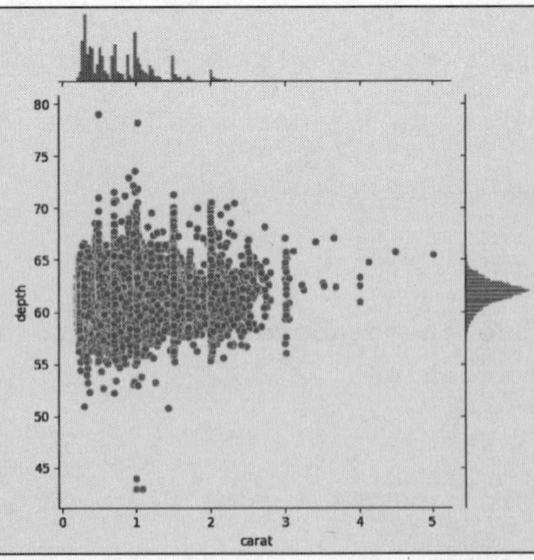

6.11.2 Hexbin plot

Hexagonal binning is used in bivariate data analysis when the data is sparse in density i.e., when the data is very scattered and difficult to analyze through scatterplots. We just need to pass an addition parameter called 'kind' and value 'hex' to plot the hexbin plot.

```
import pandas as pd

import seaborn as sb

from matplotlib import pyplot as plt

df = sb.load_dataset('iris')

sb.jointplot(x = 'petal_length',y = 'petal_
width',data = df,kind = 'hex')

plt.show()
```

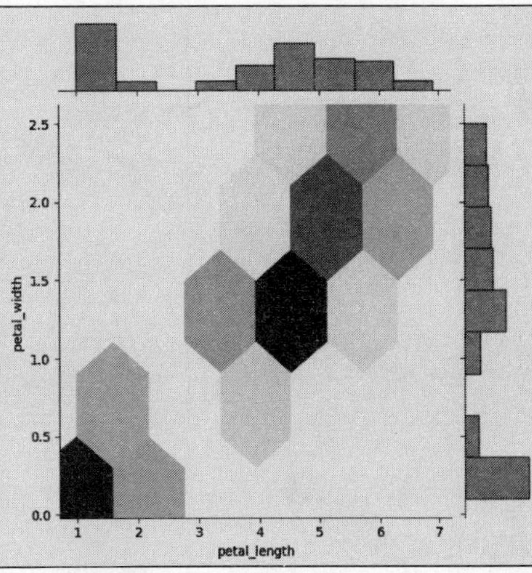

In Seaborn, users can plot a kde using jointplot(). For this, we just need to pass value 'kde' to the parameter 'kind' to plot kernel plot.

6.12 Visualizing pairwise relationship

In real-world data sets, there may be many variables. In such a scenario, the relation between each and every variable should be analyzed. But, plotting Bivariate Distribution for (n,2) combinations will be a very complex and time taking process. Therefore, seaborn offers the pairplot() function, which can be used to plot multiple pairwise bivariate distributions in a dataset.

The function depicts relationship for (n,2) combination of variable in a DataFrame as a matrix of plots and the diagonal plots are the univariate plots. Syntax of pairplot() function can be given as,

```
seaborn.pairplot(data, hue, palette, diag_kind)
```

where,

`data` is the data frame. It is the only mandatory parameter. Rest of the parameters are optional.

`hue` is used to plot data in the data frame to map to different colors

`palette` is a set of colors that will be used to map data

`diag_kind` specifies the kind of plot for the diagonal subplots. {'hist', 'kde'}

```
import pandas as pd

import seaborn as sb

from matplotlib import pyplot as plt

df = sb.load_dataset('iris')

sb.set_style("ticks")

sb.pairplot(df,hue = 'species',diag_kind = "kde",kind = "scatter",palette =
"husl")

plt.show()
```

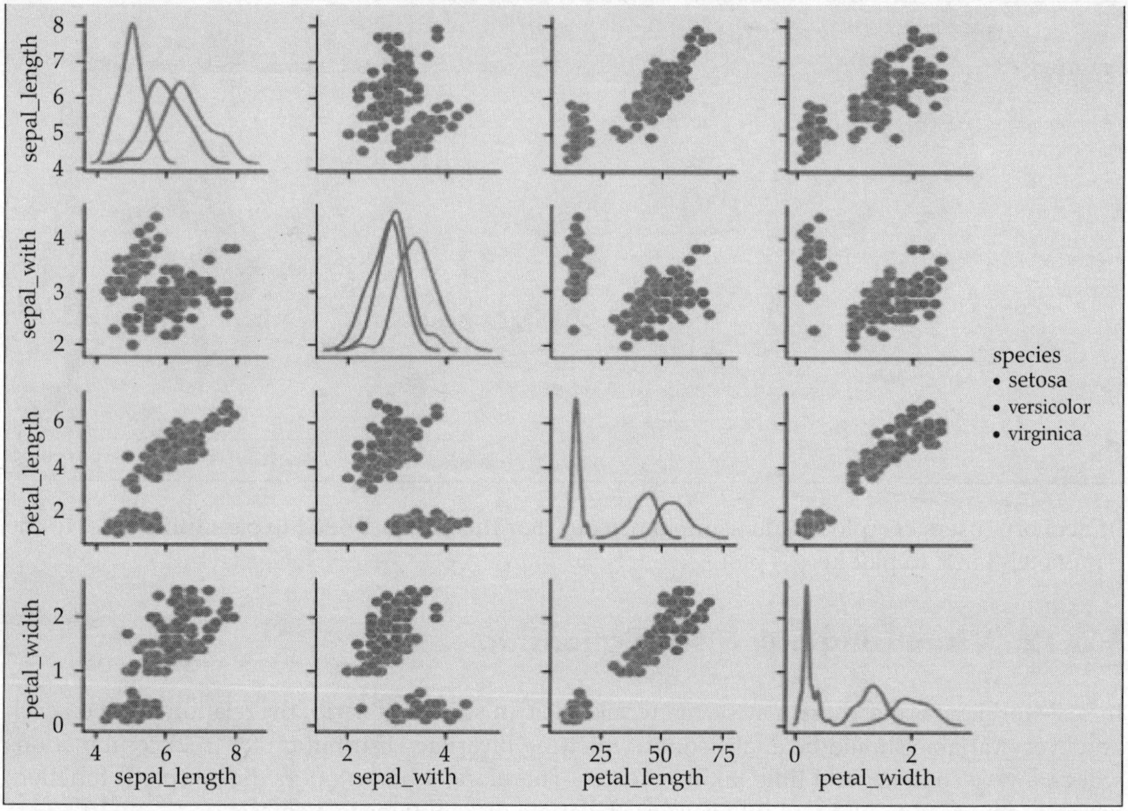

The above plot is generally used to study variation in data. The plots are displayed in a matrix format where the X axis has the row names and Y axis depicts the column names. The diagonal plots are kernel density plots, whereas other plots are scatter plots.

6.13 Box Plot in Seaborn

A box plot is the best tool to visualize distribution of data through their quartiles. These plots have whiskers, which are nothing but lines extending from the boxes to indicate variability outside the upper and lower quartiles. For this reason, box plots are also known as box-and-whisker plot. Any outliers in the data are plotted as individual points.

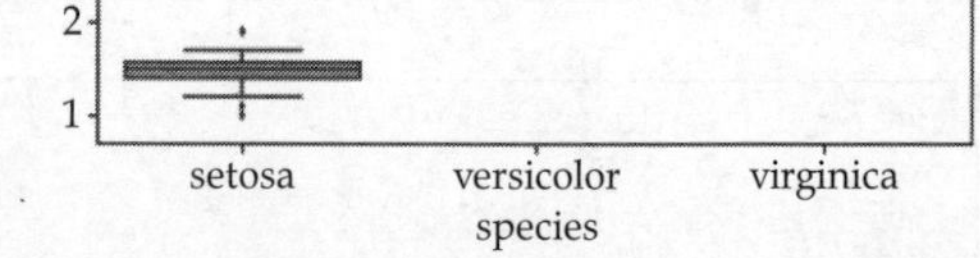


```
import pandas as pd
import seaborn as sb
from matplotlib import pyplot as plt
df = sb.load_dataset('iris')
sb.boxplot(x = "species", y = "petal_length", data = df)
plt.show()
```

Note that to draw a horizontal boxplot, we need to set orient parameter to "h."

Example: Draw a horizontal boxplot for gammas data set.

```
import pandas as pd

import seaborn as sb

from matplotlib import pyplot as plt

df = sb.load_dataset('gammas')

sb.boxplot(orient = 'h', data = df)

plt.show()
```

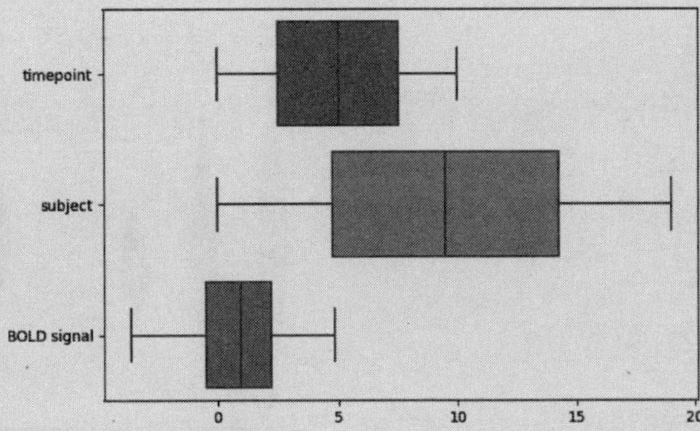

6.14 Violin plots

Violin Plots are a combination of the box plot with the kernel density estimates. They allow users to conveniently analyze and understand the distribution of the data.

```
import pandas as pd

import seaborn as sb

from matplotlib import pyplot as plt

df = sb.load_dataset('flights')

sb.violinplot(x = "year", y =
"passengers", data=df)

plt.show()
```

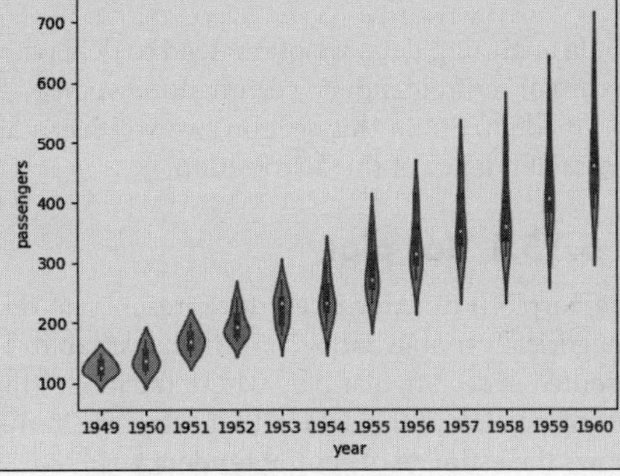

Note that in a violin plot, quartile and whisker values are shown inside violin (unlike the boxplot). from the box plot are shown inside the violin. As the violin plot uses KDE, the wider portion of violin indicates the higher density and narrow region represents relatively lower density.

Let us now add plot the violin plot with respect to three variables.

```
import pandas as pd

import seaborn as sb

from matplotlib import pyplot as plt

df = sb.load_dataset('attention')
```

```
sb.violinplot(x = "score", y = "subject",hue = 'attention', data = df)

plt.show()
```

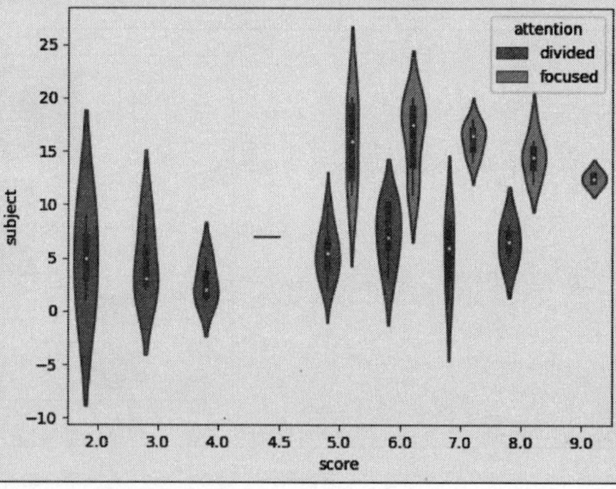

From the above plot, we can clearly make out that focused students score higher than divided students. If the hue variable has only two classes, then the plot can be beautified and made clearly readable by using violin plots.

6.15 Statistical estimation

While analyzing data, we often need to deal with estimations of the whole distribution of the data. In case of central tendency estimation, we need to summarize the distribution by calculating mean and median. So, in this section, we will learn about the plots that can help users to estimate the central tendency of the distribution.

6.15.1 Bar plot

The barplot() function used to represent the relation between a categorical variable and a continuous variable. The data are represented in rectangular bars where the length the bar represents the proportion of the data in that category. In this way, a bar plot shows the estimate of central tendency.

> The Inter-Quartile range in boxplot and higher density portion in kde fall in the same region of each category of violin plot

Example: Let us plot a bar graph to represent total_bill on Y axis, day on X axis and colored based on sex of the payer.

```
import pandas as pd

import seaborn as sb

from matplotlib import pyplot as plt

df = sb.load_dataset('tips')

sb.barplot(x = "day", y="total_bill",hue = 'sex', data = df)

plt.show()
```

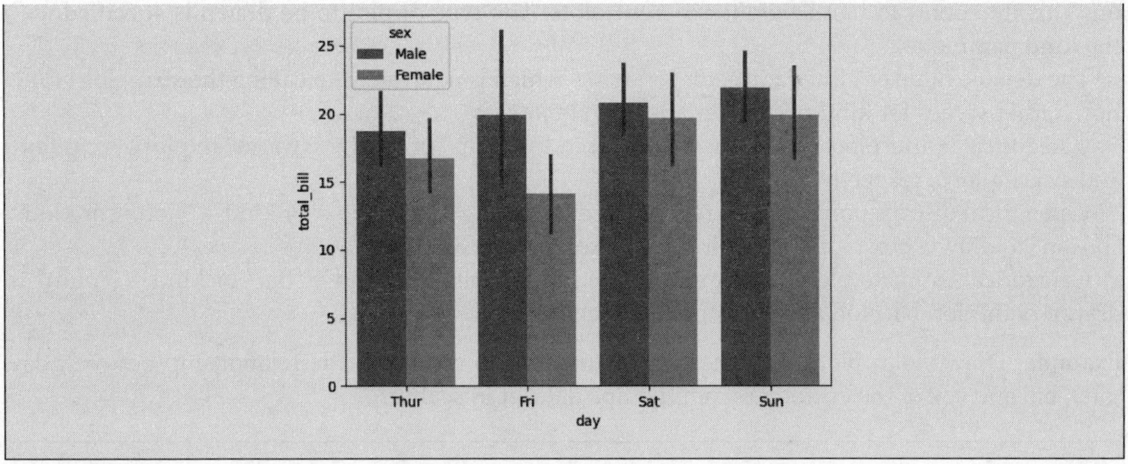

From the above graph, we can conclude that on an average, men pay more bill than women. Moreover, a higher amount is paid during weekends than on weekdays.

We can use the countplot() function, which is a special case in barplot, that shows the number of observations in each category rather than computing a statistic for a second variable.

6.15.2 Point plots

Point plots serve the same purpose that bar plots serve. But they are drawn in a different style. Rather than drawing a full bar, value of the estimate is represented by a point at a certain height on the other axis.

Example: Plotting a point plot to depict the relationship between sex and class of travel of the passengers who survived in the titanic.

```
import pandas as pd
import seaborn as sb
from matplotlib import pyplot as
plt
df = sb.load_dataset('titanic')
sb.pointplot(x = "sex", y =
"survived", hue = "class", data =
df)
plt.show()
```

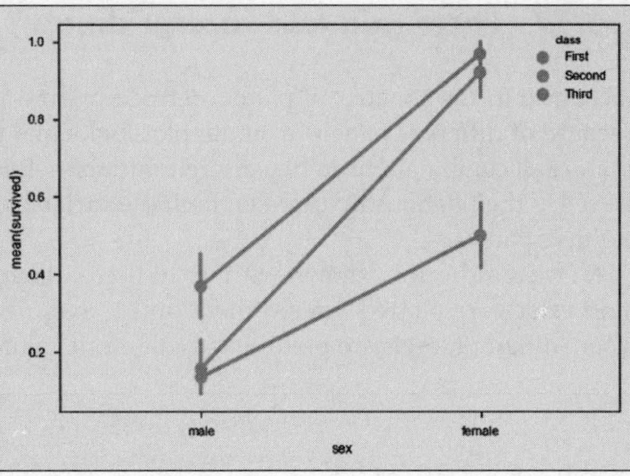

6.16 Plotting categorical data

The **catplot()** function provides a framework to plot several types of plots to represent relationship between numerical variable and one or more categorical variables, like boxplot, stripplot, and so on. This function can handle eight different plots. The type of plot to be drawn is specified with the **kind** parameter.

The default value of kind parameter is "strip," which is equivalent to calling the stripplot() function. Other values for kind parameter are given below.

Categorical scatterplots can be drawn with kind = "strip" or kind = "swarm" to plot a stripplot() and swarmplot(), respectively.

Categorical distribution plots are represented by setting kind = "box" or kind = "violin" or kind = "boxen" to draw a box plot, violin plot or a boxen plot, respectively.

Categorical estimate plots are plotted with kind = "point" or kind = "bar" or kind = "count" to draw a pointplot, barplot, and countplot, respectively.

Example: Draw violin plot using the catplot function to represent the relationship between day, total_bill and sex of the customer from the tips dataset in seaborn.

```
import pandas as pd

import seaborn as sb

from matplotlib import pyplot as plt

df = sb.load_dataset('tips')

sb.catplot(x = "day", y = "total_bill",
hue = "sex", kind = "violin", data = df);

plt.show()
```

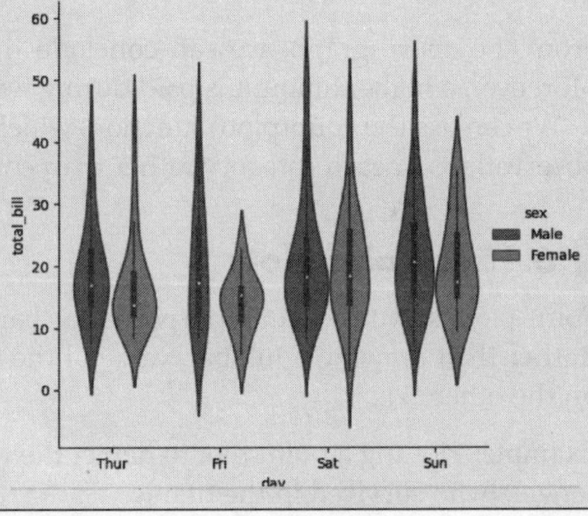

6.17 Facet grid and facetgridmap()

Facet grid forms a matrix of panels defined by row and column formed by dividing the variables. Because of different panels, a single plot looks like multiple plots. A facet grid is very helpful to analyze all combinations in two discrete variables. It is used to visualize distribution of one variable as well as the relationship between multiple variables separately within subsets of the dataset using multiple panels.

A FacetGrid can be drawn with up to three dimensions- row, col, and hue. While row and column values are plotted against the X and Y axes respectively. Hue is plotted along a depth axis, where different levels are plotted with different colors.

```
import pandas as pd

import seaborn as sb

from matplotlib import pyplot as plt

df = sb.load_dataset('attention')

sb.factorplot(x = "subject", y = "score", hue = "attention", kind = "strip",
col = "solutions", data = df)
```

```
plt.show()

print(df.head())
```

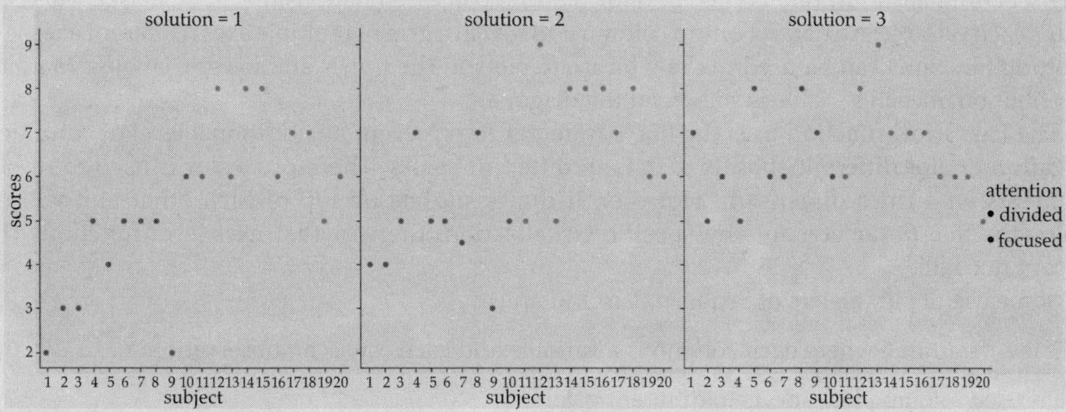

Note that the above plot is divided into three plots based on variable called "attention" using the "col" parameter. We can make many column facets and align them with the rows of the grid.

We can even use the FacetGrid map() method for visualizing data on the Facet Grid. Although the FacetGrid() object is a slightly more complex, yet it is more powerful and is built on the same idea.

We have seen that FacetGrid() function can map any plotting function onto each segment of our data. We can draw a histogram, scatter plot, or any other plot as specified in the kind parameter.

The FacetGrigmap() is used to map a dataset onto multiple axes arrayed in a grid of rows and columns that correspond to *levels* of variables in the dataset. The resultant plot is therefore called "lattice," "trellis," or "small-multiple" graphics.

The function represents levels of a third variable with the hue parameter, which plots different subsets of data in different colors. Although, the color resolve elements on a third dimension, it only draws subsets on top of each other and will not tailor the hue parameter for the specific visualization. The basic workflow of the FacetGridmap() is to initialize the **FacetGrid** object with the dataset and the variables that are used to structure the grid.

```
import pandas as pd

import seaborn as sb

from matplotlib import
pyplot as plt

df = sb.load_dataset('tips')

g = sb.FacetGrid(df, col =
"smoker", hue = "sex")

g.map(plt.hist,
"total_bill")

plt.show()
```

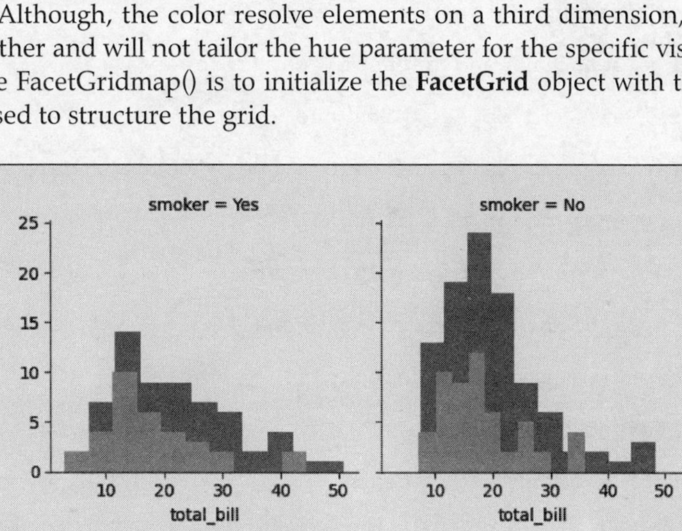

The number of plots is more than one because of the parameter col.

6.18 Pair grid

The seaborn.PairGrid() function is used for plotting pairwise relationships in a dataset. This class maps each variable in a dataset onto a column and row in a grid of multiple axes. Different axes-level plotting functions can be used to draw bivariate plots in the upper and lower triangles. Marginal distribution of each variable is shown on the diagonal.

The PairGrid() function uses the hue parameter to represent an additional level of conditionalization to plot different subsets of data in different colors. Therefore, color is used to resolve elements on a third dimension. However, it draws subsets on top of each other and will not tailor the hue parameter for the specific visualization, the way that axes-level functions that accept hue will.

Some useful parameters of Seaborn.PairGrid are,

data is a dataframe where each column is a variable and each row is an observation.

hue is used to map plot aspects to different colors.

palette is a set of colors for mapping the "hue" variable

vars specifies variables within data to be used. Otherwise, every column with a numeric datatype is used.

dropna means dropping missing values from the data before plotting

```
import seaborn

import matplotlib.pyplot as plt

  # loading dataset

df = seaborn.load_dataset('car_crashes')

  # PairGrid object with hue

graph = seaborn.PairGrid(df, hue ='total', vars = )

# type of graph for diagonal

graph = graph.map_diag(plt.hist)

# type of graph for non-diagonal

graph = graph.map_offdiag(plt.scatter)

# to add legends

graph = graph.add_legend()

# to show

plt.show()
```

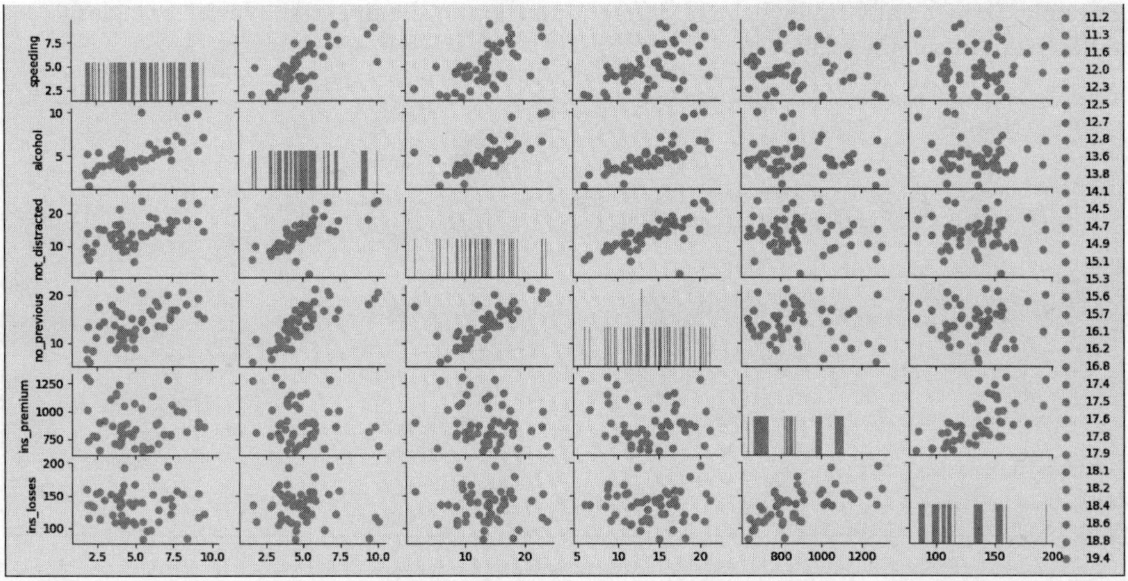

Thus, we see that a PairGrid allows us to draw a grid of subplots using the same plot type to better visualize data. The usage of pairgrid is similar to facetgrid. It first initialises the grid and then passes the grid to the plotting function. However, unlike FacetGrid, Pair Grid uses different pair of variables for each subplot. Also known as a scatterplot matrix, PairGrid forms a matrix of sub-plots.

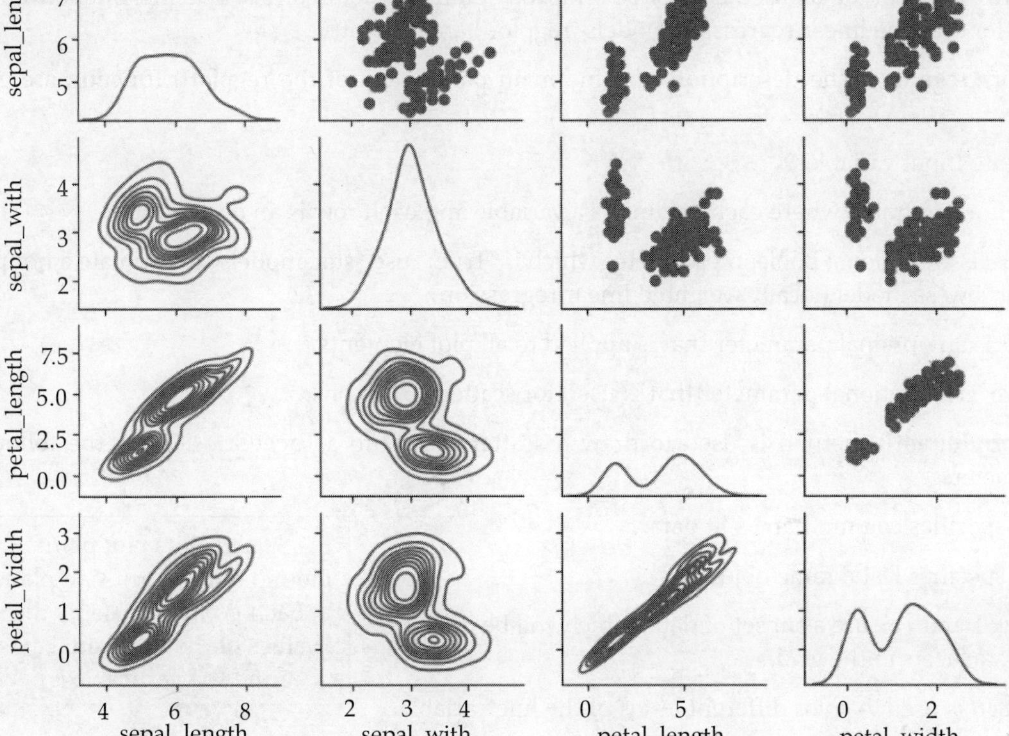

Example: Draw a PairGrid by using a different function in the upper and lower triangles to see different aspects of the relationship.

```
import pandas as pd
import seaborn as sb
from matplotlib import pyplot as plt
df = sb.load_dataset('iris')
g = sb.PairGrid(df)
g.map_upper(plt.scatter)
g.map_lower(sb.kdeplot)
g.map_diag(sb.kdeplot);
plt.show()
```

6.19 Linear relationships

As stated earlier, real-world datasets Most of the times, we use datasets contain multiple quantitative variables. To understand the relationship between those variables, we need to draw regression lines. Moreover, while building the regression models, we need to check for multicollinearity to deduce the correlation between all the combinations of continuous variables. In case multicollinearity exists in the dataset, it must be removed before further analysis. Seaborn offers two functions for drawing linear regression models- regplot() and lmplot().

seaborn.regplot(): The description of some main parameters of the regplot() function are given below:

`x, y` are Input variables.

`Data` is a dataframe where each column is a variable and each row is an observation.

`Lowess` is an optional Boolean parameter which if "True," use "statsmodels" to estimate a nonparametric lowess model (locally weighted linear regression).

`Color` is an optional parameter that is applied to all plot elements.

`Marker` is an optional parameter that is used for scatterplot glyphs.

seaborn.lmplot() method is used to draw a scatter plot onto a FacetGrid. It has the following parameters.

`x, y` specifies column names in data.

`data` specifies DataFrame object.

`hue`, `col` and `row` are a subset of data, which will be drawn on separate facets in the grid.

`Palette` is used to color different levels of the hue variable.

> Scatterplots plot points plotted in the Cartesian plane. Each point represents the values of the horizontal axis and the vertical axis.

`col_wrap` is an optional parameter of int type. It is used to wrap the column variable at this width, so that the column facets span multiple rows.

`height` is an optional parameter that specifies height (in inches) of each facet.

`aspect` is an optional parameter that specifies aspect ratio of each facet. Note that aspect * height gives the width of each facet in inches.

`markers` is an optional parameter used for a scatterplot. If markers is specified as a list then each marker in the list will be used for each level of the hue variable.

`legend` is an optional paramater of Boolean type. If legend = True and a hue variable is present then a legend is added.

`scatter` is an optional paramater of Boolean type. If true, it draws a scatterplot with the underlying observations.

`fit_reg` is an optional parameter of Boolean type. If true, the function estimates and plots a regression model relating the x and y variables.

`Order` is an optional parameter which if greater than 1, use numpy.polyfit to estimate a polynomial regression.

`logistic` is an optional paramater of Boolean type. If True, it treats y as a binary variable and use statsmodels to estimate a logistic regression model. A logistic regression model is substantially more computationally intensive than linear regression.

`lowess` is an optional paramater of Boolean type. If true, statsmodels is used to estimate a nonparametric lowess model (locally weighted linear regression).

`robust` is an optional parameter of Boolean type. If true, statsmodels is used to estimate a robust regression that will deweight outliers. This model is substantially more computationally intensive than standard linear regression.

`logx` is an optional parameter of Boolean type. If true, the function estimates a linear regression of the form y ~ log(x). Note that x must be positive for this to work.

`truncate` is an optional parameter of Boolean type. If true, the regression line is bounded by the data limits else it extends to the x axis limits.

Example: Plot a regression plot between x and y variables of diamonds data set.

```
import seaborn as sns

import matplotlib.pyplot as plt

# loading dataset

data = sns.load_dataset("diamonds")

# draw regplot

sns.regplot(x = "x",y = "y",data = data)

# show the plot

plt.show()
```

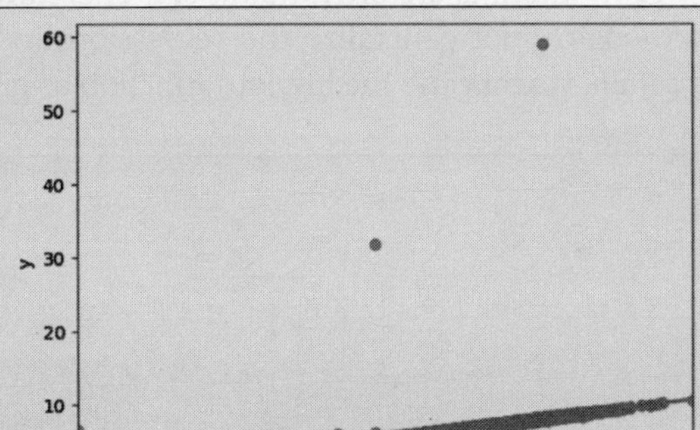

Example: Draw lmplot to represent relationship between total_bill and tip paid on gender basis.

```
import seaborn as sns
import matplotlib.pyplot as plt
# loading dataset
data = sns.load_dataset("tips")
# draw regplot
sns.lmplot(x ='total_bill', y ='tip',
hue = 'sex', data = data)
# show the plot
plt.show()
```

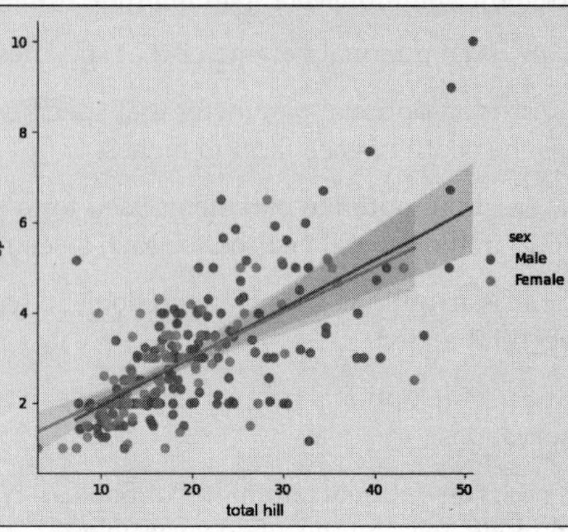

6.19.1 regplot() vs lmplot()

While regplot() performs a simple linear regression model fit and plot, lmplot() combines regplot() and FacetGrid. Technically, lmplot() is more computationally intensive and is intended as a convenient interface to fit regression models across conditional subsets of a dataset.

However, regplot() accepts the x and y variables in a variety of formats including simple numpy arrays, pandas Series objects, or as references to variables in a pandas DataFrame. But the lmplot() function accepts data provided as strings. The plots drawn by the two functions differ in size- regplot() function's plot is bigger than that of lmplot's plot.

> Boxplots are a measure of how well distributed the data in a data set. It divides the data set into three quartiles- minimum, maximum, median, first quartile and third quartile.

6.19.2 Fitting different kinds of models

The simple linear regression model used above is very simple to fit. But this may not be applicable in every situation as real-world data are often nonlinear. Therefore, the above methods cannot generalize the regression line. In such a situation, we may use the lmplot() function as given below.

```
import pandas as pd
import seaborn as sb
from matplotlib import pyplot as plt
df = sb.load_dataset('anscombe')
sb.lmplot(x="x", y="y", data=df.query
("dataset == 'I'"))
plt.show()
```

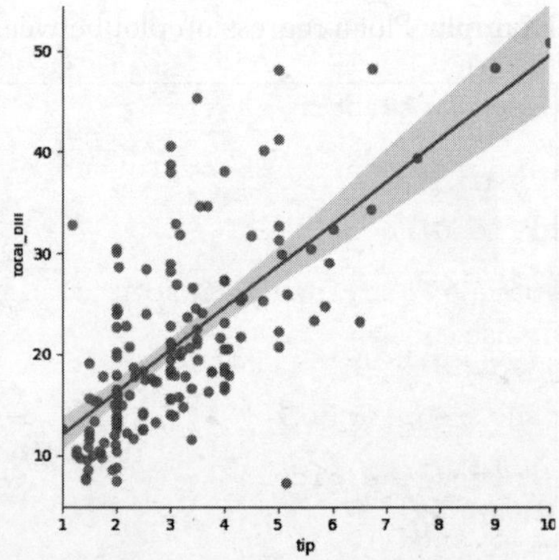

As seen from the plot, the data are good fit for linear regression model with less variance. But try for the same code with dataset = "II" and then see the result.

6.20 Heatmap

Heatmap is a fantastic visualization tool that represents each value to be plotted using various shades of the same color. Usually, the darker shades of the chart represent higher values than the lighter shade. Therefore, every different value is represented using a completely different color. Technically, heatmap is a two-dimensional graphical representation of data in which the values are stored in a matrix and are represented as colors.

A heatmap is created using the heatmap() function present in the seaborn package. The heatmap() function accepts certain parameters, which are given below.

data is a 2D dataset

annot is an array of same shape as that of data and is used to annotate the heatmap. If annot is set to true, the data value will be written on each cell. If the labels for each cell is defined, you can assign those labels to the annot attribute.

cmap is a matplotlib colormap object that is used to map the data values to the color space.

fmt is a string formatting code that is used to add annotations.

linewidths sets the width of the lines that will divide each cell.

robust is used to set contrast levels based on quantiles and works like an "auto-contrast" for choosing good values.

6.20.1 The cmap attribute

Seaborn heatmap offers three different types of colormaps.

Sequential colormap: It is used when the data ranges from a low value to a high value. The sequential color map contains the following colors.

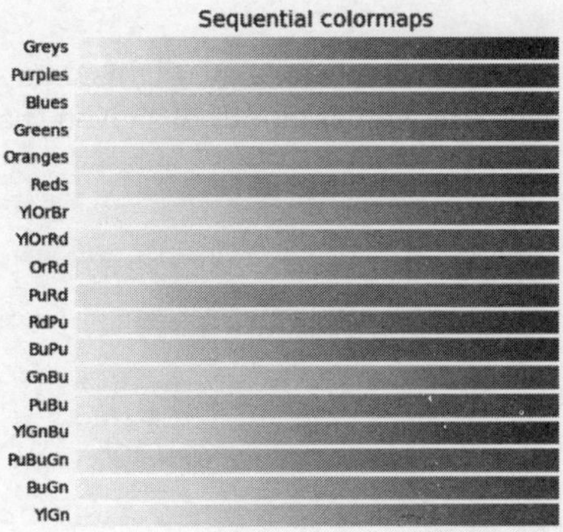

Sequential cubehelix palette: It is a form of the sequential color map that can be used when brightness is increased linearly, and there is a slight difference in hue. *The cubehelix palette looks as given below.*

To use cubehelix in your heatmap, you can write,

```
heat_map = sb.heatmap(data, cmap="cubehelix")
```

Diverging color palette: It is used when the high and low values are important in the heatmap. The divergent palette contains two different shades in a graph to represent low and high values.

To use a diverging color palette, we will write,

sb.palplot(sb.diverging_palette(200, 100, n=11))

in the above line of code, 200 is the value for the palette on the left side, and 100 is the code for the palette on the right side. The variable n defines the number of blocks. In our case, it is 11. The palette will be as follows:

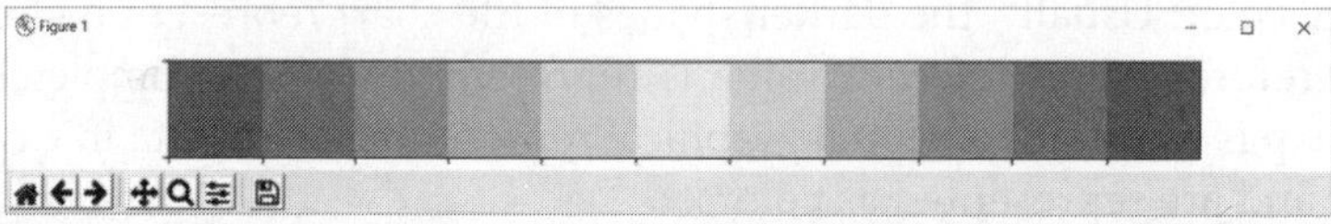

Example: Let us create an array with random values and then draw a heatmap to represent those values.

```
import numpy as np
import seaborn as sb
import matplotlib.pyplot as plt
data = np.random.rand(4, 6)
heat_map = sb.heatmap(data, cmap = "YlGnBu",
annot=True)
plt.xlabel("X - AXIS .....")
plt.ylabel("Y - AXIS .....")
plt.show()
```

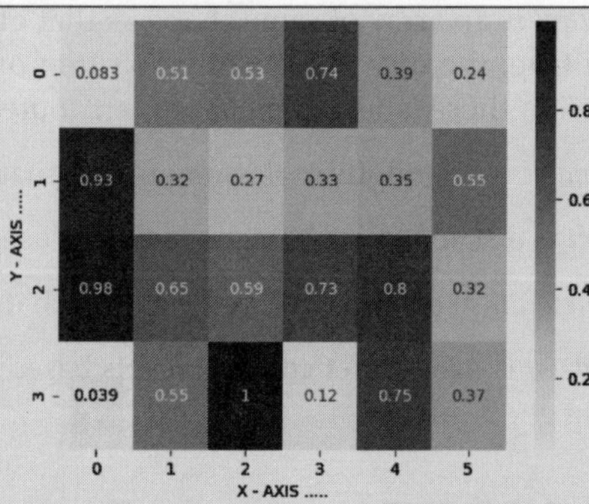

Example: Let us take the flights data set and draw a heatmap to represent number of passengers in every individual month of a given year.

```
import pandas as pd
import seaborn as sns
import matplotlib.pyplot as plt
df = pd.pivot_table(data=sns.load_dataset("flights"),
                    index='month',
                    values='passengers',
                    columns='year')
df.head()


sns.heatmap(df, cmap='coolwarm', annot=True, fmt=".1f")
plt.show()
```

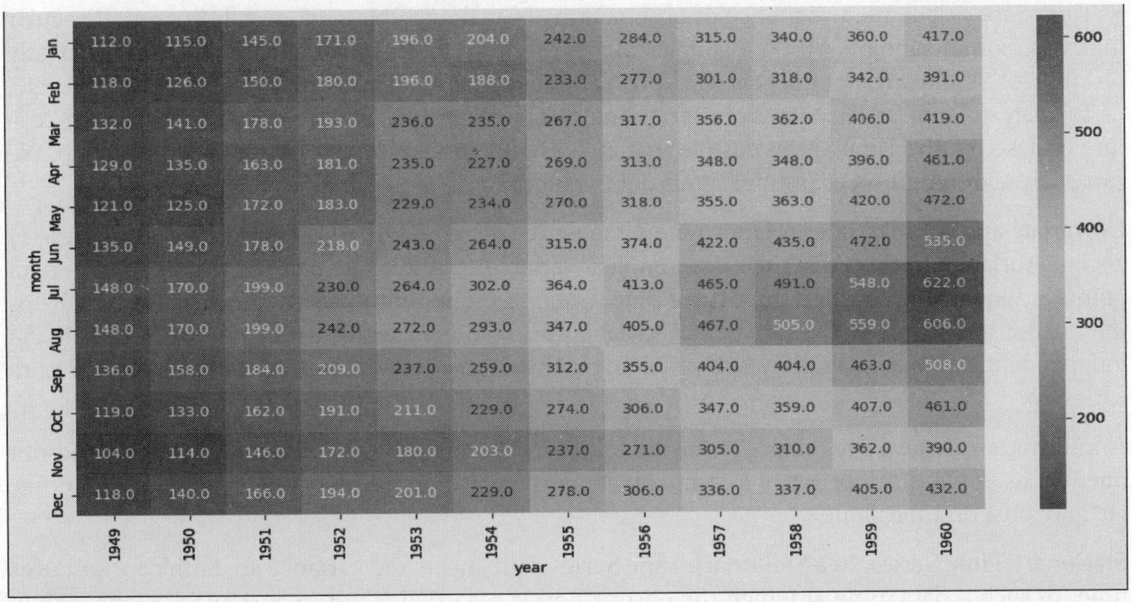

6.21 Bubble chart

A bubble chart is used to display data as a cluster of circles. We just need to supply X and Y coordinates, size, and color of the bubbles. A bubble chart is primarily used to depict and show relationships between numeric variables. In the example given below, we have created a bubble chart using some random values. Note that a bubble chart is plotted using the scatter() function that we have used for creating a scatter plot.

Example: Creating a Bubble Chart

```
import matplotlib.pyplot as plt
import numpy as np

# create data
x = np.random.rand(50)
y = np.random.rand(50)
z = np.random.rand(50)
colors = np.random.rand(50)
# use the scatter function
plt.scatter(x, y, s=z*1000,c=colors)
plt.show()
```

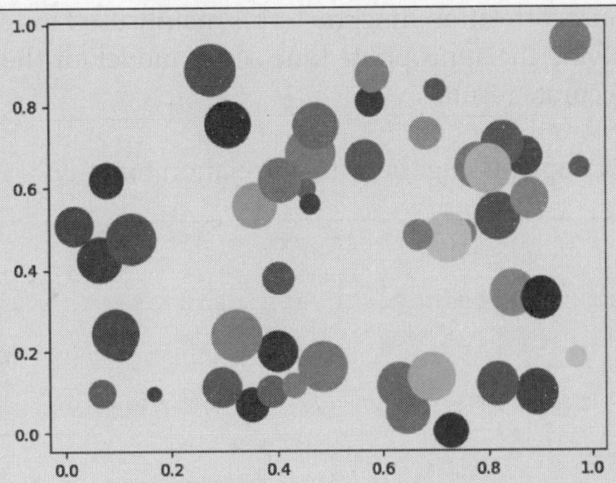

6.22 Plotting time series data

To formulate a better forecasting model, we need to explore our data in depth. Time series data are key to data analysis and visualization. We can plot line charts and a suite of other plots to understand the trends, cycles, and seasonality variations that exist in the data.

Time Series data are a sequence of observations over time, which are usually spaced at regular intervals. Some commonly used examples of time series data include daily stock prices, quarterly revenues of a company, monthly car sales of an automaker, annual unemployment rate of a state, etc.

To analyze Time Series data, time series analysis is performed to develop models that best capture or describe the Time Series data so that meaningful and accurate forecasts could be made. We can analyze different types of time series data, including:

Univariate and Multivariate: A Univariate Time Series refers to the set of observations over time of a single variable. In this case, time is an implicit variable. A univariate analysis is useful when data points are equally spaced, and thus, there is no need to express time explicitly. Such an analysis helps the analyst to learn how the dependent variable (price) differs with respect to time, which is the independent variable. Example, stock prices in past years can be used to predict prices for the future correctly.

A multivariate Time Series refers to the set of observations over time of several variables and not one. For example, stock prices of a company depend on fashion trend, occasion, global conditions, etc and joust on time alone.

Stationary Time Series: In a Stationary Time Series data, mean and variance are both constant over time. In such a data, time at which the observation is recorded is not important. Stationary time series data are easy to predict as it is a flat series without trend, with constant variance over time.

NonStationary: A nonstationary Time Series is one where either mean or variance or both are not constant over time. Two types of tests that can be used to check whether a given Time Series is stationary are autocorrelation function (ACF) test and partial autocorrelation function (PACF) test.

Autocorrelation function (ACF) Test checks for correlation between two different data points of a time series separated by a lag "h." For example, the ACF will check for correlation between points 1 and 2, 2 and 3, so on and so forth. Similarly, for lag 2, the ACF function will check between points 1 and 3, 2 and 4, 3 and 5, etc.

Autocorrelation function test is mainly used for detecting nonrandomness in the data and for identifying the appropriate time series model for the particular dataset. Such a test therefore provides accurate results.

Example: Using the auto-correlation function

```
from matplotlib import pyplot

from statsmodels.graphics.tsaplots
import plot_acf

import yfinance as yf

tesla = yf.download('T
SLA','2019-01-27', '2020-02-11')

plot_acf(tesla['Close'], lags=20)

pyplot.show()
```

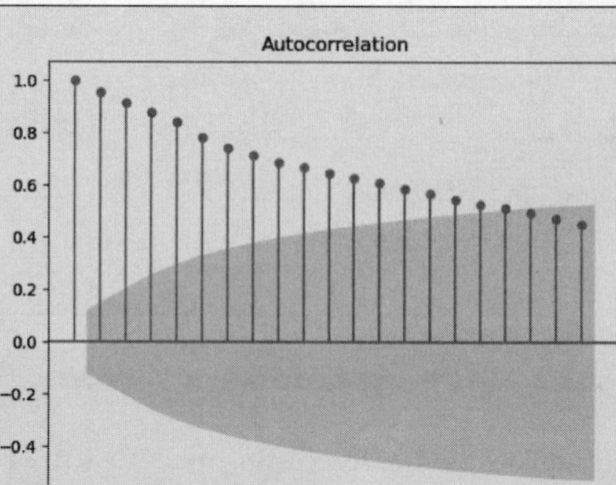

Partial autocorrelation function (PACF) is used in situations where the effect of autocorrelation at smaller lags influences the estimate of autocorrelation at longer lags.

Points to remember:

- The values of ACF and PACF vary between +1 to -1.
- If ACF or PACF is closer to +1 or -1, then it indicates a strong correlation.
- For a stationery Time Series data, ACF will drop to zero relatively quickly as and when compared to nonstationary Time Series.
- ACF considers past values to calculate correlation but PACF considers only one past value for computation not all.
- While ACF does not remove the problems associated with shorter lags, PACF does removes that problem.

In this section, we will focus on univariate time series data, but the techniques discussed here are applicable even on multivariate time series (that is when we have more than one observation at each point in time).

```
import matplotlib.pyplot as plt
import datetime
import numpy as np
x = np.array([datetime.datetime(2013, 9, 28, i, 0) for i in range(24)])
y = np.random.randint(100, size=x.shape)
plt.plot(x,y)
plt.show()
```

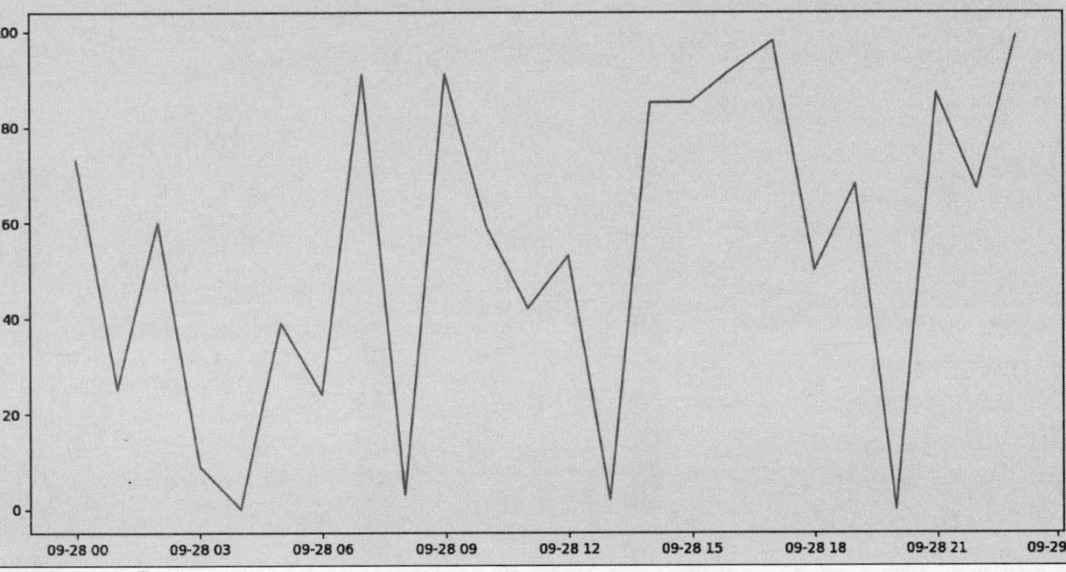

Example: Open a text file and write the following data in it. Save it as "dollar_to_rupee.csv" and use this time series data for plotting a variety of graphs.

```
18-07-2018, 68.625
19-07-2018, 68.9453
20-07-2018, 68.745
21-07-2018, 68.747
22-07-2018, 68.7415
23-07-2018, 68.9449
24-07-2018, 68.9486

import pandas as pd
from matplotlib import pyplot
series=pd.read_csv('dollar_to_rupee.csv',header=0)
series.plot()
pyplot.show()
```

To plot a histogram, we need to write,

```
import pandas as pd
from matplotlib import pyplot
series=pd.read_csv('dollar_to_rupee.csv',header=0)
series.hist()
pyplot.show()
```

To plot a kde write,

```
import pandas as pd
from matplotlib import pyplot
series=pd.read_csv('dollar_to_rupee.csv',header=0)
series.plot(kind='kde')
pyplot.show()
```

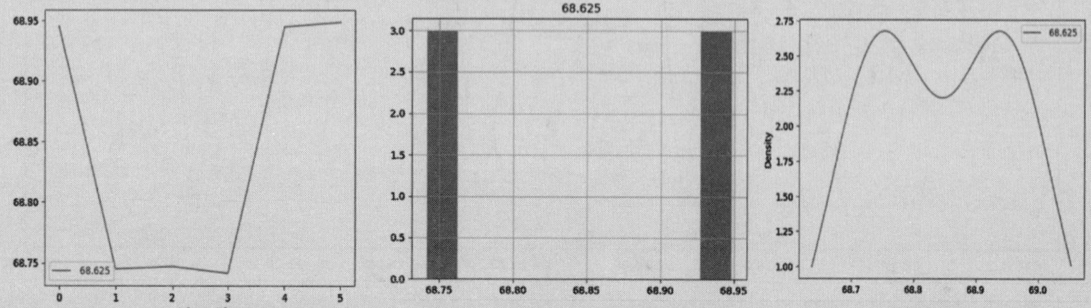

Line Chart Histogram KDE Plot

6.23 Visualizing sparse matrix

The Spy() function in the matplotlib library is used to visualize the sparse array. Note that *sparse matrix* is a matrix where most of the elements are zero.

$$\begin{bmatrix} 0 & 0 & 3 & 0 & 4 \\ 0 & 0 & 5 & 7 & 0 \\ 0 & 0 & 0 & 0 & 0 \\ 0 & 2 & 6 & 0 & 0 \end{bmatrix} \Rightarrow$$

Row	0	0	1	1	3	3
Column	2	4	2	3	1	2
Value	3	4	5	7	2	6

Sparse matrix and its representation (Change digits)

The spy() function uses two plotting styles to visualize the sparse matrix, Image style and marker style. For a full array, both the styles are used but for a sparse matrix only the marker style works. Syntax of spy() function can be given as,

matplotlib.pyplot.spy(Z, precision=0, marker=None, markersize=None, aspect='equal', origin= 'upper', **kwargs)

where,

`Z` is the array to be plotted.

`Precision` The default value of precision is 0. For sparse matrices, if precision is "present," then any value present in the array will be plotted, even if it is identically zero.

`Upper`, the value can be lower or upper. Default value is upper.

`Aspect` controls the aspect ratio of the axes. This value is important as otherwise it may result in a distorted image. If aspect is "equal" then aspect ratio is 1 and pixels will be square. In case aspect is "`auto`" then axes is kept fixed and is adjusted to fit data in the axes. In this case, nonsquare pixels are plotted.

kwargs are additional parameters that helps to get different plotting styles.

Example: Plotting sparse matrix

```
import numpy as np
import matplotlib.pyplot as plt
x = np.random.randn(75,75)
x[25, :] = 0.
x[:, 25] = 0.
plt.spy(x)
plt.show()
```

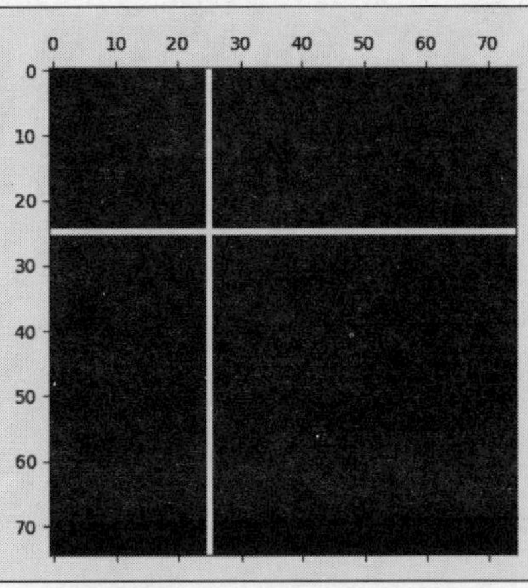

Example: Plotting sparse matrix with additional parameters

```
import numpy as np
import matplotlib.pyplot as plt
x = np.random.randn(75,75)
x[25, :] = 0.
x[:, 25] = 0.
  plt.spy(x, precision = 0.1, markersize = 5)
plt.show()
```

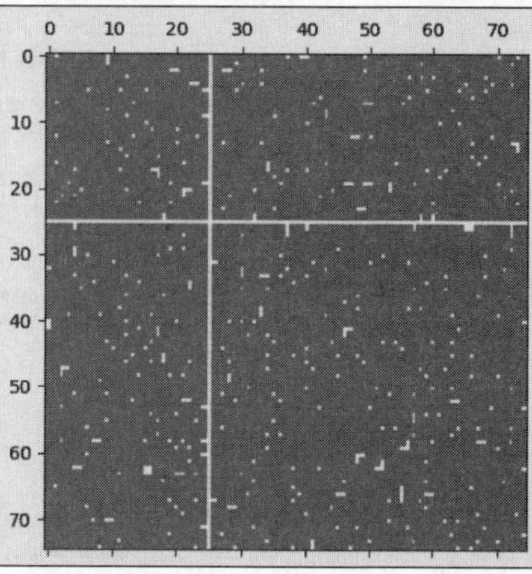

6.24 2D Pixel Plot

Pixel plots are used to represent 2-dimensional data set where each pixel refers to a different value in a data set. The pixel plot is created by using the cmap and interpolation parameters of the imshow() method in matplot.pyplot module. The syntax to create a pixel plot can be given as,

*matplotlib.pyplot.imshow(X, cmap=None, norm=None, aspect=None, interpolation=None, alpha=None, vmin=None, vmax=None, origin=None, extent=None, shape=, filternorm=1, filterrad=4.0, imlim=, resample=None, url=None, *, data=None, **kwargs)*

Write a program to generate a 2D pixel plot from a matrix created using random() method.

```
import numpy as np
import matplotlib.pyplot as plt
data = np.random.random((4, 10))
pixel_plot = plt.figure() # create a plot
pixel_plot.add_axes()       # plot axes
plt.title("pixel_plot")
pixel_plot = plt.imshow(data, cmap = 'twilight', interpolation = 'nearest')
plt.colorbar(pixel_plot)
plt.savefig('pixel_plot.png') # save a plot
plt.show(pixel_plot)  # show plot
```

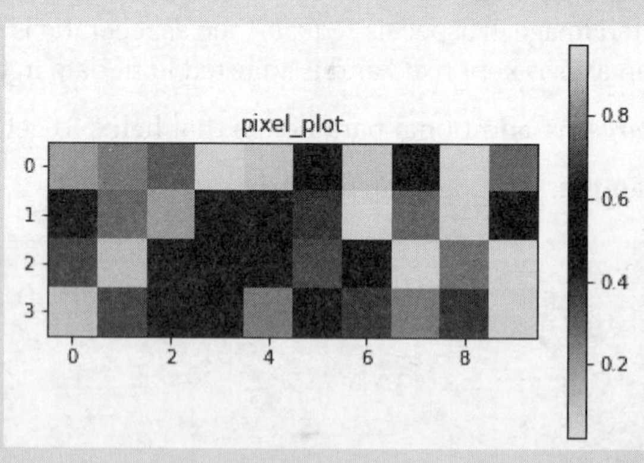

6.25 3D Data visualization

3D data visualization is used to create three-dimensional graphical representations of data. This helps to see data points plotted along three axes (X, Y, and Z) to get a more comprehensive view of the relationships within the data. 3D data visualization facilitates data exploration and analysis from different perspectives, offering better insights and decision-making.

3D data visualization provides depth and spatial context that 2D visualizations lack. They help users to understand spatial relationships, patterns, and correlations within the data. Some key techniques in 3D data visualization include:

6.25.1 3D Scatter Plots

3D scatter plots display data points in a three-dimensional space, using the X, Y, and the Z axis. Each axis represents a different variable, and every point in the plot corresponds to a single observation. Scatter plots are usually used to identify

- clusters in data. For example, market researchers segment customers based on demographics, purchase behavior, etc.
- detect correlations between three variables that cannot be uncovered by 2D plots. For example, scientific researchers analyze a scatter plot to visualize relationships between experimental variables.
- spot outliers.

```
import matplotlib.pyplot as plt
from mpl_toolkits.mplot3d import Axes3D
import numpy as np
x = np.random.rand(100)
y = np.random.rand(100)
z = np.random.rand(100)
fig = plt.figure()
# 111 represents number of rows, columns
and index of subplot
ax = fig.add_subplot(111, projection='3d')
ax.scatter(x, y, z, c='r', marker='o')
ax.set_xlabel('Mathematics')
ax.set_ylabel('Physics')
ax.set_zlabel('Chemistry')
plt.show()
```

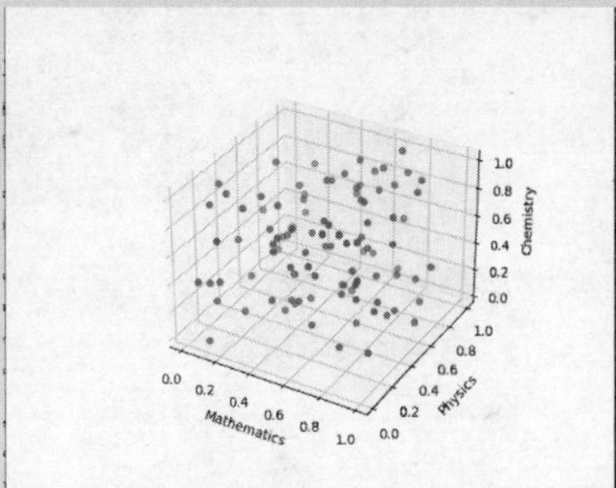

6.25.2 3D Surface Plots

3D surface plots represent a three-dimensional surface that plots the relationship between three continuous variables. The plot is usually used to learn how a dependent variable (Z) changes its value with respect to two independent variables (X and Y). Such plots are often used for the following:

- create models of surfaces, such as geographic terrain, temperature distributions, or any other data that varies continuously over a region.
- visualize and analyze how a dependent variable is affected due to interaction between two independent variables. For example, economic modelling is used to visualize changes in key economic indicators.

```
import matplotlib.pyplot as plt
import numpy as np
# Define grid for X and Y
x = np.linspace(-10, 10, 100)
y = np.linspace(-10, 10, 100)
x, y = np.meshgrid(x, y)
# Define function for Z values
z = np.sin(np.sqrt(x**2 + y**2))
# Create figure and 3D axis
fig = plt.figure(figsize=(9, 7))
ax = fig.add_subplot(projection='3d')
# Create the surface plot with customizations
ax.plot_surface(x, y, z, cmap='coolwarm', edgecolor='red', alpha=0.6)
# Labels
ax.set_xlabel('X Axis')
ax.set_ylabel('Y Axis')
ax.set_zlabel('Z Axis')
ax.set_title('3D Surface Plot of sin(sqrt(x² + y²))')
plt.show()
```

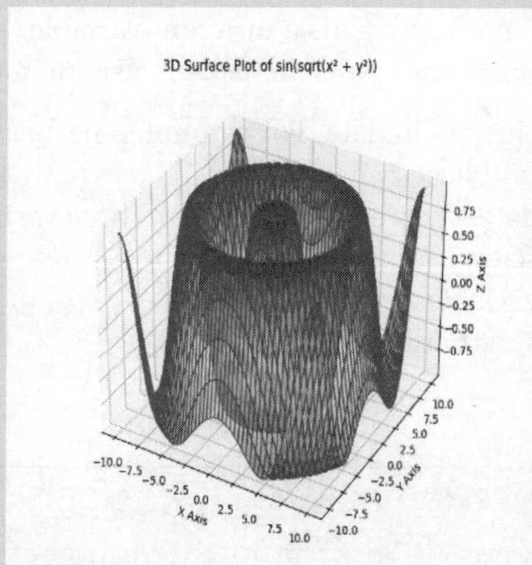

6.25.3 3D Bar Charts

3D bar charts extend traditional bar charts into the third dimension. The bars have height, width, and depth to represent three different variables. Each bar corresponds to a category and shows the magnitude across multiple dimensions. 3D bar charts are extensively used to visualize and compare multiple categories across different dimensions. For example, these graphs are used to,

- ❑ analyze sales performance across different regions and time periods.
- ❑ compare population demographics across different countries and age groups.
- ❑ visualize financial metrics across departments and time frames.

```
import matplotlib.pyplot as plt
from mpl_toolkits.mplot3d import Axes3D
import numpy as np
x = np.arange(10)
y = np.arange(10)
x, y = np.meshgrid(x, y)
z = np.zeros_like(x)
dx = dy = 0.5
dz = np.random.rand(10, 10)
# Create 3D bar chart
fig = plt.figure()
ax = fig.add_subplot(111, projection='3d')
ax.bar3d(x.flatten(), y.flatten(), z.flatten(), dx, dy, dz.flatten(), color='b')
# Add labels
ax.set_xlabel('X Label')
ax.set_ylabel('Y Label')
ax.set_zlabel('Z Label')
plt.show()
```

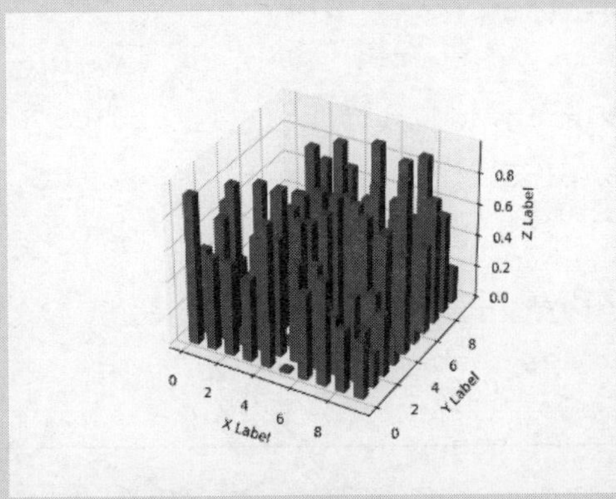

6.25.4 3D Line Graphs

3D line graphs are used to plot lines in a three-dimensional space. This helps to visualize trends over time or relationships among three variables. Each line in the graph depicts the progression of data points over time or under different conditions. The graph is an excellent tool to view how variables change and interact with each other in a 3D space. 3D line graphs are extensively used to,

- ❑ analyze stock market data to understand price movements over time for different stocks.
- ❑ visualize changes in pollution levels over different regions and time periods.
- ❑ monitor changes in system parameters over time.

```
import matplotlib.pyplot as plt
from mpl_toolkits.mplot3d import Axes3D
import numpy as np
t = np.linspace(0, 10, 100)
x = np.sin(t)
y = np.cos(t)
z = t
# Create 3D line plot
fig = plt.figure()
ax = fig.add_subplot(111, projection='3d')
ax.plot(x, y, z)
ax.set_xlabel('X Label')
ax.set_ylabel('Y Label')
ax.set_zlabel('Z Label')
plt.show()
```

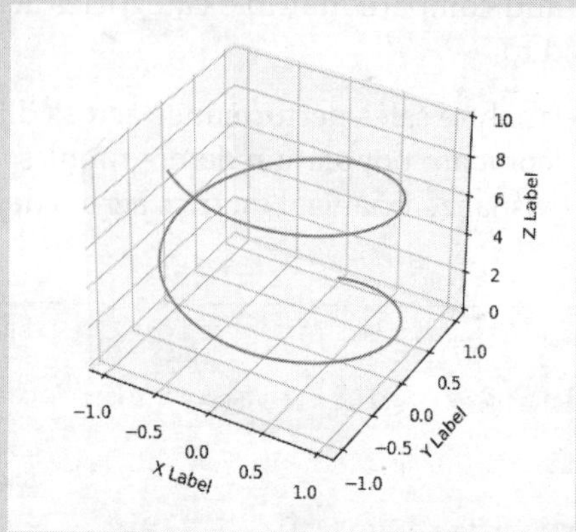

6.25.5 3D Pie Charts

3D pie charts add a third dimension to traditional pie charts. These graphs help the users to visualize data proportions and see how different parts contribute to a whole in a more detailed way. 3D pie charts are used in the following scenarios:

- analyze market share to see how the sales are distributed among different products.
- visualize budget allocation to understand the distribution of funds across different departments.
- represent survey results to demonstrate the proportion of responses in different categories.

```
import matplotlib.pyplot as plt
import numpy as np
# Create a dummy dataset
labels = ['A', 'B', 'C', 'D']
sizes = [25, 30, 35, 10]
# Create 3D pie chart
fig, ax = plt.subplots()
ax.pie(sizes, labels=labels, autopct='%1.1f%%',
shadow=True, startangle=90)
ax.axis('equal')  # Equal aspect ratio ensures that pie is drawn as a circle.
plt.show()
```

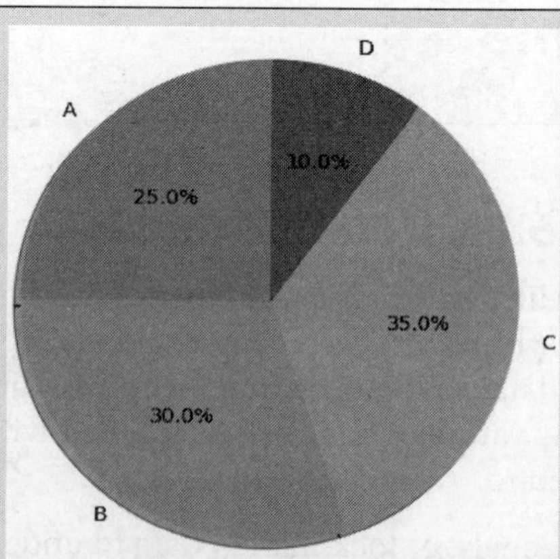

6.26 Wireframe Models

Wireframe models use lines and points to form the basic structure of a 3D shape. Since they do not fill in the surfaces, the underlying geometry and overall framework can be visualized clearly. This feature makes wireframe models preferable in engineering and architectural design applications. They help to easily understand and analyze complex geometric shapes and the underlying structure of complex data.

While engineers use wireframe models to create and analyze prototypes of structures, architects use them to visualize building layouts and designs. Wireframe models are also used in computer graphics for modelling and animation.

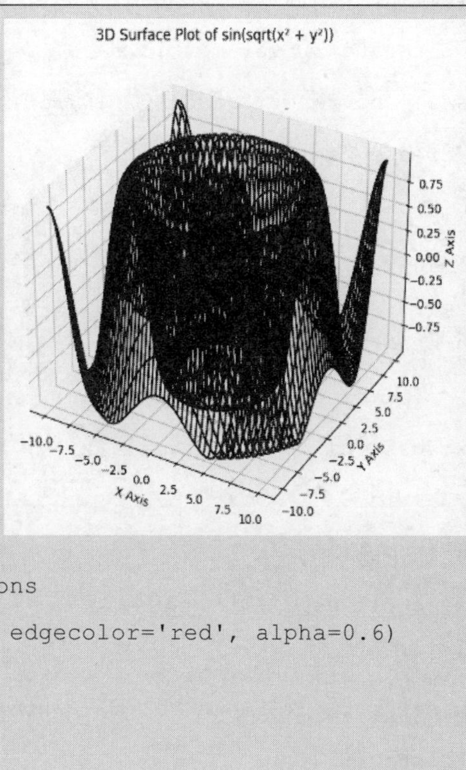


```
import matplotlib.pyplot as plt
import numpy as np
# Define grid for X and Y
x = np.linspace(-10, 10, 100)
y = np.linspace(-10, 10, 100)
x, y = np.meshgrid(x, y)
# Define function for Z values
z = np.sin(np.sqrt(x**2 + y**2))
# Create figure and 3D axis
fig = plt.figure(figsize=(9, 7))
ax = fig.add_subplot(projection='3d')
ax.plot_wireframe(x, y, z, color='black')
# Create the surface plot with customizations
#fig.plot_surface(x, y, z, cmap='coolwarm', edgecolor='red', alpha=0.6)
ax.set_xlabel('X Axis')
ax.set_ylabel('Y Axis')
ax.set_zlabel('Z Axis')
ax.set_title('3D Surface Plot of sin(sqrt(x² + y²))')
plt.show()
```

6.27 Volume Rendering

Volume rendering creates a semi-transparent 3D representation of volumetric data. In these graphs, each voxel (volumetric pixel) has a value. Since, the graph is semi-transparent, internal structures can be easily seen. Volume rendering is often used in the following areas:

- ❑ medical imaging applications where there is a need for detailed visualization of internal body structures (organs and tissues) using MRI and CT scans data.
- ❑ study geological formations
- ❑ analyze geological surveys to visualize underground structures.
- ❑ visualize meteorological data, and other complex 3D data.
- ❑ fluid dynamics research to study flow patterns.

```
import numpy as np
import matplotlib.pyplot as plt
from mpl_toolkits.mplot3d import Axes3D
# Generate 3D volumetric data
data = np.random.rand(10, 10, 10)
# Create figure
fig = plt.figure()
ax = fig.add_subplot(111, projection='3d')
# Extract coordinates where data is above a
threshold
x, y, z = np.where(data > 0.5)
ax.scatter(x, y, z, c=data[x, y, z], cmap='viridis', marker='o')
# Labels
ax.set_xlabel('X')
ax.set_ylabel('Y')
ax.set_zlabel('Z')
ax.set_title('Simple Volume Rendering')
plt.show()
```

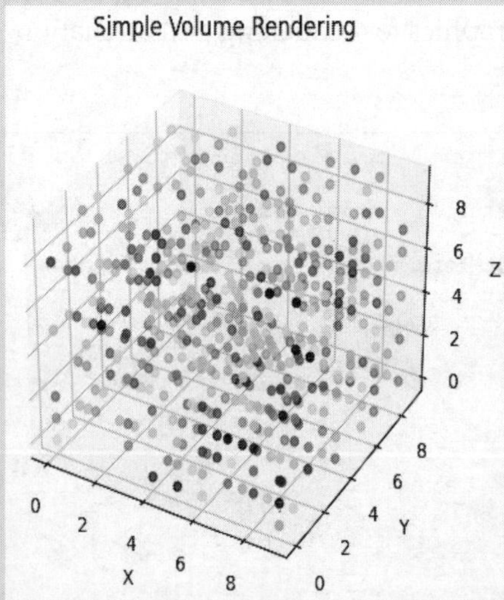

6.28 3D Heatmaps

3D heatmaps use color to represent data density or intensity in a 3D space. This helps a person to easily identify areas of high and low concentration by looking at the variations in color intensity. These maps are popularly used for,

- ❑ tracking disease outbreak patterns.
- ❑ identifying congestion points in transportation networks.
- ❑ monitoring the environment by visualizing pollution levels.

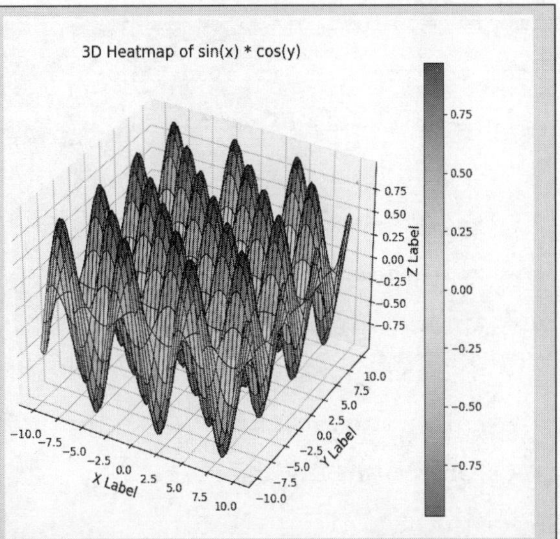


```
import matplotlib.pyplot as plt

from mpl_toolkits.mplot3d import Axes3D

import numpy as np

# Create a dummy dataset

x = np.linspace(-10, 10, 100)

y = np.linspace(-10, 10, 100)

x, y = np.meshgrid(x, y)

z = np.sin(x) * np.cos(y)

# Create 3D heatmap with improved visualization

fig = plt.figure(figsize=(10, 7))

ax = fig.add_subplot(111, projection='3d')

heatmap = ax.plot_surface(x, y, z, cmap='coolwarm', edgecolor='k', linewidth=0.5, alpha=0.8)

# Add labels and title

ax.set_xlabel('X Label', fontsize=12)

ax.set_ylabel('Y Label', fontsize=12)

ax.set_zlabel('Z Label', fontsize=12)

ax.set_title('3D Heatmap of sin(x) * cos(y)', fontsize=14)

# Add color bar

fig.colorbar(heatmap)

plt.show()
```

6.29 Bubble Charts

Bubble charts add a third axis and use the size of each bubble to represent a fourth variable. Each bubble corresponds to an observation, with its position based on three variables and its size indicating the fourth. Thus, bubble charts are useful in multivariate analysis for displaying relationships among four variables. For this reason, it finds application in the following areas:

- Visualizing customer segments based on multiple criteria during market analysis.
- Comparing different investment plans based on risk, return, and other factors involved in financial analysis.
- Studying relationships between demographic variables in social science research.

```
import matplotlib.pyplot as plt
from mpl_toolkits.mplot3d import Axes3D
import numpy as np
# Create a dummy dataset
np.random.seed(0)
x = np.random.rand(10)
y = np.random.rand(10)
z = np.random.rand(10)
s = np.random.rand(10) * 50
# Create 3D bubble chart
fig = plt.figure()
ax = fig.add_subplot(111, projection='3d')
bubble = ax.scatter(x, y, z, s=s, c='b', marker='o', alpha=0.9)
# Add labels
ax.set_xlabel('X Label')
ax.set_ylabel('Y Label')
ax.set_zlabel('Z Label')
plt.show()
```

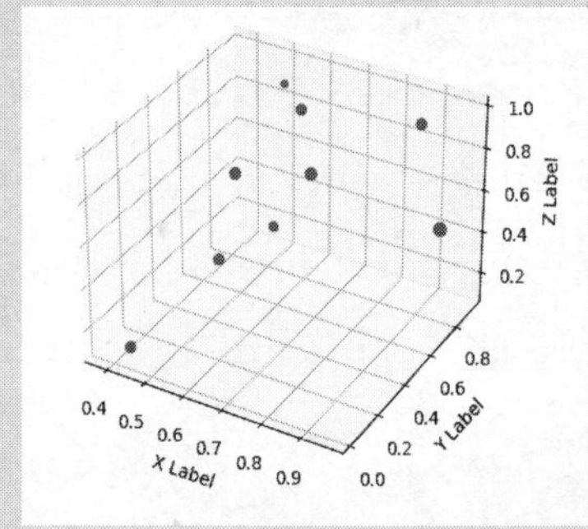

6.30 Choosing the Right 3D Visualization Technique

Choosing the appropriate 3D visualization technique depends on multiple factors like the type of analysis to be performed, the type of data, its dimensions, and distribution. These factors can be explained as given below.

Data Type: Different types of data (numerical, categorical, temporal, spatial, relational, hierarchical) can be visualized using different techniques. For example, scatter plots are suitable for numerical data, while relational data can be better visualized using network diagrams.

Data Dimension: The number of variables or attributes affects the choice of visualization technique. For instance, 3D scatter plots are preferred for visualizing three variables, but to analyze more complex relationships, surface plots perform better.

Data Distribution: Data distribution (normal, skewed, bimodal, uniform, discrete) influences the choice of graph used to effectively represent patterns, trends, and outliers. For example, histograms and heat maps are useful to visualize distribution of data.

Data Analysis Tasks: The specific questions or hypotheses to be proved/rejected determine the visualization technique to be used. For example, to explore correlations, parallel coordinates are useful.

Advantages of 3D Data Visualization:

- Simplifies complex information to make it understandable.
- Identifies hidden trends which were not visible in 2D charts.
- Improves understanding by analyzing data from different angles.
- Facilitates decision making by giving deeper insights.
- Makes data exploration interesting and engaging.

Disadvantages of 3D Visualizations:

- Sometimes data interpretation becomes more complicated than usual.
- Adding the third or even the fourth dimension may result in visual clutter, thereby making it difficult to focus on key information.
- Can result in misinterpretation due to depth perception.
- These charts are not supported by all devices or platforms. This restricts its usage.
- Creating and rendering 3D visualizations calls for more computational resources resulting in slower performance.
- The third dimension may be overemphasized while neglecting other important attributes.
- 3D graphs require more user training and expertise to navigate effectively.

> 3D visualization is crucial in the entertainment industry for creating lifelike characters, environments, and special effects in animated movies and video games. They are used to enhance the immersive experience for viewers and gamers.

Icon-based Visualization Techniques

Icon-based visualization techniques use small graphical symbols (icons) to represent data points. They are an effective tool for the users to perceive patterns, trends, and relationships that exist in the data. Icon-based visualization techniques are commonly used to visualize data and do exploratory analysis.

Write a program to create a radar plot

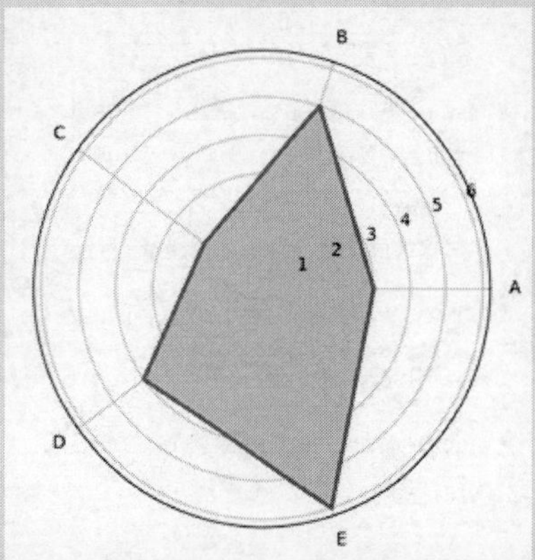


```
import matplotlib.pyplot as plt
# for plotting graphs

import numpy as np
#  for  mathematical  operations,  like  creating
angles

values = [3, 5, 2, 4, 6]

labels = ['A', 'B', 'C', 'D', 'E']


# To generate evenly spaced angles (in radians)
for each value

angles = np.linspace(0, 2 * np.pi, len(values), endpoint=False)

# Since it is a circular plot, the angles go from 0 to 2π (full circle).
```

```
# First value and first angle are repeated to ensure that the shape closes
properly
values += values[:1]                # Repeat the first value at the end
angles = np.append(angles, angles[0]) # Repeat the first angle at the end

# Polar coordinate system creates a circular plot instead of a rectangular
fig, ax = plt.subplots(subplot_kw={'projection': 'polar'})
ax.plot(angles, values, 'b-', linewidth=2)
ax.fill(angles, values, 'b', alpha=0.3)
ax.set_xticks(angles[:-1])
ax.set_xticklabels(labels)

plt.show()
fig, ax = plt.subplots(subplot_kw={'projection': 'polar'})
plt.show()
```

Chernoff Faces: Chernoff faces use facial features like eyes, nose, mouth, etc. to represent multi-dimensional data.

```
def chernoff_face(eyes, eyebrows, mouth):
    # Define facial features using emojis
    eye_options = ["• •", "◕ ◕", "◉ ◉"]  # Small, Medium, Large Eyes
    eyebrow_options = ["¯ ¯", "— —", "↖ ↗"]  # Different Eyebrows
    mouth_options = ["‿", "◡", "▾"]  # Smiling, Neutral, Sad

    # Select features based on values
    eye = eye_options[min(eyes, 2)]
    eyebrow = eyebrow_options[min(eyebrows, 2)]
    mouth = mouth_options[min(mouth, 2)]

    # Display face
    print(f"  {eyebrow}")
    print(f" ( {eye} )")
    print(f"   {mouth}")
```

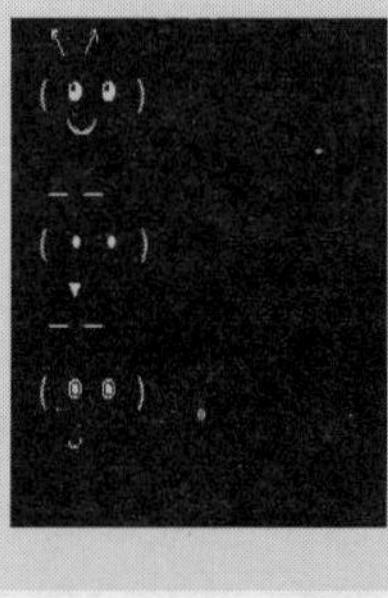

```
# Example data
chernoff_face(eyes=1, eyebrows=2, mouth=0)
chernoff_face(eyes=0, eyebrows=1, mouth=2)
chernoff_face(eyes=2, eyebrows=0, mouth=1)
```

Stick Figures (Stick Glyphs): In a stick figure, each data point is represented by a stick figure, where different body parts correspond to different variables.

```
import matplotlib.pyplot as plt


def draw_stick_figure(ax, x, y, height, width):
    ax.plot([x, x], [y, y + height], 'k-', lw=2)  # Body
    ax.plot([x - width/2, x + width/2], [y + height - width, y + height - width], 'k-', lw=2)  # Arms
    ax.plot([x - width/3, x], [y, y - height/2], 'k-', lw=2)  # Left Leg
    ax.plot([x + width/3, x], [y, y - height/2], 'k-', lw=2)  # Right Leg
    ax.scatter([x], [y + height], s=100, color='black')  # Head


fig, ax = plt.subplots(figsize=(5, 5))
draw_stick_figure(ax, 0, 0, 1, 0.5)
ax.set_xlim(-1, 1)
ax.set_ylim(-1, 2)
ax.axis('off')
plt.show()
```

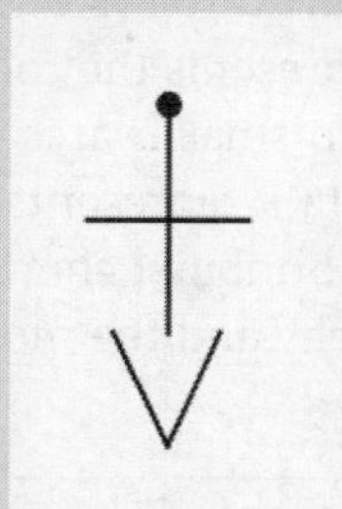

6.31 What is Hierarchical Data?

Hierarchical data is organized in a hierarchical or tree-like structure. Each data point or record is related to one or more other data points/records thereby forming a parent–child relationship. Such a structure has following use cases.

Organizational Structure: In an organizational structure, there is a hierarchy, where each employee has a manager and a manager may have several subordinates working under them. In such a scenario, the manager is like the parent node and the subordinates are like the child nodes in the hierarchy (children).

File Systems: The files stored in the computer are often organized hierarchically where, the directories (folders) contain files and subdirectories, which in turn contain additional files and directories, thereby forming a tree-like structure.

Biological Taxonomy: In biology, species are grouped into genera, genera into families, families into orders, class, phylum, kingdom, and domain. This hierarchical structure reflects the evolutionary relationships between different organisms.

Nested Data: In databases and data formats, such as JSON and XML, hierarchy in data exists between data elements that can be nested within one another. This hierarchy can be represented as relationships or groupings.

Network Routing: In computer networks, routing and organizing network resources use hierarchical data. For example, routers are organized hierarchically into domains, subdomains, and individual network segments.

Genealogical Records: Even the genealogical data is represented using a hierarchical structure. Every individual is organized into families, families into clans or lineages, and lineages into larger groups.

Sales Analysis: Business uses hierarchical data to analyze sales in different groupings like area code, city, state, country, and continent. Sales figures can also be analyzed by product category and time period. Such an analysis helps to identify the areas of growth and opportunities for improvement.

Website Traffic: Website traffic can be analyzed by geographic location, referral source, and pages visited. This helps to identify the most popular pages, referral sources, and geographic locations.

Visualizing Hierarchical Data

In this section, we will study about two different ways to visualize hierarchical data.

One of the most popular techniques to visualize hierarchical data is the Sunburst chart. The chart displays data in a circular format representing the hierarchy with rings. The innermost ring represents the root node, and the child nodes are the subsequent rings. Each arc is in turn divided into smaller arcs that represent the child nodes. The size of each arc depends on the value of the data it represents.

Sunburst charts allow users to visualize the relationship between the different levels of the hierarchy and the most prominent parts of the data. Given below is a code to plot a sunburst chart.

```
import plotly.express as px
import pandas as pd
# Sample Data: Hierarchical Structure
data = pd.DataFrame({
    "Category": ["", "A", "B", "B", "C", "C", "C1", "C1", "C2", "D", "D"],
# Added root
     "Subcategory": ["SALES", "A2", "B1", "B2", "C1", "C2", "C1a", "C1b",
"C2a", "D1", "D2"],
    "Value": [50, 20, 10, 5, 8, 5, 7, 3, 8, 4, 6]  # Adjusted values
})
# Create Sunburst Chart
```

```
fig = px.sunburst(data, path=["Category", "Subcategory"], values="Value", title="Sunburst Chart")
# Show the Chart in interactive mode
fig.show()
```

In the above code, the px.sunburst() function is used to generate the Sunburst chart. The DataFrame has three columns: "Category" (parent nodes), "Subcategory" (child nodes), and "Value" (size of each node). While Category and Subcategory define the hierarchy, "values" specifies the size of each segment. Note that the empty string in Category (" ") represents the root node.

To witness the interactive feature of the chart, hover the mouse over segments, you will see that segment's labels and values. You can even click on a segment to zoom into that level.

Sankey diagram: It is a flow diagram, in which the width of arrows is proportional to the flow quantity. This helps to visualize the contributions to a flow by defining source node, the target node, value to set the flow volume, and label to display the name of the node.

```
import plotly.graph_objects as go
# Define Nodes (categories)
nodes = ["Source A", "Source B", "Intermediate 1", "Intermediate 2", "Destination X", "Destination Y"]
# Define Links (flows between nodes)
links = {
    "source": [0, 1, 0, 1, 2, 2, 3],  # Indices of source nodes
    "target": [2, 2, 3, 3, 4, 5, 5],  # Indices of target nodes
    "value":  [10, 15, 8, 12, 5, 10, 15]  # Flow values
}
```

```
# Create Sankey Diagram
fig = go.Figure(go.Sankey(node = dict(pad = 15, thickness = 20, line = dict(color
= "black", width = 0.5), label = nodes), link=dict(source = links["source"],
target = links["target"], value = links["value"])))
# Title and Show Plot
fig.update_layout(title_text="Basic Sankey Diagram", font_size=12)
fig.show()
```

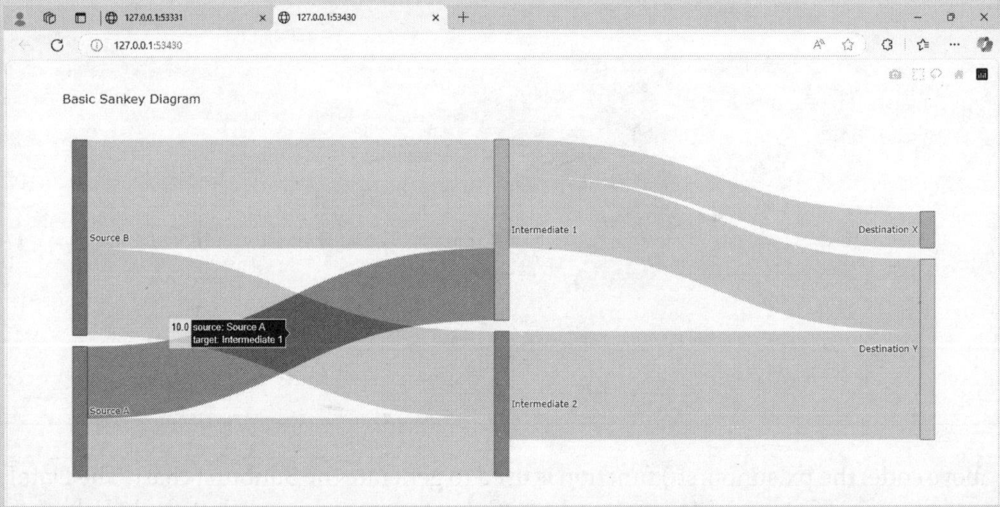

Business Scenario: Optimizing Sales and Customer Insights

XYZ Ecommerce, leveraging Python for data visualization can transform their decision-making processes. By utilizing the power of libraries like matplotlib, seaborn, and plotly, the company can create clear, actionable insights that will enable them to:

Track and forecast sales trends.

Segment and understand customer behavior.

Optimize inventory and avoid stockouts or overstocking.

Improve marketing and sales strategies by focusing on high-margin products.

The actionable visual insights can lead to more informed decisions, better resource allocation, and ultimately improve the company's bottom line.

Sales Performance Analysis

```
import pandas as pd
import matplotlib.pyplot as plt
import seaborn as sns
# Dummy sales data
data = {
    'Date': pd.date_range('2024-01-01', periods=100, freq='D'),
```

```
    'Product': ['Product A', 'Product B', 'Product C', 'Product D'] * 25,
    'Sales': [200, 150, 300, 100, 250, 200, 350, 450, 500, 600] * 10
}
df = pd.DataFrame(data)
# Sales over time (Line Chart)
plt.figure(figsize=(10, 6))
df.groupby('Date')['Sales'].sum().plot(kind='line', color='b')
plt.title('Sales Over Time')
plt.xlabel('Date')
plt.ylabel('Total Sales')
plt.grid(True)
plt.xticks(rotation=45)
plt.tight_layout()
plt.show()
# Sales by Product Category (Bar Chart)
plt.figure(figsize=(10, 6))
sns.barplot(x='Product', y='Sales', data=df, estimator=sum, ci=None)
plt.title('Sales by Product Category')
plt.xlabel('Product')
plt.ylabel('Total Sales')
plt.tight_layout()
plt.show()
import numpy as np
# Dummy customer data
customer_data = {
    'Age': np.random.randint(18, 65, size=100),
    'Total Spend': np.random.randint(100, 1000, size=100)
}
df_customers = pd.DataFrame(customer_data)
# Customer Segmentation (Scatter Plot)
plt.figure(figsize=(10, 6))
sns.scatterplot(x='Age', y='Total Spend', data=df_customers)
plt.title('Customer Age vs Total Spend')
plt.xlabel('Age')
plt.ylabel('Total Spend ($)')
plt.tight_layout()
plt.show()
# Dummy inventory data
inventory_data = {
    'Product': ['Product A', 'Product B', 'Product C', 'Product D'],
    'Inventory': [150, 200, 50, 75]
}
```

```
df_inventory = pd.DataFrame(inventory_data)
# Inventory Levels (Bar Chart)
plt.figure(figsize=(10, 6))
sns.barplot(x='Product', y='Inventory', data=df_inventory, palette='viridis')
plt.title('Inventory Levels by Product')
plt.xlabel('Product')
plt.ylabel('Inventory Level')
plt.tight_layout()
plt.show()
# Dummy revenue and profit data
revenue_data = {
    'Product': ['Product A', 'Product B', 'Product C', 'Product D'],
    'Revenue': [1000, 1500, 800, 600],
    'Cost': [600, 900, 400, 300]
}
df_revenue = pd.DataFrame(revenue_data)
# Calculating Profit
df_revenue['Profit'] = df_revenue['Revenue'] - df_revenue['Cost']
# Stacked Bar Chart for Revenue and Profit
df_revenue.set_index('Product')[['Revenue', 'Profit']].plot(kind='bar', stacked=True, figsize=(10,
6), color=['blue', 'green'])
plt.title('Revenue and Profit Comparison by Product')
plt.xlabel('Product')
plt.ylabel('Amount ($)')
plt.tight_layout()
plt.show()
# Identifying anomalies in sales data using a Box Plot
plt.figure(figsize=(10, 6))
sns.boxplot(x='Product', y='Sales', data=df)
plt.title('Sales Distribution by Product')
plt.xlabel('Product')
plt.ylabel('Sales ($)')
plt.tight_layout()
plt.show()
```

Therefore, remember that

- Pixel plots are used to represent 2-dimensional data set where each pixel refers to a different value in a data set.
- 3D data visualization facilitates data exploration and analysis from different perspectives, offering better insights and decision-making.
- Wireframe models use lines and points to form the basic structure of a 3D shape.
- Volume rendering creates a semi-transparent 3D representation of volumetric data.

- ❑ Bubble charts are useful in multivariate analysis for displaying relationships among four variables
- ❑ Icon-based visualization techniques use small graphical symbols (icons) to represent data points.

Key Terms

Aesthetics: A set of principles concerned with the nature and appreciation of beauty, especially in art.

Bar Chart: A bar graph is a chart or graph that presents categorical data with rectangular bars.

Box Plot: Also known as a whisker plot, it displays a summary of a set of data containing the minimum, first quartile, median, third quartile, and maximum.

Correlation Matrix: A plot that represents which variable is having a high or low correlation in respect to another variable.

Frequency Polygon: A graphical form of data representation that gives an idea about the shape of the data and the trends that a particular data set follows.

Histogram: A graphical representation which is quite similar to a bar graphs. It is a great tool for assessing probability distribution of a continuous variable that is easily understood by people looking at it.

Scatter Plot: A chart which plots each value in the data set by a dot.

Stacked Bar Chart: Stack bars that represent different groups on top of each other. The height of the resulting bar shows the combined result of the groups.

Time Series Data: A sequence of observations over time, which are usually spaced at regular intervals.

Univariate Time Series Data: A set of observations over time of a single variable.

Chapter Highlights

- ★ pyplot module is a sub-module of the matplotlib module.
- ★ Matplotlib is the most widely used scientific plotting library in Python.
- ★ The main advantage of plotting a bar graph is that it depicts comparisons among discrete categories.
- ★ The bar() function allow users to specify a starting value for a bar. Instead of running from zero to a value, it will go from the bottom to the value. In the code, the first call to pyplot.bar() plots the blue bars. The second call to pyplot.bar() plots the green bars, with the bottom of the blue bars being at the top of the green bars.
- ★ plt.cla() function is used to clear the axis and plt.close() to close a window that has popped up to show you your plot.
- ★ Frequency polygons can be used to compare two sets of data and are best for comparing two data sets that have the same sample size.
- ★ To draw a frequency polygon with a histogram, first draw rectangular bars against the given class intervals. Then, join the midpoints of the bars to obtain the frequency polygon.
- ★ In a box plot, a vertical line goes through the box at the median. The whiskers go from each quartile to the minimum or maximum.
- ★ Correlation is used to find out relationship between two variables.

* The distplot() function allows users to plot univariate distribution. The function can plot a histogram that fits the kernel density estimation of the data. Technically, the distplot() function is used to visualize the parametric distribution of a dataset.
* KDE is used to estimate the probability density function of a continuous random variable for non-parametric analysis. A density plot is like a histogram but has a smooth curve drawn through the top of each bin. We can call such a histogram as an abstracted histogram.
* Bivariate Distribution determines the relation between two variables and understand how one variable is behaving with respect to the other.
* Point plots serve the same purpose that bar plots serve. But they are drawn in a different style. Rather than drawing a full bar, value of the estimate is represented by a point at a certain height on the other axis.
* The **catplot()** function provides a framework to plot several types of plots to represent relationship between numerical variable and one or more categorical variables
* Facet grid forms a matrix of panels defined by row and column formed by dividing the variables. It can be drawn with up to three dimensions- row, col, and hue.
* A Bubble chart is used to display data as a cluster of circles. It is primarily used to show relationships between numeric variables.
* Autocorrelation function test is mainly used for detecting non-randomness in the data and for identifying the appropriate time series model for the particular dataset.

Review Questions

1. How does plotting graphs helpful in statistics?
2. What is pyplot? Give its uses.
3. What is a bar chart? How is it useful in interpreting data?
4. Explain the syntax of hist() function.
5. How will you calculate appropriate number of bins when plotting a histogram?
6. How will you plot a frequency polygon without a histogram?
7. How will you plot a frequency polygon with a histogram?
8. What information is revealed by a box plot?
9. How is a scatter plot drawn?
10. How is the seaborn library better than matplotlib?
11. With the help of an example explain the use of pairplot(), jointplot(), and distplot() functions.
12. Explain the utility of a facet grid.
13. How does cmap attribute make heatmaps more meaningful?
14. Differentiate between univariate and multi-variate time series data.
15. How is autocorrelation function important for data analysis?
16. How is 3D visualization different from 2D?
17. How does volume rendering help in visualization?
18. Explain the factors which help us to choose the right type of 3D visualization technique.
19. Give any three merits and three demerits of 3D visualization.

Programming Exercise

1. Plot a vertical bar graph depicting bronze, silvers and gold medals won by India in the last Asian Games.
2. Plot a horizontal bar graph depicting bronze, silvers and gold medals by China in last Asian Games.
3. Plot a vertical bar graph depicting bronze, silvers and gold medals by China and India in last Asian Games.
4. Plot a stacked bar graph depicting bronze, silvers and gold medals by China, India, Japan and Pakistan in last Asian Games.
5. Draw a scatter plot depicting year of launch and speed of the car.
6. Draw a scatter plot to compare the performance of boys and girls in a class test. From the graph, tell who performed better and were there any outliers.
7. Draw a scatter plot representing Unemployment Rate vs Stock Index Price. These two data sets should specified using pandas data frame.
8. Write a Python program to draw a scatter plot for three different groups comparing weights and heights.
9. Plot a stacked histogram showing marks obtained by 4 students in five different subjects.
10. Display a Box Plot representing marks obtained by 4 students in five different subjects.
11. Use the iris data set to plot a histogram along with kde to represent petal_length.
12. Use the iris data set to plot a scatter plot to represent relationship between peatl_lengt and petal_width.
13. Draw a violinplot to depict the relationship between tip paid on each day of the week.
14. Draw a violinplot to depict the relationship between total_bill, day of the week and sex.
15. Draw a countplot() that shows the count o class in the Titanic data set.
16. Draw a horizontal boxplot or the iris data set.
17. Draw a facet grid to represent the relationship between columns of tips data set.
18. Draw a regression plot to show the regression line between age and fare values of the titanic dataset.
19. Compare the regression plots obtained by posing a query for dataset I and II in the anscombe data set while plotting for x and y values.
20. Draw a scatter plot through a facet grid depicting total_bill and tip with columns representing gender and colored by smoker or a non-smoker. Refer dataset tips.
21. Draw a PairGrid for the iris data set. Customize color of the plot using a categorical variable (like species). Also use a different function on the diagonal to show the univariate distribution of the variable in each column.
22. Use the gapminder dataset to draw heatmaps for the following to perform the following analysis.
    a. a heatmap showing life expectancy of each continent over the years
    b. a heatmap showing life expectancy of each country over the years
    c. a heatmap showing life expectancy of each country over the years. The index should be both country as well as continent.

23. Download the daily-min-temperatures.csv that has time series data and plot a line chart, histogram, kdeplot and boxplot.
24. Plot a line graph to represent the time series data given in the file.
25. Plot a scatter matrix to represent data from the diabetes.csv file.
26. Create a file stock.csv and put the following data into it.

Value Date	Price
01-09-2022,	1042.05
02-09-2022,	1033.55
03-09-2022,	1029.7
04-09-2022,	1021.3
05-09-2022,	1015.4
06-09-2022,	1161.3
07-09-2022,	1167.6
08-09-2022,	1155.25
09-09-2022,	1154

27. Write a program to plot a 2D pixel plot with 100 random data points.
28. Use a simple mathematical function, z=sin(x) × cos(y) to generate a 3D surface plot.
29. Write a program to plot a 3D bar chart for random values of X, Y, and Z axis.
30. Write a program to plot a 3D pie chart to represent the market share of five companies in the smartphone industry, with each company holding a certain percentage of the global market share.
31. Write a program to plot a 3D Wireframe for $z = x^2 + y^2$.
32. Write a program to plot the correlation heatmap of the features present in iris dataset.
33. Write a program to create a small dataset for cars, which includes columns like horsepower, weight, and price. Plot a bubble chart to represent the features.
34. Write a program to plot and represent the ratings for each category in the radar plot.

Fill in the Blanks

1. pyplot module is a sub-module of the _______ module.
2. Matplotlib is the most widely library in Python for __________.
3. ______ function that can be used to plot a bar graph.
4. The _____ function is used to plot a horizontal bar graph.
5. The range or limit of the x axis can be set by using the _______.
6. To make ideal number of bin's width, set bins = ______.
7. _______ function is used to get the same set of random numbers each time the program is executed. Ans. seed()
8. The formula for calculating class mark is ________.
9. A box from the first quartile to the ______ quartile.
10. _______ are usually used to represent the correlation between two or more variables.
11. ________ is used to find out relationship between two variables.
12. The _______ function in the Numpy module returns a matrix of correlations of x with x, x with y, y with x and y with y.

13. A correlation matrix depicting correlations between different variables in a dataframe can be created using the ______ function.
14. To better visualize data, we can make the plots look attractive using by figure ________.
15. To build a color palette, the _________ function is used.
16. _____ is used to estimate the probability density function of a continuous random variable for non-parametric analysis.
17. ______ Distribution determines the relation between two variables and understand how one variable is behaving with respect to the other.
18. ________ binning is used in bivariate data analysis when the data is sparse in density.
19. The three dimensions in a facet grid are _____, ______ and ______.
20. _____ is used to map plot aspects to different colors.
21. ________ is a set of colors for mapping the "hue" variable.
22. In a heatmap, darker shades of a chart represent _______ (higher/lower) values than the lighter shade.
23. A bubble chart is plotted using the _______ function.
24. _______ data is a sequence of observations over time, which are usually spaced at regular intervals.
25. ________ function test is mainly used for identifying the appropriate time series model for the particular dataset.
26. The _____ function in the matplotlib library is used to visualize the sparse array.
27. 3D surface plots the relationship between three _______ variables.
28. ______ models use lines and points to form the basic structure of a 3D shape.
29. voxel means ________.
30. ______ charts are useful in multivariate analysis for displaying relationships among four variables.
31. _________ visualization techniques use small graphical symbols to represent data points.

State True or False

1. A bar graph presents categorical data with rectangular bars.
2. In a bar graph, bars can be drawn only vertically.
3. The bar() function is used to draw a stacked bar chart.
4. The labels for x axis can be specified using the ylabel().
5. Histograms assess probability distribution of a non-continuous variable.
6. Histogram plots the frequency distribution of numeric array by splitting it to small equal-sized bins.
7. Frequency polygon is always drawn along with a histogram. Ans. False
8. When drawing a frequency plot, frequency is plotted on x-axis.
9. Frequency is plotted against the class mark and not the upper or lower limit of any class.
10. We can make horizontal box plot.
11. If $\rho = -1$, then there is no relation between X and Y.
12. A correlation plot is like a histogram having a smooth curve drawn through the top of each bin.

13. pairplot() function is used to plot multiple pairwise bivariate distributions in a dataset.
14. Unlike FacetGrid, Pair Grid uses different pair of variables for each subplot.
15. Multicollinearity is good for a data set.
16. A logistic regression model is substantially more computationally intensive than linear regression.
17. A bubble chart is primarily used to depict and show relationships between categorical variables.
18. A multivariate analysis is useful when data points are equally spaced.
19. 3D visualization can be used to identify outliers.
20. 3D surface plots create a semi-transparent 3D representation of volumetric data.
21. Stick figure represents a parent–child relationship.

Fill in the Blanks to Complete the Code

1.
```
import matplotlib.pyplot as plt
__________ = [22,55,62,45,21,22,34,42,42,4,99,102,110,120,121,122,130,111,115,112,80,75,65,54,44,43,42,48]
plt.hist(population_ages, bins = ____, histtype = ____, rwidth=0.8)
plt.xlabel('___')
plt._____('y')
plt.________('Interesting Graph\nCheck it out')
plt.legend()
plt._____()
```

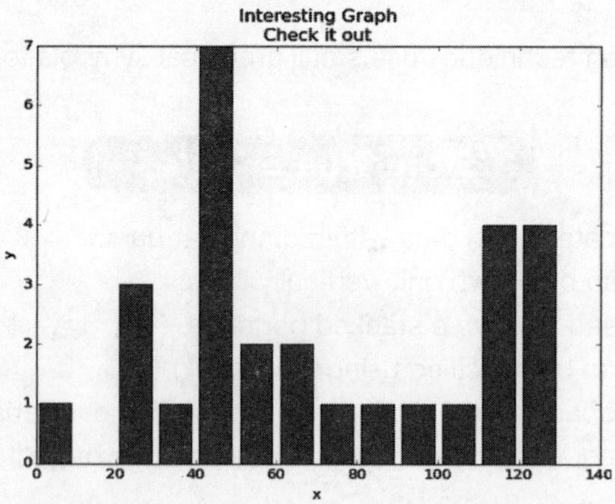

2.
```
import matplotlib.pyplot as plt
plt.____([1,3,5,7,9],[5,2,7,8,2], label="Example one")
plt.bar([2,4,6,8,10],[8,6,2,5,6], _______ = "Example two", color='____')
_____.legend()
plt._____ ('bar number')
plt.ylabel(______)
____.show()
```

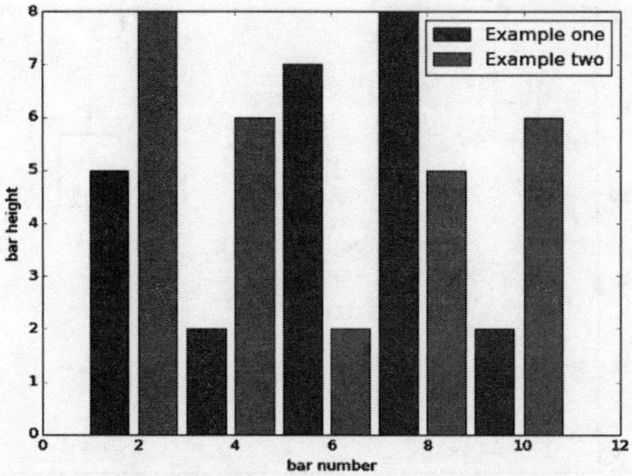

3.
```
import _________ as plt
import numpy ____ np
np._______.seed(1)
x = ____.arange(0.0, 50.0, 2.0)
y = x ** 1.3 + np.random.rand(*x.shape) * 30.0
s = np.random.rand(*x.shape) * 800 + 500
plt.scatter(x, ___, s, ______ = "green", ______=0.5, _____=r'$\
clubsuit$',______ ="Luck")
plt.xlabel("__________")
plt.________("Gold")
_____.legend(loc='upper left')
plt.show()
```

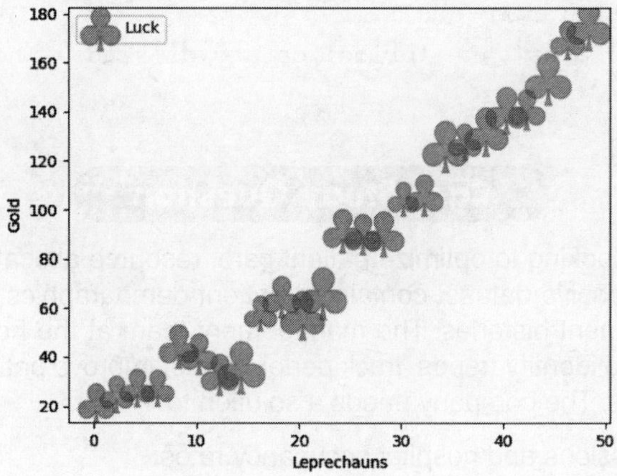

4.
```
import matplotlib.pyplot as ____
import numpy as np
sequence1 = ____.random.random_integers(0,100,100)
________ = np.random.random_integers(25,75,100)
sequence3 = np.__________.random_integers(50,80,100)
plot.boxplot((_________, sequence2, sequence3))
plot.show()
```

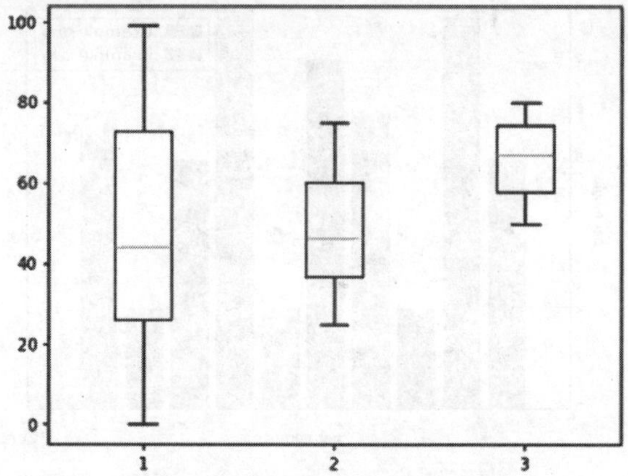

Give the Output

1.
```
import pandas as pd
import seaborn as sb
from matplotlib import pyplot as plt
df = sb.load_dataset('iris')
sb.distplot(df['petal_length'],hist=False)
plt.show()
```
2.
```
import pandas as pd
import seaborn as sb
from matplotlib import pyplot as plt
df = sb.load_dataset('diamonds')
sb.jointplot(x = 'carat',y = 'price',data = df,kind = 'hex')
plt.show()
```

Case Study Question

A healthcare provider, is looking to optimize patient care, resource allocation, and operational efficiency. They have an extensive dataset containing patient demographics, treatment data, hospital admissions, and appointment histories. The management team at the hospital wants to use data visualization techniques to identify trends, track performance, improve patient satisfaction, and predict future resource needs. The company needs a solution to:

- ❑ Monitor patient admissions and hospital occupancy rates.
- ❑ Visualize treatment effectiveness and patient outcomes.
- ❑ Track seasonal trends in patient visits and disease occurrences.
- ❑ Analyze patient demographics and their impact on healthcare services.

CHAPTER

7 File Handling

Data Automation

In today's scenario, companies rely heavily on data to make informed decisions. Data is often stored in a variety of files including CSV, JSON, XML, or Excel files. The company uses Python to efficiently handle file so that the data can be stored, retrieved, processed, and manipulated seamlessly.

Assume that ABC Retail Ltd. has several files containing transactional data, including customer orders, inventory logs, and sales reports stored in CSV and text file formats. As the volume of transactions is continuously growing, manually processing these files has become time-consuming and error-prone. The business is looking for an automated solution to handle files efficiently. Write the code to perform the following tasks.

- **Read** and **write** customer orders and sales data from/to CSV files.
- **Update** inventory levels based on the sales data.
- **Generate** reports for sales performance on a weekly basis.

The data that we already have in a row and column format can be easily converted into rows and columns of a database or spreadsheet file (CSV, TXT, XLS) so that this structured data can be used later for further processing and analysis. These files have a delimiter and support either fixed or variable width data in which missing values are represented as blanks in between the delimiters.

Even unstructured data obtained from HTML pages, images, PDF files, a feed from Twitter or a plain text document from a news feed can be converted into more usable data by using different built-in functions from various Python libraries.

In this chapter, we will therefore read about the basic operations on a text file. These operations include opening a file either by using relative or absolute file path in the desired mode, reading, appending, manipulating data stored in a text file and performing standard input/output operations on them.

We will also discuss these basic operations on a binary file, read about the Pickle Module for loading and dumping data in a binary file. Operations on CSV files are also illustrated in this chapter. All these files are very critical to storing and processing large chunks of data for analysis and knowledge extraction.

7.1 Introduction

A **file** is a collection of data stored on a secondary storage device like a hard disk. Till now, we had been processing data that was entered through the computer's keyboard using the input(). But this task can become very tedious, especially when there is a huge amount of data to be processed. A better solution, therefore, is to combine all the input data into a file and then design a Python program to read this data from the file whenever required.

When a program is being executed, its data is stored in *random access memory* (RAM). Though RAM can be accessed faster by the CPU, it is also **volatile**, which means that when the program ends, or the computer shuts down, all the data is lost. If you want to use the data in future, then you need to store this data on a permanent or non-volatile storage media like the hard disk, USB drive, DVD, etc.

Data on **non-volatile** storage media is stored in named locations on the media called **files**. You can think of working with files as working with a notebook. To use a notebook, you must first open it. Once the notebook is opened, you can read the contents that you had previously written in it or write some new content into it. After using the notebook, you close it. The same concept can be applied to files. We first open a file, read or write to it and then finally close it.

A file is basically used because real life applications involve large amounts of data and in such situations the console oriented I/O operations pose two major problems:

- First, it becomes cumbersome and time consuming to handle huge amount of data through terminals.
- Second, when doing I/O using terminal, the entire data is lost when either the program is terminated or the computer is turned off. Therefore, it becomes necessary to store data on a permanent storage (the disks) and read whenever necessary, without destroying the data.

In order to use files, we have to learn file input and output operations, that is, how data is read or written to a file. Although file I/O operations are almost same as terminal I/O, the only difference is that when doing file I/O, the user must specify the name of the file from which data should be read/written.

7.2 File path

The files that we use are stored on a storage medium like the hard disk in such a way that they can be easily retrieved as and when required. Most file systems that are used today store files in a tree (or *hierarchical*) structure. At the top of the tree is one (or more) root node(s). Under the root node, there are other files and folders (or **directories**) and each folder can in turn contain other files and folders. Even these folders can contain other files and folders and this can go on to nearly a limitless depth. Consider the tree structure given in Figure 7.1.

> Folder names and file names are case sensitive in Windows but they are case insensitive in Linux

Every file is identified by its path that begins from the root node or the root folder. In Windows, C:\ (also known as C drive) is the root folder, but you can also have a path that starts from other drives like D:\, E:\, etc. The **file path** is also known as the pathname. For example, in the figure, the file BTech_CS.docx file is stored in the C:\. The C drive has a folder Students which in turn has a subfolder (folder within a folder) named Graduate. The subfolder Graduate has the desired file. So the path of this file can be written as,

C:\Students\Under Graduate\BTech_CS.docx

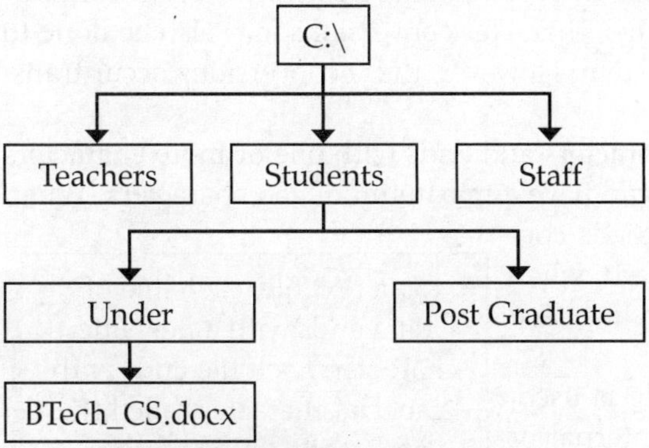

Figure 7.1 Files and Folders

> The characters after the dot forms the extension of the file. It is used to indicate the type of file. For example, docx tells that the file is a Word document)

Note that the character used to separate the folder names (also called the **delimiter**) is specific to the file system. For example, while Solaris OS uses the forward slash (/), Microsoft Windows on the other hand uses the backslash (\).

7.2.1 Relative path and absolute path

> A relative path is specified relative to the program's current working directory

A file path can be either *relative* or *absolute*. While an absolute path always contains the root and the complete directory list to specify the exact location of the file, relative path on the other hand, needs to be combined with another path in order to access a file. That is, relative pathname starts with respect to the current working directory and therefore lacks the leading slashes. For example, C:\Students\Under Graduate\BTech_CS.docx is the absolute path as all of the information needed to locate the file is contained in the path, but Under Graduate\BTech_CS.docx is a relative path as only a part of the complete path is specified.

Note that when a relative file path is specified, the relative path is joined with the current directory to create an absolute file path. Therefore, in our example, if the current working directory is C:\Students, then the relative path Under Graduate\BTech_CS.docx is equivalent to using its absolute path.

7.3 Types of files

Like C and C++, Python also supports two types of files – text files and binary files.

7.3.1 ASCII text files

A **text file** is a stream of characters that can be sequentially processed by a computer in forward direction. For this reason a text file is usually opened for only one kind of operation (reading, writing, or appending) at any given time. As text files only process characters, they can only read or write data, one character at a time. In Python, a text stream is treated as a special kind of file.

Depending on the requirements of the operating system and on the operation that has to be performed (read/write operation) on the file, newline characters may be converted to or from carriage-return/linefeed combinations. Besides this, other character conversions may also be done to satisfy the storage requirements of the operating system. However, these conversions occur transparently to process a text file.

In a text file, each line contains zero or more characters and ends with one or more characters that specify the end of line. Each line in a text file can have a maximum of 255 characters. When data is written to a text file, each newline character is converted to a carriage return/line feed character. Similarly, when data is read from a text file, each carriage return/ line feed character is converted in to newline character.

> In a text file, each line of data ends with a new line character. Each file ends with a special character called the end-of-file (EOF) marker.

Another important thing is that when a text file is used, there are actually two representations of data – internal or external. For example, an integer value will be represented as a number that occupies 2 or 4 bytes of memory internally, but externally the integer value will be represented as a string of characters representing its decimal or hexadecimal value.

7.3.2 Binary files

A binary file is a file which may contain any type of data, encoded in binary form for computer storage and processing purposes. It includes files like word processing documents, PDFs, images, spreadsheets, videos, zip files and other executable programs. Like a text file, a binary file is a collection of bytes. A binary file is also referred to as a character stream with following two essential differences.

- A binary file does not require any special processing of the data and each byte of data is transferred to or from the disk unprocessed.
- Python places no constructs on the file, and it may be read from, or written to, in any manner the programmer wants.

While text files can be processed sequentially, binary files, on the other hand, can be either processed sequentially or randomly depending on the needs of the application. In Python, to process a file randomly, the programmer must move the current file position to an appropriate place in the file before reading or writing data. For example, if a file is used to store records (using structures) of students, then to update a particular record, the programmer must first locate the appropriate record, read the record into memory, update it and finally write the record back to disk at its appropriate location in the file.

> The contents of a binary file are not human readable. If you want that data stored in the file must be human-readable, then store the data in a text file.

> Binary files store data in the internal representation format. Therefore, an integer value will be stored in binary form as 2 byte value. The same format is used to store data in memory as well as in file. Like text file, binary file also ends with an EOF market.

In a text file, an integer value 123 will be stored as a sequence of three characters – 1, 2 and 3. So each character will take 1 byte and therefore, to store the integer value 123 we need 3 bytes. However, in a binary file, the integer value 123 will be stored in 2 bytes in the binary form. This clearly indicates that binary files take less space to store the same piece of data and eliminate conversion between internal and external representations and are thus more efficient than the text files.

Thus, we see that text files contain only basic characters and do not store any information about the color, font and size of the text. Examples of text files include files with .txt or .py extension. These files can be opened with Windows Notepad. These files can be easily read and the contents of the file are treated as an ordinary string value. Binary files, on the other hand, cannot be read by text editors like Notepad. If you open a binary file in Notepad, you will see some scrambles and absurd data.

7.4 Opening and closing files

Python has many built-in functions and methods to manipulate files. These functions and methods basically work on a file object.

> Binary files are mainly used to store data beyond text, like images, executables, etc.

7.4.1 The open() function

Before reading from or writing to a file, you must first open it using Python's built-in open() function. This function creates a file object, which will be used to invoke methods associated with it. The syntax of open() is:

fileObj = open(file_name [, access_mode])

Where,

file_name is a string value that specifies name of the file that you want to access.

access_mode indicates the mode in which the file has to be opened, i.e., read, write, append, etc. Table 1 lists other possible values of access mode argument.

Note that the open() function returns a file object. This file object will be used to read, write or perform any other operation on the file. It works like a file handle.

You can also print the details of file object as shown in the code given below.

```
file = open("File1.txt", "rb")
print(file)
OUTPUT
<open file 'File1.txt', mode 'rb' at 0x02A850D0>
```

> Access mode is an optional parameter and the default file access mode is read(r).

Note that a **file handle** is different from a file. Try to understand it by using an analogy of TV and the TV remote control. You can use the remote control to switch channels, change the volume, etc. But whatever changes you try to do using remote control are actually applied on the TV. So, your file handle or the file object acts as a remote control of your file (TV). Whatever changes you want to perform on the file is actually carried out through the file object.

Table 1: || Access Modes

Mode	Purpose
r	This is the default mode of opening a file which opens the file for reading only. The file pointer is placed at the beginning of the file.
rb	This mode opens a file for reading only in binary format. The file pointer is placed at the beginning of the file.

(Continued)

Table 1: || *(Continued)*

Mode	Purpose
r+	This mode opens a file for both reading and writing. The file pointer is placed at the beginning of the file.
rb+	This mode opens the file for both reading and writing in binary format. The file pointer is placed at the beginning of the file.
w	This mode opens the file for writing only. When a file is opened in w mode, two things can happen. If the file does not exist, a new file is created for writing. If the file already exists and has some data stored in it, the contents are overwritten.
wb	Opens a file in binary format for writing only. When a file is opened in this mode, two things can happen. If the file does not exist, a new file is created for writing. If the file already exists and has some data stored in it, the contents are overwritten.
w+	Opens a file for both writing and reading. When a file is opened in this mode, two things can happen. If the file does not exist, a new file is created for reading as well as writing. If the file already exists and has some data stored in it, the contents are overwritten.
wb+	Opens a file in binary format for both reading and writing. When a file is opened in this mode, two things can happen. If the file does not exist, a new file is created for reading as well as writing. If the file already exists and has some data stored in it, the contents are overwritten.
a	Opens a file for appending. The file pointer is placed at the end of the file if the file exists. If the file does not exist, it creates a new file for writing.
ab	Opens a file in binary format for appending. The file pointer is at the end of the file if the file exists. If the file does not exist, it creates a new file for writing.
a+	Opens a file for both reading and appending. The file pointer is placed at the end of the file if the file exists. If the file does not exist, it creates a new file for reading and writing.
ab+	Opens a file in binary format for both reading and appending. The file pointer is placed at the end of the file if the file exists. If the file does not exist, a new file is created for reading and writing.

7.4.2 The file object attributes

Once a file is successfully opened, a *file* object is returned. Using this file object, you can easily access various types of information related to that file. This information can be obtained by reading values of specific attributes of the file. Table 2 lists attributes related to file object.

Table 2: || File Object Attributes

Attribute	Information obtained
fileObj.closed	Returns true if the file is closed and false otherwise
fileObj.mode	Returns access mode with which file has been opened
fileObj.name	Returns name of the file

Program to open a file and print its attribute values.

```
file = open("File1.txt", "wb")
print("Name of the file: ", file.name)
print("File is closed.", file.closed)
print("File has been opened in ", file.mode, "mode")
OUTPUT
Name of the file:  File1.txt
File is closed. False
File has been opened in wb mode
```

7.4.3 The close() method

The close() method as the name suggests is used to close the file object. Once a file object is closed, you cannot further read from or write into the file associated with the file object. While closing the file object the close() flushes any unwritten information (which means transfers the data to file that was supposed to be written in the file but has not yet been transferred). Although, Python automatically closes a file when the reference object of a file is reassigned to another file, but as a good programming habit you should always explicitly use the close() method to close a file. The syntax of close() is

fileObj.close()

The close() method frees up any system resources like file descriptors, file locks, etc. that are associated with the file. Moreover, there is an upper limit to the number of files a program can open. If that limit is exceeded, then the program may even crash or work in an unexpected manner. Thus, you can waste lots of memory if you keep many files open unnecessarily and also remember that open files always stand a chance of corruption and data loss.

Once the file is closed using the close() method, any attempt to use the file object will result in an error.

Program that tries to access a file after it is closed.

```
file = open("File1.txt", "wb")
print("Name of the file: ", file.name)
print("File is closed.", file.closed)
print("FIle is now being closed.. You cannot
use the File Object")
file.close()
print("File is closed.", file.closed)
print(file.read())

OUTPUT
Name of the file:  File1.txt
File is closed. False
FIle is now being closed.. You cannot use the
File Object
File is closed. True
Traceback (most recent call last):
  File "C:\Python27\Try.py", line 7, in <module>
    print(file.read())
ValueError: I/O operation on closed file
```

> Python has a garbage collector to clean up unreferenced objects but still it is our responsibility to close the file and release the resources consumed by it

7.5 Reading and writing files

The read() and write() are used to read data from file and write data to files, respectively. In this section, we will study both these functions to manipulate data through files.

7.5.1 write() and writelines() methods

The write() method is used to write a string to an already opened file. Of course, this string may include numbers, special characters or other symbols. While writing data to a file, you must remember that the write() method does not add a newline character ('\n') to the end of the string. The syntax of write() method is:

fileObj.write(string);

As per the syntax, the string that is passed as an argument to the write() is written into the opened file.

Program to write a small program that writes a message in the file.

```
file = open("File1.txt", "w")
file.write("Hello  All,  hope  you  are  enjoying
learning Python")
file.close()
print("Data Written into the file.......")
OUTPUT
Data Written into the file......."
```

> The write( ) method returns None

Now, if you open the File1.txt, you will see that it has the contents, "Hello All, hope you are enjoying learning Python" written in it. The file is created in the same directory where your program file (.py file) is stored, that is in the C:\Python27 folder.

The writelines() method is used to write a list of strings.

Program to write to a file using the writelines() method

```
file = open("File1.txt", "w")
lines = ["Hello World, ", "Welcome to the world of Python", "Enjoy Learning
Python"]
file.writelines(lines)
file.close()
print("Data written to file........")
OUTPUT
Data written to file.......
```

7.5.2 append() method

Once you have stored some data in a file, you can always open that file again to write more data or append data to it. To append a file, you must open it using 'a' or 'ab' mode depending on whether it is a text file or a binary file. Note that if you open a file in 'w' or 'wb' mode and then start writing data into it, then its existing contents would be overwritten. So always open the file in 'a' or 'ab' mode to add more data to existing data stored in the file.

Appending data is especially essential when creating a log of events or combining a large set of data into one file. The code given below appends data to our File1.txt file.

Program to append data to an already existing file

```
file = open("File1.txt", "a")
file.write("\n Python is a very simple yet
powerful language")
file.close()
print("Data appended to file.......")
OUTPUT
Data appended to file......."
```

If you open a file in append mode then the file is created if it did not exist.

7.5.3 The read() and readline() methods

The read() method is used to read a string from an already opened file. As said before, the string can include alphabets, numbers, characters or other symbols. The syntax of read() method is

fileObj.read([cout])

In the above syntax, count is an optional parameter which if passed to the read() method specifies the number of bytes to be read from the opened file. The read() method starts reading from the beginning of the file and if count is missing or has a negative value then, it reads the entire contents of the file (i.e., till the end of file).

Program to print the first 10 characters of the file File1.txt.

```
file = open("File1.txt", "r")
print(file.read(10))
file.close()
OUTPUT
Hello All,
Note that if you try to open a file for reading
that does not exist, then you will get an error,
as shown below.
file1 = open("file2.txt","r")
print(file2.read())
OUTPUT
Traceback (most recent call last):
  File "C:\Python27\Try.py", line 1, in <module>
    file1 = open("file2.txt","r")
IOError: [Errno 2] No such file or directory:
'file2.txt'
```

read() method returns newline as '\n'.

The readline() method is used to read a single line from the file. The method returns an empty string when the end of the file has been reached. Note that a blank line is represented by \n and the readline() method returns a string containing only a single newline when a blank line is encountered in the file.

Consider adding a few more lines in the file File1.txt and read its contents using the readline() method. The contents of the file are,

```
Hello All,
Hope you are enjoying learning Python
We have tried to cover every point in detail
to avoid confusion
Happy Reading
file = open("File1.txt", "r")
print("First Line : ", file.readline())
print("Second Line : ", file.readline())
print("Third Line : ", file.readline())
file.close()
OUTPUT
First Line :  Hello All,

Second Line :

Third Line :  Hope you are enjoying learning
Python
```

Binary files are more efficient than text files so we have opened the files using rb and wb access modes. You could have also opened using r or w access mode to work with text files.

You can also use the readlines() method to read all the lines in the file. The code for doing so is given below.

Program to demonstrate readlines() function

```
file = open("File1.txt", "r")
print(file.readlines())
file.close()
OUTPUT
['Hello All,\r\n', '\r\n', 'Hope you are enjoy-
ing learning Python\r\n', '\r\n', 'We have
tried to cover every point in detail to avoid
confusion\r\n', '\r\n', 'Happy Reading\r\n']
```

After reading a line from the file using the readline() method, the control automatically passes to the next line. That is why, when you call the readline() again, the next line in the file is returned

The list() method is also used to display entire contents of the file. You just need to pass the file object as an argument to the list() method.

Program to display the contents of the file File1.txt using the list() method.

```
file = open("File1.txt", "r")
print(list(file))
file.close()
OUTPUT
['Hello All,\r\n', '\r\n', 'Hope you are enjoying learning Python\r\n',
'\r\n', 'We have tried to cover every point in detail to avoid confusion\
r\n', '\r\n', 'Happy Reading\r\n']
```

The last and probably a very fast, simple and efficient way to display a file is to loop over the file object to print every line in it. This is shown in the code given below.

Program to display the contents of a file

```
file = open("File1.txt", "r")
for line in file:
    print(line)
file.close()
OUTPUT
Hello All,
Hope you are enjoying learning Python
We have tried to cover every point in detail to
avoid confusion
Happy Reading
```

> All reading methods return an empty string when end of file (EOF) is reached. That is, if you have read the entire file and then again call readline(), an empty string would be returned.

7.5.4 Opening Files using with keyword

It is good programming habit to use with keyword when working with file objects. This has the advantage that the file is properly closed after it is used even if an error occurs during read or write operation or even when you forget to explicitly close the file. This difference is clearly evident from the code given below.

```
with open("File1.txt", "rb") as
file:
    for line in file:
        print(line)
print("Let's check if the file is
closed : ", file.closed)
OUTPUT
Hello World

Let's check if the file is closed
: True
```

```
file = open("File1.txt", "rb")
for line in file:
        print(line)
print("Let's check if the file is
closed : ", file.closed)
OUTPUT
Hello World

Let's check if the file is closed
: False
```

In the first code, the file is opened using with keyword. After the file is used in the for loop, it is automatically closed as soon as the block of code comprising the for loop is over. But when the file is opened without with keyword, it is not closed automatically. You need to explicitly close the file after using it.

```
with open("file1.txt","r") as file:
    print(file.read()) # file is already closed after the last line is read
file.close()           # attempt to close a file that is already closed
OUTPUT
Hello
Welcome to the world of Programming
```

7.5.5 Splitting words

Python allows you to read line(s) from a file and splits the line (treated as a string) based on a character. By default, this character is space but you can even specify any other character to split words in the string.

Program to split the line into a series of words and use space to perform the split operation

```
with open('File1.txt', 'r') as file:
    line = file.readline()
    words = line.split()
    print(words)
OUTPUT
['Hello', 'World,', 'Welcome', 'to', 'the',
'world', 'of', 'Python', 'Programming']
```

> Calling close() on a file object that is already closed does not raise any error but fails silently.

Program to perform split operation whenever a comma is encountered

```
with open('File1.txt', 'r') as file:
    line = file.readline()
    words = line.split(',')
    print(words)
OUTPUT
['Hello World', ' Welcome to the world of Python
Programming\n']
```

> When you open a file for reading or writing the file is searched in the current working directory. If the file exist somewhere else then you need to specify the path of the file

7.5.6 Some other useful file methods

Table 3 discusses some additional file methods.

Table 3: || File Methods

Method	Description	Example
fileno()	Returns the file number of the file (which is an integer descriptor)	file = open("File1.txt", "w") print(file.fileno()) OUPUT 3
flush()	Flushes the write buffer of the file stream	file = open("File1.txt", "w") file.flush()
isatty()	Returns True if the file stream is interactive and False otherwise	file = open("File1.txt", "w") file.write("Hello") print(file.isatty()) OUTPUT False
readline(n)	Reads and returns one line from file. N is optional. If n is specified then atmost n bytes are read	file = open("Try.py", "r") print(file.readline(10)) OUTPUT file = ope

(Continued)

Table 3: || *(Continued)*

Method	Description	Example
truncate(n)	Resizes the file to n bytes	file = open("File.txt", "w") file.write("Welcome to the world of programming....") file.truncate(5)
rstrip()	Strips off whitespaces including newlines from the right side of the string read from the file.	file = open("File.txt") line = file.readline() print(line.rstrip()) OUTPUT Greetings to All !!!

7.6 File positions

With every file, the file management system associates a pointer often known as *file pointer* that facilitates the movement across the file for reading and/or writing data. The file pointer specifies a location from where the current read/write operation is initiated. Once the read/write operation is completed, the pointer is automatically updated.

Python has various methods that tells or sets the position of the file pointer. For example, the tell() method tells the current position within the file at which the next read or write operation will occur. It is specified as number of bytes from the beginning of the file. When you just open a file for reading, the file pointer is positioned at location 0, which is the beginning of the file.

Table 4: || From and its Position

From	Reference position
0	From the beginning of the file
1	From the current position of
2	From the end of the file

The seek(offset[, from]) method is used to set the position of the file pointer or in simpler terms, move the file pointer to a new location. The *offset* argument indicates the number of bytes to be moved and the *from* argument specifies the reference position from where the bytes are to be moved. Table 4 specifies the value of from argument and its corresponding interpretation. Note that the from value 2 is especially important when working with MP3 files that stores tags at the end of the file, so you directly issue a command to move the file pointer to a position 128 bytes from the end of the file.

Program that tells and sets the position of the file pointer.

```
file = open("File1.txt", "rb")
print("Position of file pointer before reading is : ", file.tell())
print(file.read(10))
print("Position of file pointer after reading is : ", file.tell())
print("Setting 3 bytes from the current position of file pointer")
file.seek(3,1)
print(file.read())
file.close()
OUTPUT
Position of file pointer before reading is : 0
Hello All,
Position of file pointer after reading is : 10
Setting 3 bytes from the current position of file pointer
pe you are enjoying learning Python
```

PROGRAMMER'S ZONE

Program 7.1: Write a program that copies first 10 bytes of a binary file into another.

> In Python, you don't need to import any library to read and write files. Just create a file object and call the open function to read/write to the file.

```
with open("File1.txt", "rb") as file1:
    with open("file2.txt","wb") as file2:
            buf = file1.read(10)
            file2.write(buf)
print("File Copied")
```

OUTPUT

```
File Copied
```

Program 7.2: Write a program that copies one Python script into another in such a way that all comment lines are skipped and not copied in the destination file

```
with open("First.py", "rb") as file1:
    with open("Second.py","wb") as file2:
        while True:
            buf = file1.readline()
            if len(buf)!=0:
                if buf[0] == '#':
                    continue
                else:
                    file2.write(buf)
            else:
                break
print("File Copied")
```

OUTPUT

```
File Copied
```

Program 7.3: Write a program that accepts filename as an input from the user. Open the file and count the number of times a character appears in the file

```
filename = input("Enter the filename : ")
with open(filename) as file:
    text = file.read()
    letter = input("Enter the character to be searched : ")
    count = 0
    for char in text:
        if char == letter:
                count += 1
print(letter, "appears ", count, " times in file")
```

OUTPUT

```
Enter the filename : File1.txt
Enter the character to be searched : a
a appears  7  times in file
```

Program 7.4: Write a program that reads data from a file and calculates the percentage of vowels and consonants in the file

```
filename = input("Enter the filename : ")
```

```
with open(filename) as file:
    text = file.read()
    count_vowels = 0
    count_consonants = 0
    for char in text:
        if char in "aeiou":
            count_vowels += 1
        else:
            count_consonants += 1
print("Number of vowels = ", count_vowels)
print("Number of consonants = ", count_consonants)
print("Total Length of File = ", len(text))
print("Percentatge of vowels in the file = ", ((count_vowels)*100)/
len(text),"%")
print("Percentatge of consonants in the file = ", ((count_consonants)*100)/
len(text), "%")
OUTPUT
Enter the filename : File1.txt
Number of vowels = 31
Number of consonants = 77
Total Length of File = 108
Percentatge of vowels in the file = 28 %
Percentatge of consonants in the file = 71 %
```

7.7 Renaming and deleting files

The os module in Python has various methods that can be used to perform file-processing operations like renaming and deleting files. To use the methods defined in the os module, you should first import it in your program then call any related functions.

7.7.1 The rename() Method

The *rename()* method takes two arguments, the current filename and the new filename. Its syntax is:

os.rename(old_file_name, new_file_name)

Program to rename file "FILE1.TXT" to "STUDENTS.TXT"

```
import os
os.rename("File1.txt", "Students.txt")
print("File Renamed")
OUTPUT
File Renamed
```

The file object provides functions to manipulate files

You can check whether the above code renamed the right file by checking in the C:\Python27 directory. Now, there is no file named File1.txt but does have a file named Students.txt.

7.7.2 The remove() Method

This method can be used to delete file(s). The method takes a filename (name of the file to be deleted) as an argument and deletes that file. Its syntax is:

os.remove(file_name)

Program to delete a file named File1.txt

```
import os
os.remove("File1.txt")
print("File Deleted")
OUTPUT
File Deleted
Check the contents of the directory. The file name File1.txt no longer exists.
```

PROGRAMMER'S ZONE

Write a program that counts the number of tabs, spaces and new line characters in a file.

```
filename = input("Enter the filename : ")
with open(filename) as file:
    text = file.read()
    count_tab = 0
    count_space = 0
    count_nl = 0
    for char in text:
        if char == '\t':
                count_tab += 1
        if char == ' ':
                count_space += 1
        if char == '\n':
               count_nl += 1
print("TABS = ", count_tab)
print("SPACES = ", count_space)
print("NEW LINES = ", count_nl)
OUTPUT
Enter the filename : File1.txt
TABS =  3
SPACES =  22
NEW LINES =  5
```

Write a program that generates a Quiz and uses Two Files- Questions.txt and Answers.Txt. The program opens Questions.txt and reads a question and displays the question with options on the screen. The program then opens the Answer.txt file and displays the correct answers.

```
file1 = open("Questions.txt", "r")
file2 = open("Answers.txt", "r")
ques = file1.read()
qlines= ques.split('\n')
```

```
for lines in qlines:
   print(lines)
ans = file2.read()
alines= ans.split('\n')
print("CORRCT ANSWERS")
for lines in alines:
   print(lines)
```

Write a program that computes the total size of all the files in C:\Python27 folder.

```
import os
totalSize = 0
for file in os.listdir("C:\Python27"):
    totalSize += os.path.getsize(os.path.join("C:\Python27",file))
print("Total size of all the files in C:\\Python27 folder = ", totalSize)
```

OUTPUT

```
Total size of all the files in C:\Python27 folder =  799866
```

Program 7.6: Write a program to check if flash drive is connected to your computer.

```
import os
print("os.path.exists(\"G:\\") = ", os.path.exists("G:\\"))
```

OUTPUT

```
os.path.exists("G:\\") =  True
```

Write a program that reads a file line by line. Each line read from the file is copied to another file with line numbers specified at the beginning of the line.

```
file1 = open("file1.txt","r")
file2 = open("File.txt","w")
num = 1
for line in file1:
    file2.write(str(num) + " : " + line)
    num = num + 1
file1.close()
file2.close()
```

Write a program that fetches data from a specified url and prints it on screen.

```
import urllib.request
x = urllib.request.urlopen('https://www.google.com/')
print(x.read())
```

Program 7.8: Write a program that fetches data from a specified url and writes it in a file.

```
Hint: Use the urllib2 module that handles the url
import urllib.request
url = 'https://www.google.com/search?q=python'
headers = {}
headers['User-Agent'] = "Mozilla/5.0 (X11; Linux i686) AppleWebKit/537.17
(KHTML, like Gecko) Chrome/24.0.1312.27 Safari/537.17"
```

```
Request = urllib.request.Request(url, headers = headers)
Response = urllib.request.urlopen(Request)
Data = Response.read()
File = open('URL_File.txt','w')
File.write(str(Data))
File.close()
```

7.8 Comma separated values (CSV)

A **CSV file** is a plain text file that contains data (including text and numbers) which can be easily exported in different applications. Although most often a comma is used to separate (or delimit) data, but sometimes other characters, such as semicolons can also be used. As the name suggests, CSV files are saved with a .csv extension.

A CSV file has a very simple structure – data separated by commas. And this simplicity is its biggest strength. Data in a CSV file is human-readable and can be easily viewed with a text editor like Notepad or a spreadsheet program like Microsoft Excel, Google Sheets or LibreOffice.

Spreadsheet programs present the contents of a CSV file as if it were formatted in rows and columns. While an xlsx file or any other spreadsheet file can have multiple sheets, a CSV file can only have a single sheet. Moreover, unlike a spreadsheet file, CSV files do not store data in rows and columns. Despite these drawbacks, CSV files are popular because they can be easily created by website developers, easily imported in other applications and better organize large amounts of data.

Name	Class	State	Marks	Fees
Sahil	2018	Odisha	92	3.75
Bina Madan	2017	West Bengal	84	3.52
Jivham	2018	Karnataka	17	3.20
Krish	2019	Tamil Nadu	65	3.48

```
Sahil,2018,Odisha,92,3.75

Bina Madan,2017,West Bengal,84,3.52

Jivham,2018,Karnataka,17,3.20

Krish,2019,Tamil Nadu,45,3.48
```

Figure 7.2 (Left): Contents of XLSX File; (Right): Contents of CSV File

Figure 7.2 shows how a spreadsheet file is represented in a CSV file. Note that the fields of data in each row are delimited with a comma and individual rows are separated by a newline. Since the CSV file is a text file, it can be created and edited using any text editor.

7.8.1 Difference between Excel vs CSV

Excel	CSV
❑ It is a binary file.	❑ It is a plain text format with a series of values separated by commas.
❑ An Excel file allows operations on the data	❑ A CSV file is just a text file that only stores data. It does not allow formatting or other operations on data stored in it.

(Continued)

Excel	CSV
❑ Excel is a spreadsheet that saves files with extension .xlsx	❑ CSV files are saved with extension .csv
❑ Excel files cannot be opened or edited using text editors.	❑ CSV files can be opened or edited by text editors.
❑ It is very difficult to parse Excel data. The process of parsing is also very slow.	❑ CSV data can be easily parsed at a relatively faster speed.
❑ Excel files consume more memory while importing data.	❑ CSV files can be processed much faster, and consume less memory.
❑ Reading large files and manipulating Excel data is simpler in Excel for the end user (for example, selecting individual cells for import, convert dates and time automatically, reading formulas and their results, filters, sorting, etc).	❑ Reading large files is slower. Moreover, CSV file does not permit automatically formatting data in the desired format.
❑ Besides, data, Excel files can store charts and graphs.	❑ CSV cannot store charts or graphs.
❑ Excel file can be opened with Microsoft Excel only.	❑ CSV can be opened with any text editor or even with spreadsheet software like MS Excel.

7.8.2 Working with CSV files

Before reading data from or writing data to a CSV file, we must import the csv module. This module has some important functions that help users to handle CSV files in their programs.

7.8.3 Reading CSV files with CSV

A CSV file is read using the `reader` object. The reader accepts the csv filename as input and returns a reader object.

The CSV file is opened as a text file with Python's built-in `open()` function, which returns a file object. The file object is then passed to the `reader`, for reading data from the file.

```
import csv
with open('File1.txt') as csv_file:
    file = csv.reader(csv_file)
    line_count = 0
    for row in file:
        print(row)
        line_count + = 1
print(f'Processed {line_count} lines.')
```

```
OUTPUT
['Welcome to the world of ....']
['Programming in Python !!!!']
['HAPPY PROGRAMMING']
Processed 4 lines.
```

7.8.4 Optional Python CSV reader parameters

Some additional parameters in the CSV `reader` object are:

- `delimiter` which specifies the character used to separate each field. By default, comma (,) is used.
- `quotechar` which specifies the character that will be used to surround fields that contain the delimiter character. By default, a double quote (") is used.
- `Escapechar` which specifies the character used to escape the delimiter character if quotes are not used.

For example, if joining_year is written as Nov,2011 then there are three different ways to handle this situation.

- Use a different delimiter by using the delimiter option.
- Wrap the data in quotes because the chosen delimiter is ignored in quoted strings. The character to be used for quoting is specified with the `quotechar` parameter. You must use a quotechar that does not appear in the data.
- Escape the delimiter characters in the data using the `escapechar` parameter.

7.8.5 Reading CSV files into a dictionary with CSV

The CSV DictReader method is used to read a dictionary.

```
import csv
with open('emp.txt', mode='r') as csv_file:
    file = csv.DictReader(csv_file)
    line_count = 0
    for row in file:
        print(f'{row["name"]} works in the {row["department"]} department,
and was born in {row["joining_year"]}.')
        line_count += 1
    print(f'Processed {line_count} lines.')
OUTPUT
Kiyan works in the Accounting department, and was born in 2011.
Manan works in the HR department, and was born in 2012.
Karishma works in the IT department, and was born in 2013.
Processed 3 lines.
```

7.8.6 Writing CSV files with CSV

Data can be written to a CSV file using a `writer` object and the `.writerow()` method. The writer accepts a csv filename as input and returns a writer object. The writer object converts the user's data into a delimited string. This string can later be used to write into CSV files using writerow() function.

```
import csv
with open('emp1.csv', mode='w') as employee_file:
    file = csv.writer(employee_file)
    file.writerow('The file contains details about employees')
    file.writerow(['Kiyan','Accounting',2011])
    file.writerow(['Manan','HR',2012])
    file.writerow(['Karishma','IT',2013])
print("DATA WRITTEN SUCCESSFULLY.......")
OUTPUT
DATA WRITTEN SUCCESSFULLY.......
```

Like the reader object, the writer object also has `quotechar` as an optional parameter that tells the `writer` which character is used to quote fields when writing to the file. However, whether to use quoting or not, is determined by the `quoting` optional parameter. That is,

- If `quoting` is set to `csv.QUOTE_MINIMAL`, then `.writerow()` will quote fields only if they contain the `delimiter` or the `quotechar`. This is the default case.
- If `quoting` is set to `csv.QUOTE_ALL`, then `.writerow()` will quote all fields.
- If `quoting` is set to `csv.QUOTE_NONNUMERIC`, then `.writerow()` will quote all fields containing textual data. It will also convert all numeric fields to the `float` data type.
- If `quoting` is set to `csv.QUOTE_NONE`, then `.writerow()` will escape delimiters instead of quoting them. So, another optional parameter `escapechar` must be specified in this case.

```
import csv
with open('emp1.csv', mode='w') as employee_file:
    file = csv.writer(employee_file)
    file.writerow('The file contains details about employees')
    file.writerow(['Kiyan','Accounting',2011])
    file.writerow(['Manan','HR',2012])
    file.writerow(['Karishma','IT',2013])
print("DATA WRITTEN SUCCESSFULLY.......")
OUTPUT
DATA WRITTEN SUCCESSFULLY.......
```

7.8.7 Writing CSV file from a dictionary with CSV

We can even write a dictionary to a csv file using the DictWriter method as shown below. Note that here, the fieldnames parameter is required because this parameter uses the keys in `fieldnames` to write out the first row as column names. The DictWriter accepts a csv filename and fieldnames as parameters.

The writeheader() method can be used to write the first row of csv file using the pre-specified fieldnames. Subsequently, the **writerows()** method is used to write all the rows. In each row, only the values are written. Keys are not written in every row.

```
import csv
with open('employee_file2.csv', mode='w') as csv_file:
    fieldnames = ['emp_name', 'dept', 'joining_year']
    writer = csv.DictWriter(csv_file, fieldnames=fieldnames)
        writer.writerow({'emp_name':  'Veronica',  'dept':  'Accounting',
'joining_year': 2009})
    writer.writerow({'emp_name': 'Natasha', 'dept': 'IT', 'joining_year':
2015})
print("DATA WRITTEN SUCCESSFULLY......")
OUTPUT
DATA WRITTEN SUCCESSFULLY......
```

7.8.8 Input as CSV file

The CSV file is a text file in which the values in the columns are separated by a comma. Let's consider the following data present in the file named **input.csv**.

You can create this file using windows notepad by copying and pasting this data. Save the file as **input.csv** using the save As All files (*.*) option in notepad.

```
id,name,salary,start_date,dept
1,Rick,623.3,2012-01-01,IT
2,Dan,515.2,2013-09-23,Operations
3,Tusar,611,2014-11-15,IT
4,Ryan,729,2014-05-11,HR
5,Gary,843.25,2015-03-27,Finance
6,Rasmi,578,2013-05-21,IT
7,Pranab,632.8,2013-07-30,Operations
8,Guru,722.5,2014-06-17,Finance
```

7.8.9 Reading specific data from a CSV file

We have seen that the **read_csv()** function of the pandas library is used to read the contents of a CSV file into the pandas DataFrame. The same function can be used to read only certain portion of the contents.

Let us create a sample csv file with some arbitrary data as given below.

```
id,name,salary,joining_date,dept
1,Reyansh,95000,2016-01-04,IT
2,Daniel,50000,2015-10-23,Operations
3,Tush,61000,2014-11-05,HR
4,Riya,72000,2015-05-18,IT
5,Goransh,84000,2018-04-27,Finance
6,Rasmi,57800,2016-05-29,HR
7,Pranab,63280,2014-11-31,Operations
8,Jivham,72200,2015-01-17,Finance
```

To create this file, just type this comma-separated data in a Notepad file and save it as input.csv. Use the read_csv() method to view the contents of this file in Python environment to ensure that everything is working perfectly well till here. Now let us choose a specific portion the in following ways:

Reading Specific Rows: The read_csv() function is used to read some specific rows for a given column by slicing the data frame. For example, to read the first 3 rows for the column named dept, we will write,

```
import pandas as pd
data = pd.read_csv('input.csv')
print (data[0:3]['dept'])
OUTPUT
0            IT
1            Operations
2            HR
Name: dept, dtype: object
```

Reading Specific Columns: To read some specific columns of the csv file, we will use the multi-axes indexing method called **.loc()**. For example, to display name and department of all employees (all the rows), we will write,

```
import pandas as pd
data = pd.read_csv('input.csv')
# Use the multi-axes indexing funtion
print (data.loc[:,['name','dept']])
OUTPUT
      name        dept
0  Reyansh          IT
1  Daniel   Operations
2  Tush             HR
3  Riya             IT
4  Goransh     Finance
5    Rasmi          HR
6   Pranab  Operations
7   Jivham     Finance
```

Reading Specific Columns and Rows: To read specific rows and columns using the `read_csv()` function, a combination of the above two techniques is used. For example, to read name and salary of 2nd, 4th and 6th employee, we will write,

```
import pandas as pd
data = pd.read_csv('input.csv')
# Use the multi-axes indexing funtion
print (data.loc[[2,4,6],['name','salary']])
OUTPUT
      name  salary
2     Tush   61000
4  Goransh   84000
6   Pranab   63280
```

7.8.10 Reading specific columns for a range of rows

To read some specific columns and a range of rows, we will use multi-axes indexing method, that is, .loc(). For example, to display name and department of rows from the third to the sixth row, we will write,

```
import pandas as pd
data = pd.read_csv('input.csv')
# Use the multi-axes indexing funtion
print (data.loc[2:5,['name','salary']])
OUTPUT
      name  salary
2     Tush   61000
3     Riya   72000
4  Goransh   84000
5    Rasmi   57800
```

7.9 Pickle module

Python pickle module is used for serializing and de-serializing Python objects. The process of converting any kind of Python object (example Booleans, Integers, Floats, Complex numbers, Strings, Tuples, Lists, Sets, and dictionary) into byte streams (in the form of 0s and 1s) is called pickling or **serialization** or flattening or marshalling. Correspondingly, the process of converting byte stream (generated through pickling) back into Python objects is known as unpickling or **de-serialization**.

Pickling and unpickling are very important processes as they allow users to easily transfer data from one server/system to another and then store it in a file or database.

However, one must always make sure that you should not unpickle data received from an untrusted source as they may pose a serious threat to security. The pickle module has no way of knowing or raising alarm while pickling malicious data.

To pickle or unpickle a data object in Python, we must first import the pickle module.

```
import pickle
L = ['a', 'b', 'c', 'd']
with open('datafile.txt', 'wb') as file:
    pickle.dump(L, file)
print("Data Written Successfully .......")
```

In the above program, list L contains four elements ('a', 'b', 'c', 'd'). A binary file named "datafile.txt" is created in write mode in the current working directory. The list is pickled or serialized using the dump() method of pickle module and written to the file.

The pickle.dump() method takes three arguments. The first argument is the object that has to be serialized. The second argument is the file object that is obtained while opening the binary file in write mode. The third argument is the key-value argument which defines the protocol. There are two type of protocol – **pickle.HIGHEST_PROTOCOL** and **pickle.DEFAULT_PROTOCOL**.

The program given below unpickles the contents of datafile.txt and stores it in a list object that is then printed on the screen.

```
import pickle
file = open ("datafile.txt", "rb")
L = pickle.load(file)
print(L)
OUTPUT
['a', 'b', 'c', 'd']
```

Write a program to pickle a dictionary object.

```
import pickle
stud = {'RollNo': 1, 'Name':"Zack", 'Marks': 65, 'Course':"IT"}
file = open("Student.pickle","wb")
pickle.dump(stud, file)
file.close()
print("DATA WRITTEN SUCCESSFULLY .....")
file = open("Student.pickle", 'rb')
stud_details = pickle.load(file)
print(stud_details)
OUTPUT
DATA WRITTEN SUCCESSFULLY .....
{'RollNo': 1, 'Name': 'Zack', 'Marks': 65, 'Course': 'IT'}
```

7.9.1 Pickle exceptions

While executing programs, we may get some exceptions (in simple terms error, though technically exception is different from error). Some of them are discussed below.

- Pickle.PicklingError is raised when the pickle object doesn't support pickling.
- Pickle.UnpicklingError if the file contains bad or corrupted data.
- EOFError if end of file is detected.

7.9.2 Advantages of pickling

- Can be used to save large amount of complicated data in the hard disk for future use.
- Can be used to securely share large amount of data over a computer network.
- Easy to use and can be done in just a few lines of code.
- The pickled file is not human-readable until it is unpickled. In this way, a pickled file provides some data security.

In Python, even functions and classes can be serialized.

7.9.3 Disadvantages of pickling

- Languages other than Python may not able to unpickle pickled files and will thus be unusable for them.

- There is always a security threat when unpickling data from malicious or untrusted sources. Moreover, an attacker can access and modify the stored pickled files from caches, file systems, or databases.

7.10 JSON

A JSON or JavaScript Object Notation file is one that stores data as text in human-readable format. We can read a JSON file in Python environment using the `read_json()` function defined in pandas module.

JSON stores information in an organized and easy-to-access manner. For example, if we write

```
var student = {
    "roll_no" : "21",
    "name" : "Missy",
    "course" : "BTech"
};
```

then, an object that we access using the variable student is created. The object can have one or more properties that can be defined using a `"name":"value"` pairing, separated by commas.

JSON is the standard data interchange format that is primarily used for transmitting data between a web application and a server. JSON files can be edited using a text editor.

Though JSON format was originally based on a subset of JavaScript, it is considered a language-independent format as it is supported by many different programming Application Programming Interfaces (APIs). It is becoming increasingly popular as an alternative to XML.

7.10.1 Applications of JSON files

JavaScript based applications use .json files in browser extensions and websites.

- JSON format is used for serializing and transmitting structured data over network connection.
- JSON files are easy to access for reading and writing data.
- JSON is language independent and can be used with any language including C#, Python, Java, etc.
- JSON files are used to store configurations and settings for a particular application. For example, to create a Google Chrome App, a JSON file called manifest.json is included that specifies the name of the app, its description, current version, and other properties and settings.

Although many applications use JSON files for data interchange, they may not actually save those files on the hard drive as data interchange occurs between client and server. However, some applications do permit users to save .json files. For example, Google+ uses JSON files to save user's profile data. After logging in, users may select the "Data liberation" page to download their profile data.

Mozilla Firefox saves bookmark backups using JSON files. The files are saved to the Firefox user profile directory within a folder called bookmarkbackups.

7.10.2 How to open a JSON file?

Since JSON files are plain text files, they can be easily opened in any text editor, including Microsoft Notepad on Windows, Apple TextEdit on Mac, Vim on Linux or on GitHub Atom (cross-platform). JSON files can also be opened in the Google Chrome and Mozilla Firefox web browsers.

7.10.3 Creating a JSON file

Let us create a .json file to store information related to students. But before creating a .json file, observe the JSON object given below that stores details of a student.

```
{
    "student": [

        {
            "roll_no":"01",
            "name": "Jiom",
            "course": "MTech",
            "subject": "CS"
        },
        {
            "roll_no":"02",
            "name": "Shreon",
            "course": "BTech",
            "subject": "IT"
        }
    ]
}
```

Now, type the data given below into a text editor like notepad and save the file as student. json extension. Do not forget to choose the file type as all files (*.*).

```
{
    "ID":["1","2","3","4","5","6","7","8" ],
    "Name":["Rocky","Danish","Mikal","Raima","Gauri","Neon","Siya","Garv"
],
    "Cource":["BCA","BTech","MCA","MTech","Bsc","MSc","BE","ME" ],
    "Subject":[ "IT","Electronics","SE","Data Sciences","Data Analytics","CS",
        "Electronics","Electrical"]
}
```

Reading a JSON file

The read_json() function of the pandas library is used to read the JSON file into a pandas DataFrame. The code to read the student.json file is given below.

```
import pandas as pd
data = pd.read_json('student.json')
print (data)
OUTPUT
    ID    Name Cource          Subject
0   1    Rocky    BCA               IT
1   2   Danish  BTech      Electronics
2   3    Mikal    MCA               SE
3   4    Raima  MTech    Data Sciences
4   5    Gauri    Bsc   Data Analytics
5   6     Neon    MSc               CS
6   7     Siya     BE      Electronics
7   8     Garv     ME       Electrical
```

To read specific data from a JSON file, we can use the slice operation and multi-axes indexing method called .loc(). Code given below illustrates accessing the name and subject of third, fifth and sixth student.

```
import pandas as pd
data = pd.read_json('student.json')
print (data.loc[[2,4,6],['Name','Subject']])
OUTPUT
    Name          Subject
2  Mikal             SE
4  Gauri   Data Analytics
6   Siya      Electronics
```

To read a JSON file as a collection of individual records, use the to_json() function along with parameters – orient and lines, as shown in the code given below.

```
import pandas as pd
data = pd.read_json('student.json')
print(data.to_json(orient='records', lines=True))
OUTPUT
{"ID":1,"Name":"Rocky","Cource":"BCA","Subject":"IT"}
{"ID":2,"Name":"Danish","Cource":"BTech","Subject":"Electronics"}
{"ID":3,"Name":"Mikal","Cource":"MCA","Subject":"SE"}
{"ID":4,"Name":"Raima","Cource":"MTech","Subject":"Data Sciences"}
{"ID":5,"Name":"Gauri","Cource":"Bsc","Subject":"Data Analytics"}
{"ID":6,"Name":"Neon","Cource":"MSc","Subject":"CS"}
{"ID":7,"Name":"Siya","Cource":"BE","Subject":"Electronics"}
{"ID":8,"Name":"Garv","Cource":"ME","Subject":"Electrical"}
```

7.10.4 Writing JSON to a file in Python

Table 5: || Python object and their corresponding JSON object

Python object	JSON object
dict	object
list, tuple	array
str	string
int, long, float	numbers
True	true
False	false
None	null

Serializing JSON means transforming data into a series of bytes (hence serial) so that it can be easily stored or transmitted across a network. JSON library in Python provides dump() or dumps() function to convert the Python objects into their respective JSON object so that data in them can be easily written to files. Table lists Python objects and their corresponding JSON objects.

json.dumps(): The json.dumps() function in the JSON package that is supported by Python helps in converting a dictionary to a JSON object. The function takes two parameters:

dictionary specifies name of dictionary to be converted to JSON object.

indent defines the number of units for indentation.

Once the dictionary is converted to a JSON object, it is written to a file using the write() function.

Example: Write details of a student in a JSON File using the dumps() method.

```
# Python program to write JSON to a file
import json
# Data to be written
Dict ={
    "roll_no":"01",
    "name": "Jiom",
    "course": "MTech",
    "subject": "CS"
    }
# Serializing json
JSONObj = json.dumps(Dict, indent = 4)
# Writing to sample.json
with open("student_new.json", "w") as outfile:
    outfile.write(JSONObj)
outfile.close()
print("Data Written ..........")
```

Serialization converts an object into a special format which is suitable for transmitting over the network or storing in file or database is called Serialization.

Note that the dumps() method returns a string which will be converted into JSON format.

Using json.dump()

An alternate way of writing JSON data to a file is by using the json.dump() method. This method is defined in the JSON package and is used to directly write a dictionary to the JSON file. In such a case, there is no need to convert the dictionary into an actual JSON object. The function takes two parameters:

`dictionary` specifies name of dictionary which should be converted to JSON object.

`file pointer` refers to pointer of the file opened in write or append mode.

Example: Write a code to serialize a dictionary object using dump() method.

```
# Python program to write JSON to a file
import json
# Data to be written
Dict ={
    "roll_no":"01",
    "name": "Jiom",
    "course": "MTech",
    "subject": "CS"
    }
# Serializing json
with open("sample.json", "w") as outfile:
    json.dump(Dict, outfile)
print("Data Written ..........")
```

Note that the dump() accepted two parameters here. A Python dictionary and a Python file as argument. The dump() method however, does not write file in readable format. So, we need to specify some additional parameters to make the contents more readable. These additional parameters are,

`indent` used for indentation in json file. Its value is a positive integer which specifies the amount of indentation of key-value pairs at each level. This is just used for making the output more clearly readable especially in case of deeply nested data structures. The default value of indent is None. However, note that increasing indentation also increases the size of the data. So, avoid using indent in the production environment.

`sort_keys` is used for sorting keys in ascending order. It is basically a Boolean flag, which when True returns a JSON string ordered by keys, instead of being randomly ordered. Its default value is False.

`Skipkeys` is used to skip the non-string keys. Basically, JSON format expects the keys to be a string. In case the key is neither string nor can be converted to a string (like tuple) then a

`TypeError` exception is raised. To prevent the exception from being raised, set the skipkeys argument to True.

`key_separator` is a string that is used to separate keys and values in a dictionary. By default, the separators set to (',', ': ').

Look at the same code with additional parameters in the dump() method.

```
# Python program to write JSON to a file
import json
# Data to be written
Dict ={
    "roll_no":"01",
    "name": "Jiom",
    "course": "MTech",
    "subject": "CS"
    }
# Serializing json
with open("sample.json", "w") as outfile:
      json.dump(Dict, outfile, sort_keys = True,
indent = True)
print("Data Written ..........")
```

> Since dictionary doesn't preserve the order of elements, the order in which you get the keys may vary.

7.10.5 Reading JSON from a file using Python

De-serialization, opposite of serialization, uses load() method to convert a JSON object into their corresponding Python objects. The load() method can easily de-serialize JSON data from another program or obtained as a string format of JSON file into a dictionary. The method takes one parameter – File pointer that points to a JSON file. Its syntax is as follows:

```
load(fp) -> a Python object
```

Example: Reading a JSON file

```
import json
  # Opening JSON file
with open('sample.json', 'r') as openfile:
    Reading from json file
    JSONObj = json.load(openfile)
print(JSONObj)
print(type(JSONObj))
OUTPUT
{'roll_no':  '01',  'name':  'Jiom',  'course':
'MTech', 'subject': 'CS'}
<class 'dict'>
```

Deserialization converts the special format returned by the serialization back into a usable object.

While working with Python, every JSON file is considered as a string.

Write a code to create a dictionary with nested name:value entries. Write this dictionary data in a json file. Also write the code to read this file and display its content on the monitor.

```
# Python program to write JSON to a file
import json
# Data to be written
candidate = {
    "firstName": "Jivham",
    "lastName": "Chaudhary",
    "age": 22,
    "address": {
    "streetAddress": "21 2nd Street",
        "city": "Mumbai",
        "state": "Maharashtra",
        "postalCode": "400018"
    },
    "phoneNumbers": [
        {
            "type": "home",
            "number": "0222 555123"
        },
        {
            "type": "mobile",
            "number": "123 456-7890"
        }
    ],
    "siblings": [],
    "specialization": None
}
```

loads() function is as same as load() but instead of deserializing the JSON string from a file, it deserializes from a string.

```
# Serializing json
with open("candidate01.json", "w") as outfile:
    json.dump(candidate, outfile, sort_keys = True, indent = True)
print("Data Written ..........")
print(open('candidate01.json', 'r').read())   # reading JSON object as
string
```

OUTPUT

```
Data Written ..........
{
 "address": {
  "city": "Mumbai",
  "postalCode": "400018",
  "state": "Maharashtra",
  "streetAddress": "21 2nd Street"
 },
 "age": 22,
 "firstName": "Jivham",
 "lastName": "Chaudhary",
 "phoneNumbers": [
  {
   "number": "0222 555123",
   "type": "home"
  },
  {
   "number": "123 456-7890",
   "type": "mobile"
  }
 ],
 "siblings": [],
 "specialization": null
}
```

Write a code that stores multiple key:value pairs in a person dictionary to a json file. Also load the file and display its contents.

```
import json

data = {}
data['people'] = []
data['people'].append({
    'name': 'Saransh',
    'interest': 'painting',
    'sport': 'basket ball'
})
```

The dumps() function works exactly like dump(), but instead of sending the output to a file-like object, it returns the output as a string.

```
data['people'].append({
    'name': 'Aditya',
    'interest': 'Gaming',
    'sport': 'Tennis'
})
data['people'].append({
    'name': 'Tarasha',
    'interest': 'adventure',
    'sport': 'High Jump'
})

with open('data.txt', 'w') as outfile:
    json.dump(data, outfile)

with open('data.txt') as json_file:
    data = json.load(json_file)
    for p in data['people']:
        print('Name: ' + p['name'])
        print('Interest: ' + p['interest'])
        print('Sport: ' + p['sport'])
        print('')
```

OUTPUT

```
Name: Saransh
Interest: painting
Sport: basket ball
Name: Aditya
Interest: Gaming
Sport: Tennis

Name: Tarasha
Interest: adventure
Sport: High Jump
```

Use the use the html parser parameter to read the entire html file and the beautifulsoup library to search for the values of html tags and get specific data like title of the page and the list of headers in the page.

```
import urllib.request
from bs4 import BeautifulSoup
response = urllib.request.urlopen('http://
tutorialspoint.com/python/python_overview.htm')
html_doc = response.read()
soup = BeautifulSoup(html_doc, 'html.parser')
print (soup.title)
print(soup.title.string)
print(soup.a.string)
print(soup.b.string)
```

Serializing objects convert a Python object into a JSON string and deserialization builds up the Python object from its JSON string representation.

OUTPUT

```
<title>Python - Overview - Tutorialspoint</title>
Python - Overview - Tutorialspoint
None
Python is Interpreted
```

Business Scenario: Sales Data Processing

QuickSales receives daily sales reports in CSV format from multiple branches. There is now an urgent requirement to aggregate, clean, and analyze these reports for real-time insights. The manual process was time-consuming and prone to error(s). To make this task computerized, we can execute the following code.

```
import os

import pandas as pd

# Directory containing sales files

directory = 'sales_reports/'

sales_data = []

# Reading all CSV files in the directory

for filename in os.listdir(directory):

  if filename.endswith('.csv'):

    filepath = os.path.join(directory, filename)

    df = pd.read_csv(filepath)

    sales_data.append(df)

# Combining all data into a single DataFrame

combined_sales_data = pd.concat(sales_data, ignore_index=True)

print(combined_sales_data.head())

# Handling missing values

combined_sales_data.fillna(0, inplace=True)

# Removing duplicate entries

combined_sales_data.drop_duplicates(inplace=True)

# Converting date columns to datetime format

combined_sales_data['Date'] = pd.to_datetime(combined_sales_data['Date'], errors='coerce')

# Filtering sales data for the current month

current_month_data = combined_sales_data[combined_sales_data['Date'].dt.month == pd.Timestamp.now().month]
```

Key Terms

CSV file: A plain text file that contains data (including text and numbers) which can be easily exported in different applications. Though most often a comma is used to separate (or delimit) data, other characters, like semicolons can also be used.

De-serialization: The process of converting byte stream (generated through pickling) back into Python objects is known as unpickling or de-serialization.

Delimiter: One or more characters used to specify the boundary between different parts of text.

Directory: Collection of files, also called a folder. A directory can have other files and directories within it.

File: A stream of information that is usually stored on a permanent storage media like hard drive, floppy disk, CD-ROM, etc.

File handle: An object that allows you to manipulate/read/write/close the file.

File path: A sequence of directory names that specifies the exact location of a file.

Non-volatile memory: Memory that can store data even when the power supply to the computer system is switched off. Hard drives, flash drives, and rewritable compact disks (CD-RW) are each examples of non-volatile memory.

Serialization: The process of converting any kind of Python object (example Booleans, Integers, Floats, Complex numbers, Strings, Tuples, Lists, Sets, and dictionary) into byte streams (in the form of 0s and 1s) is called pickling or serialization or flattening or marshalling.

Text file: A file having printable characters organized into lines separated by newline characters.

Volatile memory: Memory that loses data as soon as the computer system is switched off. RAM is an example of volatile memory.

Chapter Highlights

- ✶ If you want to use the data in future, then you need to store this data on a permanent or non-volatile storage media like the hard disk, USB drive, DVD, etc.
- ✶ At the top of the tree is one (or more) root node(s). Under the root node, there are other files and folders (or directories) and each folder can in turn contain other files and folders.
- ✶ Every file is identified by its path that begins from the root node or the root folder.
- ✶ A file path can be either *relative* or *absolute*. While an absolute path always contains the root and the complete directory list to specify the exact location of the file, relative path on the other hand, needs to be combined with another path in order to access a file.
- ✶ Each file ends with a special character called the end-of-file (EOF) marker.
- ✶ A binary file is a file which may contain any type of data, encoded in binary form for computer storage and processing purposes.
- ✶ open() function creates a file object, which will be used to invoke methods associated with it.
- ✶ The close() method is used to close the file object. Once a file object is closed, you cannot further read from or write into the file associated with the file object.
- ✶ Python has a garbage collector to clean up unreferenced objects but still it is our responsibility to close the file and release the resources consumed by it.
- ✶ To append a file, you must open it using 'a' or 'ab' mode depending on whether it is a text file or a binary file.
- ✶ The read() method is used to read a string from an already opened file.
- ✶ The file pointer specifies a location from where the current read or write operation is initiated.
- ✶ The tell() method tells the current position within the file at which the next read or write operation will occur. It is specified as number of bytes from the beginning of the file.
- ✶ The getcwd() method is used to display the current working directory.
- ✶ A CSV file is read using the `reader` object. The reader accepts the csv filename as input and returns a reader object.
- ✶ Python pickle module is used for serializing and de-serializing Python objects.

* A JSON or JavaScript Object Notation file is one that stores data as text in human-readable format.
* De-serialization, opposite of serialization, uses load() method to convert a JSON object into their corresponding Python objects.

Review Questions

1. What are files? Why do we need them?
2. Explain the significance of root node?
3. Differentiate between absolute and relative file path.
4. Differentiate between a file and folder.
5. Differentiate between text and binary files.
6. Explain the utility of open() function.
7. What are different access modes in which you can open a file?
8. With the help of an example explain any three attributes of file object.
9. Is it mandatory to call the close() method after using the file?
10. Explain the syntax of read() method.
11. Give the significance of with keyword.
12. Write a short note on different methods to read data from a file.
13. With the help of suitable examples explain different ways in which you can write data in a file.
14. Discuss some directory methods present in the os module.
15. In the file, identify the delimiter and the line terminator characters.
16. Compare an Excel file with a CSV file.
17. Differentiate between serialization and de-serialization with the help of an example.
18. What exceptions may be raised while pickling/unpickling data in Python?
19. What are JSON files?

Programming Exercise

1. Write a program that reads text from a file and writes it into another file but in the reverse order.

   Hint: Make the first line in the original file as the last line in the copied file.
2. Write a program that reads a file and prints only those lines that have the word print.
3. Write a program that has several lines. Each line begins with a line number. Now read this file line by line and copy the line in another file but do not copy the numbers.
4. Write a program to compare two files.
5. Write a program to copy one file into another. Copy one character at a time.
6. Write a program to read and write the details of a student in a file.
7. Write a program to count the number of records stored in file employee.
8. Write a program to read a file that contains small case characters. Then write these characters into another file with all lower case characters converted into upper case.
9. Write a program to merge two files into a third file.
10. Write a program that reads a file and copies its contents in another file. While copying, replace all full stops with commas.
11. Write a program that exchanges the contents of two files.

12. Write a program that writes data to a file in such a way that each character after a full stop is capitalized and all numbers are written in brackets.
13. Write a program that takes a list of data values from the user and serializes it in a file. Also write the code to load this data and display it on the screen.
14. Write a program to create a dictionary that stores data of employee. Demonstrate the process of loading and dumping this data.
15. Create a .json file to store information related to books based on their topic and edition.
16. Create an emp.json file with properties ID, Name, Salary, Start_Date, Dept and perform the following operations.
    (a) Read the JSON file into a data frame.
    (b) Print name and salary of 5th and 7th employee.
    (c) Read the JSON file content into individual records.
17. Create a dictionary object storing details of an employee. Serialize it in a .json file using the dumps() method.
18. Create a dictionary object with nested entries storing details of an employee. Serialize it in a .json file using the dump() method. Also write the code to read this file and display its content on the screen.

Fill in the Blanks

1. _______ function is used to access files.
2. Fill in the blanks to read a file using the "with" keyword.
   ___open("File.txt")__file:
3. Fill in the blanks to open a file called "abc.bin" in binary read mode.
   File = open(______,__)
4. How many characters would be printed by this code (one character is one byte)?
   file=open("fILE.txt","r")
   for i in range(100):
   print(file.read(10))
   file.close()
5. Fill in the blanks to open a file, read its content and print its length.
   file=_____("File.txt","r")
   text = file.______()
   print (___(text))
   file.close()
6. Fill in the blanks to open a file for reading using the with statement.
   _____open("File.txt")__file:
   print(file.____())
7. Most file systems that are used today stores files in a ________ structure.
8. Every file is identified by its path that begins from the _______.
9. In Windows, __________ is the root folder.
10. A relative path is specified relative to the program's ____________.
11. _________ pathnames start with respect to the current working directory.

12. Each file ends with a special character called the_________.
13. open() function returns a _________.
14. The _______ method frees up any system resources like file descriptors, file locks, etc.
15. Any attempt to use the file object will result in a _______________.
16. The write() method returns _______.
17. If you try to open a file for reading that does not exist, then you will get _________.
18. The readline() method returns __________ when the end of the file has been reached.
19. If you do not want the new file to be created in the current working directory, then you must specify the __________.
20. The ________specifies a location from where the current read or write operation is initiated.
21. _____ method tells the current position within the file at which the next read or write operation will occur.
22. When you open a file for reading, the file pointer is positioned at _________.
23. _______ method is used to delete a file.
24. If you try to change to a directory that does not exist _______ will be generated.
25. If you try to delete a non-empty directory, then you will get ________.
26. To remove a non-empty directory, use the _______ method defined inside the ______ module.
27. The method _________ is used to create more than one folder.
28. _________ method is used to create strings for filenames.
29. The __________ method uses the string value passed to it to form an absolute path.
30. _____ method is used for multi-axes indexing.

State True or False

1. When a program is being executed, its data is stored in ROM.
2. RAM is an example of non-volatile memory.
3. You can have only one root in all the file systems.
4. Delimiters may vary from one operating system to another.
5. Folder names and file names are case insensitive in Windows.
6. Absolute path always contains the root.
7. The contents of a binary file are human readable.
8. Text files include files like word processing documents, PDFs, images, spreadsheets, videos, zip files and other executable programs.
9. Binary files are more efficient than text files.
10. *.py files are binary files.
11. When you open a file for appending that does not exist, then a new file is created.
12. You can open any number of files without any sort of restriction.
13. The read() method starts reading from the beginning of the file.
14. If count is missing or has a negative value in the read() method then, no contents are read from the file.
15. The readline() method is used to read all the lines in the file.
16. tell() moves the file pointer to a new location.
17. Before removing a directory, it should be absolutely empty.

18. os.path.abs() method accepts a file path as an argument and returns True if the path is an absolute path and False otherwise.
19. The cwd() method is used to display the current working directory.
20. CSV is a binary file.
21. The process of converting a byte stream back into Python objects is known as pickling.
22. The pickled file is not human-readable.
23. A JSON file stores data in binary format.
24. JSON files can be edited using a text editor.
25. The dumps() function sends the output to a file-like object.

Fill in the Blanks and Identify the Usage of the Lines

1. File = open("File.txt", "r")

   The above statement _______ a text file.
2. file.read()

   The above statement _______ a text file.
3. print(file.readline())

   The above statement _______ a text file.
4. print(file.readlines())

   The above statement _______ a text file.
5. file.write("Welcome")

   The above statement _______ a text file.
6. file = open("File.txt", "w")

   The above statement _______ a text file.
7. file.writelines(lines)

   The above statement _______ a text file.
8. file = open("File.txt", "a")

   The above statement _______ a text file.
9. file.close()

   The above statement _______ a text file.
10. file.read(10)

    The above statement _______ a text file.
11. file.seek(file.tell()-10)

    The above statement _______ a text file.
12. file = open("File.txt", "r+b")

    The above statement _______ .
13. file.seek(-10,2)

    The above statement _______ .

14. file.seek(20,1)

The above statement ________ .

15. file.seek(30,0)

The above statement ________ .

Give the Output

1.
```
import os
Files = ['BTech.txt', 'BCA.csv', 'BSc.docx']
for file in Files:
   print(os.path.join('C:\\Users\\Students', file))
```

2.
```
with open("File.txt", "w") as file:
   file.write("Greetings to All !!! \n Welcome to the world of
programming\n")
with open("File.txt") as file:
   print(file.read())
```

3.
```
file=open("File.txt","r")
file.read()
text = file.read())
print(len(text))
file.close()
```

4.
```
str ="Welcome to Python Programming"
file = open("File.txt","w")
n = file.write(str)
print(n)
file.close()
```

5.
```
What will be written in the file?
a.  file.write("Oxford" + "University" + "Press")
b.  file.write(str(len("Oxford University Press")))
c.  file.write("Clue".replace('C', 'B')
d.  file.write("HELLO".lower())
```

6.
```
import csv
fields = ['Name', 'Branch', 'Year', 'CGPA']
 rows = [ ['Nikhil', 'COE', '2', '9.0'],
          ['Sanchit', 'COE', '2', '9.1'],
          ['Aditya', 'IT', '2', '9.3'],
          ['Sagar', 'SE', '1', '9.5'],
          ['Prateek', 'MCE', '3', '7.8'],
```

```
        ['Sahil', 'EP', '2', '9.1']]
    filename = "students.csv"
    # writing to csv file
with open(filename, 'w') as csvfile:
    # creating a csv writer object
    csvwriter = csv.writer(csvfile)

    # writing the fields
    csvwriter.writerow(fields)

    # writing the data rows
    csvwriter.writerows(rows)
```

7.
```
import csv
    # my data rows as dictionary objects
mydict =[{'branch': 'COE', 'cgpa': '9.0', 'name': 'Nikhil', 'year': '2'},
        {'branch': 'COE', 'cgpa': '9.1', 'name': 'Sanchit', 'year': '2'},
        {'branch': 'IT', 'cgpa': '9.3', 'name': 'Aditya', 'year': '2'},
        {'branch': 'SE', 'cgpa': '9.5', 'name': 'Sagar', 'year': '1'},
        {'branch': 'MCE', 'cgpa': '7.8', 'name': 'Prateek', 'year': '3'},
        {'branch': 'EP', 'cgpa': '9.1', 'name': 'Sahil', 'year': '2'}]
    # field names
fields = ['name', 'branch', 'year', 'cgpa']
    # name of csv file
filename = "university_records.csv"
    # writing to csv file
with open(filename, 'w') as csvfile:
    # creating a csv dict writer object
    writer = csv.DictWriter(csvfile, fieldnames = fields)
        # writing headers (field names)
    writer.writeheader()
        # writing data rows
    writer.writerows(mydict)
```

8.
```
import csv
with open("people.csv", 'r') as file:
    csv_file = csv.DictReader(file)
    for row in csv_file:
        print(dict(row))
```

9.
```
import pickle
example_dict = {1:"6",2:"2",3:"f"}
pickle_out = open("dict.pickle","wb")
pickle.dump(example_dict, pickle_out)
pickle_out.close()
```

10.
```
pickle_in = open("dict.pickle","rb")
example_dict = pickle.load(pickle_in)
print(example_dict)
print(example_dict[3])
```

11.
```
import pickle
pickle_off = open ("datafile.txt", "rb")
emp = pickle.load(pickle_off)
print(emp)
```

12.
```
import json
 student = {
    'name': 'Rajesh',
    'roll': 52,
    ‹subject': ['English', 'Science']
}
 student_dumped = json.dumps(student)
 print(student_dumped)
print(type(student_dumped))
```

Find Out the Error, If Any

1.
```
with open("File.txt") as file
     file.write("Hello World")
with open(File.txt) as f:
data = f.read()
print(data)
```

2.
```
filename = "File.txt"
file = open("filename", "r")
for line in file:
  print(line, end = ' ')
```

3.
```
filename = "File.txt"
file = open(filename, "r")
while True:
      print(file.readline())
```

4.
```
file = open("File.txt", "a")
write("Hello World again")
```

5.
```
data = {'one': 1, 'two': 2, (1,2): 3}
json.dumps(data, indent=4)
```

CHAPTER

8 Advanced Data Analytics

Forecasting Monthly Sales Using ARIMA/SARIMA

RetailNova, a retail company sells a range of goods, including home essentials, electronics, apparel, and seasonal items via online as well as offline stores.

The company realized the need for accurate demand forecasting for better inventory management, supply chain planning, marketing campaign timing, and budget allocation.

Till now, the company had been using simple methods (like year-over-year percentage change and moving averages) which were not responsive to seasonal fluctuations, holiday promotions, or economic disruptions (e.g., pandemic waves, inflation surges). Therefore, the data analyst suggested to develop a **robust time series forecasting model** that could:

- Predict monthly sales over the next 12 months.
- Account for **seasonality, trend,** and **irregular components.**
- Provide insights to support procurement, logistics, and marketing departments.

The data analytics team collected monthly sales data along with features including **Festival indicators, Promotional campaigns, and COVID-19 effects.**

The team performed the following analyses:

- **Time Plot** showed a clear upward trend with strong seasonal spikes every October due to festival sales.
- **Seasonal Decomposition (STL)** reflected seasonal (repeating annual) pattern and anomalies (during pandemic months).
- **ACF/PACF Plots were** used to determine stationarity and potential autoregressive and moving average terms.

To analyze data, an analyst can uncover patterns, make predictions, and draw meaningful conclusio ns in a variety of ways. The chapter focuses on four of them–Contingency Tables, ARIMA, Longitudinal Data Analysis, and Hypothesis Testing.

Contingency Tables are used to summarize categorical data and explore the relationships between two or more variables. ARIMA is a time series forecasting technique that is extensively used to predict future values based on historical data. It is applied in a wide range of applications ranging from finance to environmental science.

Longitudinal Data Analysis, which deals with data collected over time from the same subjects or units, is used to study changes over time. For this reason, it is widely used in areas including healthcare, economics, and social sciences.

Note: The dataset from this chapter is available online. For more details, please refer to the back cover of the book.

Hypothesis Testing, a core principle of inferential statistics, is used to assess the validity of assumptions or claims made about a population based on sample data. This is often vital for making evidence-based decisions in research, policy, and business.

Besides covering these topics in depth, the chapter will demonstrate their practical application using Python. The combination of theory and practice will help to solve real-world problems and conduct meaningful analysis.

8.1 Contingency Table

When there is a single variable to analyze, we can use statistics like mean, median, standard deviation, and variance. But for bivariate analysis that involves analysis of two variables, correlation analysis is required.

Contingency Table is a powerful tool to explore two or even more variables. Every value in the table represents the counts between two or more categorical variables. A three-variable contingency table (or three-way table) is a way to analyze the relationship between three categorical variables.

Write a Python script to create a Three-Variable Contingency Table. The dataset of students must have three categorical variables: Gender (Male, Female), Study_Hours (Low, Medium, High), Pass (Yes, No)

```
import pandas as pd
data = {
    'Gender': ['Male', 'Male', 'Female', 'Female', 'Male', 'Female',
'Male', 'Female', 'Male', 'Female'],
    'Study_Hours': ['Low', 'High', 'Medium', 'Low', 'High', 'Medium',
'Low', 'Medium', 'High', 'Low'],
    'Pass': ['No', 'Yes', 'Yes', 'No', 'Yes', 'Yes', 'No', 'Yes', 'Yes',
'No']
}

df = pd.DataFrame(data)
print("ORIGINAL DATASET")
print(df)
contingency_table = pd.crosstab(index=[df['Gender'], df['Study_Hours']],
columns=df['Pass'], margins=False)
print("CONTINGENCY TABLE")
print(contingency_table)
```

OUTPUT

```
ORIGINAL DATASET
   Gender Study_Hours Pass
0    Male         Low   No
1    Male        High  Yes
2  Female      Medium  Yes
3  Female         Low   No
4    Male        High  Yes
```

```
5  Female      Medium  Yes
6    Male         Low   No
7  Female      Medium  Yes
8    Male        High  Yes
9  Female         Low   No
CONTINGENCY TABLE
Pass                 No  Yes
Gender Study_Hours
Female Low            2    0
       Medium         0    3
Male   High           0    3
       Low            2    0
```

In the above code, note that `pd.crosstab()` is used to create the contingency table. The statement groups two categorical variables, Study_Hours and Gender, in rows and keeps the third categorical variable, Pass, in the column. `Margins = True` to add row and column totals and False otherwise.

> Contingency tables help analyze relationships between categorical variables.

For further analysis on a three-variable contingency table, we can use normalization and Chi-Square Test.

8.1.1 Chi-Square Test

The Chi-Square Test checks statistical dependence between variables. This helps determine if there is a significant relationship between categorical variables.

```
import pandas as pd
import scipy.stats as stats
data = {
     'Gender': ['Male', 'Male', 'Female', 'Female', 'Male', 'Female',
'Male', 'Female', 'Male', 'Female'],
     'Study_Hours': ['Low', 'High', 'Medium', 'Low', 'High', 'Medium',
'Low', 'Medium', 'High', 'Low'],
    'Pass': ['No', 'Yes', 'Yes', 'No', 'Yes', 'Yes', 'No', 'Yes', 'Yes',
'No']
}
df = pd.DataFrame(data)
contingency_table = pd.crosstab(index=[df['Gender'], df['Study_Hours']],
columns=df['Pass'], margins = False)
chi2, p, dof, expected = stats.chi2_contingency(contingency_table)
print("Chi-Square Statistic:", chi2)
print("P-value:", p)
print("Degrees of Freedom:", dof)
print("Expected Frequencies Table:\n", expected)
```

```
OUTPUT
Chi-Square Statistic: 10.0
P-value: 0.018566135463O4325
Degrees of Freedom: 3
Expected Frequencies Table:
 [[0.8 1.2]
 [1.2 1.8]
 [1.2 1.8]
```

In the above code, we see that the chi^2 measures how different the observed values are from expected values.

If **p < 0.05**, we reject the null hypothesis, meaning there is a significant relationship. In case, $p \geq 0.05$, the null hypothesis is approved, as there is no significant relationship between the variables. In our case, there is a strong relationship.

Degrees of Freedom (dof) is used to determine the number of independent comparisons. It is calculated using the formula, dof = (number of rows − 1) × (number of columns − 1)

> **A two-way contingency table (or cross-tabulation) shows the relationship between two categorical variables.**

Expected Frequencies Table shows the frequencies we would expect if there were no association. Formula for dof can be given as,

	Pass	Fail	Total
Male	30	20	50
Female	40	10	50
Total	70	30	100

dof = (number of rows − 1) × (number of columns − 1)
where, the contingency table has r rows and c columns:
For example, given a 2 × 2 contingency table (Gender vs. Pass Rate):
Here, Rows (r) = 2 and Columns (c) = 2

	Pass	Fail
Male	30	20
Female	40	10

Using the formula,

```
dof = (2 - 1) × (2 - 1) = 1
```

	Pass	Fail
Low	20	30
Medium	40	10
High	10	10

Let us take another example by considering a 3 × 2 contingency table. In the table, Rows (r) = 3 and Columns (c) = 2. Using the formula,

```
dof = (3 - 1) × (2 - 1) = 2
```

Expected Frequency is the number we would expect in each category if the variables were independent (i.e., no association). It is calculated using the formula,

E_{ij} = [(Row Total) × (Column Total)] / Grand Total

For example, consider the contingency table showing variables, Gender vs. Pass:

Expected Frequency for Males Who Passed can be calculated as,

$E_{Male,\ Pass}$ = (50) × (70) / 100 = 35

Expected Frequency for Males Who Failed is,

EMale, Fail = (50) × (30) / 100 = 15

Expected Frequency for Females Who Passed is calculated as,

$E_{Female,\ Pass}$ = (50) × (70) / 100 = 35

Expected Frequency for Females Who Failed can be given as,

$E_{Female, Fail}$ = (50) × (30) / 100 = 15

Thus, the Expected Frequency Table is:

	Pass	Fail	Total
Male	35	15	50
Female	35	15	50
Total	70	30	100

8.1.2 Normalizing the Contingency Table

Normalization converts counts to proportions for better comparison. This means that it shows proportions instead of row counts. A normalized contingency table is also known as Proportional (Relative Frequency) Contingency Table.

Write a program to normalize a contingency table by row total

```
import pandas as pd
import scipy.stats as stats
data = {
    'Gender': ['Male', 'Male', 'Female', 'Female', 'Male', 'Female',
'Male', 'Female', 'Male', 'Female'],
    'Study_Hours': ['Low', 'High', 'Medium', 'Low', 'High', 'Medium',
'Low', 'Medium', 'High', 'Low'],
    'Pass': ['No', 'Yes', 'Yes', 'No', 'Yes', 'Yes', 'No', 'Yes', 'Yes',
'No']
}
df = pd.DataFrame(data)

contingency_table = pd.crosstab(index=[df['Gender'], df['Study_Hours']],
columns=df['Pass'], margins = False)
normalized_table = contingency_table.div(contingency_table.sum(axis=1),
axis=0)
print(normalized_table)
```

OUTPUT

```
Pass                 No  Yes
Gender Study_Hours
Female Low          1.0  0.0
       Medium       0.0  1.0
Male   High         0.0  1.0
       Low          1.0  0.0
```

Write a program to visualize relationships in a contingency table using a stacked bar plot.

```
import pandas as pd
import scipy.stats as stats
import matplotlib.pyplot as plt

data = {
    'Gender': ['Male', 'Male', 'Female', 'Female', 'Male', 'Female',
'Male', 'Female', 'Male', 'Female'],
```

```
    'Study_Hours': ['Low', 'High', 'Medium', 'Low', 'High', 'Medium', 'Low', 'Medium', 'High', 'Low'],
    'Pass': ['No', 'Yes', 'Yes', 'No', 'Yes', 'Yes', 'No', 'Yes', 'Yes', 'No']
}
df = pd.DataFrame(data)
contingency_table = pd.crosstab(index=[df['Gender'], df['Study_Hours']], columns=df['Pass'], margins = False)
contingency_table.plot(kind='bar', stacked=True, colormap='coolwarm')
plt.title("Pass Count by Gender and Study Hours")
plt.ylabel("Count")
plt.xlabel("Gender & Study Hours")
plt.xticks(rotation=45)
plt.legend(title="Pass")
plt.show()
```

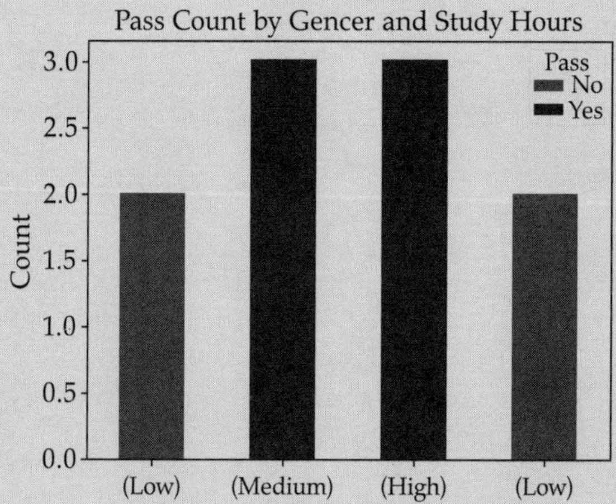

Write a program to visualize relationships in a contingency table using a heatmap.

> In a heatmap, darker shades represent higher frequencies. Such a chart is useful for spotting patterns and trends.

```
import pandas as pd
import scipy.stats as stats
import matplotlib.pyplot as plt
data = {
    'Gender': ['Male', 'Male', 'Female', 'Female', 'Male', 'Female', 'Male', 'Female', 'Male', 'Female'],
    'Study_Hours': ['Low', 'High', 'Medium', 'Low', 'High', 'Medium', 'Low', 'Medium', 'High', 'Low'],
    'Pass': ['No', 'Yes', 'Yes', 'No', 'Yes', 'Yes', 'No', 'Yes', 'Yes', 'No']
}
df = pd.DataFrame(data)
contingency_table = pd.crosstab(index=[df['Gender'], df['Study_Hours']], columns=df['Pass'], margins = False)
import seaborn as sns
sns.heatmap(contingency_table, annot=True, cmap="coolwarm", fmt="d")
```

```
plt.title("Three-Way Contingency Table Heatmap")
plt.show()
```

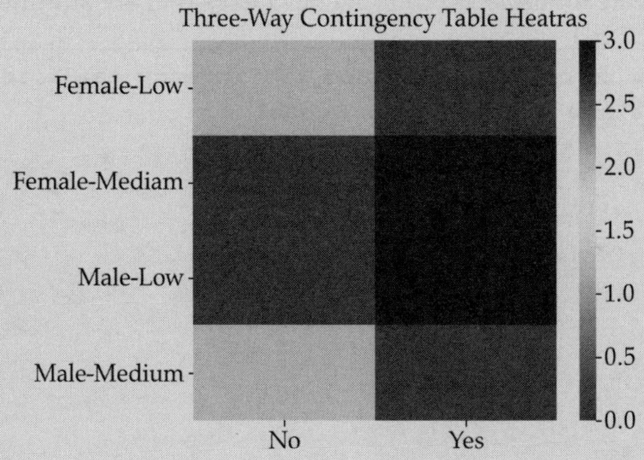

8.1.3 Multi-way (Higher-dimensional) Contingency Tables

These tables show relationship between four or more categorical variables. This relationship cannot be visualized using crosstab(). For this, pivot tables are used. The pivot_table() helps to analyze complex relationships between multiple categorical variables.

Write a program to display the Four-Way Contingency Table

```
import pandas as pd
data = {
    'Gender': ['Male', 'Female', 'Male', 'Female', 'Male', 'Female',
'Male', 'Female', 'Male', 'Female'],
    'Study_Hours': ['Low', 'High', 'Medium', 'Low', 'High', 'Medium',
'Low', 'Medium', 'High', 'Low'],
    'Pass': ['No', 'Yes', 'Yes', 'No', 'Yes', 'Yes', 'No', 'Yes', 'Yes', 'No'],
    'School': ['A', 'B', 'A', 'B', 'A', 'B', 'A', 'B', 'A', 'B']
}
df = pd.DataFrame(data)
# Using pivot table to analyze four variables
pivot_table = df.pivot_table(index=['Gender', 'Study_Hours'],
columns=['Pass', 'School'], aggfunc=len, fill_value=0)
print(pivot_table)
```

OUTPUT

```
Pass                 No     Yes
School                A  B   A  B
Gender Study_Hours
Female High           0  0   0  1
       Low            0  2   0  0
       Medium         0  0   0  2
Male   High           0  0   2  0
       Low            2  0   0  0
       Medium         0  0   1  0
```

Chi-Square Test checks if categorical variables are dependent.

8.1.4 Stratified Contingency Tables

In this approach, we create multiple 2D contingency tables that are stratified by another variable.

Write a program to create stratified contingency table in which attributes Gender and Pass are stratified by School

```
import pandas as pd
data = {
    'Gender': ['Male', 'Female', 'Male', 'Female', 'Male', 'Female',
'Male', 'Female', 'Male', 'Female'],
    'Study_Hours': ['Low', 'High', 'Medium', 'Low', 'High', 'Medium',
'Low', 'Medium', 'High', 'Low'],
    'Pass': ['No', 'Yes', 'Yes', 'No', 'Yes', 'Yes', 'No', 'Yes', 'Yes',
'No'],
    'School': ['A', 'B', 'A', 'B', 'A', 'B', 'A', 'B', 'A', 'B']
}
df = pd.DataFrame(data)
for school in df['School'].unique():
        sub_table = pd.crosstab(df[df['School'] == school]['Gender'],
df[df['School'] == school]['Pass'])
    print(f"Contingency Table for School {school}:\n{sub_table}\n")
```

OUTPUT

```
Contingency Table for School A:
Pass    No  Yes
Gender
Male     2    3
Contingency Table for School B:
Pass    No  Yes
Gender
Female   2    3
```

Cramér's V test measures association strength among variables.

8.1.5 Statistical Tests for Contingency Tables

Once we have created the contingency tables and visualized the data, we can apply statistical tests to verify relationships.

We have already learnt how to apply the Chi-Square Test of Independence. In this section, we will read about two more tests.

Fisher's Exact Test (For Small Data): If we have small samples (<5 counts in some cells), then we can use the Fisher's Exact Test instead of the Chi-Square Test. The Fisher's test gives more accurate results for small datasets. Even in this test, $p < 0.05$ means variables are related.

```
oddsratio, p_value = stats.fisher_exact(contingency_table)
print("Fisher's Exact Test P-value:", p_value)
```

Cramér's V (Effect Size): The Cramér's V measures the strength of association in a Chi-Square Test. The formula to compute the Cramér's V value is,

```
cramers_v = np.sqrt(chi2 / (n * (min(contingency_table.shape) - 1)))
```

where, `n = contingency_table.sum().sum() # Total sample size`

Once obtained, the Cramér's V value is interpreted as,

Value	Strength of Association
0.1–0.3	Weak
0.3–0.5	Moderate
>0.5	Strong

8.2 Time Series Methods

Time series and forecasting have always been a challenging problem in statistics and Data Science. A data is said to be a time series data, when it is sampled on a time-bound attribute like days, months, and years inherently giving it an implicit order.

Forecasting means analyzing data to predict future values. We often use ARIMA and SARIMA algorithms for forecasting. While ARIMA considers the past values (autoregressive, moving average) to predict future values, SARIMA uses past values as well as any seasonality patterns. This makes SARIMA significantly more powerful than ARIMA in forecasting complex data spaces containing cycles.

8.2.1 Data preprocessing for time series forecasting

Time series data is messy. Any algorithm requires clean data for accurate results. Even in case of ARIMA and SARIMA, data has to be cleaned using the following techniques.

Detrending/Stationarity: Models built on stationary data are usually more robust. Adding stationary component in the varying time-series data, helps to ensure that the statistical properties of a model do not vary depending on when the sample was taken.

Anomaly detection: Outliers present in the data might skew the forecasting results. To avoid such a scenario, outliers are identified and normalized.

Checking sampling frequency: The regularity of sampling is checked to avoid considering irregular data for forecasting. If irregularity in data is found, then data has to be imputed or made uniform, as otherwise it may result in broken integrity of the time series. Moreover, irregular data does not fit well with the models.

Missing data: Missing data values must be addressed before modeling. A time series data can be visualized as shown in the figure (with missing values looks like this):

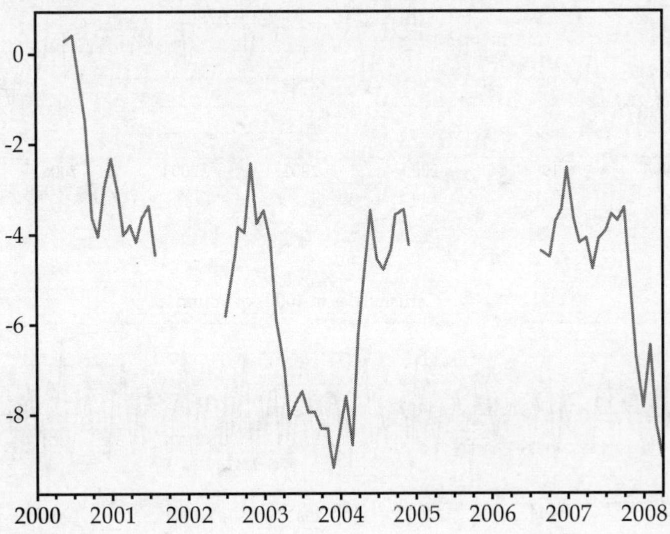

8.3 ARIMA - Autoregressive Integrated Moving Average

ARIMA model is a class of linear models that use historical values to forecast future values. In this section, we will discuss, each of them.

Autoregressive (AR): In an autoregression model, the variable of interest is forecasted using a linear combination of past values of that variable. The term autoregression means a regression of the variable against itself. This means that lagged values of the target variable are used as input variables to forecast values for the future. An autoregression model of order p will look like:

$$m_t = {}_0 + {}_1m_{t-1} + {}_2m_{t-2} + {}_3m_{t-3} + \ldots + {}_pm_{t-p}$$

In the above equation, the currently observed value of *m* is a linear function of its past *p* values. [0, p] are the regression coefficients that are determined after training. We can determine the optimal values of *p* using standard techniques. One of these include analyzing **Autocorrelation** and **Partial Autocorrelation** function plots.

The autocorrelation function (ACF) is the correlation between the current and the past values of the same variable. It takes into account the translative effect that are carried by values with time apart from a direct effect. For example, the cost of oil the day before yesterday had affected the cost yesterday, and yesterday's cost had an effect on the cost today. The cost of oil day before yesterday that affected today's cost is measured by ACF, considering the translative effect.

Partial Autocorrelation (PACF) measures only the direct correlation between past values and current values. This means that PACF only measures the effect of the cost the day before yesterday on today's cost with no translative effect.

Therefore, ACF and PACF plots help the analysts to determine past value dependency, so that the value of *p* in AR can be optimally deduced.

Integrated (I): Integrated represents any differencing applied to make the data stationary. A Dickey-Fuller test technique is applied to the data to check for stationarity, and then experiments with different differencing factors. A differencing factor, d = 1 means a lag of mt - mt-1. The figure illustrates the plot of original vs. differenced data. The differenced data is more stationary than the original data since the mean and variance are approximately consistent over the years.

Catfish Sales in 1000s of Pounds

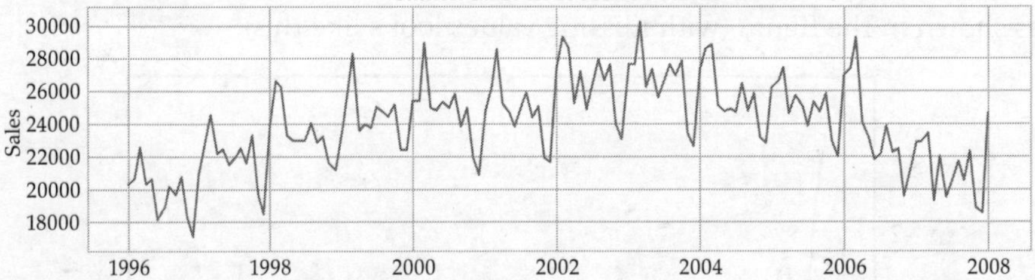

Original Data

Catfish Sales in 1000s of Pounds

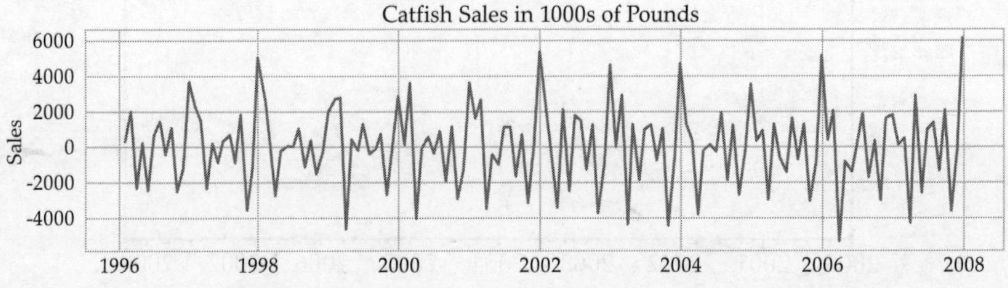

After applying d = 1

Moving Average (MA): Moving average models uses past forecast errors rather than past values in a regression-like model to forecast future values. A moving average model, MA(q), can be denoted by the following equation:

$$m_t = {}_0 + {}_1e_{t-1} + {}_2e_{t-2} + {}_3e_{t-3} + \ldots + {}_qe_{t-q}$$

Here, *e* is the *error*. The value of the error represents the random residual deviations between the model and the target variable. Since error is determined after fitting the model, it is an unobservable parameter. Therefore, a better alternative to solve the MA equation is iterative techniques like Maximum Likelihood Estimation.

Write a program to implement ARIMA. Also plot ACF and PACF

```
import numpy as np
import pandas as pd
import matplotlib.pyplot as plt
import seaborn as sns
from statsmodels.tsa.arima.model import ARIMA
from statsmodels.tsa.stattools import adfuller, acf, pacf
from statsmodels.graphics.tsaplots import plot_acf, plot_pacf
# Generate synthetic time series data
def generate_data(n=100):
    np.random.seed(42)
    time_series = np.cumsum(np.random.randn(n))  # Random walk
    return pd.Series(time_series, index=pd.date_range(start='2023-01-01',
periods=n, freq='D'))
# Check stationarity
def check_stationarity(series):
    result = adfuller(series)
    print("ADF Statistic:", result[0])
    print("p-value:", result[1])
    if result[1] > 0.05:
        print("The series is non-stationary. Differencing is required.")
    else:
        print("The series is stationary.")
# Plot ACF and PACF
def plot_acf_pacf(series, lags=20):
    fig, axes = plt.subplots(1, 2, figsize=(12, 5))
    plot_acf(series, lags=lags, ax=axes[0])
    plot_pacf(series, lags=lags, ax=axes[1])
    axes[0].set_title("Autocorrelation Function (ACF)")
    axes[1].set_title("Partial Autocorrelation Function (PACF)")
    plt.show()
# Train ARIMA model
def train_arima(series, order=(1,1,1)):
    model = ARIMA(series, order=order)
    model_fit = model.fit()
```

```
    print(model_fit.summary())
    return model_fit
# Forecast future values
def forecast(model_fit, steps=10):
    forecast_values = model_fit.forecast(steps=steps)
    return forecast_values
if __name__ == "__main__":
    # Generate data
    series = generate_data()
    # Check stationarity
    check_stationarity(series)
   # Plot ACF and PACF
    plot_acf_pacf(series)

    # Train ARIMA model
    model_fit = train_arima(series, order=(2,1,2))
        # Forecast
    steps = 10
    forecast_values = forecast(model_fit, steps=steps)
        # Plot results
    plt.figure(figsize=(10,5))
    plt.plot(series, label='Original Series')
    plt.axvline(series.index[-1], color='r', linestyle='--',
label='Forecast Start')
    plt.plot(pd.date_range(start=series.index[-1], periods=steps+1,
freq='D')[1:],
             forecast_values, label='Forecast', color='g')
    plt.legend()
    plt.show()
```

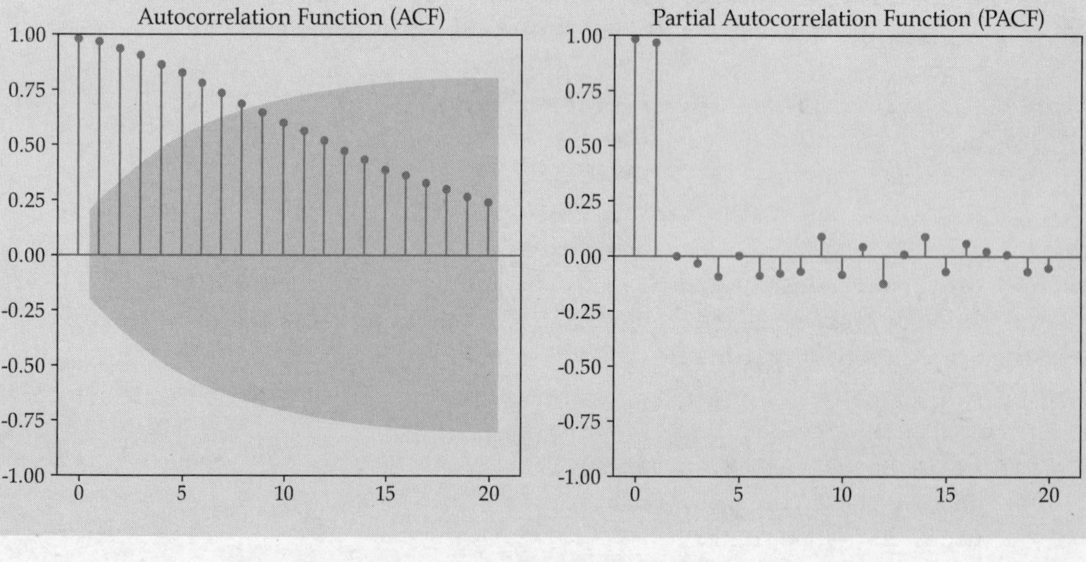

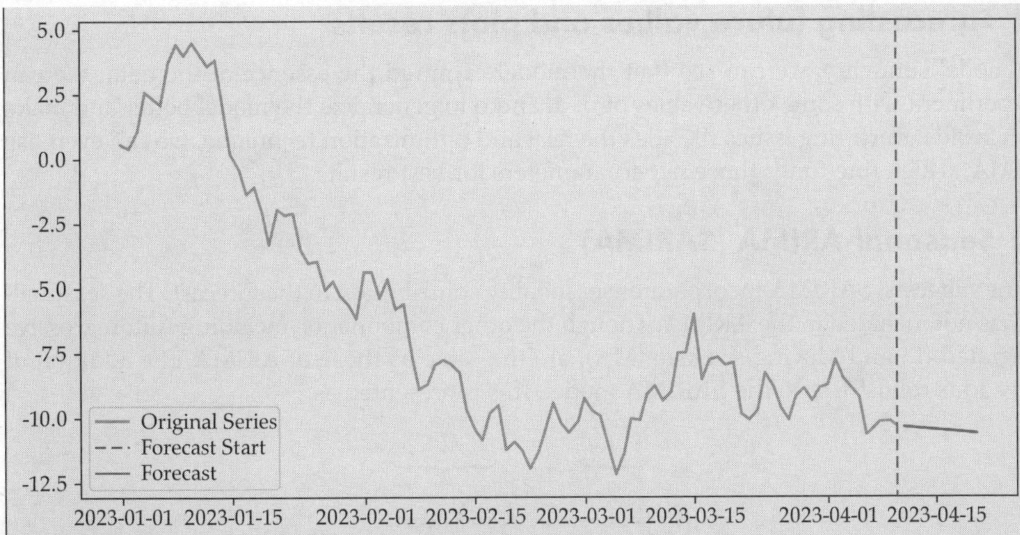


```
ADF Statistic: -1.3583317659818985
p-value: 0.6020814791099101
The series is non-stationary. Differencing is required.
```

```
                               SARIMAX Results
==============================================================================
Dep. Variable:                      y   No. Observations:                  100
Model:                 ARIMA(2, 1, 2)   Log Likelihood                -130.434
Date:                Fri, 14 Feb 2025   AIC                            270.868
Time:                        21:18:35   BIC                            283.844
Sample:                    01-01-2023   HQIC                           276.118
                         - 04-10-2023
Covariance Type:                  opg
==============================================================================
                 coef    std err          z      P>|z|      [0.025      0.975]
------------------------------------------------------------------------------
ar.L1          0.1317      0.283      0.465      0.642      -0.423       0.686
ar.L2          0.8665      0.230      3.768      0.000       0.416       1.317
ma.L1         -0.0600      0.355     -0.169      0.866      -0.757       0.637
ma.L2         -0.9347      0.304     -3.072      0.002      -1.531      -0.338
sigma2         0.8138      0.162      5.013      0.000       0.496       1.132
===================================================================================
Ljung-Box (L1) (Q):                   0.46   Jarque-Bera (JB):                 0.33
Prob(Q):                              0.50   Prob(JB):                         0.85
Heteroskedasticity (H):               1.02   Skew:                            -0.14
Prob(H) (two-sided):                  0.96   Kurtosis:                         3.07
===================================================================================
```

From the output of the above code, we can observe that if the p-value is **greater than 0.05**, the series is non-stationary and requires differencing.

The **ARIMA Model Summary** shows the model details including coefficients, AIC, BIC, etc. Key features of this program are,

- Generation of synthetic time series data (random walk).
- Checking stationarity using **Augmented Dickey-Fuller test**.
- **Plotting ACF and PACF** to determine ARIMA parameters. While the ACF plot shows significant lags where autocorrelation is high, PACF plot, on the other hand, helps to identify AR terms by removing indirect relationships.

8.3.1 Forecasting future values and plots results

From the model summary, we can see that the model captured the essence of the data. We can further experiment with some other values of p, d, and q to generalize the model better and make sure that it avoids overfitting issues. Besides the trial and optimization technique, we can even use **Auto-ARIMA,** which fine-tunes those hyperparameters for best results.

8.3.2 Seasonal-ARIMA (SARIMA)

As the name suggests, SARIMA incorporates seasonality contribution to the forecast. The seasonality factor was not included in the ARIMA. Though the other components, including Autoregressive (AR), Integrated (I), and Moving Average (MA), are the same as those of ARIMA, the addition of Seasonality adds robustness to the SARIMA model. It is represented as:

$$\text{ARIMA} \quad \underbrace{(p,d,q)}_{\substack{\uparrow \\ \text{Non-seasonal part} \\ \text{of the model}}} \quad \underbrace{(P,D,Q)_m}_{\substack{\uparrow \\ \text{Seasonal part of} \\ \text{of the model}}}$$

Here, m is the number of observations per year. The other values like P, D, Q are similar to that used in ARIMA.

```
Implementing SARIMA
import pandas as pd
import numpy as np
import matplotlib.pyplot as plt
import statsmodels.api as sm
from statsmodels.tsa.statespace.sarimax import SARIMAX
from sklearn.metrics import mean_squared_error

df = pd.read_csv('AirPassengers.csv' parse_dates=["Month"],
index_col="Month")

# Plot dataset
plt.figure(figsize=(10, 5))
plt.plot(df, label='Air Passengers')
plt.xlabel('Year')
plt.ylabel('Passengers')
plt.title('Air Passengers Over Time')
plt.legend()
plt.show()

# Train-Test Split (80% train, 20% test)
train_size = int(len(df) * 0.8)
train, test = df.iloc[:train_size], df.iloc[train_size:]
```

```
# Define SARIMA parameters (p, d, q) x (P, D, Q, s)
p, d, q = 1, 1, 1  # Non-seasonal components
P, D, Q, s = 1, 1, 1, 12  # Seasonal components (s=12 for monthly data)

# Fit SARIMA model on training data
model = SARIMAX(train["Passengers"], order=(p, d, q), seasonal_order=(P,
D, Q, s))
sarima_result = model.fit()

# Print model summary
print(sarima_result.summary())

# Make predictions on test data
test_pred = sarima_result.get_prediction(start=test.index[0], end=test.
index[-1]).predicted_mean

# Ensure the predicted values match the test set length
if len(test) == len(test_pred):
    # Compute RMSE
    rmse = np.sqrt(mean_squared_error(test, test_pred))
    print(f"Root Mean Square Error (RMSE): {rmse:.2f}")
else:
    print(f"Error: Mismatch in lengths - Test: {len(test)}, Predictions:
{len(test_pred)}")

# Forecast the next 24 months
forecast_steps = 24
forecast = sarima_result.get_forecast(steps=forecast_steps)
forecast_index = pd.date_range(test.index[-1], periods=forecast_steps +
1, freq='M')[1:]
forecast_values = forecast.predicted_mean

# Plot test predictions and future forecast
plt.figure(figsize=(10, 5))
plt.plot(df, label="Original Data")
plt.plot(test.index, test_pred, label="Test Predictions", color='orange')
plt.plot(forecast_index, forecast_values, label="Forecast", color='red')
plt.xlabel("Year")
plt.ylabel("Passengers")
plt.title("SARIMA Test Predictions & Future Forecast")
plt.legend()
plt.show()
```

OUTPUT

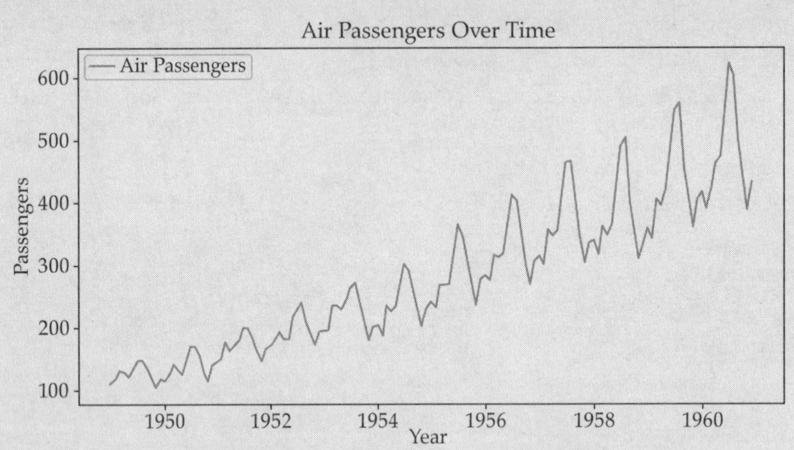

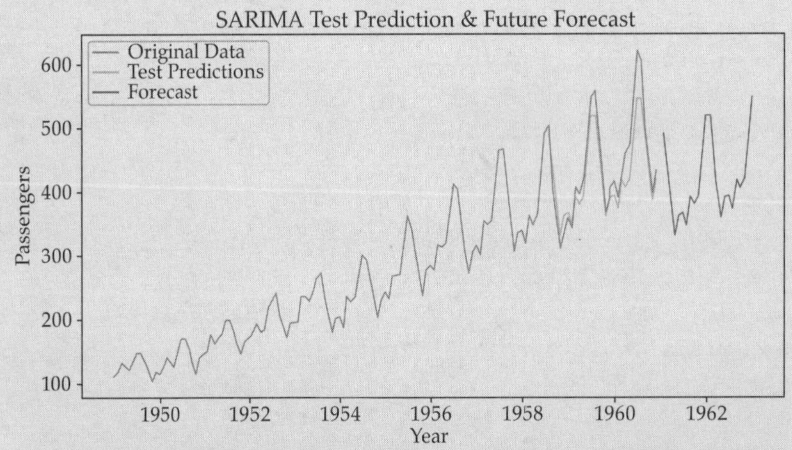


```
                                     SARIMAX Results
==========================================================================================
Dep. Variable:                         Passengers   No. Observations:                  115
Model:             SARIMAX(1, 1, 1)x(1, 1, 1, 12)   Log Likelihood                -374.130
Date:                            Sat, 15 Feb 2025   AIC                            758.260
Time:                                    20:41:44   BIC                            771.385
Sample:                                01-01-1949   HQIC                           763.575
                                     - 07-01-1958
Covariance Type:                              opg
==============================================================================
                 coef    std err          z      P>|z|      [0.025      0.975]
------------------------------------------------------------------------------
ar.L1         -0.6368      0.334     -1.909      0.056      -1.291       0.017
ma.L1          0.4609      0.372      1.238      0.216      -0.269       1.190
ar.S.L12      -0.3547      0.670     -0.529      0.597      -1.669       0.959
ma.S.L12       0.2283      0.721      0.317      0.751      -1.184       1.641
sigma2        89.5804     14.374      6.232      0.000      61.407     117.753
===================================================================================
Ljung-Box (L1) (Q):                   0.01   Jarque-Bera (JB):                 2.63
Prob(Q):                              0.92   Prob(JB):                         0.27
Heteroskedasticity (H):               1.18   Skew:                             0.33
Prob(H) (two-sided):                  0.64   Kurtosis:                         2.59
===================================================================================

Warnings:
[1] Covariance matrix calculated using the outer product of gradients (complex-step).
Root Mean Square Error (RMSE): 30.14
```

8.3.4 Pros and cons of ARIMA and SARIMA models

The linear nature of both the algorithms makes them easy to use in the industry for experimentation and understanding the data, creating baseline forecasting scores. When tuned right with lagged values (p, d, q), these models perform significantly better. The simple and explainable nature of ARIMA/SARIMA makes them popular among the analysts and data scientists.

Pros of ARIMA and SARIMA

Easy to understand and interpret: The ARIMA and SARIMA models are simple and interpretable. The results generated by them rank high in terms of quality.

Limited variables: The models use few hyperparameters making the model easy to maintain when in production.

Cons of ARIMA and SARIMA

Exponential time complexity: As the value of p and q increases, there are equally more coefficients to fit. This in turn increases the time complexity thereby making it difficult to put into production. In such a scenario, data scientists look for other algorithms.

Complex data: The algorithms may fail to give results if the data is too complex and there is no optimal solution for p and q.

Amount of data needed: ARIMA/SARIMA requires considerable amount of data to work on. Just three years of historical data is not enough for an accurate forecast.

8.3.5 Real-world use-cases of ARIMA and SARIMA

ARIMA and SARIMA are popularly used econometrics models for forecasting stock prices, product-demand, and even the spread of infectious diseases. When one does not know the underlying mechanisms or if the mechanism is too complicated to understand, then ARIMA is a good alternative. These models are much simpler than complex deep algorithms like RNNs. Given below are a few examples in which applying ARIMA gives better results.

1. ARIMA model was used to forecast COVID-19 case numbers in India. The only shortcoming of using ARIMA was that it forecasts only by considering the past values. But the dynamics of COVID-19 changed shape with time and number of cases depended on a lot of other behavioral factors other than past values that ARIMA was not able to capture.
2. The SARIMA model is also used to predict Daily and Monthly Average Global Solar Radiation based on the hourly solar radiation data obtained from the Korean Meteorological Administration over 37 years.

   ARIMA and SARIMA models are used for disease management. For example, these models were used by a hospital in Singapore to accurately predict the number of beds that will be needed in the next three days during the SARS epidemic. This information helped the hospital to optimize resources and staff schedules.

   ARIMA models are used to examine patient's medical data to check for early signs of health issues and tailor-fit treatment strategies.
3. These models are frequently used in food companies to model and forecast demand for consumer goods and services. This information helps to optimize production planning to control inventory.
4. ARIMA models can analyze financial time series data that often contain complex autocorrelations and interactions between multiple economic indicators. This makes these models suitable for forecasting volatile metrics like stock prices or exchange rates.
5. ARIMA models are used to predict the future of a country or global economy. This information helps to formulate economic policy decisions.
6. ARIMA models analyze historical weather data (about air–sea interactions and many other factors) to identify the trends in the climate and predict what the future climates will look like.
7. In supply-chain operations, ARIMA models are used to forecast supply chain disruptions by analyzing the interactions between multiple variables like transport delays or demand fluctuations.

8.4 Longitudinal Data Analysis

Longitudinal data consists of repeated observations of the same subjects over time. It finds applications in different areas including medicine, social sciences, and finance. Longitudinal data is very useful in analyzing trends, transitions, and event occurrences over time.

Longitudinal analysis when applied in finance, helps to calculate a portfolio's value at risk (VaR), using the historic simulation method. The simulation demonstrates how the value of the current portfolio would have fluctuated over previous time periods. For this, it is important to have the historical fluctuations of the assets in the portfolio during those times. Such a simulation-based observation provides an estimate of the maximum likely loss over the next time period.

In event studies, longitudinal data is used to analyze the factors that result in abnormal stock returns over time or observe the fluctuations in stock prices when there is any announcement for a merger and/or performance in the last quarter.

Longitudinal data is also used to measure poverty and income inequality by tracking individual households. Another application of longitudinal data is assessing teacher's effectiveness and other factors affecting student performance. The data for this analysis can be collected from standardized test scores.

Moreover, social scientists use longitudinal data to understand the causation of events that have occurred in the past. For example, understanding the effect of a new law on crime statistics, or the birth rate after a natural disaster in a particular area.

Also known as panel data, longitudinal data, is collected by a series of repeated observations of the same subjects over some extended time frame. Longitudinal data is extensively used in the social sciences, including by economists, political scientists, and sociologists. For example, a company uses longitudinal data to track profitability, risk, and to identify the effect of economic shocks. In economics and financial studies, longitudinal data is used to measure how long an event lasts and observe facts such as, whether the same group of individuals or a different set of people remain unemployed during a recession.

Longitudinal data is different from cross-sectional data. While longitudinal data covers the same sample over time, cross-sectional data studies different samples at each point in time. Thus, a cross-sectional data set will always draw a new random sample.

Longitudinal data is collected sequentially from the same respondents over time. This helps in analyzing trends and changes over time. Correspondingly, a longitudinal study involves repeated observations of the same variables (such as people) over long time periods. It is usually an observational study that can also be structured as a longitudinal randomized experiment. Longitudinal study or longitudinal survey or panel study helps the researchers to identify the developments or changes in the characteristics of the target population at both the group and the individual level. For example, it can be used to understand the similarities or differences between identical twins who are brought up together vs. identical twins who are not. In this study, several variables are observed. The only constant is that all the participants have identical twins.

8.4.1 Techniques for Collection and Exploration of Longitudinal Data

Longitudinal data is collected by the following ways.

- Surveys and Interviews to collect measurements from individuals over time.
- Clinical Trials in which the patients are observed at multiple time points.
- Sensor Data collected from IoT devices to track behavior over time.

- Financial Data, for example, stock market data that are used to analyze trends over a period of months/years.

```
import pandas as pd
#Sample Longitudinal Data
data = {
    'Subject_ID': [1, 1, 1, 2, 2, 2, 3, 3, 3],
    'Time': [1, 2, 3, 1, 2, 3, 1, 2, 3],
    'Measurement': [10, 12, 14, 20, 22, 25, 30, 32, 35]
}
df = pd.DataFrame(data)
print(df.head())  # View first few records
import matplotlib.pyplot as plt

for subject in df['Subject_ID'].unique():
    subset = df[df['Subject_ID'] == subject]
    plt.plot(subset['Time'],     subset['Measurement'],        marker='o',
label=f'Subject {subject}')

plt.xlabel('Time')
plt.ylabel('Measurement')
plt.title('Longitudinal Data Trends')
plt.legend()
plt.show()
```

```
   Subject_ID  Time  Measurement
0           1     1           10
1           1     2           12
2           1     3           14
3           2     1           20
4           2     2           22
```

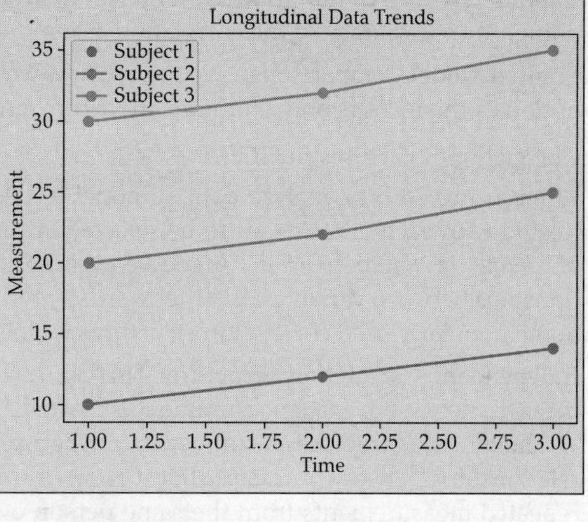

8.4.2 Techniques to Analyze Longitudinal Data

Two methods are usually preferred for analyzing longitudinal data–GEE and MER. Both these techniques use time-invariant predictors that never change (e.g., gender, genotype) and time-varying predictors (e.g., age) for analysis. Moreover, both the techniques can easily handle irregularly timed and missing data without the need for explicit imputation.

8.4.2.1 Generalized Estimating Equations (GEE)

GEEs are a statistical tool used to understand how different factors (like age, medication, or other covariates) affect repeated measurements taken from the same subjects over time. It is extensively used in medical or psychological research, where data from multiple visits or observations from the same person are analyzed.

The focus of GEEs is not on how these repeated measurements are related to each other, but on the relationship between the factors (like medication or age) and the outcomes (like cognitive scores or disease progression). For example, GEEs are popular in fields like neurodegenerative diseases. For example, GEEs are used in the treatment of neurodegenerative diseases by analyzing how cognitive scores change over time based on factors like education or age, or how medication affects different aspects of brain function (like motor skills or cognition).

The accuracy of the correlation model plays and important role in getting reliable estimates of how the factors affect the outcomes.

Advantages:

Tolerant of Mistakes in Correlation Modeling: Even when one is not totally right about how things are correlated, GEEs can still give good estimates for the relationships.

Easy to Compute: Compared to other complicated methods (like MER), GEEs are much easier to calculate and less demanding computationally.

Handles Missing Data Well: GEEs perform well even in case of missing data.

Limitations:

Missing Data Assumptions: GEEs assume that missing data is completely random, which is not always the case, especially in case of diseases where certain factors might cause people to drop out of studies. In this case, more advanced methods are useful.

Cannot Test Correlation Models: GEEs do not directly estimate how well the correlation model is doing, so the accuracy of the correlation assumptions cannot be tested.

Limited Model Comparisons: To compare how well different models fit the data, GEEs is not a good option as the focus is only on the relationship between factors and outcomes, not the correlations.

Correlation Structures in GEE

When using GEE to analyze data, a model to describe how the repeated measurements are correlated with each other needs to be selected at the beginning of the analysis. This model is called a *working correlation structure.* A good correlation structure gives us reliable estimates for the relationships between variables. In other words, it reflects the actual correlations as closely as possible. Some popularly used correlation structures include:

Independent Correlation Structure: This assumes that there is no correlation between repeated measurements. So, each measurement is treated as if it is completely independent from the others.

Though the structure is simple, it can be used in initial analyses to get a quick look at the relationships between variables. But it is often unrealistic for most real-world data as we do need repeated measurements from the same person over time. Therefore, the independent correlation structure can lead to inaccurate results for time-varying data.

Exchangeable Correlation Structure: This assumes that all repeated measurements within a group (or "cluster") are equally correlated. For example, if you have participants grouped by disease category, this structure assumes that any two participants within the same disease category are equally correlated, no matter which two participants you pick.

The exchangeable correlation structure works well when "things" in the same group (like people in the same disease category) are similar to each other. However, it does not always work well for data over time, like measurements taken years apart. For example, while studying people's health over 10 years, we cannot assume that the correlation between measurements taken in the first year and the tenth year will be the same. Measurements taken at shorter intervals (like every consequent year) are typically more similar than those taken far apart (like year 1 and year 10).

The structure is better-suited for situations where all measurements within a group are similarly related, like measurements from people in the same disease category or people in the same study site.

Autoregressive Correlation Structure: This structure is used when the measurements taken closer in time are more strongly related to each other than measurements taken further apart. So, the correlation decreases as the time between measurements increases.

The model is often used when working with time-based data, like measuring someone's health over several years. For example, the health scores in year 1 and year 2 are probably more similar than the scores in year 1 and year 10.

Unstructured Correlation Structure: This is the most flexible structure because it does not make any assumptions about how the correlations look. It estimates a different correlation for each pair of time points. But flexibility comes at the cost of being computationally expensive. The structure requires more processing power and time to calculate. However, it is best suited for data with only a few time points (since calculating correlations for many time points can be overwhelming).

8.4.2.2 Mixed Effects Regression (MER)

MER models are a powerful tool for studying relationships between factors (like age, medication, or other covariates) and repeated measurements over time, just like GEEs. However, MER models go a step further. They not only estimate the relationship between covariates and repeated responses but also account for the correlations between those repeated measurements over time.

MER models do this by using "random effects" to represent differences that exist between individuals or groups (called *clusters*). For example, while studying people, MER models can capture how each person's measurements change over time and how different groups might behave differently. These random effects help to make more accurate predictions and account for individual variability.

MER models are used in fields like neurodegenerative disease research. Researchers have used MER models to understand how different health outcomes change over time. For example, how motor skills or brain scans change for each person's unique progression.

Advantages:

Multi-level Predictions: MER models can handle data at different levels (like individual measurements, groups of people, or research sites) and make predictions at each level. This helps in understanding how things vary not just between people but also across different groups.

Hypothesis Testing: Since MER models estimate both the relationship between covariates and responses *and* the correlation structure, hypotheses about the correlation parameters can be tested. This helps to check how well the model captures relationships between repeated measurements.

Better Model Comparison: Different models can be easily compared using techniques like likelihood ratio tests and information criteria (AIC/BIC). Model comparison is not possible with GEEs because GEEs do not estimate the correlation structure directly.

Better Handling of Missing Data: MER models are more flexible when dealing with missing data. This helps make MER models more applicable to real-world data, where missing values are quite common.

Limitations:

Computational Complexity: MER models are more complex and require more computation.

Model Specification: The accuracy of results from MER models depends on the accuracy of the relationship and the correlation structure of the repeated measurements.

Modeling Correlation

In Mixed Effects Regression (MER) models, the correlation between repeated measurements is captured using random effects. These random effects represent the unique characteristics of each individual or group (like each person's disease progression) that affect the outcome over time. The modeling of random effects is the key for accurate results. Theoretically, random effects follow a normal distribution but practically, following a strictly normal distribution is not possible.

If the random effects and the covariates (the factors being analyzed, like medication or age) are independent, then even if the random effect distribution is wrong, the model still gives valid estimates. A valid estimate means biased or incorrect results.

If the random effects and covariates are dependent, then the model might give biased results which are always inaccurate.

The relationship between the random effects and the covariates can be tested using a Hausman Chi-Squared Test. If this test shows that the random effects and covariates are independent, then the random effects follow a normal distribution. Otherwise, statistics need to be applied for flexible modeling.

8.4.2.3 Time-Varying Predictors

GEEs and MERs are both great for analyzing how things change over time, such as medication use, dosage changes, blood pressure, or weight. These are examples of time-varying predictors because they can change during the study period and impact the outcomes. To model these time-varying predictors, we often use **splines**. Think of a spline as a flexible curve that smoothly connects two or more points to capture the changes in a predictor (like medication usage) over time. This curve helps to understand how the predictor is changing and how that impacts the disease progression.

There are different types of splines, but we should select the one that flexibly captures changes over time without being too rigid. Another important decision is the number of splines to be used. While too few splines might miss important changes, too many splines, on the other hand, may make the curve less meaningful. Therefore, the best approach is to use P-splines. P-splines are a specific type of spline that balances smoothness and precision. It selects right number of splines automatically to maximize accuracy without overcomplicating things.

Write a program to analyze patients' blood pressure over multiple visits, considering the fixed effect as the effect of treatment on blood pressure and the correlation structure, which includes measurements from the same patient that are correlated.

```
import pandas as pd
import numpy as np
import statsmodels.api as sm
from statsmodels.genmod.generalized_estimating_equations import GEE
from statsmodels.genmod.families import Gaussian
from statsmodels.genmod.cov_struct import Exchangeable
```

```
# Generate synthetic data
np.random.seed(42)
num_patients = 50
num_visits = 5
total_observations = num_patients * num_visits

# Create patient IDs (repeated measures)
patients = np.repeat(np.arange(num_patients), num_visits)

# Treatment (randomly assigned to patients)
treatment = np.random.choice([0, 1], num_patients)
treatment_effect = np.array([treatment[i] for i in patients])

# Visit number
visits = np.tile(np.arange(1, num_visits + 1), num_patients)

# Generate blood pressure (dependent variable)
baseline_bp = 120 + treatment_effect * (-5)  # Treatment reduces BP by 5
units
measurement_noise = np.random.normal(0, 3, total_observations)
blood_pressure = baseline_bp + measurement_noise

# Create DataFrame
df = pd.DataFrame({
    "Patient": patients,
    "Visit": visits,
    "Treatment": treatment_effect,
    "BloodPressure": blood_pressure
})

# Define GEE model with an Exchangeable correlation structure
model = GEE(
    endog=df["BloodPressure"],        # Dependent variable
    exog=sm.add_constant(df[["Treatment", "Visit"]]),    #  Independent
variables
    groups=df["Patient"],             # Clustered by patient
   family=Gaussian(),              # Continuous outcome (Gaussian family)
    cov_struct=Exchangeable()         # Assumes equal correlation between
visits
)
# Fit the model
result = model.fit()

# Print summary
print(result.summary())
```

OUTPUT

```
                         GEE Regression Results
==============================================================================
Dep. Variable:           BloodPressure   No. Observations:                 250
Model:                             GEE   No. clusters:                      50
Method:                    Generalized  Min. cluster size:                   5
                  Estimating Equations  Max. cluster size:                   5
Family:                       Gaussian  Mean cluster size:                 5.0
Dependence structure:     Exchangeable  Num. iterations:                     2
Date:                 Sat, 01 Mar 2025  Scale:                           8.870
Covariance type:                robust  Time:                         13:54:48
==============================================================================
                 coef    std err          z      P>|z|      [0.025      0.975]
------------------------------------------------------------------------------
const        120.1969      0.543    221.320      0.000     119.132     121.261
Treatment     -5.0910      0.376    -13.546      0.000      -5.828      -4.354
Visit          0.0602      0.154      0.391      0.696      -0.241       0.362
==============================================================================
Skew:                          0.2110   Kurtosis:                      -0.0027
Centered skew:                 0.2375   Centered kurtosis:              0.3554
==============================================================================
```

Write a program to analyze students' test scores across different schools using MER. The fixed effect is the impact of study hours on test scores and for random effect, use school-specific differences in test scores.

```
import pandas as pd
import numpy as np
import statsmodels.api as sm
from statsmodels.formula.api import mixedlm

# Create synthetic data
np.random.seed(42)
num_schools = 10
num_students_per_school = 20
total_students = num_schools * num_students_per_school

# Generate school IDs
schools = np.repeat(np.arange(num_schools), num_students_per_school)

# Generate study hours (fixed effect)
study_hours = np.random.uniform(1, 10, total_students)

# Generate random school-specific effects
school_effects = np.random.normal(0, 5, num_schools)
school_random_effect = np.array([school_effects[i] for i in schools])
```

```
# Generate scores with both fixed and random effects
scores = 50 + 5 * study_hours + school_random_effect + np.random.normal
(0, 3, total_students)

# Create DataFrame
df = pd.DataFrame({
    "School": schools,
    "StudyHours": study_hours,
    "Scores": scores
})

# Fit a Mixed-Effects Model
model = mixedlm("Scores ~ StudyHours", df, groups=df["School"],
re_formula="1")
result = model.fit()

# Print model summary
print(result.summary())
```

OUTPUT

```
         Mixed Linear Model Regression Results
==========================================================
Model:             MixedLM Dependent Variable: Scores
No. Observations: 200      Method:             REML
No. Groups:        10      Scale:              8.2790
Min. group size:   20      Log-Likelihood:     -514.6708
Max. group size:   20      Converged:          Yes
Mean group size:   20.0
----------------------------------------------------------
             Coef.  Std.Err.   z    P>|z| [0.025 0.975]
----------------------------------------------------------
Intercept    50.519    1.593 31.723 0.000 47.398 53.641
StudyHours    5.011    0.078 64.539 0.000  4.859  5.163
Group Var    23.217    3.963
```

Write a program for Event history analysis to model the timing of events.

```
import numpy as np
import pandas as pd
import matplotlib.pyplot as plt
from lifelines import KaplanMeierFitter, CoxPHFitter

# Generate synthetic survival data
np.random.seed(42)
num_patients = 100
# Generate survival times (in months)
survival_times = np.random.exponential(scale=12, size=num_patients)
# Censoring indicator (1 = event occurred, 0 = censored)
censored = np.random.choice([0, 1], size=num_patients, p=[0.3, 0.7])
```

```
# Treatment group (random assignment)
treatment = np.random.choice(["A", "B"], size=num_patients)
# Create DataFrame
df = pd.DataFrame({
    "SurvivalTime": survival_times,
    "Censored": censored,
    "Treatment": treatment
})
# Kaplan-Meier Survival Analysis
kmf = KaplanMeierFitter()
plt.figure(figsize=(8, 5))
# to take rows belonging to the current treatment group
for group in df["Treatment"].unique():
    mask = df["Treatment"] == group
   kmf.fit(df["SurvivalTime"][mask], event_observed=df["Censored"][mask],
label=f"Treatment {group}")
    kmf.plot_survival_function()
plt.title("Kaplan-Meier Survival Curve")
plt.xlabel("Time (Months)")
plt.ylabel("Survival Probability")
plt.legend()
plt.show()
```

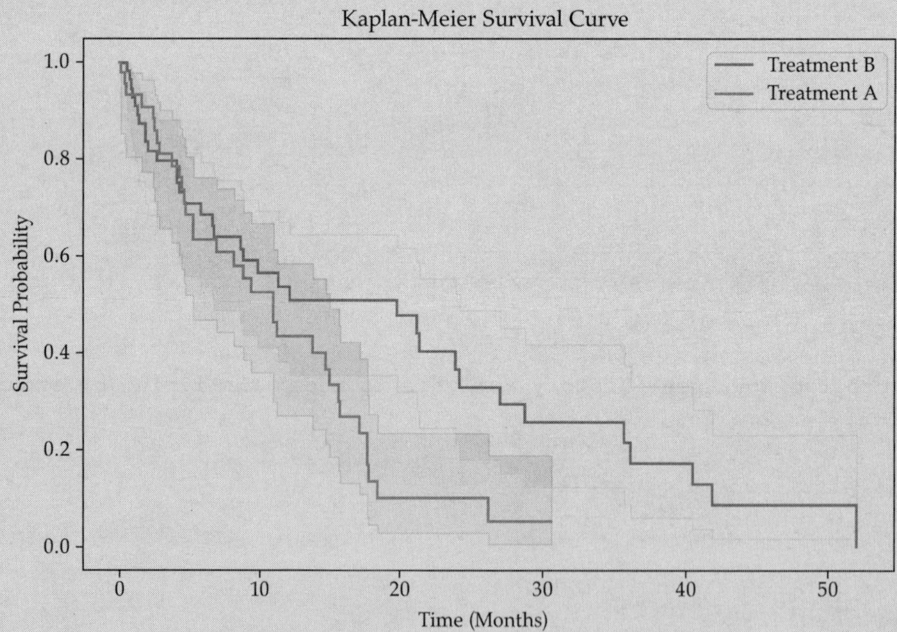

df["SurvivalTime"][mask] selects the survival times of the current treatment group.
df["Censored"][mask] indicates whether an event (death or failure) has occurred (1) or if the data is censored (0).

8.5 Hypothesis Testing with Python: T-Test, Z-Test, and P-Value

Data is the fuel that drives decision-making, and hypothesis testing is the technique that helps to optimize these decisions. It allows the data scientists to confirm if their findings, theories, and assumptions occurred by chance or by accurate statistical analysis. Areas including Pharmaceuticals, Manufacturing, Insurance, and Research use hypothesis testing to make better predictions and accurate conclusions from the data.

Any hypothesis testing tries to find answer for the question, "Based on what is known, what will happen?". A hypothesis is a prediction or assumption based on what we already know. It is not just a random guess or a simple question. Rather, it is a thoughtful statement that raises a question and suggests a possible answer. For example, the statement "women have more patience than men" is a hypothesis. A strong hypothesis is clear, testable, and flexible enough to be refined as more data is gathered and analyzed.

Hypotheses have two variables, the independent variable (cause) and the dependent variable (effect). The independent variable affects what happens to the dependent variable.

In the above statement, hypothesis ("women are more prone to cancer than men") is true but has to be tested. This can be done by conducting a survey on people who have suffered from cancer and then performing a hypothesis test.

8.5.1 Parts of a Hypothesis

There are two parts of a Hypothesis:

Null Hypothesis or H_o: A null hypothesis assumes that there is no effect or difference between the variables of two more samples being studied. For example, the statement, "BMI does not impact health status" means that whether someone has BMI 10 or 40, their health will be the same. The null hypothesis, denoted as H_o, is what researchers test to determine whether it should be accepted or rejected based on the data.

Alternative Hypothesis or H_1: An alternative hypothesis is the opposite of the null hypothesis. It suggests that there is a meaningful effect or difference between the variables of two more samples being studied. For example, the statement, "BMI impacts health status" is an alternative hypothesis.

8.5.2 Key Terminology

Some important terms frequently used in hypothesis testing are,

Level of Significance or the threshold level, specifies how far the sample statistic must deviate from the null hypothesis for the result to be considered statistically significant. Therefore, *it is the probability of making the wrong decision when* H_o *is true.* The significance level, 'α', is set to 5% (0.05) by default, but can be set to any other value before testing the hypothesis.

P-value: The p-value represents the probability of obtaining the observed results during hypothesis testing. It indicates the strength of the evidence against the null hypothesis. If the p-value is less than the threshold value, the H_o is rejected and H_1 is accepted, implying that there is a significant effect. Correspondingly, if the p-value is greater than the threshold value then H_o cannot be rejected, as there is not enough evidence to support H_1.

Confidence Level: Confidence level is defined as the percentage of probability that the confidence interval will contain the true population parameter when a random sample is drawn from the population multiple times.

For example, given a population of sufferers of cancers, the confidence level is the probability that irrespective of the number of times random samples are drawn from the population, there will always be a higher percentage of women suffering from cancer. The formula for confidence level is 1- α, where 'α' is usually set as 5%. Hence, the confidence level is 95%.

> Confidence level can be zero, but significance level cannot be zero.

Confidence Interval: When random samples are drawn from the population of people suffering from cancer, we get different values due to variation between the variables in the population. So, it is better to express the population estimate as a range of numbers. This range is known as the confidence interval.

The confidence interval is a range of values determined by the confidence level, indicating the likelihood that a specific population parameter falls within that range.

8.5.3 Steps in Hypothesis Testing

As discussed, hypothesis testing is performed to either accept or reject a statement made about a sample drawn from a population. That is, the hypothesis test verifies the credibility of the hypothesis. To perform hypothesis testing, we need to follow the steps given below.

Step 1: State the null and the alternative hypotheses.

Step 2: Set an appropriate value for the significance level, "α" which is usually 5% (0.05).

Step 3: Collect and analyze data.

Step 4: Calculate the p-value and either accept or reject the null hypothesis.

Once the hypothesis testing is complete, we may get two types of errors–Type I and Type II errors.

Type I error or α-error occurs when the null hypothesis is true but is rejected. For example, a medical test incorrectly detects a disease in a healthy person.

Type II error or β-error occurs when the null hypothesis is false but it is accepted. For example, a medical test fails to detect a disease in a sick person.

Minimizing one type of error may increase the likelihood of the other. So, based on the context of the hypothesis test, a balance needs to be made.

8.5.4 The T-Test in Hypothesis Testing

A T-test is a statistical test that is used to compare the means of two groups and determine if the difference between them is statistically significant. The test is often used when,

1. the sample size is small, say <=30
2. the population standard deviation is unknown
3. the data follows a normal or Gaussian distribution indicating that the data is distributed symmetrically.

There are three different types of T-tests. Depending upon *the nature of the data or the design* of the experiment, we select one that is most appropriate in the current context. Let us see all of them.

One-Sample T-test:The test compares the mean value of a sample with a known mean or average. Therefore,

Null Hypothesis: $\mu = M$

Alternative Hypothesis: $\mu \neq M$

where, μ = sample mean and M = known mean.

Independent Sample T-test: The test compares the mean values of two different samples from two different populations to see if there is a significant difference.

Null Hypothesis: $\mu_1 = \mu_2$
Alternative Hypothesis: $\mu_1 \neq \mu_2$
where, μ_1 and μ_2 are the sample means for the two independent samples.

Dependent or Paired Sample T-test: The test compares the means of two dependent samples taken from the same population at different points in time.
Null Hypothesis: $\mu_2 - \mu_1 = 0$
Alternative Hypothesis: $\mu_2 - \mu_1 \neq 0$
where μ_1 and μ_2 are the sample means for the two dependent samples.

Assumptions of a T-Test:
T-tests do assume that:

1. The data are continuous.
2. The samples are randomly selected from the dataset.
3. The variances of the two groups are equal.
4. The distribution is approximately normal.

> For two-sample T-tests, we must have independent samples. If the samples are not independent, then a paired T-test may be appropriate.

The test statistic is calculated as:

$$t = \frac{\bar{X}_1 - \bar{X}_2}{\sqrt{\frac{s_1^2}{n_1} + \frac{s_2^2}{n_2}}}$$

Where:

- ❑ $\bar{X}_1, \bar{X}_2$ = Sample means
- ❑ s_1^2, s_2^2 = Sample variances
- ❑ n_1, n_2 = Sample sizes

Example: In a class, the average score obtained by the students in the math exam is **75**. A sample of 10 students has the following scores:

Scores: 72, 78, 80, 76, 74, 69, 82, 77, 73, 75

Assuming a 5% significance level ($\alpha = 0.05$) and critical value ±2.262, check if the average is 75 or not.

Solution:

Step 1: State Hypotheses
Null Hypothesis, H_0: $\mu = 75$
Alternative Hypothesis, H_1: $\mu \neq 75$

Step 2: Calculate Sample Mean ($\bar{x}$) and Standard Deviation (s)
Mean, $\bar{x}$ = (72 + 78 + 80 + 76 + 74 + 69 + 82 + 77 + 73 + 75) / 10 = 75.6
Sample standard deviation,

$$s = \sqrt{\frac{\sum (x_i - \bar{x})^2}{n-1}}$$

Using calculations, **s ≈ 4.14**

Step 3: Calculate t-score

$$t = \frac{\overline{x} - \mu}{s / \sqrt{n}}$$

$$t = \frac{75.6 - 75}{4.14 / \sqrt{10}} = \frac{0.6}{1.31} = 0.458$$

Step 4: Compare with the Critical Value. Since |0.458| < 2.262, the null hypothesis is not rejected, as there is no significant evidence to say that the mean score is different from 75.

Example: Assume that two teaching methods were tested on two groups of students. The test scores are:

1. Method A: 85, 87, 90, 78, 88
2. Method B: 80, 83, 86, 79, 81

At $\alpha = 0.05$ and critical value = ±2.306, test whether the two methods produce different results.

Solution:

Step 1: State Hypotheses

Null hypothesis, H_o: $\mu_1 = \mu_2$ (Both methods have the same mean score)

Alternative hypothesis, H_1: $\mu_1 \neq \mu_2$ (The means are different)

Step 2: Compute Sample Statistics

For Method A:

$$\overline{x}_1 = \frac{85 + 87 + 90 + 78 + 88}{5} = 85.6$$

$$s_1 = 4.98$$

For Method B:

$$\overline{x}_2 = \frac{80 + 83 + 86 + 79 + 81}{5} = 81.8$$

$$s_2 = 3.42$$

Step 3: Compute T-Statistic

$$t = \frac{\overline{x}_1 - \overline{x}_2}{\sqrt{\frac{s_1^2}{n_1} + \frac{s_2^2}{n_2}}}$$

$$t = \frac{85.6 - 81.8}{\sqrt{\frac{4.98^2}{5} + \frac{3.42^2}{5}}}$$

$$t = \frac{3.8}{\sqrt{4.96 + 2.34}} = \frac{3.8}{7.3} = \frac{3.8}{2.7} = 1.41$$

Step 4: Compare with the Critical Value. Since |1.41| < 2.306, the null hypothesis cannot be rejected, as there is no significant difference between the two methods.

Example: A weight-loss program was tested on 6 individuals. Their weights before and after the program are:

Person	Berfore (kg)	After (kg)
1	85	80
2	90	87
3	78	75
4	88	85
5	95	92
6	84	81

At $\alpha = 0.05$ and critical value = ±2.571, test if the weight-loss program was effective.

Solution:

Step 1: State Hypotheses

Null hypothesis, H_o: μ_d = 0 (No weight loss)

Alternative hypothesis, H_1: μ_d ≠ 0 (Weight loss occurred)

Step 2: Compute Differences (d = Before - After)

Person	Berfore	After	d
1	85	80	5
2	90	87	3
3	78	75	3
4	88	85	3
5	95	92	3
6	84	81	3

$$\overline{x}_d = \frac{5+3+3+3+3+3}{6} = 3.33$$

Sample standard deviation of **differences** (s_d):

$$s_d = \sqrt{\frac{\sum (d_i - \overline{x}_d)^2}{n-1}} = 0.82$$

Step 3: Compute T-Statistic

$$t = \frac{\overline{x}_d - 0}{s_d / \sqrt{n}}$$

$$t = \frac{3.33}{0.82/\sqrt{6}}$$

$$t = \frac{3.33}{0.33} = 10.09$$

Step 4: Compare with the Critical Value. Since 10.09 > 2.571, the null hypothesis is rejected and we conclude that the weight-loss program was effective.

```
Write a program to perform independent sampled t-test
import scipy.stats as stats
# Example data: Test scores of two different groups
group1 = [85, 90, 88, 92, 87, 95, 91, 89]
group2 = [80, 85, 83, 86, 82, 88, 84, 81]
```

```
# Perform an Independent t-test (Two-sample t-test)

t_stat, p_value = stats.ttest_ind(group1, group2)

print("Independent t-test results:")
print(f"T-statistic: {t_stat:.4f}")
print(f"P-value: {p_value:.4f}")

alpha = 0.05  # Significance level
if p_value < alpha:
    print("\n Null hypothesis rejected for independent t-test.")
    print("\n The means of the two independent groups are significantly
different.")
else:
   print("\n Null hypothesis accepted for independent t-test.")
   print("\n No significant difference between the two independent groups.")
```

OUTPUT

```
Independent t-test results:
T-statistic: 4.1378
P-value: 0.0010
Null hypothesis rejected for independent t-test.
The means of the two independent groups are significantly different.
```

Write a program to perform paired sample t-test

```
import scipy.stats as stats
# Example data: Before and after test scores of the same group (Paired
t-test)
before = [78, 82, 85, 88, 84, 79, 81, 83]
after  = [80, 85, 87, 90, 86, 82, 84, 85]

# Perform a Paired t-test
t_stat_paired, p_value_paired = stats.ttest_rel(before, after)

print("\nPaired t-test results:")
print(f"T-statistic: {t_stat_paired:.4f}")
print(f"P-value: {p_value_paired:.4f}")

# Significance level (alpha)
alpha = 0.05

# Interpretation for Paired t-test
if p_value_paired < alpha:
  print("\nNull hypothesis rejected for paired t-test.")
  print("The paired samples are significantly different (before vs after).")
else:
  print("\nNull hypothesis accepted for paired t-test.")
  print("No significant difference in the paired samples (before vs after).")
```

```
OUTPUT
Paired t-test results:
T-statistic: -12.9795
P-value: 0.0000
Null hypothesis rejected for paired t-test.
The paired samples are significantly different (before vs after).
```

8.5.5 Z-Test

A Z-test is a statistical test that helps us to determine if the mean of two populations is different when the variances are known and the sample size is large. The test can also compare one mean to a hypothesized value. Given below are the assumptions that are often made for the Z-test.

1. The data follows a normal distribution
2. The value of variance and standard deviation should be known before the test.

How Z-test is different from t-test?

1. Z-tests are performed when an experiment has a large sample size. T-tests are suitable for datasets with small size.
2. To apply Z-tests, the standard deviation should be known. But T-tests assumes that standard deviation is not known.
3. All data points should be independent of one another
4. The samples being compared should have the same variance.

The Z-score is calculated with the formula:

$z = (x - \mu) / \sigma$

where:

z = Z-score

x = the value being evaluated

μ = the mean

σ = the standard deviation

We have two types of Z-tests. One-sample Z-test that compares the mean of a single sample to a known population mean. And Two-sample Z-test that compares the means of two independent samples.

Example: A company claims that the average battery life of their new smartphone is 12 hours. The testing team tests 100 phones and finds that the average life of the battery was indeed 11.8 hours with a standard deviation of 0.5 hours. Assuming a 5% threshold value and the critical value for a two-tailed test to be ±1.96, can a customer present the evidence to refute the company's claim?

Solution:

Step 1: State the hypotheses

Null hypothesis, $H_o : \mu = 12$

Alternative hypothesis, $H_1 : \mu \neq 12$

Step 2: Calculate the Z-score

$Z = (\bar{x} - \mu) / (\sigma / \sqrt{n})$

$= (11.8 - 12) / (0.5 / \sqrt{100})$

$= -0.2 / 0.05$

$= -4$

Step 3: Compare Z-score with critical value

|-4| > 1.96, so the null hypothesis is rejected. This means that there is sufficient evidence to refute the company's claim about battery life.

Example: Consider a scenario to compare the effectiveness of two different medications for controlling diabetes. Medication A is tested on 50 patients, resulting in a mean reduction of 15 mmHg with a standard deviation of 3 mmHg. Medication B is tested on 60 patients, resulting in a mean reduction of 13 mmHg with a standard deviation of 4 mmHg. Assuming a 1% significance level and the critical score for the two-tailed Z-test to be ±2.576, check if there is a significant difference between the two medications?

Solution:

Step 1: State the hypotheses

Null hypothesis, H_o: $\mu_1 - \mu_2 = 0$

Alternative hypothesis, H_1: $\mu_1 - \mu_2 \neq 0$

Step 2: Calculate the Z-score

$Z = (\bar{x}_1 - \bar{x}_2) / \sqrt{((\sigma_1^2/n_1) + (\sigma_2^2/n_2))}$

$= (15 - 13) / \sqrt{((3^2/50) + (4^2/60))}$

$= 2 / \sqrt{(0.18 + 0.2667)}$

$= 2 / 0.6455$

$= 3.10$

Step 3: Compare Z-score with critical value. Since, 3.10 > 2.576, the null hypothesis is rejected, indicating that there is a significant difference between the effectiveness of the two medications.

Write a program to apply z-test on a list of values

```
import numpy as np
from statsmodels.stats.weightstats import ztest
# Example Data: Test scores of two different groups
group1 = [85, 90, 88, 92, 87, 95, 91, 89, 86, 93, 88, 90, 92, 94, 87, 89,
91, 85, 88, 90]
group2 = [80, 85, 83, 86, 82, 88, 84, 81, 79, 87, 85, 83, 84, 86, 80, 82,
83, 85, 81, 84]
# Perform a Two-sample Z-test
z_stat, p_value = ztest(group1, group2)
print("Two-sample Z-test results:")
print(f"Z-statistic: {z_stat:.4f}")
print(f"P-value: {p_value:.4f}")
# Significance level (alpha)
alpha = 0.05
if p_value < alpha:
    print("\nNull hypothesis rejected for the Z-test.")
    print("The means of the two groups are significantly different.")
else:
    print("\nNull hypothesis accepted for the Z-test.")
    print("No significant difference between the two groups.")
```

```
OUTPUT
Two-sample Z-test results:
Z-statistic: 7.2664
P-value: 0.0000
Null hypothesis rejected for the Z-test.
The means of the two groups are significantly different.
```

Business Scenario: Analyzing Customer Satisfaction Based on Product Categories

Imagine that you are working as a data analyst for a retail company. You have been assigned the task to analyze the relationship between product category (e.g., Electronics, Clothing, and Groceries) and customer satisfaction. Customer satisfaction is categorized as either "Satisfied" or "Dissatisfied." The company had done a customer survey. Use contingency table to analyze how product categories influence customer satisfaction.

Product Category	Satisfied	Dissatisfied	Total
Electronics	50	30	80
Clothing	40	20	60
Groceries	60	40	100
Total	**150**	**90**	**240**

```
import pandas as pd
import numpy as np
from scipy.stats import chi2_contingency
data = {
    'Product  Category':  ['Electronics',  'Electronics',  'Clothing',
'Clothing', 'Groceries', 'Groceries'],
    'Satisfaction': ['Satisfied', 'Dissatisfied', 'Satisfied', 'Dissatisfied',
'Satisfied', 'Dissatisfied'],
    'Count': [50, 30, 40, 20, 60, 40]
}
# Create a DataFrame
df = pd.DataFrame(data)
# Create the contingency table
contingency_table  =  pd.pivot_table(df,  values='Count',  index='Product
Category', columns='Satisfaction', aggfunc=np.sum)
print("Contingency Table:")
print(contingency_table)
# Chi-square test to see if there is a relationship between product cat-
egory and satisfaction
chi2, p, dof, expected = chi2_contingency(contingency_table)
print("\nChi-Square Test Results:")
print(f"Chi2 Statistic: {chi2}")
print("P-Value: ",p)
```

```
print("Degrees of Freedom: ",dof)
print("Expected Frequencies: ", expected)
if p < 0.05:
    print("\nThere is a significant relationship between product category
and customer satisfaction.")
else:
    print("\nThere is no significant relationship between product category
and customer satisfaction.")
```

OUTPUT

```
Contingency Table:
Satisfaction       Dissatisfied  Satisfied
Product Category
Clothing                     20         40
Electronics                  30         50
Groceries                    40         60
Chi-Square Test Results:
Chi2 Statistic: 0.7111111111111111
P-Value:   0.7007840105925329
Degrees of Freedom:  2
Expected Frequencies:  [[22.5 37.5]
 [30.  50. ]
 [37.5 62.5]]
There is no significant relationship between product category and customer
satisfaction.
```

Business Scenario: Hypothesis Testing for Sales Promotion Effectiveness

Suppose that you are a data analyst for an e-commerce company. To increase the average sales per customer, the marketing team has recently launched a promotional campaign offering a 10% discount on all products. As the analyst, it is now your job to test if there is a significant change in average sales per customer due to promotional activity.

Null Hypothesis (H_0): The average sales per customer before the promotion is equal to the average sales per customer during the promotion period.

Alternative Hypothesis (H_1): The average sales per customer during the promotion is greater than the average sales per customer before the promotion.

```
import numpy as np
import pandas as pd
import matplotlib.pyplot as plt
from scipy.stats import ttest_ind
np.random.seed(42)
# Simulating sales data for before and during the promotion period
sales_before = np.random.normal(loc=100, scale=15, size=200) # mean=100,
std=15, n=200
```

```
sales_during = np.random.normal(loc=110, scale=15, size=200)  # mean=110,
std=15, n=200
# Perform Hypothesis Testing (One-tailed t-test)
t_stat, p_value = ttest_ind(sales_before, sales_during, alternative='less')
print("P-value: ", p_value)
alpha = 0.05 # Significance level
if p_value < alpha:
    print("\nReject the null hypothesis: There is a significant increase
in sales during the promotion.")
else:
    print("\nFail to reject the null hypothesis: There is no significant
increase in sales during the promotion.")
OUTPUT
P-value:  1.0249831620681065e-15
Reject the null hypothesis: There is a significant increase in sales dur-
ing the promotion.
```

Business Scenario: Forecasting Monthly Sales Using ARIMA/SARIMA

FreshMart, a mid-sized grocery retail chain, faced recurring challenges in inventory management. Seasonal fluctuations and unpredictable demand patterns led to frequent stockouts of high-demand items like fresh produce, and overstock of non-perishables. These inefficiencies were causing customer dissatisfaction and unnecessary losses.

The company had been relying on simple forecasting methods like moving averages, which failed to account for complex patterns such as seasonality and trend shifts. As a result, managers often made decisions based on gut feeling or outdated data.

FreshMart's data team introduced ARIMA (AutoRegressive Integrated Moving Average) and SARIMA (Seasonal ARIMA) models into their demand forecasting process. These models were selected for their ability to handle both long-term trends and seasonal cycles.

By analyzing three years of historical sales data across different product categories and locations, the SARIMA model revealed clear seasonal patterns such as spikes in fresh fruit sales during summer and increased demand for baking goods around holidays.

Within three months of implementing SARIMA-based forecasts, FreshMart reported a 25% reduction in stockouts and a 15% decrease in excess inventory. Store managers felt more confident in planning, especially during high-traffic periods. Customers noticed improved product availability, leading to a measurable boost in satisfaction scores.

Key Terms

Contingency Tables: Data analytics tool to summarize categorical data and explore the relationships between two or more variables.

ARIMA: A time series forecasting technique that is extensively used to predict future values based on historical data. It is applied in a wide range of applications ranging from finance to environmental science.

Longitudinal Data Analysis: Data analytics tool that deals with data collected over time from the same subjects or units, to study changes over time. For this reason, it is widely used in areas including healthcare, economics, and social sciences.

Hypothesis Testing: A core principle of inferential statistics used to assess the validity of assumptions or claims made about a population based on sample data. This is often vital for making evidence-based decisions in research, policy, and business.

Expected frequency: Number in each category if the variables were independent (i.e., no association).

Time series data: Data that is sampled on a time-bound attribute like days, months, and years inherently giving it an implicit order.

Forecasting: Analyzing data to predict future values.

ARIMA model: A class of linear models that use historical values to forecast future values.

Spline: To model the time-varying predictors, splines are used. Spline is a flexible curve that smoothly connects two or more points to capture the changes in a predictor over time.

Hypothesis: A prediction or assumption based on what we already know. It is not just a random guess or a simple question. Rather, it is a thoughtful statement that raises a question and suggests a possible answer.

T-test: A statistical test that is used to compare the means of two groups and determine if the difference between them is statistically significant.

Z-test: A statistical test that help us to determine if the mean of two populations is different when the variances are known and the sample size is large.

Chapter Highlights

* When there is a single variable to analyze, we can use statistics like mean, median, standard deviation, and variance. But for bivariate analysis that involves analysis of two variables, correlation analysis is required.
* The chi^2 measures how different the observed values are from the expected values.
* If $p < 0.05$, we reject the null hypothesis.
* If we have small samples (<5 counts in some cells), then we can use the Fisher's Exact Test instead of the Chi-Square Test on contingency tables.
* The Cramér's V measures the strength of association in a Chi-Square Test.
* Degrees of Freedom (dof) is used to determine the number of independent comparisons.
* The pivot_table() helps to analyze complex relationships between multiple categorical variables.
* While ARIMA considers the past values (autoregressive, moving average) to predict future values, SARIMA uses past values as well as any seasonality patterns.
* Outliers present in the data might skew the forecasting results. To avoid such a scenario, outliers are identified and normalized.
* The term autoregression means a regression of the variable against itself. This means that lagged values of the target variable are used as input variables to forecast values for the future.
* Longitudinal data analysis is used to measure how long an event lasts and observe facts such as, whether the same group of individuals or a different set of people remain unemployed during a recession.
* Two methods are usually preferred for analyzing longitudinal data–GEE and MER. Both these techniques use time-invariant predictors that never change (e.g., gender, genotype) and time-varying predictors (e.g., age) for analysis. Moreover, both the techniques can easily handle irregularly timed and missing data without the need for explicit imputation.

* MER models are a powerful tool for studying relationships between factors (like age, medication, or other covariates) and repeated measurements over time, just like GEEs. They not only estimate the relationship between covariates and repeated responses but also account for the correlations between those repeated measurements over time.
* An alternative hypothesis is the opposite of the null hypothesis. It suggests that there is a meaningful effect or difference between the variables of two more samples being studied.

Review Questions

1. How do we analyze a single variable dataset?
2. Explain any technique to analyze a dataset with two or more variables.
3. How is p-value significant in case of hypotheses testing?
4. What do you understand by time series data?
5. Explain the different techniques in which time-series data is cleaned.
6. Define the term autoregression.
7. Differentiate between the following.
   a. ARIMA and SARIMA b. ACF and PACF c. α-error and β-error
8. Explain the meaning of A, R, I, M, and A in ARIMA.
9. Give the pros and cons and applications of ARIMA/SARIMA.
10. Define longitudinal data? How is it different from cross-sectional data?
11. How can one analyze longitudinal data?
12. Explain the correlation structures in GEE.
13. How is MER better than GEE?
14. Explain the significance of P-splines.
15. Define hypotheses and explain its parts.
16. List the steps in hypotheses testing.
17. Write short notes on T-test and Z-test.

Programming Exercise

1. Create a contingency table and calculate the chi-square statistic.
2. Fit an ARIMA model to a time series data and make predictions.
3. Fit a SARIMA model to seasonal data and forecast values.
4. Perform a two-sample T-test on two datasets to compare their means.
5. Perform a Z-test to compare the mean of a sample with a known population mean.
6. Perform a Chi-Square Test for independence on a contingency table.
7. Create a multi-way contingency table and compute the chi-square statistic.
8. Stratify a contingency table and perform a Chi-Square Test.
9. Perform Generalized Estimating Equations (GEE) on longitudinal data.
10. Fit a mixed-effects model to data.

Fill in the Blanks

1. _______ is a time series forecasting technique that is extensively used to predict future values based on historical data.

2. The _______ is used to create the contingency table.
3. On a three-variable contingency table, we can use normalization and _______ Test.
4. The _______ x measures how different the observed values are from expected values.
5. _______ is used to determine the number of independent comparisons.
6. _______ is the number in each category if the variables were independent.
7. _______ shows proportions instead of row counts.
8. The Cramér's V measures the _______ in a Chi-Square Test.
9. _______ means analyzing data to predict future values.
10. _______ considers just the past values to predict future values.
11. Outliers present in the data might skew the forecasting results. So, outliers should be _______.
12. _______ means a regression of the variable against itself.
13. _______ incorporates seasonality contribution to the forecast.
14. _______ Correlation Structure is used when the measurements taken closer in time are more strongly related to each other than measurements taken further apart.
15. _______ models uses "random effects" to represent differences that exist between individuals or groups.
16. _______ are splines that balance smoothness and precision.
17. A _______ hypothesis assumes that there is no effect or difference between the variables of two more samples being studied.
18. If the _______ is less than the threshold value, the H_0 is rejected and H_1 is accepted.
19. _______ error occurs when the null hypothesis is true but is rejected.
20. _______ T-test compares the mean value of a sample with a known mean or average.

State True or False

1. Longitudinal Data Analysis deals with data collected over time from different subjects or units, to study changes over time.
2. Hypothesis testing uses descriptive statistics.
3. Correlational analysis is used in data analysis tasks that involves a single variable.
4. If $p < 0.05$, we reject the null hypothesis.
5. In a heatmap, darker shades represent lower frequencies.
6. The Fisher's test gives more accurate results for small datasets as compared to Chi-Square Test.
7. Time series data is sampled on a performance-bound attribute.
8. SARIMA uses past values as well as any seasonality patterns to predict future values.
9. Models built on stationary data are usually more robust.
10. ACF takes into account the translative effect that are carried by values with time apart from a direct effect.
11. For ARIMA/SARIMA just three years of historical data is not enough for an accurate forecast.
12. Cross-sectional data studies different samples at each point in time.
13. GEEs perform well even in case of missing data.
14. Autoregressive Correlation Structure assumes that all repeated measurements within a group are equally correlated.
15. Hypotheses is a fact already known to us.
16. Confidence level can be zero, but significance level cannot be zero.
17. Type I error occurs when the null hypothesis is false but it is accepted.

18. Independent Sample T-test compares the mean values of two different samples from two different populations to see if there is a significant difference.
19. A T-test is a statistical test that help us to determine if the mean of two populations is different when the variances are known and the sample size is large.
20. Z-tests are performed when an experiment has a large sample size. T-tests are suitable for datasets with small size.

CHAPTER

9 Interfacing Python with MySQL

Employee Management System

Employee management of any organization maintains accurate records of employees, their roles, payroll, and performance. These days, such systems are computerized. MySQL database, combined with Python is used to automate and streamline tasks involved in employee data management.

Imagine that you are a DBA of a mid-sized company with around 200 employees. The HR department needs a computer-based system to manage employee records such as personal details, job titles, salary, performance evaluations, and leave balances. Write the code to perform CRUD (Create, Read, Update, Delete) operations on the following employee data:

Employee Information: Basic personal and job details
Payroll Information: Salary, bonuses, deductions
Leave Management: Leave balances, leave requests, and approvals
Performance Records: Employee evaluations and feedback

Now that we already studied basic concepts of **databases** and DBMS, and have also covered SQL through MySQL database, let us move a step ahead and see how we can work with our MySQL tables and manipulate data stored in it using scripts (or programs) written in Python. However, before starting to code, let us first quickly recapitulate the basics that we have already learned.

9.1 Interfacing Python with MySQL

To work with MySQL database through our Python program, we need to first connect with MySQL. Only then it will be possible to execute our **SQL** queries to create tables, insert data into it, retrieve data, update or delete the data and execute all other queries that we have already studied in the previous chapter.

To connect MySQL database with Python programs, we must follow the steps given below.

Step 1: Connect to the database.
Step 2: Create a database object.
Step 3: Execute the SQL query and get the results.
Step 4: Fetch records from the results obtained in Step 3.
Step 5: Save any changes made in the Database.

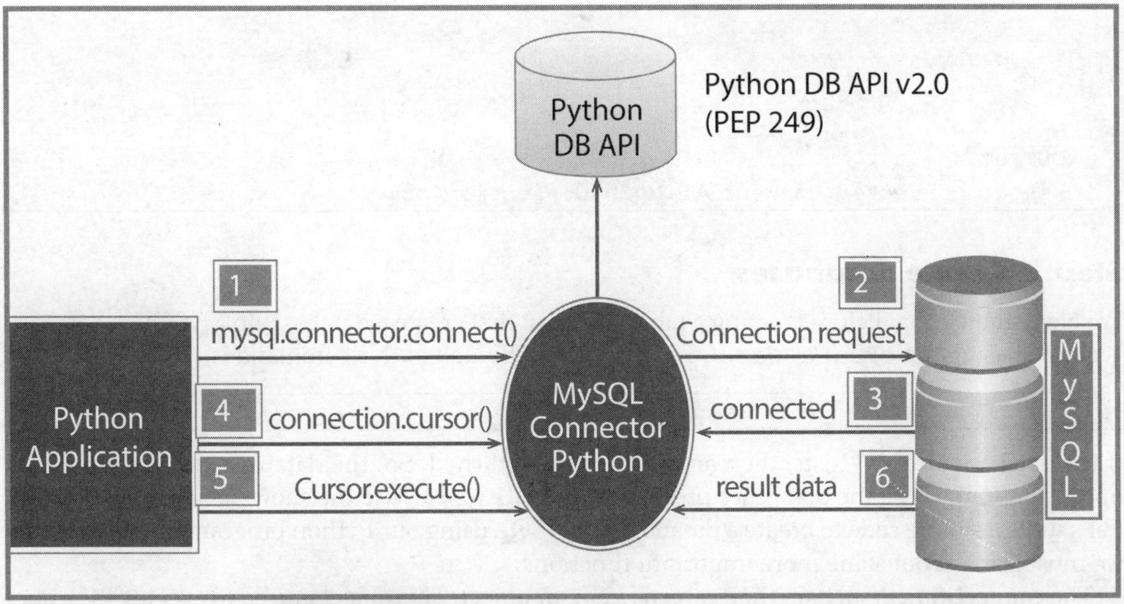

Figure 9.1 MySQL database connection in Python

> is_connected() is the method of the MySQLConnection class through which we can verify is our python application connected to MySQL.

All these steps are elaborated below and summarized in Figure 9.1. However, before starting make sure that the MySQL-connector-python package is installed in your computer. In Windows this can be done by writing and executing the pip install MySQL-connector-python command in the Command Prompt.

Step 1: Connect to database

The connect() method is used to establish a connection between MySQL database and Python program. Once a connection is established, an object of MySQLConnection is returned. This object is then used to perform various operations on the MySQL Database.

However, the connect() method throws an exception if the connection could not be established. For example, if one of the required parameters (like user name, password) is wrong. In our programs, we have obtained the connection object in variable db.

We can use the **username** and **password** of **MySQL** to connect to the database. In case you don't know these details then create a new **user** with the specified password. The create user command has the following syntax,

```
CREATE USER user_name
IDENTIFIED BY 'password';
```

Here, user_name is name of the user and password is the chosen password. You can use any value for these two parameters.

```
import mysql.connector as mysql
# connect to the database
db = mysql.connect(
    host = "localhost",
```

```
        user = "reema",
        passwd = "*******"
)
print(db)
OUTPUT
<mysql.connector.connection.MySQLConnection object at 0x036B2580>
```

Step 2: Create databases

We have studied that before creating a table, we must first create a database. In MySQL, a database is created using the `create database` command. Syntax of this command is,

```
CREATE DATABASE database_name
```

If the database already exists, then an error will be returned. So, the database_name should be a unique one. To see all the databases present in MySQL, we can use the show databases command. Let's write a simple code to create a database in MySQL using our Python program. But before that we must learn about some more important functions.

The **connection.cursor()** method returns a cursor object. This object is used to execute SQL queries. The cursor object uses MySQLConnection object to interact with the MySQL **server**.

cursor.close() method is used to close the cursor object. Once this is done, you will not be able to execute SQL queries.

Similarly, **connection.close()** method is used to close the MySQL database connection.

```
import mysql.connector as mysql
# connect to the database
db = mysql.connect(
        host = "localhost",
        user = "reema",
        passwd = "*******"
)
cursor = db.cursor()
# executing SQL query using 'execute()' method
cursor.execute("SHOW DATABASES")
# 'fetchall()' method fetches all the rows from the results obtained after
# executing the last query
databases = cursor.fetchall()
# a list of all databases present is printed
print(databases)
## to print the database in a for loop, we can write
for database in databases:
                                                                print(database)
OUTPUT
[('information_schema',), ('mydb',), ('mysql',), ('performance_schema',),
('sys',)]
('information_schema',)
('mydb',)
('mysql',)
('performance_schema',)
('sys',)
```

Here, **Username** is the username that you use to work with MySQL on your computer. The default username for the MySQL database is a **root.**

Password is specified by the user while installing the MySQL database. User working as root does not need password.

Host Name is the server name or IP address on which MySQL is running. You can specify it as localhost or 127.0.0.0, if you are running MySQL on your own computer.

Database Name is name of the database to which you are trying to connect. Here we are using database mydb.

Step 3: Execute the query

The cursor.execute() method is used to run or execute an SQL query through a Python program. Another method, cursor.executemany(operation, seq_of_parameters) is used to prepare a database query and execute it against all parameter sequences available in the sequence specified by `seq_of_params`. In simple words, the method iterates through the sequence of parameters and in each iteration, the current parameter is passed to the `execute()` method.

9.2 Creating tables

A database can have one or more tables. Our data is stored in these tables. However, before creating a table, first select the database in which it has to be created.

In MySQL, table is created using the `CREATE TABLE table_name`. Again, name of the table should be unique. To see the table_name, we can use the `show tables` command.

The basic syntax of this statement can be given as,

```
CREATE TABLE table_name(
    column1 datatype,
    column2 datatype,
    column3 datatype,
    .....
    columnN datatype,
    PRIMARY KEY(one or more columns )
);
```

Within the opening and closing brackets, list of columns and their corresponding data types are specified.

9.3 Setting primary key

A table can be deleted using the DROP TABLE statement. The syntax of DROP TABLE statement is, DROP TABLE table_name:

We have studied that primary key helps us to uniquely identify each record in the table. While creating the table, we can set one or more columns as the primary key. However, we should remember two things while specifying values for a primary key. First, it should contain unique values. Second, it cannot have NULL values.

The code given below creates a table STUDENT in mydb database.

```
import mysql.connector as mysql
# connect to the database
db = mysql.connect(
    host = "localhost",
    user = "reema",
    passwd = "*******",
    database = "mydb"
)
cursor = db.cursor()
# create a table 'STUDENT' in the 'mydb' database
cursor.execute("CREATE TABLE STUDENT (ROLLNO INT(11) NOT NULL PRIMARY KEY,
NAME VARCHAR(30), MARKS INT)")
# 'DESC table_name' gives information about all columns
cursor.execute("DESC STUDENT")
# print all the columns
print(cursor.fetchall())
OUTPUT
[('ROLLNO', 'int', 'NO', 'PRI', None, 'auto_increment'), ('NAME', 'varchar(30)
', 'YES', '', None, ''), ('MARKS', 'int', 'YES', '', None, '')]
```

Now to make sure that our table is created, we have used the show tables command in the code given below.

```
import mysql.connector as mysql
# connecting to the database
db = mysql.connect(
    host = "localhost",
    user = "reema",
    passwd = "********",
    database = "mydb"
)
cursor = db.cursor()
# get a list of all the tables in 'mydb' database
cursor.execute("SHOW TABLES")
tables = cursor.fetchall()
for table in tables:  # display the tables
  print(table)
OUTPUT
('student',)
```

In case you have forgotten to add the primary key constraint while creating the table, you can still make one or more columns as the primary key by using the ALTER TABLE command. The syntax for ALTER TABLE command can be given as,

```
ALTER TABLE table_name
ADD PRIMARY KEY (column_name);
import mysql.connector as mysql
# connect to the database
db = mysql.connect(
    host = "localhost",
    user = "reema",
```

```
    passwd = "*******",
    database = "mydb"
)
cursor = db.cursor()
cursor.execute("ALTER TABLE STUDENT ADD COLUMN ROLLNO INT(11) NOT NULL
PRIMARY KEY")
cursor.execute("DESC STUDENT")
print(cursor.fetchall())
OUTPUT
[('ROLLNO', 'int', 'NO', 'PRI', None, ''), ('NAME', 'varchar(30)', 'YES',
'', None, ''), ('MARKS', 'int', 'YES', '', None, '')]
```

9.4 Dropping primary key

If we wish to remove the primary key constraint from our table, then the DROP PRIMARY KEY command is used with the ALTER TABLE statement. The general syntax of this command can be given as,

```
ALTER TABLE table_name
DROP PRIMARY KEY;
```

Look at the code give below and carefully observe the output. ROLLNO is no longer the primary key of the table STUDENT.

```
import mysql.connector as mysql
# connecting to the database
db = mysql.connect(
    host = "localhost",
    user = "reema",
    passwd = "********",
    database = "mydb"
)
cursor = db.cursor()
cursor.execute("ALTER TABLE STUDENT DROP ROLLNO")
cursor.execute("DESC STUDENT")
print(cursor.fetchall())
OUTPUT
None
[('NAME', 'varchar(30)', 'YES', '', None, ''), ('MARKS', 'int', 'YES', '',
None, '')]
```

9.5 Inserting data

Before inserting values in a table, it must first be created using the CREATE TABLE command. We use the `INSERT INTO` statement to add new rows of data in an existing table. Syntax of INSERT INTO statement can be given as,

```
INSERT INTO TABLE_NAME VALUES (value1,value2,value3,...valueN);
```

The code given below inserts a row in the table STUDENT that we created in mydb database.

```
import mysql.connector as mysql
# connect to the database
db = mysql.connect(
    host = "localhost",
    user = "reema",
   passwd = "******",
    database = "mydb"
)
cursor = db.cursor()
query = r'INSERT INTO STUDENT VALUES(1,"PARAS",54)'
# execute query
cursor.execute(query)
# to make permanent changes in the database we use the 'commit()' method
db.commit()
print(cursor.rowcount, "records inserted")
OUTPUT
1 records inserted
```

9.5.1 inserting multiple rows

executemany() method is used to insert multiple rows into the table. The method takes a **query** as the first argument and a list of **tuples** containing record as the second parameter. Code given below illustrates inserting multiple rows in a table.

```
import mysql.connector as mysql
# connect to the database
db = mysql.connect(
    host = "localhost",
    user = "reema",
    passwd = "********",
    database = "mydb"
)
cursor = db.cursor()
query = "INSERT INTO STUDENT (ROLLNO, NAME, MARKS) VALUES (%s,%s, %s)"
# values stored in a variable
values = [
    (1,"PARAS",56), (2,"NEON",68), (3,"MEERA", 99), (4,"SHIV", 89)  ]
# execute the query
cursor.executemany(query, values)
# save changes to the database permanently
db.commit()
print(cursor.rowcount, "records inserted")
4 records inserted
```

9.6 Retrieve or select data

The **SELECT** statement in SQL is used to fetch or retrieve data from one or more tables in the database. The result of the SELECT statement is in the form of a table known as the result-set. The syntax of the SELECT statement can be given as,

```
SELECT column1, column2, columnN FROM table_name;
```

Here, column1, column2 ... are the fields of the table from which data has to be fetched. To fetch all the fields from the table, the syntax is

```
SELECT * FROM table_name;
Before
```

Step 4: Fetch records from the result

To read data from a table, we need to fetch records stored in the database. After database connection is established, we can execute an appropriate query (using the SELECT statement). The results of this query can then be accessed using any of the two methods. fetchone() method that fetches a single record. fetchall() method fetches multiple values from a database table.

fetchone(): This method fetches the next row of the result-set. Note that a result-set is an object returned when a query is executed using the cursor object.

fetchall(): It retrieves/fetches all the rows in the result-set.

rowcount: It gives the number of rows that were affected by an execute() method. It is a read-only attribute.

```
import mysql.connector as mysql
# connect to the database
db = mysql.connect(
    host = "localhost",
    user = "reema",
    passwd = "********",
    database = "mydb"
)
cursor = db.cursor()
query = "SELECT * FROM STUDENT"
# get records from the table
cursor.execute(query)
# fetch all records from the 'cursor' object
records = cursor.fetchall()
# display the result
for record in records:
    print(record)
OUTPUT
(1, 'PARAS', 54)
(2, 'HEENA', 68)
(3, 'MANAB', 75)
(4, 'ZYAN', 81)
```

9.6.1 Retrieving selected columns

To select a few columns from the table, the **SELECT** statement is used. For example, let us get the username column from the **STUDENT** table.

```
import mysql.connector as mysql
# connect to the database
db = mysql.connect(
    host = "localhost",
    user = "reema",
    passwd = "********",
    database = "mydb"
)
cursor = db.cursor()
# formulate the Query
query = "SELECT NAME, MARKS FROM STUDENT"
# retrieve the columns 'NAME', 'MARKS' from the table
cursor.execute(query)
# fetch all records from the 'cursor' object
data = cursor.fetchall()
# Display the results
for pair in data:
    print(pair)
OUTPUT
('PARAS', 56)
('NEON', 68)
('MEERA', 99)
('SHIV', 89)
```

9.6.2 Where clause

The WHERE clause is used in the SELECT statement to specify a condition for retrieving data from one or more tables. The WHERE clause filters the records in the table to fetch only those rows that meet the specified criteria.

In addition to the SELECT statement, the WHERE clause is also used with the UPDATE and DELETE statements. The basic syntax of the SELECT statement with the WHERE clause can be given as,

```
SELECT column1, column2, columnN
FROM table_name
WHERE [condition]
```

We can even use comparison and logical operators in the WHERE clause. Let's see a couple of queries to see how the SELECT statement with WHERE clause actually works.

```
import mysql.connector as mysql
# connect to the database
db = mysql.connect(
    host = "localhost",
    user = "reema",
    passwd = "********",
    database = "mydb"
)
```

```
cursor = db.cursor()
# form the Query
query = "SELECT * FROM STUDENT WHERE MARKS > 75"
# retrieve columns NAME', 'MARKS' from the table
cursor.execute(query)
# fetch all records from the 'cursor' object
data = cursor.fetchall()
# display the data
for pair in data:
    print(pair)
OUTPUT
(3, 'MEERA', 99)
(4, 'SHIV', 89)
```

9.7 Order by clause

The ORDER BY statement in SQL is used to sort the retrieved data in either ascending or descending order. We can sort the values in the result-set by one or more columns using the ORDER BY clause.

By default, ORDER BY sorts the data in ascending order. To sort in descending order, we can use the keyword DESC. To specifically state ascending as the sorting order, the keyword ASC is used.

Let us discuss different ways in which ORDER BY clause can be used with the SELECT statement.

Sort according to one column: To sort in ascending or descending order we can use the keywords ASC or DESC, respectively. The syntax for this can be given as,

```
SELECT expressions
FROM tables
[WHERE conditions]
ORDER BY expression [ ASC | DESC ]
```

Where, **Expressions** specifies the columns to be retrieved.

Tables is the table from which the records have to be retrieved. At least one table must be listed in the FROM clause.

WHERE condition is optional. If specified, the condition must be satisfied for the records to be selected.

ASC is optional as it is the default sorting order. ASC sorts the result-set in ascending order by expression.

DESC is optional. If present, it sorts the result-set in descending order by *expression*.

Sort according to multiple columns: To sort with respect to multiple columns, use comma (,) to separate the names of columns. The syntax can be given as,

```
SELECT * FROM table_name ORDER BY column1 ASC|DESC , column2 ASC|DESC
import mysql.connector as mysql
# connect to the database
```

```
db = mysql.connect(
    host = "localhost",
    user = "reema",
    passwd = "*******",
    database = "mydb"
)
cursor = db.cursor()
# form the Query
query = "SELECT * FROM STUDENT ORDER BY MARKS DESC"
# retrieve columns 'NAME', 'MARKS' columns from the table
cursor.execute(query)
# fetch all records from the 'cursor' object
data = cursor.fetchall()
for record in data:
    print(record)
OUTPUT
(3, 'MEERA', 99)
(4, 'SHIV', 89)
(2, 'NEON', 68)
(1, 'PARAS', 56)
```

Step 5: Saving records

All database operations must ensure data consistency. For this, every operation must satisfy the following four properties that are also known as ACID properties:

Atomicity: Either an operation executes completely or it is not executed at all.

Consistency: Every operation must leave data in the database in a consistent state (where data is correct).

Isolation: Intermediate results of query execution are not visible outside the current transaction.

Durability: Once an operation changing database values has executed completely, then the operation is committed and changes done to the database are made permanent (even after a system failure). Python provides two methods to either *commit* or *rollback* a transaction.

Commit Operation: The commit() function is used to finalize changes in the database. After this operation, changes cannot be reverted. To use the commit() method, we can write db.commit().

Rollback Operation: To undo or to revert the changes made to the database, rollback() method is used. To use the rollback() method, we can write db.rollback().

9.8 Updating the table

The SQL UPDATE statement is used to make changes in the existing data (in a table). We can even use the WHERE clause with the UPDATE query to update only selected rows. This will ensure that only the rows meeting the specified criteria (and not all) are affected. The basic syntax of the UPDATE query with a WHERE clause can be given as,

```
UPDATE table_name
SET column1 = value1, column2 = value2...., columnN = valueN
WHERE [condition];
```

Again, according to the syntax, any number of conditions can be specified using the AND or the OR operators in the WHERE clause.

```
import mysql.connector as mysql
# connect to the database
db = mysql.connect(
    host = "localhost",
    user = "reema",
    passwd = "********",
    database = "mydb"
)
cursor = db.cursor()
# form the Query
query = "UPDATE STUDENT SET NAME = 'KARAN' WHERE ROLLNO = 3"
# execute the query
cursor.execute(query)
# save the changes in the database
db.commit()
# formulate another Query
query = "SELECT * FROM STUDENT"
# execute the query
cursor.execute(query)
data = cursor.fetchall()
for record in data:
    print(record)
OUTPUT
1, 'PARAS', 56)
(2, 'NEON', 68)
(3, 'KARAN', 99)
(4, 'SHIV', 89)
```

9.9 Aggregate functions

An **aggregate function** is one that performs a calculation on multiple values and returns a single value. For example, the avg() aggregate function accepts multiple values and returns a single value – average value of those values. The general syntax of an aggregate function is,

```
function_name(DISTINCT | ALL expression)
```

where, **func_name** can be anyone from the table. Table 1 lists some commonly used aggregate functions.

DISTINCT is used to perform calculations based on distinct values.

expression can be a column or expression. This expression can include column names and arithmetic operators.

Table 1: || Aggregate functions in SQL

Aggregate function	Description
AVG()	Returns the average of non-NULL values.
BIT_AND()	Returns bitwise AND.
BIT_OR()	Returns bitwise OR.
BIT_XOR()	Returns bitwise XOR.
COUNT()	Returns the number of rows in a group, including rows with NULL values.
GROUP_CONCAT()	Returns a concatenated string.
MAX()	Returns the highest value (maximum) in a set of non-NULL values.
MIN()	Returns the lowest value (minimum) in a set of non-NULL values.
STDEV()	Returns the population standard deviation.
SUM()	Returns the summation of all non-NULL values a set.
VARIANCE()	Returns the population standard variance.

9.10 The SQL SELECT DISTINCT statement

The SELECT DISTINCT statement is used to return only distinct (different) values. Thus, this clause eliminates duplicate entries while displaying data from the table. The syntax of DISTINCT clause when used with the SELECT statement can be given as,

```
SELECT DISTINCT column1, column2,.....columnN
FROM table_name
WHERE [condition]
```

table_name specifies name of the table(s) from which data has to be retrieved. We can specify more than one table names also.

The WHERE condition is optional. If present, it specifies the conditions that must be satisfied before retrieving data.

Note that, the DISTINCT clause does not ignore NULL values. So, if a table has null values, the DISTINCT clause will include them as well in the result-set.

> The SQL DISTINCT keyword is used in conjuction with the SELECT statement to eliminate all the duplicate records and fetching only unique records

9.11 SELECT COUNT, SUM, AVG

The SELECT COUNT statement returns a count or the number of data values. The SELECT SUM returns the sum of the data values. And the SELECT AVG returns the average of the data values.

The general COUNT syntax is:

```
SELECT COUNT(column-name)
FROM table-name
```

The general SUM syntax is:

```
SELECT SUM(column-name)
FROM table-name
```

The general AVG syntax is:

```
SELECT AVG(column-name)
FROM table-name
```

9.12 SQL SELECT MIN, MAX statement

As the name suggests, the SELECT MIN statement in SQL returns the minimum value for a column. Correspondingly, the SELECT MAX statement returns the maximum value for a column.

> It is a good programming practice to close the database connection and release the resources being used.

The general MIN syntax is:

```
SELECT MAX(column-name)
FROM table-name
```

and the general MAX syntax can be given as,

```
SELECT MAX(column-name)
FROM table-name
```

The code given below uses aggregate functions on our table STUDENT stored in database mydb.

```
import mysql.connector as mysql
# connect to the database
db = mysql.connect(
    host = "localhost",
    user = "reema",
    passwd = "*******",
    database = "mydb"
cursor = db.cursor()
# form the Query
query = "SELECT COUNT(ROLLNO) FROM STUDENT WHERE MARKS > 40 AND MARKS <90"
# retrieve the values in column 'NAME', 'MARKS'
cursor.execute(query)
# fetch all records from the 'cursor' object
data = cursor.fetchall()
## Showing the data
for pair in data:
    print(pair)
# form another Query
query = "SELECT MAX(MARKS) FROM STUDENT"
# retrieve values for the column 'NAME', 'MARKS' from the table
cursor.execute(query)
# fetch all records from the result-set
data = cursor.fetchall()
print(data)
query = "SELECT MIN(MARKS) FROM STUDENT"
# get the values of column 'NAME', 'MARKS' from the table
cursor.execute(query)
```

```
# fetch all records from the result set
data = cursor.fetchall()
print(data)
# form another Query
query = "SELECT AVG(MARKS) FROM STUDENT"
# get the values of column 'NAME', 'MARKS' from the table
cursor.execute(query)
# fetch all records from the result set
data = cursor.fetchall()
print(data)
OUTPUT
(3,)
[(99,)]
[(56,)]
[(Decimal('78.0000'),)]
```

9.13 The SQL GROUP BY statement

The GROUP BY statement is used to create a summary of records. The statement groups rows that have the same values (in a column) to create summary rows. For example, we can find the number of students in each class (here we group by class), average salary of employees in IT department (here, we can group by department).

Therefore, the GROUP BY clause returns one row for each group thereby reducing the number of rows in the result-set.

The GROUP BY statement is often used with aggregate functions (COUNT, MAX, MIN, SUM, AVG) to group the result-set by one or more columns. The general syntax of GROUP BY statement can be given as,

```
SELECT column_name(s)
FROM table_name
WHERE condition
GROUP BY column_name(s)
ORDER BY column_name(s);
```

9.14 The HAVING clause

We have learnt that WHERE clause is a powerful clause that is used for selective selection. But this clause cannot be used with aggregate functions. So, SQL has another clause – the HAVING clause that can be used with aggregate functions.

Thus, the HAVING clause allows users to filter the values returned from a grouped query after applying aggregation functions. The syntax of HAVING clause can be given as,

```
SELECT expression1, expression2, ... expression_n, aggregate_function
(expression)
FROM tables
[WHERE conditions]
GROUP BY expression1, expression2, ... expression_n
HAVING condition;
```

```
import mysql.connector as mysql
## connecting to the database using 'connect()' method        OUTPUT
db = mysql.connect(                                            (3,)
    host = "localhost",
    user = "reema",                                            (3,)
    passwd = "********"
    database = "mydb"                                          (2,)
)
cursor = db.cursor()
## defining the Query                                          (2,)
query = "SELECT COUNT(*) FROM STUDENT GROUP BY CLASS"
## executing the query                                         (89,)
cursor.execute(query)
data = cursor.fetchall()                                       (97,)
for record in data:
   print(record)                                               (79,)
##defining the Query
query = "SELECT MAX(MARKS) FROM STUDENT GROUP BY CLASS"        (84,)
## executing the query
cursor.execute(query)
data = cursor.fetchall()
for record in data:
   print(record)
```

9.15 NoSQL databases

NoSQL database stands for "Not Only SQL" or "Not SQL". It was introduced by Carl Strozz in 1998. Basically, NoSQL is a non-relational database management system that does not require a fixed schema (or structure), avoids joins (or linking between two or more tables), and is easy to scale (or expand). NoSQL database is extensively used for distributed data storage and for Big data and real-time web apps. For example, companies like Twitter, Facebook and Google that collect terabytes of data everyday use NoSQL databases.

We have read that Relational Database Management System (RDBMS) uses SQL syntax to store Figure 9.2 and retrieve data. But a NoSQL database system includes a wide range of database technologies that can store structured, semi-structured, unstructured and polymorphic data.

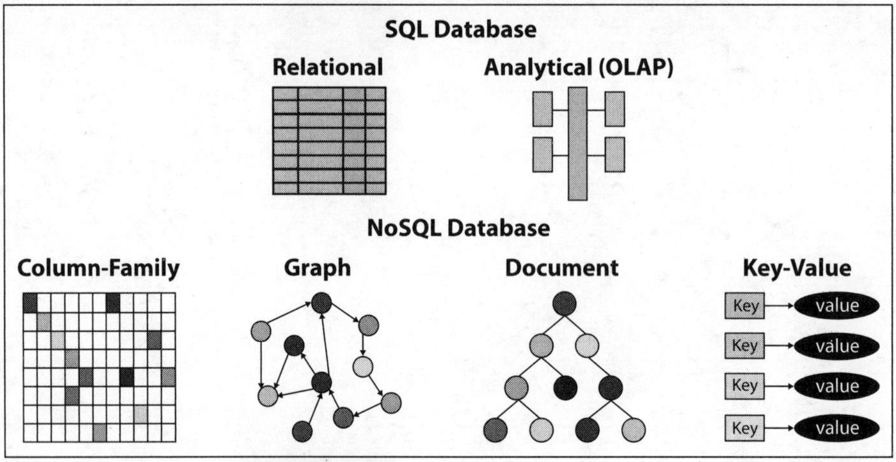

Figure 9.2 SQL & NoSQL database

9.15.1 Why NoSQL?

NoSQL databases became popular with growth of Internet-based companies like Google, Facebook, Amazon, etc. that generate and process massive amount of data every day. RDBMS response time increases while dealing with huge volumes of data. To overcome this limitation, though the system could be easily scaled up by upgrading the existing hardware, the entire process of scaling was very expensive.

Therefore, a better option is to distribute the database on multiple computers whenever the data load increases. This technique is called "scaling out." The difference between scale-up and scale-out can be easily understood from the figure given Figure 9.3.

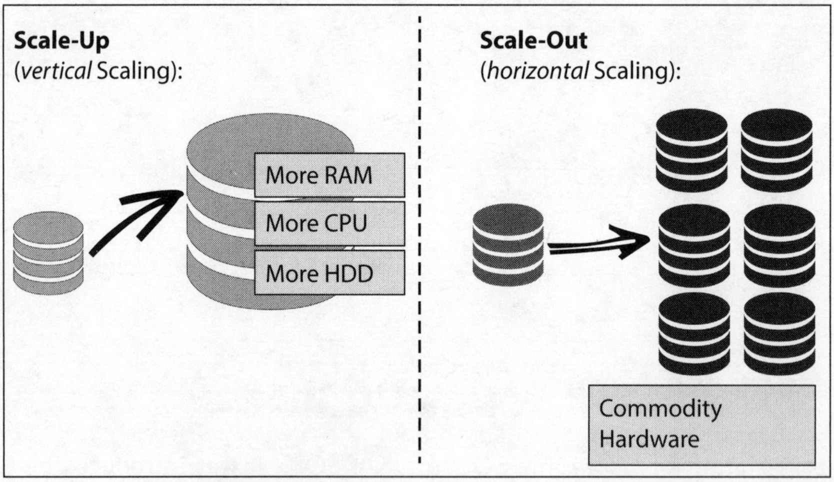

Figure 9.3 Scale-up and scale-out architecture

9.15.2 Features of NoSQL

- NoSQL databases do not follow the relational model of RDBMS. So, there is no concept of flat fixed-column records and tables.
- No complex features like query languages, referential integrity joins, query optimizers, or ACID are required.

- NoSQL databases do not define a stringent structure for storing data.
- It supports storage of heterogeneous (different) structures of data in the same domain.
- NoSQL databases provide an easy-to-use interface for storing as well as querying data.
- Optimized for web-enabled databases.
- Multiple NoSQL databases can be executed in a distributed fashion.
- Offer auto-scaling and fail-over capabilities.
- Provide better throughput (or performance) as query response time is less than that of RDBMS.
- NoSQL databases work on Shared Nothing Architecture (Refer Figure 9.4) that requires less coordination while supporting higher distribution.

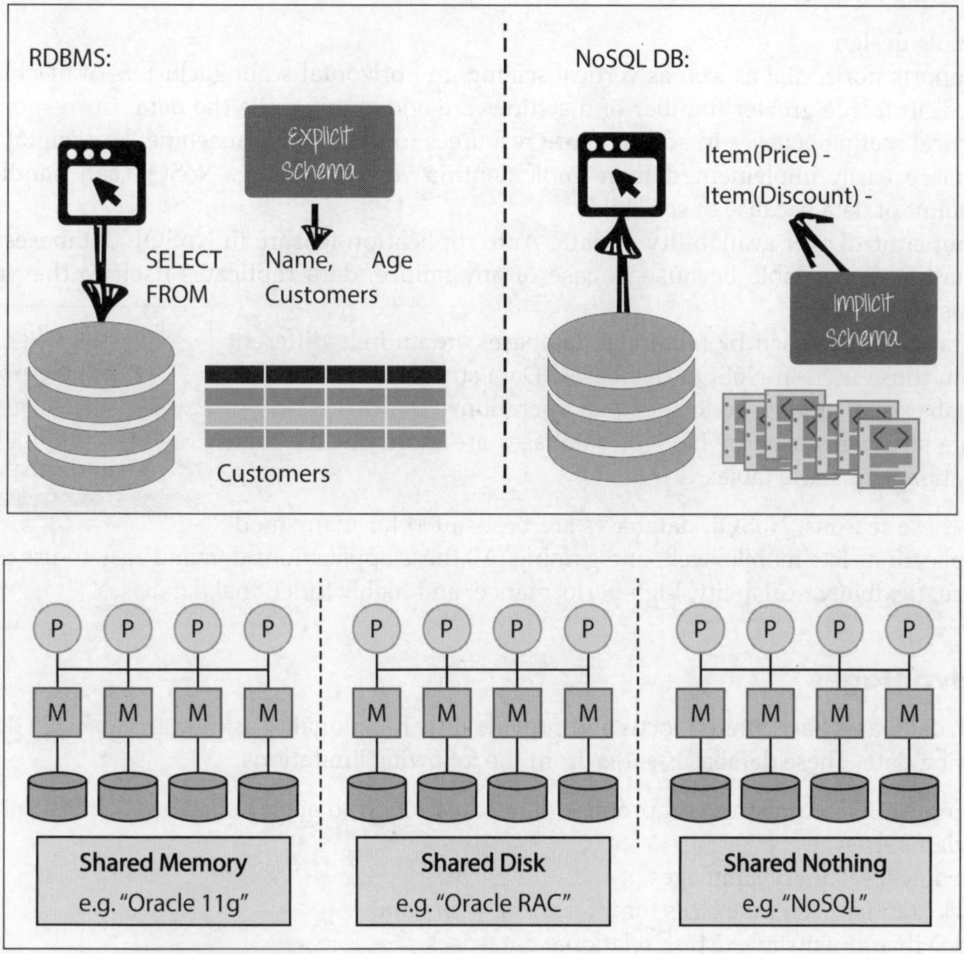

Figure 9.4 Comparison between RDBMS and NoSQL databases

9.15.3 Pros and cons of NoSQL databases

Before the NoSQL databases were introduced, RDBMS was used extensively. But soon when database applications grew in number and complexity, it was realized that the traditional DBMS will no longer be able to meet the demands of data storage and processing.

> MongoDB is the leading NoSQL database.

With an RDBMS, answering even a single simple query took lot of time. Moreover, cloud computing technology emerged at this time to replace vertical scaling with a scale-out architecture. Also, agile development techniques which aim for continuous deployment and short development cycles to facilitate quick response to user's queries, make it in high demand.

Advantages

Relational databases were not designed to address the scalability and agility issues that were being faced by modern applications. They were also not apt to exploit the availability of cheap storage and processing power through the cloud. Hence, NoSQL database was a good choice because of the following reasons.

- Simple design
- Supports horizontal as well as vertical scaling. In horizontal scaling, clusters of machines are used. In fact, a greater number of machines are added to handle the data. Correspondingly, vertical scaling believes in adding more resources to the existing machine. Horizontal scaling is more easily implemented than implementing vertical scaling. NoSQL can handle huge amount of data because of scalability.
- Finer control over availability of data. Auto replication feature in NoSQL databases makes data highly available because in case of any failure, data replicates itself to the previous consistent state.
- Data structures used by relational databases are entirely different from those used in NoSQL databases. Data structures for NoSQL databases are optimized to speed up operations.
- Data structures used by NoSQL databases are more flexible than relational database tables.

> The suitability of a given NoSQL database depends on the problem it should solve.

For all these reasons, NoSQL databases are best-suited for many modern applications like mobile, web, and gaming. All these applications demand easy-to-use intuitive interface, flexibility, scalability, high-performance, and highly functional databases.

Disadvantages

NoSQL databases have limited focus and provide little functionality as they are specially designed for storing data. These databases suffer from the following limitations.

- Many NoSQL databases compromise data consistency, to achieve data availability and speed of data retrieval.
- Use low-level query languages.
- Lack standardized interfaces for interacting with data.
- Huge investments in existing relational databases.
- Managing NoSQL data is much more complex than in a relational database.
- NoSQL is more difficult to install and manage on a daily basis than a relational database.
- Most NoSQL databases lack ACID transactions. However, some new databases like MarkLogic, Aerospike, FairCom c-treeACE, Google Spanner (a NewSQL database), Symas LMDB, and OrientDB support ACID features in their design and implementation.
- Most NoSQL databases support eventual consistency so that any changes made in the database are propagated to all the machines on which that data is stored. So queries for data may not immediately return updated data.

9.15.4 When to use NoSQL?

- If you have to store and retrieve huge amounts of data
- If the relationship between the data being stored is not relevant
- When the data keeps changing with time
- If the data to be stored is unstructured
- If there is no need to add constraints and perform joins in the data
- If the size of data is continuously increasing and the database must scale to handle the ever-expanding data

9.15.5 NoSQL database

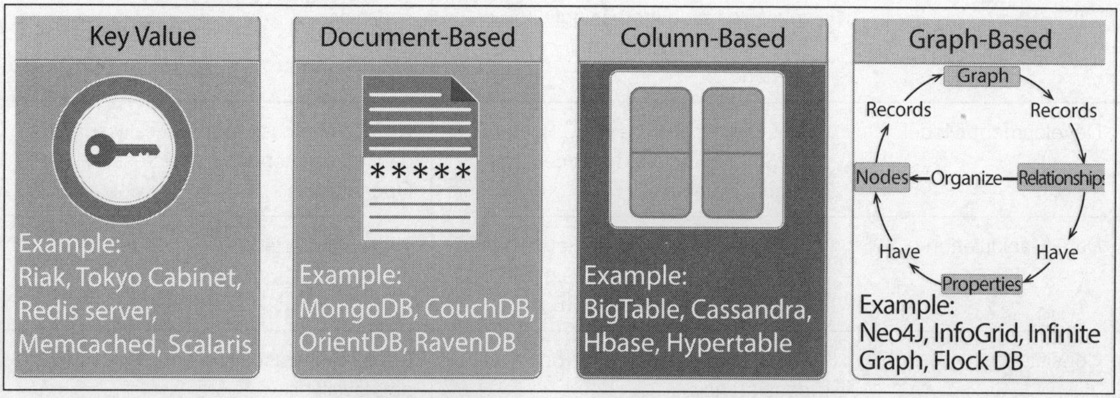

Figure 9.5 Types of NoSQL database

NoSQL databases include the following types of data (refer Figure 9.5).

- **Key-value stores** are the simplest NoSQL databases in which every item is stored as a key with its value.
- **Document** databases contain different key-value pairs, or even nested documents.
- **Wide-column** organizes data tables as columns instead of as rows. Data stored is optimized for queries. This allows wide-column to access large datasets faster than the relational databases.
- **Graph stores** are used for storing information about networks (like social connections).

These databases organize data in the form of nodes which represent records in a relational database and use edges to represent connections between nodes. Such a structure can support richer and more flexible representations of data relationships that may change with time and use. Table 2 highlights the difference between SQL and NoSQL Databases

Table 2: || Highlights the difference between SQL and NoSQL Databases

	SQL Databases	NoSQL Databases
Types	One type (SQL database) with minor variations.	Many different types inculding key-value stores, document databases, wide-column stores, and graph databases.
Development History	Developed in 1970s to deal with first wave of data storage applications.	Developed in 2000s to deal with limitations of SQL databases.

(Continued)

Table 2: || *(Continued)*

	SQL Databases	NoSQL Databases
Examples	MySQl, Postgers, Oracle Database Structure and data types are fixed in advance.	MongoDB, Cassandra, HBase, Neo4j.
Schemas	To store information about a new data item, the entire database must be altered, during which time the databases must be taken offline.	Typically dynamic. Rocords can add new information on the fly, and unlike SQL table rows, dissimilar data can be stored together as necessary.
Scaling	Vertically, meaning a single server must be made increasingly power-ful in order to deal with increased demand.	Horizontally, meaning that to add capacity.
Development Model	Mix of open-source (e.g., Postgres, MySQL) and closed source (e.g., Oracle Database).	NoSQL database automatically spreads data across servers as necessary Open-source.
Data Manipulation	Specific language using Select, Insert, and Update statements, e.g. SELECT fields FROM table WHERE…	Through interfaces.
Consistency	Can be configured for strong consistency.	Consistency usually compromised for data availability.
Optimal workloads	Relational databases are designed for transactional processing.	NoSQL databases are used for analytics over semi-structured data.
ACID properties	Supports ACID properties.	NoSQL databases often make tradeoffs by relaxing some of the ACID properties of relational databases for a more fiexible data model that can scale horizontally.
Scale	Relational databases typically scale up by increasing the compute capabilities of the hardware or scal-out by adding replicas for read-only workloads.	NoSQL databases typically are partition-able because key-value access patterns are able to scale out by using dis-tributed architecture to increase throughput that provides consitent performance at near boundless scale.

9.16 MongoDB

To support flexibility and scalability, MongoDB stores data in JSON-like documents. To practice commands in MongoDB, you either need to install it in your system from https://www.mongodb.com or use MongoDB cloud service at https://www.mongodb.com/cloud/atlas.

To access the MongoDB database from your Python code, you must also install a MongoDB driver, "PyMongo" by using the command, pip install pymongo.

Remember that Python interacts with NoSQL databases in the same way as it interacts with Relational databases. We have installed the MongoDB on our system and used host = localhost and port = 27017 as suggested by the software.

9.16.1 Create a database

> **Programming Tip**
> In MongoDB, a database is created only when it has some content in it.

To create a database in MongoDB, first create a Mongo**Client** object. Specify a connection URL by giving IP address and the name of the database to be created. MongoDB will create the database if it does not exist, and establish a connection with it.

```
import pymongo
myclient = pymongo.MongoClient("mongodb://localhost:27017/")
mydb = myclient["mydatabase"]
print(myclient.list_database_names())
OUTPUT
['admin', 'config', 'local']
```

Note that in the above code, we have created a database named mydatabase, but name of this database is not reflected in the output because MongoDB does not create a database until you actually add any table with at least one record in it. However, to check if a database exists or not, you can print names of all databases in the system by executing the command,

```
print(myclient.list_database_names())
```

9.16.2 Creating a collection

To create a collection (or a table) in MongoDB, use a database object and specify the name of the collection to be created. MongoDB will create the collection only if it does not exist in the specified database. Look at the code given below which creates a collection "customers" in the "mydatabase" and some rows (or contents) in it.

9.16.3 Insert into collection

> **Programming Tip**
> If you do not specify an _id field, then MongoDB will add one for you and assign a unique id for each document.

To insert a record (or *document)* in a collection in MongoDB, we can use the `insert_one()` method. We can create a dictionary of name and value pairs and then simply insert it in the collection. We can also add multiple records (or documents) by using a list of dictionaries. In such a case, insert_many() method will be used.

Note that the `insert_one()` method returns a InsertOneResult object, which has a property, `inserted_id`, that holds the id of the inserted document. Similarly, the `insert_many()` method returns a InsertManyResult object, having `inserted_ids` property that holds the ids of the inserted documents.

Another important point to note is that every collection may have an id field. Value of the id field should be unique. If you do not specify id, then MongoDB will itself assign unique ids for every document. The code given below inserts multiple documents in a collection with a unique id field.

```
import pymongo
myclient = pymongo.MongoClient("mongodb://localhost:27017/")
mydb = myclient["mydatabase"]
tab = mydb["customers"]
L = [
    {"_id": 1, "NAME": "Janak", "COMPANY": "Jruma" },
    {"_id": 2,  "NAME": "Raj", "COMPANY": "Tirupati Industries" },
    {"_id": 3, "NAME": "Sanjay", "COMPANY": "BomPlast" },
    {"_id": 4, "NAME": "Pranay", "COMPANY": "Accenture" },
    {"_id": 5, "NAME": "Karina", "COMPANY": "TCS" }]
x = tab.insert_many(L)
print(x.inserted_ids)
OUTPUT
[1, 2, 3, 4, 5]
```

9.16.4 Find one and find all

We use SELECT statement in SQL to select a specific data from a database table. Similarly, in MongoDB, this is done using the `find_one()` method that returns the first occurrence in the selection. For example, to find the first document in the customers collection, we will write,

```
x = tab.find_one()
```

To find all occurrences in the selection, we use the `find()` method. Code to find all occurrences in the customers table is given below.

```
import pymongo
myclient = pymongo.MongoClient("mongodb://localhost:27017/")
mydb = myclient["mydatabase"]
tab = mydb["customers"]
for x in tab.find():
  print(x)
OUTPUT
{'_id': 1, 'NAME': 'Janak', 'COMPANY': 'Jruma'}
{'_id': 2, 'NAME': 'Raj', 'COMPANY': 'Tirupati Industries'}
{'_id': 3, 'NAME': 'Sanjay', 'COMPANY': 'BomPlast'}
{'_id': 4, 'NAME': 'Pranay', 'COMPANY': 'Accenture'}
{'_id': 5, 'NAME': 'Karina', 'COMPANY': 'TCS'}
```

The `find()` method can also be used to include only selected fields in the result. For this, the second parameter of the `find()` method is an object describing fields that must be included in the result.

> **Programming Tip**
>
> In the find() method, an error occurs if you specify both 0 and 1 values in the same object. The only exception is when one of the fields is the _id field.

The code given below illustrates printing of all fields except NAME.

```
The code given below illustrates printing of all fields except NAME.
# Return only ids and companies, not the names
import pymongo
myclient = pymongo.MongoClient("mongodb://localhost:27017/")
mydb = myclient["mydatabase"]
tab = mydb["customers"]
for x in tab.find({},{ "COMPANY": 0 }):
  print(x)
OUTPUT
{'_id': 1, 'NAME': 'Janak'}
{'_id': 2, 'NAME': 'Raj'}
{'_id': 3, 'NAME': 'Sanjay'}
{'_id': 4, 'NAME': 'Pranay'}
{'_id': 5, 'NAME': 'Karina'}
```

9.16.5 Filter the result

IN SQL, you use the WHERE clause and other clauses in the query to filter the result. In MongoDB, we can do this using the find() method. The first argument of the find() method is a query object that is often used to limit the search. The code given below displays the document where company name is Jruma.

```
import pymongo
myclient = pymongo.MongoClient("mongodb://localhost:27017/")
mydb = myclient["mydatabase"]
tab = mydb["customers"]
myQuery = { "COMPANY": "Jruma" }
val = tab.find(myQuery)
for x in val:
  print(x)
OUTPUT
{'_id': 1, 'NAME': 'Janak', 'COMPANY': 'Jruma'}
```

9.16.6 Advanced query

To make advanced queries, we can even use modifiers as values in the query object. For example, in the code given below, we have printed documents where the value of COMPANY starts with the letter "T" or alphabetically higher than it. Here, we have used the greater than modifier for this purpose.

```
import pymongo
myclient = pymongo.MongoClient("mongodb://localhost:27017/")
mydb = myclient["mydatabase"]
tab = mydb["customers"]
```

```
myQuery = { "COMPANY": { "$gt": "T" } }
val = tab.find(myQuery)
for x in val:
  print(x)
OUTPUT
{'_id': 2, 'NAME': 'Raj', 'COMPANY': 'Tirupati Industries'}
{'_id': 5, 'NAME': 'Karina', 'COMPANY': 'TCS'}
```

Note that you could have done the same task using a regular expression as given below. Here, we have printed documents where COMPANY starts with alphabet 'T'.

```
import pymongo
myclient = pymongo.MongoClient("mongodb://localhost:27017/")
mydb = myclient["mydatabase"]
tab = mydb["customers"]
myQuery = { "COMPANY": { "$regex": "^T" } }
val = tab.find(myQuery)
for x in val:
  print(x)
OUTPUT
{'_id': 2, 'NAME': 'Raj', 'COMPANY': 'Tirupati Industries'}
{'_id': 5, 'NAME': 'Karina', 'COMPANY': 'TCS'}
```

9.16.7 Sort the result

The `sort()` method is used to sort the result in ascending or descending order. The method takes the "fieldname" based on which the documents are to be sorted and "direction" to specify whether sorting has to be done in ascending or descending order. Default value of direction is ascending.

```
import pymongo
myclient = pymongo.MongoClient("mongodb://localhost:27017/")
mydb = myclient["mydatabase"]
tab = mydb["customers"]
val = tab.find().sort("NAME")
for x in val:
  print(x)
OUTPUT
{'_id': 1, 'NAME': 'Janak', 'COMPANY': 'Jruma'}
{'_id': 5, 'NAME': 'Karina', 'COMPANY': 'TCS'}
{'_id': 4, 'NAME': 'Pranay', 'COMPANY': 'Accenture'}
{'_id': 2, 'NAME': 'Raj', 'COMPANY': 'Tirupati Industries'}
{'_id': 3, 'NAME': 'Sanjay', 'COMPANY': 'BomPlast'}
```

Note that you can even write sort("fieldname", 1) for sorting in ascending order and sort("fieldname", -1) for sorting in descending order.

9.16.8 Delete document

To delete one document, the `delete_one()` method is used. We just need to specify a query object defining which document to delete as the parameter of this method. Note that in the code given below, we have inserted one document and then deleted it.

> **Programming Tip**
> As the name suggests, update_one() updates only the first occurrence of the document.

```
import pymongo
myclient = pymongo.MongoClient("mongodb://localhost:27017/")
mydb = myclient["mydatabase"]
tab = mydb["customers"]
Dict = {"_id":6,"NAME": "Sanchita", "COMPANY": "WIPRO" }
x = tab.insert_one(Dict)
print(x.inserted_id)
myQuery = { "COMPANY": "WIPRO" }
tab.delete_one(myQuery)
```

Moving ahead, note that to delete more than one document, the `delete_many()` method is used. Like `delete_one()`, the `delete_many()` accepts a query object defining which documents to delete.

Again going a step further, all documents in a collection can be easily deleted by passing an empty query object to the `delete_many()` method. To know how many documents were actually deleted, we can write,

```
x = tab.delete_many({})
print(x.deleted_count, " documents deleted.")
```

9.16.9 Update collection

To update a record, or document in MongoDB, the `update_one()` method is used. This method accepts a query object as the first parameter. The query defines which document to update. The second parameter is an object defining new values of the document. Look at the code given below that changes COMPANY to Cognizant where it was initially TCS.

```
import pymongo
myclient = pymongo.MongoClient("mongodb://localhost:27017/")
mydb = myclient["mydatabase"]
tab = mydb["customers"]
myQuery = {"COMPANY": "TCS" }
newval = { "$set": { "COMPANY": "Cognizant" } }
tab.update_one(myQuery, newval)
#print "customers" after the update:
for x in tab.find():
  print(x)
OUTPUT
{'_id': 1, 'NAME': 'Janak', 'COMPANY': 'Jruma'}
```

```
{'_id': 2, 'NAME': 'Raj', 'COMPANY': 'Tirupati Industries'}
{'_id': 3, 'NAME': 'Sanjay', 'COMPANY': 'BomPlast'}
{'_id': 4, 'NAME': 'Pranay', 'COMPANY': 'Accenture'}
{'_id': 5, 'NAME': 'Karina', 'COMPANY': 'Cognizant'}
```

As stated, `update_one()` method will update only the first occurrence of a document. To update multiple or in fact all the documents meets a particular criteria (as specified in the query object), the `update_many()` method is used. So, when we execute the following statements, a number of documents modified will be displayed.

```
x = tab.update_many(myQuery, newvalues)
print(x.modified_count, "documents updated.")
```

9.16.10 Limit the result

To limit the result in MongoDB, the `limit()` method is used. This method just takes a number defining how many documents to return. Only specified number of documents will then be displayed. For example, the code given below displays only two documents.

```
import pymongo
myclient = pymongo.MongoClient("mongodb://localhost:27017/")
mydb = myclient["mydatabase"]
tab = mydb["customers"]
res = tab.find().limit(2)
#print the result:
for x in res:
  print(x)
OUTPUT
{'_id': 1, 'NAME': 'Janak', 'COMPANY': 'Jruma'}
{'_id': 2, 'NAME': 'Raj', 'COMPANY': 'Tirupati Industries'}
```

Business Scenario: Interfacing with MySQL using Python

Data is the fuel for decision-making. MySQL is a widely used relational database management system that helps businesses to store and manage large amounts of data. Imagine that an e-commerce company wants to track orders, customer information, and inventory in a MySQL database. The DBA has to automate the process of inserting, updating, deleting, and fetching data using Python.

1. Create Customers table in SQL

```
CREATE TABLE Customers (
    CustomerID INT PRIMARY KEY AUTO_INCREMENT,
    FirstName VARCHAR(100),
    LastName VARCHAR(100),
    Email VARCHAR(100),
    PhoneNumber VARCHAR(15)
);
```

2. Create Orders table in SQL

```
    CREATE TABLE Orders (
```

```
    OrderID INT PRIMARY KEY AUTO_INCREMENT,
    CustomerID INT,
    OrderDate DATE,
    TotalAmount DECIMAL(10, 2),
    FOREIGN KEY (CustomerID) REFERENCES Customers(CustomerID)
);
```

3. Create Inventory table

```
CREATE TABLE Inventory (
    ProductID INT PRIMARY KEY AUTO_INCREMENT,
    ProductName VARCHAR(100),
    Quantity INT,
    Price DECIMAL(10, 2)
);
```

Python code to connect to the database

```
pip install mysql-connector-python
import mysql.connector

# Connect to the MySQL database
db_connection = mysql.connector.connect(
    host="localhost",  # The MySQL host, 'localhost' if running locally
    user="root",       # Your MySQL username
    password="password",  # Your MySQL password
    database="ecommerce"  # The name of your database
)
# Create a cursor object to execute SQL queries
cursor = db_connection.cursor()
```

Insert Data into the Database

```
def add_customer(first_name, last_name, email, phone_number):
    query = """ INSERT  INTO  Customers  (FirstName,  LastName,  Email,
PhoneNumber)
    VALUES (%s, %s, %s, %s); """
    values = (first_name, last_name, email, phone_number)
    cursor.execute(query, values)
    db_connection.commit() # Commit the changes to the database
    print("Customer added successfully!")
```

Fetch Data from the Database

```
def get_customer_by_id(customer_id):
    query = "SELECT * FROM Customers WHERE CustomerID = %s;"
    cursor.execute(query, (customer_id,))
    result = cursor.fetchone()  # Fetch a single result
    if result:
        print(" Customer ID: ", result[0], " Name: ", result[1], " ",
result[2], " Email: ", result[3], " Phone: ", result[4])
    else:
        print("Customer not found.")
```

Update Data in the Database

```
def update_customer_phone(customer_id, new_phone_number):
    query = "UPDATE Customers SET PhoneNumber = %s WHERE CustomerID = %s;"
    cursor.execute(query, (new_phone_number, customer_id))
    db_connection.commit()
    print("Customer phone number updated successfully!")
```

Delete Data from the Database

```
def delete_customer(customer_id):
    query = "DELETE FROM Customers WHERE CustomerID = %s;"
    cursor.execute(query, (customer_id,))
    db_connection.commit()
    print(f"Customer {customer_id} deleted successfully!")
```

Close the Connection

```
# Close the cursor and connection
cursor.close()
db_connection.close()
```

Key Terms

Aggregate Function: Function that performs a calculation on multiple values and returns a single value.
Clients: Computers that install and run RDBMS software are called clients.
Database: A collection of related tables.
NoSQL: A non-relational database management system that does not require a fixed schema (or structure), avoids joins (or linking between two or more tables), and is easy to scale (or expand).
Servers: To access data, clients connect to more powerful machines called servers.
SQL: A database query language.

Chapter Highlights

* MySQL is an open-source software so users do not have to pay to use it.
* SQL queries (or statements) can be used to perform operations like retrieving, inserting, updating and deleting data. They can be also used to create tables or modify the structure of existing tables. However, to use SQL queries, you must first install a database, like Oracle, MySQL, MongoDB, PostGres SQL, SQL Server, DB2, etc.
* In MySQL, every client can make a request to a server that responds with the desired output.
* We can use the SQL SELECT statement to perform mathematical calculations.
* A database is created using the CREATE DATABASE statement.
* To select a particular database and start using it, we need the use database command.
* In SQL, the CREATE TABLE statement is used to create a table.
* A table can be deleted using the DROP TABLE statement. When a table is deleted, all its definition, data, indexes, views, triggers, constraints and permission specifications are removed from the database.

- ✶ INSERT INTO statement is used to add new rows of data in a table that exists in the database.
- ✶ The SELECT statement in SQL is used to fetch or retrieve data from one or more tables in the database.
- ✶ SELECT DISTINCT statement eliminates duplicate entries while displaying data from the table.
- ✶ The WHERE clause is used in the SELECT statement to specify a condition for retrieving data from one or more tables.
- ✶ The ORDER BY statement in SQL is used to sort the retrieved data in either ascending or descending order.
- ✶ The SQL UPDATE statement is used to modify the existing data in a table.
- ✶ The DELETE query in SQL is used to delete existing record(s) from a table in the database.
- ✶ PRIMARY KEY constraint helps us to uniquely identify each record in the table. The primary key must contain UNIQUE values, and cannot have NULL values.
- ✶ A table can have only one primary key and the primary key may consist of one or more fields.
- ✶ To set PRIMARY KEY constraint on an already created table, the ALTER TABLE command is used.
- ✶ The cursor.execute() method is used to run or execute an SQL query through a python program. Another method, cursor.executemany(operation, seq_of_parameters) is used to prepare a database query and executes it against all parameter sequences found in the sequence seq_of_params.
- ✶ The results of this query can then be accessed using either fetchone() method to fetch single record or fetchall() method to fetch multiple values from a database table.
- ✶ The GROUP BY statement is used to create a summary of records. The statement groups rows that have the same values (in a column) to create summary rows.

Review Questions

1. What is SQL? Why is it used?
2. MySQL and SQL are the same. Comment on this statement.
3. Give some features of MySQL that makes it a popular database.
4. Why do we need to specify data type? List some data types used in SQL.
5. Differentiate between char and varchar.
6. List the steps for interfacing Python with MySQL.
7. How can we create a database in SQL?
8. Explain the syntax of the SELECT statement.
9. With the help of an example explain how you will use the ORDER BY clause to sort data based on multiple columns.
10. What does primary key constraint state? How can we enforce such a constraint in SQL?
11. Differentiate between execute and executemany().
12. How is fetchone() different from fetchall() function?
13. How is durability ensured while working with MySQL?
14. With the help of an example explain the significance of GROUP BY and HAVING clause.

15. Write the SQL statements that you will use to:

a. create a database.
b. see a list of all the databases present in MySQL.
c. change to another database.
d. delete a database.
e. create a table.
f. return values that match values in a list or a sub-query.
g. sort the retrieved data in either ascending or descending order.
h. remove records from a table.
i. return the maximum value for a column.
j. return the minimum value for a column.
k. return a count of the number of data values.
l. return the sum of the data values.
m. return the average of the data values.
n. set PRIMARY KEY constraint on an already created table.
o. drop a PRIMARY KEY constraint.
p. filter the values returned from a grouped query based on the results of aggregation functions.

	status	COUNT(*)
►	Cancelled	6
	Disputed	3
	In Process	6
	On Hold	4
	Resolved	4
	Shipped	303

16. Consider the table given below and write a query that returns the number of orders in each status.

17. Consider the `orders` and `orderdetails` table. Write a query to get the total amount of all orders by status. (***Hint:*** join the `orders` table with the `orderdetails` table). Also write the query that returns the order numbers and the total amount of each order.

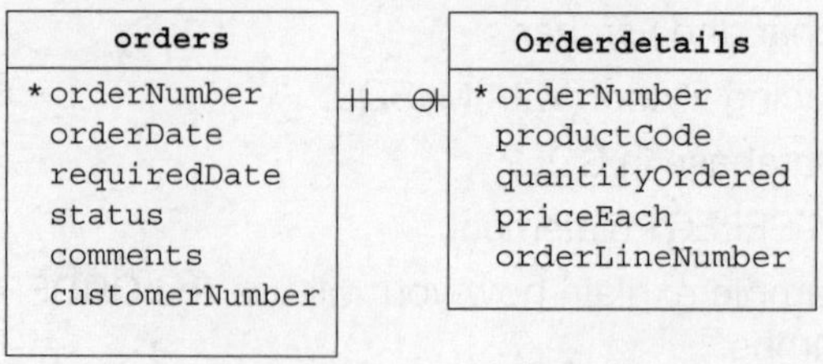

18. Explain the given query.

a.
```
SELECT YEAR(orderDate) AS year, SUM(quantityOrdered * priceEach) AS
total
FROM orders
INNER JOIN orderdetails
    USING (orderNumber)
```

```
WHERE status = 'Shipped'
GROUP BY    year
HAVING year > 2003;
```

b.
```
import mysql.connector
connection = mysql.connector.connect(host='localhost',
        database='Electronics',
        user='pynative',
        password='pynative@#29')
mySql_Create_Table_Query = """CREATE TABLE Laptop (
    Id int(11) NOT NULL, Name varchar(250) NOT NULL,
    Price float NOT NULL, Purchase_date Date NOT NULL,
    PRIMARY KEY (Id)) """
cursor = connection.cursor()
result = cursor.execute(mySql_Create_Table_Query)
print("Laptop Table created successfully ")
if (connection.is_connected()):
   cursor.close()
   connection.close()
   print("MySQL connection is closed")
```

c.
```
select bst.start_station_name, count(*) as num_trips
from modeanalytics.sf_bike_share_trip bst
group by bst.start_station_name
```

d.
```
select bst.start_station_name, count(*) as num_trips, avg(bst.duration)
as avg_duration_seconds, min(bst.duration) as min_duration_seconds,
  max(bst.duration) as max_duration_seconds
from modeanalytics.sf_bike_share_trip bst
group by bst.start_station_name
```

e.
```
select  bst.start_station_name, bst.end_station_name, count(*) as
num_trips,
  avg(bst.duration) as avg_duration_seconds, min(bst.duration) as min_
duration_seconds, max(bst.duration) as max_duration_seconds
from modeanalytics.sf_bike_share_trip bst
group by bst.start_station_name,bst.end_station_name
```

f.
```
select bst.start_station_name, bst.end_station_name, count(1) as num_
trips, avg(duration) as avg_duration_seconds,min(duration) as min_
duration_seconds, max(duration) as max_duration_seconds
from modeanalytics.sf_bike_share_trip bst
group by 1,2
having count(1) > 1000
```

g.
```
import MySQLdb
db = MySQLdb.connect("localhost","testuser","test123","TESTDB" )
cursor = db.cursor()
cursor.execute("SELECT VERSION()")
data = cursor.fetchone()
print "Database version : %s " % data
db.close()
```

h.
```
import MySQLdb
db = MySQLdb.connect("localhost","testuser","test123","TESTDB" )
cursor = db.cursor()
cursor.execute("DROP TABLE IF EXISTS EMPLOYEE")
```

19. What do you understand by the term NoSQL?
20. Differentiate between scale-up and scale-out techniques of upgrading the existing hardware.

Programming Exercise

1. Write a program that creates a table Employee with attributes FIRST_NAME, LAST_NAME, AGE, SEX, and INCOME.
   a. Insert at least 10 rows in the table.
   b. Display all the records from EMPLOYEE table having salary more than 1000.
   c. Increase AGE of all the males by one year.
   d. Delete all the records from EMPLOYEE where AGE is more than 20.
2. Create a database having two tables with the specified fields, to computerize a library system of a Delhi University College.
   LibraryBooks (Accession number, Title, Author, Department, Purchase Date, Price)
   IssuedBooks (Accession number, Borrower)
   a. Identify primary and foreign keys. Create the tables and insert at least 5 records in each table.
   b. Delete the record of book titled "Database System Concepts".
   c. Change the Department of the book titled "Discrete Maths" to "CS".
   d. List all books that belong to "CS" department.
   e. List all books that belong to "CS" department and are written by author "Navathe".
   f. List all computer (Department="CS") that have been issued.
   g. List all books which have a price less than Rs. 500 or purchased between "01/01/1999" and "01/01/2004".
3. Create a database having three tables to store the details of students of Computer Science Department in your college. Personal information about Student (College roll number, Name of student, Date of birth, Address, Marks (rounded off to whole number in percentage at 10 + 2), Phone number, Paper Details (Paper code, Name of the Paper) Student's Academic and Attendance details (College roll number, Paper code, Attendance, Marks in home examination).
   a. Identify primary and foreign keys. Create the tables and insert at least 5 records in each table.
   b. Design a query that will return the records (from the second table) along with the name of student from the first table, related to students who have more than 75% attendance and more than 60% marks in Paper 2.
   c. List all students who live in "Delhi" and have marks greater than 60, in Paper 1.
   d. Find the total attendance and total marks obtained by each student.
   e. List the name of the student who has got the highest marks in Paper 2.
4. Create the following tables and answer the queries given below: Customer (CustID, email, Name, Phone, ReferrerID), Bicycle (BicycleID, DatePurchased, Color, CustID, ModelNo), BicycleModel (ModelNo, Manufacturer, Style), Service (StartDate, BicycleID, EndDate)
   a. Identify primary and foreign keys. Create the tables and insert at least 5 records in each table.

b. List all the customers who have the bicycles manufactured by the manufacturer "Honda".
c. List the bicycles purchased by the customers who have been referred by customer "C1".
d. List the manufacturer of red colored bicycles.
e. List the models of the bicycles given for service.

5. Create the following tables, enter at least 5 records in each table and answer the queries given below. EMPLOYEE (Person_Name, Street, City), WORKS (Person_Name, Company_Name, Salary), COMPANY
(Company_Name, City), MANAGES
(Person_Name, Manager_Name)
a. Identify primary and foreign keys.
b. Alter table employee, add a column "email" of type varchar(20).
c. Find the name of all managers who work for both Samba Bank and NCB Bank.
d. Find the names, street address and cities of residence and salary of all employees who work for "Samba Bank" and earn more than $10,000.
e. Find the names of all employees who live in the same city as the company for which they work.
f. Find the highest salary, lowest salary and average salary paid by each company.
g. Find the sum of salary and number of employees in each company.
h. Find the name of the company that pays the highest salary.

6. Create the following tables, enter at least 5 records in each table and answer the queries given below. Suppliers (SNo, Sname, Status, SCity), Parts (PNo, Pname, Colour, Weight, City), Project (JNo, Jname, Jcity), Shipment (Sno, Pno, Jno, Quantity)
a. Identify primary and foreign keys.
b. Get supplier numbers for suppliers in Paris with status>20.
c. Get supplier details for suppliers who supply part P2. Display the supplier list in the increasing order of supplier numbers.
d. Get supplier names for suppliers who do not supply part P2.
e. For each shipment get full shipment details, including total shipment weights.
f. Get all the shipments where the quantity is in the range 300 to 750 inclusive.
g. Get part numbers for parts that either weigh more than 16 pounds or are supplied by suppliers S2, or both.
h. Get the names of the cities that store more than five red parts.
i. Get full details of parts supplied by a supplier in Delhi.
j. Get part numbers for the part supplied by a supplier in Allahabad to a project in Chennai.
k. Get the total number of project supplied by a supplier (say, S1).
l. Get the total quantity of a part (say, P1) supplied by a supplier (say, S1).

7. Perform the following instructions in a MongoDB database.
a. Create a MongoDB database named Employees.
b. Add at least 10 documents in it one by one. Every document must store name, age and address of each employee.
c. Update the document of employees having age > 42.
d. Delete data of employee having name "Prajakta".
e. Display 5 documents.
f. Display details of employees whose names start with 'R'.

Fill in the Blanks

1. ________ is a database query language.
2. _______ language is used to create or modify database objects (like tables, views, indexes, users, etc).
3. Data type _____ is used to define fixed length strings.
4. ________ statement is used to see a list of all the databases present in MySQL.
5. In SQL, the ________ statement is used to create a table.
6. Once the table is created, we can use the ______ command to see the description of the newly created table.
7. _________ statement is used to add new rows of data in a table that exists in the database.
8. The _______ statement in SQL is used to fetch or retrieve data from one or more tables in the database.
9. ______ statement eliminates duplicate entries while displaying data from the table.
10. The ___________ method returns a cursor object which is then used to execute SQL queries.
11. The default username for the MySQL database is ______.
12. To insert multiple rows into the table, _________ method is used.
13. __________ is a read-only attribute and returns the number of rows that were affected by an execute() method.
14. _________ function is used to finalize changes in the database.
15. The GROUP BY statement is often used with ________ functions.
16. NoSQL database works on _______ Architecture.
17. The ________ property of the InsertOneResult object, holds the id of the inserted document. In MongoDB, the value of the ____ field must be unique.

State True or False

1. MySQL is a proprietary software.
2. MySQL can be used only on Windows.
3. MySQL satisfies ACID property.
4. MySQL is a database query language.
5. The server application responds with the requested information that is displayed on the client machine.
6. DDL is used to manipulate data.
7. Char performs faster than varchar.
8. The ALL keyword is used to compare any applicable value in the list.
9. The WHERE clause can be used retrieve data only from a single table.
10. The ORDER BY clause can be used to sort data according to multiple columns.
11. The primary key must contain NULL values.

12. A table can have only one primary key and the primary key may consist of one or more fields.
13. We can execute query even after the cursor object is closed.
14. User working as root does not need password.
15. fetchone() method fetches all the rows in a result-set.
16. commit() method is used to revert the changes made to the database.
17. In MongoDB, a database is not created until it gets some content in it.
18. In MongoDB, it is mandatory to specify an _id field in collection.

CHAPTER 10

Introduction to Machine Learning

Detecting Fraudulent Transactions with Outlier Analysis

XYZ Retail is a company that operates both online and in physical stores. As the company grows, the volume transaction data is also escalated. Over time, the company observed decline in profit owing to the growing number of fraudulent transactions. XYZ Retail then hired a data analyst to detect these frauds early and minimize losses.

The analyst used outlier analysis to detect transactions that deviate significantly from typical patterns. By flagging these outliers, the analyst can investigate suspicious transactions, thereby preventing fraudulent activities in real time.

The era in which we are living right now is the 'age of data'. Today, we have massive amount of data that is constantly increasing every day, better computational power and more storage resources. However, the real challenge is to make a sense of all the data. Therefore, companies are busy building intelligent systems using concepts and methodologies from Computer science, Data Mining and Machine learning. Machine learning is the buzzword today. It involves application of algorithms that provides sense to the data.

Machine Learning (ML) enables computer systems to provide sense to data in much the same way as human beings do. It is a branch of artificial intelligence that extracts patterns from raw data by using a well-defined algorithm. ML allows computers to learn from experience without human intervention.

10.1 Need for machine learning

We all know that human beings are the most intelligent species on this planet. Humans can think, evaluate and solve complex problems. Therefore, humans now want to imbibe this intelligence in machines so that even they can think, analyze and act to deduce solutions to otherwise complex problems.

- In continuation to this, ML aims at enabling the machines make decisions, based on data, with efficiency and scale particularly to automate the data-driven decision-making process. Some factors which had escalated the growth and application of ML techniques are discussed below.
- Lack of availability of human expertise, or in situations where it is not safe or practically feasible for humans to work. For example, navigation in unknown territories or spatial planets.

- Dynamic scenarios where conditions keep changing fast and humans are quite slow to respond. Apart from other reasons, it may also be due to limited network connectivity or inadequate availability of infrastructure in the organization.
- Difficulty faced by humans to provide 100% accurate results especially for computational tasks. For example, in applications like handwriting recognition, voice recognition, face recognition, so on and so forth.

10.1.1 Machine learning model

We can better understand the role of ML techniques through a very simple definition given by Professor Mitchell –

"A computer program is said to learn from experience E with respect to some class of tasks T and performance measure P, if its performance at tasks in T, as measured by P, improves with experience E." Based on this definition, the Machine Learning Model can be given as shown in Figure 10.1. Here,

Task (T), is the real-world problem to be solved. For example, predicting sales of a product, classifying an email as spam or not a spam, etc. Technically, examples of ML-based tasks are Classification, Regression, Clustering, Recognition, etc.

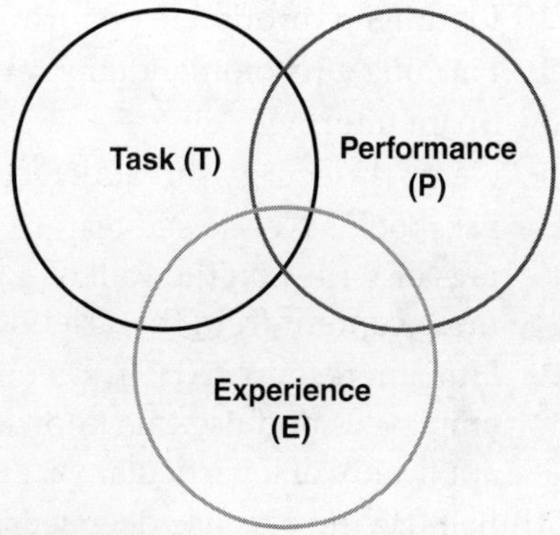

Figure 10.1 Machine learning model

Experience (E) is the knowledge gained from data provided to the algorithm or model. Once data is provided, the model runs iteratively to learn some inherent patterns. Therefore, like humans, machines now learn from experience by analyzing situation, relationships, etc. Supervised, unsupervised and reinforcement learning are some ways to learn or gain experience. Experience acquired through ML model or algorithm is used to solve task T.

Performance (P) is a measure that indicates how well a particular ML algorithm has performed the given task T using experience E. Performance is analyzed based on well-defined metrics including accuracy, F1 score, confusion matrix, precision, recall, sensitivity, etc.

10.1.2 Challenges in machines learning

All is not good with respect to ML. There are multiple issues with respect to cyber security. Apart from this, other significant factors can be given as,

- Availability of good-quality data for application of ML algorithms.
- Time-consuming and exhaustive set of tasks involved in data acquisition, feature extraction and retrieval.
- Lack of expertise as ML is still in its infancy stage.
- No clear objective for formulating business problems, is another big challenge for applying ML techniques.
- Issue of overfitting and underfitting the model.
- Too many features or variables or columns in the data set pose a big challenge.

10.1.3 Applications of machine learning

As stated before, ML is a growing area. Its application to solve real-world problems is constantly rising. These days, ML is being extensively used for

- Emotion analysis
- Sentiment analysis
- Error detection and prevention
- Weather forecasting and prediction
- Stock market analysis and forecasting
- Speech synthesis
- Speech recognition
- Customer segmentation
- Object recognition
- Fraud detection and prevention
- Recommendation of products to customer in online shopping
- Identifying profitable opportunities or dangerous risks
- Forming a recommendation engine to personalize online ad delivery in almost real time
- Spam filtering
- Network security threat detection
- Facebook's News Feed feature uses ML to personalize each member's feed. If a user frequently tags or writes on the wall of a particular friend, the News Feed changes its behavior to display more content from that friend.
- Human resource (HR) systems use ML algorithms to identify characteristics of effective employees and use this knowledge to select the best suitable candidate from the set of all the applicants of a particular vacant post.
- Self-driving cars use deep learning neural networks to identify objects and determine optimal actions for safely steering a vehicle down the road.
- Tumor detection, drug discovery, and DNA sequencing
- Predicting price and load of electricity that will be consumed in an area
- Voice recognition system
- Diagnosing diseases (like diabetes, cancer) based on the symptoms of patients
- Identifying frequently selling products or products that sell well together so that lucrative discounts can be given to further boost their sales

10.2 Types of machine learning algorithms

Machine learning algorithms can be categorized as supervised or unsupervised.

Supervised ML algorithms as the name indicates have a supervisor as teacher. These algorithms apply learning from past data (or experiences) to new data using labeled examples.

> Supervised learning should be used when output of data in the training set is known.

Technically, supervised learning algorithms learn an association between input data and output. For example, if we have input variable(s) X and output variable (Y), then the mapping function from input to output can be given as, Y = f(x). This mapping function can be used to predict the output value for any new input after learning from the existing data.

Supervised learning algorithms start with analyzing a known training dataset, to produce an inferred function that can be used to predict future data values. The learning algorithm then compares the predicted output with actual output to find errors and modify the model accordingly.

For example, if you have a basket filled with different variety of fruits then the first step is to train the machine to identify a fruit. Now, our machine can easily identify an apple and a banana. Supervised learning algorithms can be further classified into two categories:

Classification algorithm: A classification algorithm classifies data into a particular group. Classification techniques predict discrete categories. The output will be based on what the model has learned in training phase – for example, classifying a fruit as either an apple or a banana.

In real world applications, classification can be used in medical imaging, speech recognition, hand-writing recognition, credit scoring, predicting if an incoming email is authentic or spam, or whether a tumor is cancerous or benign.

Classification algorithms are best used if data can be tagged, categorized, or separated into specific groups or classes. Commonly used classification algorithms include support vector machine (SVM), decision trees, *k*-nearest neighbor (KNN), Naïve Bayes, discriminant analysis, to name a few.

> In supervised learning, clear instructions are giving specifying what needs to be learnt and how it needs to be learnt.

Regression: A regression algorithm predicts a real value. The output value is based on what the model has learned in its training phase. In contrast to classification algorithms, regression predicts continuous values – for example, the cost of a product, the value of a stock, changes in temperature or fluctuations in power demand. Commonly used regression analysis algorithms include logistic regression, neural networks, etc.

Thus, in supervised ML algorithm, data input and desired output, along with a feedback about the accuracy of predictions during algorithm training are provided. Data scientists can select variables or features that can be used by the model to analyze data and make predictions. For example, supervised learning can be used by a company to identify customers who are likely to churn. It can also be used by insurance companies to predict the likelihood of occurrence of a mishap and determine the Total Insurance Value.

Unsupervised learning: Unsupervised learning trains the machine using information that is neither classified nor labeled. In this case, the ML algorithm works on that information without any guidance. The unsorted information is grouped based on similarities, patterns and differences without any prior training of data. For example, if we give an image of mango and an orange, then initially the machine has no idea about how a mango looks and how the orange looks (Figure 10.2).

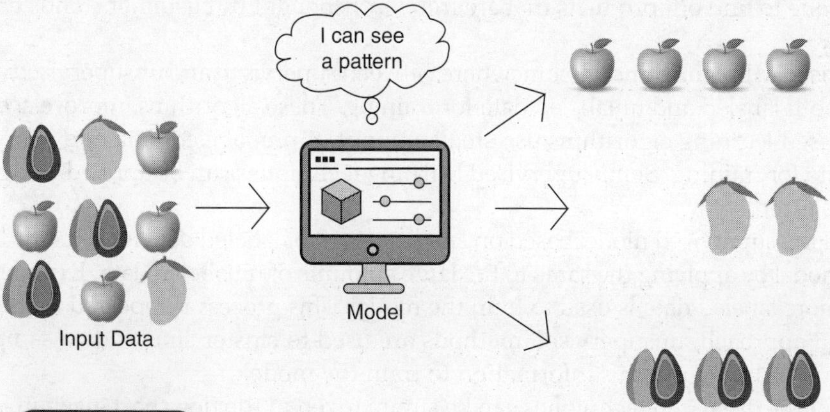

Figure 10.2 Unsupervised learning looks patterns in the absence of labels

Unsupervised ML algorithm learns through observation and finding structures in the data. That is, the model automatically finds patterns and relationships in the dataset by creating clusters in it. For example, if given a dataset of pictures of both mangoes and oranges, the algorithm can make two clusters – one containing only pictures of oranges and the other of mangoes. What an unsupervised ML cannot do is specifying labels to the clusters. That is, it can only segregate the pictures but cannot tell that this is a real-world orange and that is a mango.

Unsupervised learning can be categorized into two sets of algorithms:

- *Clustering:* In clustering, the aim is to discover inherent groupings in the data or discover hidden patterns. It is one of the most useful unsupervised ML techniques as it finds similarity as well as relationship in the underlying data. For example, a company may like to group its customers by their purchasing behavior, a cell phone company can use clustering to optimally decide the locations where they can build cell phone towers (these clusters can depict the number of people relying on their towers). Other applications include gene sequence analysis, market research, and object recognition. Commonly used clustering algorithms include k-means, k-medoids, hierarchical clustering, etc.
- *Association Analysis:* In association mining (or analysis), the aim is to discover rules that describe large portions of data. For example, a company can use association analysis to conclude that the customer who buys X also buys product Y.
- *Dimensionality Reduction:* It is used to reduce the number of feature variables for the data set. It is done by selecting a set of principal or representative features. Dimensionality reduction is very important technique especially when the data set has a large number (millions). Principal Component Analysis (PCA), KNN and discriminant analysis are some popular algorithms used for dimensionality reduction.
- *Anomaly Detection:* This technique is used to find out the occurrences of rare events or observations that generally do not occur. Application of learned knowledge in anomaly detection techniques helps to differentiate between anomalous or a normal data point. Generally, clustering (more specifically, KNN) is used to detect anomalies based in data.

Thus, unsupervised ML algorithms (also called neural networks) are used when the information used to train is neither classified nor labelled. These algorithms use an iterative approach called deep learning to review data and arrive at conclusions. Unsupervised learning algorithms are used for more complex tasks than supervised learning systems. For example, these algorithms are used in image recognition, speech-to-text and natural language processing applications, predicting the probability of presence of a particular disease, etc. A retailer can use unsupervised learning technique to find out products that are frequently bought by customers tends to be bought more frequently.

Semi-supervised ML algorithms fall somewhere between supervised and unsupervised algorithms, since they use both labeled and unlabeled data for training. These algorithms improve accuracy.

Semi-supervised learning algorithms use small amount of pre-labeled data and a large number of unlabeled data for training. Semi-supervised learning techniques can be applied using any of the two approaches given below.

First, to build the supervised model based on small amount of labeled data followed by building an unsupervised model by applying the same to the large amounts of unlabeled data. Experience gained by generating more labeled data is used to train the model. This process is repeated multiple times.

In the second approach, unsupervised methods are used to cluster similar data samples, annotate these groups and then use this information to train the model.

Application of the discussed techniques can be summarized in the flowchart given in Figure 10.3.

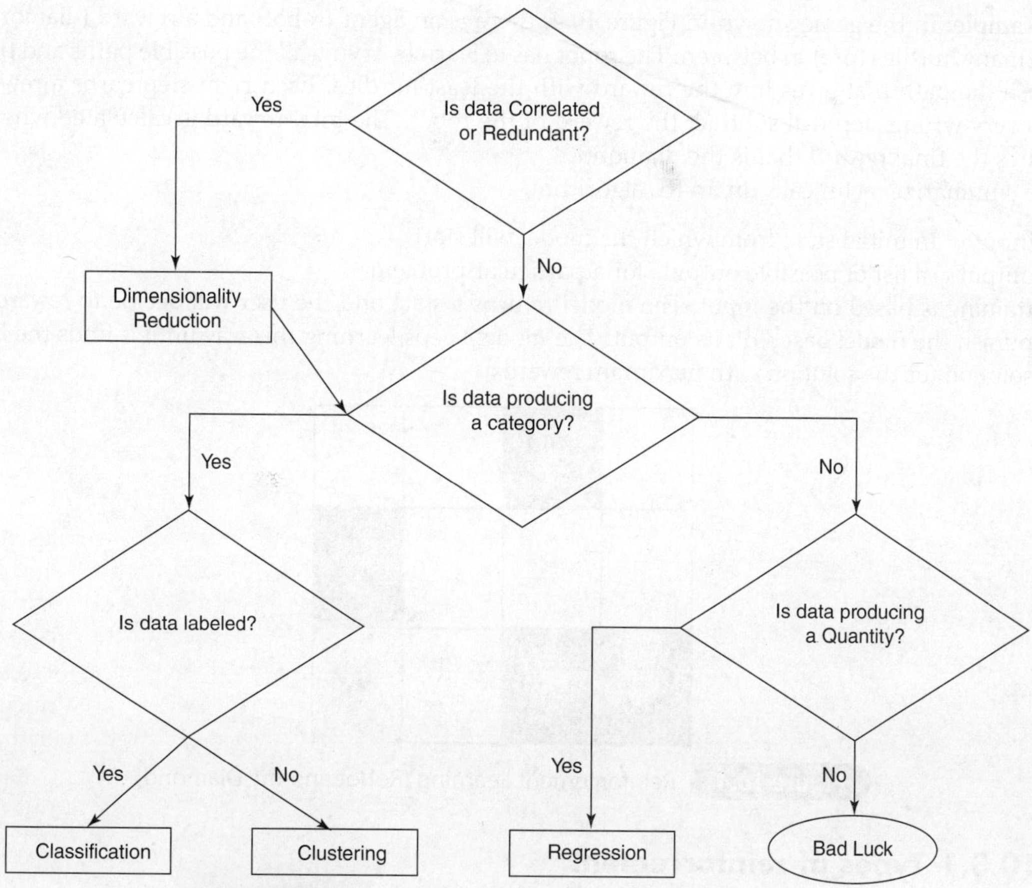

Figure 10.3 Techniques applicable in different scenarios

10.3 Reinforcement Learning (RL)

These techniques are different from the previously discussed techniques and are rarely used. In an RL algorithm, an agent is trained over a period of time so that it can interact with a specific environment.

Reinforcement learning is a type of dynamic programming that trains algorithms using a system of reward and punishment. The agent receives rewards by performing correctly and penalties for performing incorrectly. In this way, the agent learns without any human intervention to maximize its reward and minimize its penalty.

Since RL requires a lot of data, it is mostly used in areas where simulated data is readily available like gameplay, robotics, etc. In these areas, RL is used to find the best possible behavior or path that can be taken in a particular situation.

Reinforcement learning is different from supervised learning. In supervised learning, the training data has labels, so the model is trained with the correct answer; but in case of RL, the reinforcement agent decides what to do to perform the given task. In the absence of a training dataset, it is bound to learn from its own experience.

Example: In the game shown in Figure 10.4, there is an agent (robot) and a reward (diamond), with many hurdles (fire) in between. The robot has to learn by trying all the possible paths and then choose the path that gives him the reward with the least hurdles. Each right step earns a reward and every wrong step will subtract the reward of the robot. The total reward is calculated when it reaches the final reward that is the diamond.

To summarize technically, in an RL algorithm,

- input is an initial state from which the model will start.
- output is a list of possible outputs for a particular problem.
- training is based on the input. The model returns a state and the user will decide to reward or punish the model based on its output. The model keeps learning this way until it finds the best solution (or the solution with maximum rewards).

Figure 10.4 Reinforcement Learning (Robot and the Diamond)

10.3.1 Types of reinforcement

There are two types of reinforcement:

Positive Reinforcement has a positive effect on behavior. It occurs when a particular behavior increases the strength and the frequency of the behavior. Such reinforcement maximizes performance and sustains changes for a long period of time.

Negative Reinforcement is defined as strengthening a behavior by stopping or avoiding a negative condition.

10.3.2 Applications of reinforcement learning

Reinforcement Learning is used in large environments when a model of the environment is known, but an analytic solution is not available.

> RL agent perceives and interprets its environment, takes actions and learns through trial and error.

- It can be used in robotics for industrial automation.
- It is used to make machines learn.
- It is used in data-processing applications.
- It can be used to create training systems that provide custom instruction and materials according to the requirement of students.
- It is used for creating game playing software (playing chess).
- It is used in a self-driving car where the car (agent) interacts with its environment, receives a reward depending on how it performs, such as driving to destination safely. Similarly, the agent receives a penalty for performing incorrectly, such as going off the road or hitting a hurdle.

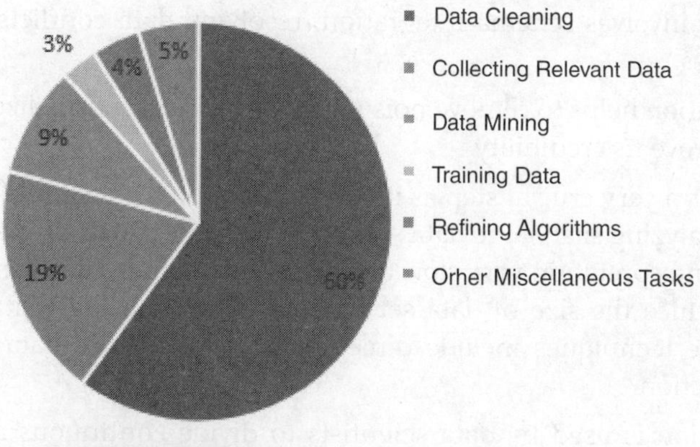

Figure 10.5 Time spent on data analysis task

10.4 Preparing data

The most important part of an ML algorithm is the data. Success of any ML model depends on the quality of data. Irrelevant, incorrect or incomplete data when fed to an ML algorithm will generate only useless results. We have learnt in junior classes that computer works on GIGO concept. That is, Garbage-In-Garbage-Out. Same is the case with ML. To get useful and accurate results we must feed right data i.e. the data in correct scale, format, containing meaningful features to solve the problem at hand. Therefore, the first step in any ML process is to prepare data.

Even CrowdFlower, surveyed about 80 data scientists to know how much time they spend on what activity. They finally came up with the results depicted in the pie chart (Figure 10.5). The survey also revealed that 57% of the data scientists consider cleaning activities boring and cumbersome and 19% of the data scientists found collecting datasets as the most mundane task.

For example, to analyze the log files of a website in finding the IP address of the spammers or to identify the demography from which the website is getting more sales, or to know in which geographic region is the website more popular, we need to know two main things – the number of hits made to the website and the IP address of the hit. But, the content of log files is not structured so we need to prepare the log data to extract data in the required format (IP address + Number of Hits) for analysis.

The amount of time to be dedicated for data preparation (also known as data wrangling, data munging, or data cleaning) depends on the quality of data available. That is, how complete it is, how many missing values are there, how clean it is and whether it is consistent or not.

10.4.1 Steps in preparing data

The entire process of preparing data for analysis can be divided into a number of steps including, Cleaning or Data Preparation.

1. **Data Cleaning:** The first step of data preparation is correcting inconsistent data by filling out missing values and removing outliers or noisy data (if any). Many-a-times, data sets do not have values for important variables, may contain inconsistent data or duplicate records or some other random error. All these factors result in low-quality data. Therefore, the first and foremost task is to mend this data to make it useful.

   To fill missing values, data scientists may either ignore the tuple or fill the mean/median value of the attribute or any global constant. Outliers are handled manually or by using regression or clustering techniques.

2. **Data Integration** involves schema integration, resolving data conflicts (if any) and handling data redundancies.
3. **Data Transformation** helps to remove noisy data (or outliers), normalize, aggregate and generalize data to improve its credibility.
4. **Data Reduction** is a very crucial step as it is very common for data sets these days to have size in peta bytes. Analyzing such large data sets not only makes analysis inefficient but also makes the task of data interpretation very slow and time consuming. Therefore, we must apply some techniques to reduce the size of data set without compromising the accuracy of the results of analysis. Some techniques include dimensionality reduction, data cube aggregation and numerosity reduction.
5. **Data Discretization** is used by data scientists to divide continuous attributes into discrete intervals. This also helps data scientists to reduce the size of data. Usually there are three types of attributes – continuous, nominal and ordinal. Some algorithms work only on categorical attributes. Therefore, data discretization is at times a necessary task that cannot be ignored.

Although many techniques and tools (like OpenRefine or GoogleRefine, DataCleaner) are already available for data preparation, automated data preparation is still a hot topic of research. Many researchers and data scientists are working together to explore better techniques to save data preparation time. International Data Corporation (IDC) predicted that by the end of 2020 the use of data preparation tools will grow 2.5 times faster than any other IT-controlled tool.

Once the data is thoroughly pre-processed, it can be further worked upon for better results. Some strategies required to make data more usable include:

Data Rescaling: Pre-processed data may contain attributes having values in different units or scales. For example, price of a product may be specified in dollars, rupees, yen, mark, euro or any other currency. But ML algorithms expect data to be in the same scale. So, we need to perform data scaling either by normalization or through standardization of data.

Normalization: Refers to rescaling of floating-point values into the range 0 to 1. It is also known as Min-Max scaling. This is even more important in algorithms in which input attributes for a model relies on the magnitude of values. For example, distance measures are used in KNN and in the preparation of coefficients in regression.

The formula used for normalization can be given as,

$$X' = \frac{X - X_{min}}{X_{max} - X_{min}}$$

where, X_{max} and X_{min} are the maximum and the minimum values of the feature, respectively.

- For very small values of X (approaching minimum value), the numerator will be 0, and hence X' is 0.
- For large values of X (approaching maximum value), the numerator is equal to the denominator and thus the value of X' is 1.
- For X between minimum and the maximum value, the value of X' is between 0 and 1.

Example: Normalizing the values of iris data set

```
# Normalize the data attributes for the Iris dataset.
from sklearn.datasets import load_iris
from sklearn import preprocessing
# load the iris dataset
iris = load_iris()
# separate the data from the target attributes
X = iris.data
y = iris.target
# normalize the data attributes
normalized_X = preprocessing.normalize(X)
print(normalized_X)
```

Normalization is mainly used in Sparse dataset that have many zero values. We can rescale such data using the help of Normalizer class of scikit-learn Python library. In ML, there are two types of normalization pre-processing techniques:

Ll Normalization: In this normalization technique, dataset values are modified in such a way that in each row the sum of the absolute values will always be up to 1. It is also called Least Absolute Deviations.

Example: Download the dataset from https://www.kaggle.com/uciml/pima-indians-diabetes-database and apply L1 normalization on the data values.

```
from pandas import read_csv
from numpy import set_printoptions
from sklearn.preprocessing import Normalizer
path = r"diabetes.csv"
data = read_csv(path)
names = ['preg', 'plas', 'pres', 'skin', 'test', 'mass', 'pedi', 'age', 'class']
array = data.values
Data_normalizer = Normalizer(norm='l1').fit(array)
Data_normalized = Data_normalizer.transform(array)
print ("\nNormalized data:\n", Data_normalized [0:3])

OUTPUT
Normalized data:
 [[1.73296710e-02 4.27465218e-01 2.07956052e-01 1.01089747e-01
  0.00000000e+00 9.70461576e-02 1.81095062e-03 1.44413925e-01
  2.88827850e-03]
[4.18495842e-03 3.55721466e-01 2.76207256e-01 1.21363794e-01
  0.00000000e+00 1.11319894e-01 1.46892041e-03 1.29733711e-01
  0.00000000e+00]
 [2.56433270e-02 5.86591104e-01 2.05146616e-01 0.00000000e+00
  0.00000000e+00 7.46861898e-02 2.15403947e-03 1.02573308e-01
  3.20541587e-03]
```

L2 Normalization: It is a normalization technique that modifies the dataset values in such a way that in each row the sum of the squares will always be up to 1. It is also called least squares.

Example: Read the diabetes.csv and perform L2 normalization on the data set values.

```
from pandas import read_csv
from numpy import set_printoptions
from sklearn.preprocessing import Normalizer
path = r"diabetes.csv"
data = read_csv(path)
names = ['preg', 'plas', 'pres', 'skin', 'test', 'mass', 'pedi', 'age', 'class']
array = data.values
Data_normalizer = Normalizer(norm='l2').fit(array)
Data_normalized = Data_normalizer.transform(array)
print ("\nNormalized data:\n", Data_normalized [0:3])
```

OUTPUT

```
Normalized data:
 [[0.03355185 0.82761219 0.40262215 0.1957191  0.         0.18789033
  0.00350617 0.27959871 0.00559197]
 [0.008424   0.71604034 0.55598426 0.24429612 0.         0.22407851
  0.00295683 0.26114412 0.        ]
 [0.04039717 0.9240852  0.32317734 0.         0.         0.11765675
  0.00339336 0.16158867 0.00504965]]
```

Data Standardization: Standardization means shifting the distribution of each attribute in such a way that it has a mean value zero and a standard deviation of one (unit variance). It is especially useful in Gaussian processes which require attributes to have standardized values.

Example: Standardize the attributes of Flowers Dataset.

```
# Normalize the data attributes for the Iris dataset.
from sklearn.datasets import load_iris
from sklearn import preprocessing
# load the iris dataset
iris = load_iris()
print(iris.data.shape)

# separate the data from the target attributes
X = iris.data
y = iris.target
# normalize the data attributes
normalized_X = preprocessing.scale(X)
print(normalized_X)
```

> It is a good programming practice to rescale data before training an ML algorithm. With rescaling, data units are eliminated, allowing you to easily compare data from different locations.

Data scaling: Also known as feature scaling is also very important when values of each feature in a dataset vary between random values. In such cases, we need to scale values to make it possible to compare identical variables belonging to different distributions and different variables. To scale data, we increase or decrease the magnitude of data.

Generally, the min-max method is used to get all of the scaled data in the range [0, 1]. The formula used to scale data with min-max method is same as that used for normalization,

$$x_{\text{scaled}} = \frac{x - x_{\min}}{x_{\max} - x_{\min}}$$

The above formula scale features between a given minimum and maximum value (here, between 0 and 1) so that the maximum absolute value of each feature is scaled to unit size. This can be done by using the pre-processing MinMaxScaler() function as shown below.

First define a `data_scaler` variable by writing,

```
data_scaler = preprocessing.MinMaxScaler(feature_range=(0, 1))
```

Now using the fit_transform() method, fit the data and then transform it as given below.

```
data_scaled = data_scaler.fit_transform(data)
```

The method returns a NumPy array of a specific shape.

For example, if data has minimum and maximum of each column in the array, it is given as

```
Min: [ 0. -1.5 -1.9 -5.4]
Max: [3. 4. 2. 2.1]
```

Note that this can be done by printing values for data.min(axis=0) and data.max(axis=0).

When we scale the data by writing data_scaled.min(axis=0), the result would be Min: [0. 0. 0. 0.]. Similarly, data by writing data_scaled.max(axis=0), the result would be Max: [1. 1. 1. 1.]

So, the best thing is to scale values between min and max so that all the feature values range between the specified values.

Though scaling is not mandatory, one must perform it to remove any disparities in data and improve the performance of ML algorithm.

> Scaling changes the size of data but does not affect the shape of the data.

Centering: It is another technique used for feature scaling especially when predicting data. For example, in linear modeling (discussed in later chapters), the intercept repr esents the estimate of the target when all predictors are at their mean value. This means that at x = 0, the predictor value will be equal to the intercept. In some situations, this is not used for the best interpretation. Like, if we use Marks obtained in Math to predict Marks obtained in Physics, then supposing that a student didn't give Math exam due to personal reasons and got 0 does not mean that his performance in Physics will be same as intercept (which may even be a negative value).

$$X_{\text{std}} = \frac{X - \overline{X}}{s_X}$$

Standardization: The most common method of scaling is standardization. To standardize a data set, we first center the data values and then divide them by the standard deviation to ensure that the standard deviation of the variable is one.

Standardizing data in this way helps the data scientist by,

- ❑ treating intercepts as the estimate when all predictors are at their mean value.
- ❑ having both coefficients and standard deviations of the original predictors of the same unit. This thereby helps data scientists to compare the magnitude of impact between different predictors.

- having more stable and faster optimization techniques.
- not bearing the overhead of regularization penalties where the magnitude of coefficients for different predictors do not have the same meaning.
- having the ease of applying KNN algorithm when features contribute equally (these models use the distance between observations calculated from the features).
- ease of applying the K-means clustering algorithm, as this algorithm is affected by the scale of the data and standardizing the features will prevent variables from dominating due to varying scales.
- ease of applying logistic regression, neural networks, and SVMs algorithms as scaled and standardized data can remove the disproportionate effect of some data points over others.

Example: Standardize the values in the iris data set

```
# Normalize the data attributes for the Iris dataset.
from sklearn.datasets import load_iris
from sklearn.preprocessing import StandardScaler
# load the iris dataset
iris = load_iris()
print(iris.data.shape)
X = iris.data
# initialize the scaler
ss = StandardScaler()
# Fit the data using scalar
Xstd = ss.fit_transform(X)
print(Xstd.mean())

OUTPUT
(150, 4)
-1.4684549872375404e-15
```

ML algorithms like gradient descent and KNN require scaled data.

Standardization transforms the data attributes with a Gaussian distribution. It differs the mean and Standard Deviation to a standard Gaussian distribution with a mean of 0 and an SD of 1.

10.4.2 Benefits of data standardization

Generally, standardization is preferred over min-max normalization. However, there are some applications where min-max scaling is more preferred.

- Neural networks prefer to have input data in the range 0 to 1.
- In some images, that require pixels to take only a specific range of RGB values, data may have to be normalized.

10.5 Binarization

As the name suggests, binarization is used to convert our data into binary values. For this, we take a binary threshold. Values above the threshold value are converted to 1. Correspondingly, values below that threshold are written as 0. For example, if threshold = 0.5, then all data values above 0.5 will become 1 and all values below this will become 0; hence, the name. Binarizing data is also known as thresholding the data. This technique is useful when we have probabilities in our dataset and want to convert them into concrete values. The scikit-learn Python library has Binarizer class to binarize the data.

Example: Program to binarize data in diabetes.csv file with a threshold value = 0.5.

```
from pandas import read_csv
from numpy import set_printoptions
from sklearn.preprocessing import Binarizer
path = r"diabetes.csv"
data = read_csv(path)
names = ['preg', 'plas', 'pres', 'skin', 'test', 'mass', 'pedi', 'age', 'class']
array = data.values
binarizer = Binarizer(threshold=0.5).fit(array)
Data_binarized = binarizer.transform(array)
print ("\nBinary data:\n", Data_binarized [0:5])

OUTPUT
Binary data:
 [[1. 1. 1. 1. 0. 1. 1. 1. 1.]
 [1. 1. 1. 1. 0. 1. 0. 1. 0.]
 [1. 1. 1. 0. 0. 1. 1. 1. 1.]
 [1. 1. 1. 1. 1. 1. 0. 1. 0.]
 [0. 1. 1. 1. 1. 1. 1. 1. 1.]]
```

10.6 Data labeling

Another important technique that is often used before applying ML program is data labeling. This is especially useful in classification problems, where a number of labels (textual or numeric) are available with the data.

Most of the scikit-learn functions expect data to have numeric labels rather than textual labels. Therefore, we need to convert all textual labels into numeric labels. This process is called label encoding. In Python, label encoding of data is performed using the LabelEncoder() function of scikit-learn Python library.

Example: Program to demonstrate label encoding

```
import numpy as np
from sklearn import preprocessing
input_labels = ['justice','patience','justice','truth','patience',
'loyalty','perseverance']
encoder = preprocessing.LabelEncoder()
encoder.fit(input_labels)
test_labels = ['truth','justice','patience','loyalty']
encoded_values = encoder.transform(test_labels)
print("\nLabels =", test_labels)
print("Encoded values =", list(encoded_values))
encoded_values = [2,0,4,3]
decoded_list = encoder.inverse_transform(encoded_values)
print("\nEncoded values =", encoded_values)
print("\nDecoded labels =", list(decoded_list))
```

```
OUTPUT
Labels = ['truth', 'justice', 'patience', 'loyalty']
Encoded values = [4, 0, 2, 1]
Encoded values = [2, 0, 4, 3]
Decoded labels = ['patience', 'justice', 'truth', 'perseverance']
```

10.7 Data feature selection

The performance of any ML model directly depends on data features (or attribute features) that are used to train that model. Selecting all features or irrelevant features for training the model will negatively affect the performance of the ML model. On the contrary, selecting relevant data features increases the accuracy of model, especially in case of linear and logistic regression.

Python is a very strong programming language. It facilitates users to automatically select relevant features from the data set. Relevant features are the features in the data that are most relevant to the output or for predicting value(s) for another variable.

Advantages:
Benefits of automatic feature selection before executing the ML model include:

- Overfitting issues get reduced
- Increased accuracy of ML model.
- Reduced times to train the ML model.

10.7.1 Feature selection techniques

Python uses the following techniques for automatic feature selection that can be used in an ML model.

Univariate Selection: Univariate Selection selects relevant features using statistical testing. The features having strongest relationship with the prediction variables are selected as the most relevant features. SelectKBest0 class of scikit-learn Python library are used to implement univariate feature selection technique.

Example: Program to select four best features from the diabetes.csv data set using the chi-square statistical test.

```
from pandas import read_csv
from numpy import set_printoptions
from sklearn.feature_selection import SelectKBest
from sklearn.feature_selection import chi2
path = r"diabetes.csv"
data = read_csv(path)
names = ['preg', 'plas', 'pres', 'skin', 'test', 'mass', 'pedi', 'age', 'class']
array = data.values
# separate array into input and output components
X = array[:,0:8]
Y = array[:,8]
test = SelectKBest(score_func=chi2, k=4)
```

```
fit = test.fit(X,Y)
set_printoptions(precision=2)
print(fit.scores_)

OUTPUT
[ 111.52   1411.89   17.61   53.11   2175.57  127.67   5.39  181.3 ]
```

Recursive Feature Elimination (RFE): RFE technique removes the attributes recursively and builds the model with remaining attributes. The RFE class of scikit-learn Python library is used to implement RFE feature selection technique in Python.

Example: Program to select three best features from the diabetes.csv data set using RFE with logistic regression algorithm.

```
from pandas import read_csv
from sklearn.feature_selection import RFE
from sklearn.linear_model import LogisticRegression
path = r"diabetes.csv"
data = read_csv(path)
names = ['preg', 'plas', 'pres', 'skin', 'test', 'mass', 'pedi', 'age', 'class']
array = data.values
# separate array into input and output components
X = array[:,0:8]
Y = array[:,8]
model = LogisticRegression(max_iter=1000)
rfe = RFE(model,  n_features_to_select=4)
fit = rfe.fit(X, Y)
print("Num Features: %s" % (fit.n_features_))
print("Selected Features: %s" % (fit.support_))
print("Feature Ranking: %s" % (fit.ranking_))

OUTPUT
Num Features: 4
Selected Features: [ True  True False False False  True  True False]
Feature Ranking: [1 1 3 5 4 1 1 2]
```

From the output, we can conclude that RFE chooses preg, plas, mass and pedi as the first four best features. They are marked as 1 in the output.

Principal Component Analysis (PCA): PCA is a data reduction technique, which selects number of principal components (or features) in the output using linear algebra to transform the dataset into a compressed form. PCA feature selection technique is implemented with PCA class of scikit-learn Python library.

Example: Program to demonstrate PCA feature selection technique on diabetes.csv dataset.

```
from pandas import read_csv
from sklearn.decomposition import PCA
path = r"diabetes.csv"
data = read_csv(path)
names = ['preg', 'plas', 'pres', 'skin', 'test', 'mass', 'pedi', 'age', 'class']
array = data.values
```

```
# separate array into input and output components
X = array[:,0:8]
Y = array[:,8]
pca = PCA(n_components=3)
fit = pca.fit(X)
print("Explained Variance: %s" % fit.explained_variance_ratio_)
# To print all the components, write, print(fit.components_)

OUTPUT
Explained Variance: [0.88854663 0.06159078 0.02579012]
```

Feature Importance: This technique is used to select important features by using a trained supervised classifier. In Python, this is done with the ExtraTreeClassifier class of scikit-learn library.

Example: Program to use ExtraTreeClassifier to select features from the diabetes.csv dataset.

```
from pandas import read_csv
from sklearn.ensemble import ExtraTreesClassifier()
path = r"diabetes.csv"
data = read_csv(path)
names = ['preg', 'plas', 'pres', 'skin', 'test', 'mass', 'pedi', 'age', 'class']
array = data.values
# separate array into input and output components
X = array[:,0:8]
Y = array[:,8]
model = ExtraTreesClassifier()
model.fit(X, Y)
print(model.feature_importances_)

OUTPUT
[0.1075765  0.23331297 0.09862073 0.08091481 0.07459248 0.14372739
 0.11620097 0.14505416]
```

In the output, we see that there are scores for each attribute. Higher the score, higher is the importance of that attribute.

10.8 Detecting and correcting outlier

In statistics, an outlier is defined as an observation or a data-point that is distant from other observations. For example, if in a data set of 100 observations, majority has a value between 75 and 100, and 5 observations have values less than 30, then these 5 observations are treated as outliers. These outliers can be a result of a mistake during data collection or it can be just an indication of variance in your data.

Outlier detection algorithms are extremely useful in real-world applications that work on large data sets as they help to perform pattern recognition. Applications like fraud detection in finance and intrusion detection in network security makes maximum use of outlier detection techniques.

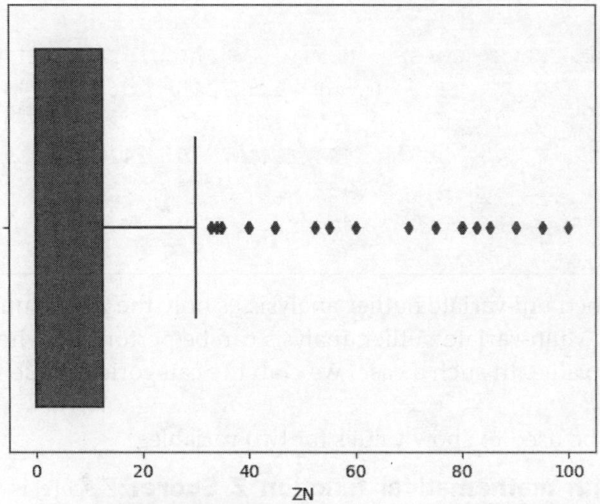

Figure 10.6 Identifying Outliers

10.8.1 Finding outliers

In a small data set outlier's identification is still fine, but for large data sets having thousands of rows and hundreds of columns, it is just impossible to find even a single outlier.

To make our work of discovering outliers easy, there are multiple techniques and easiest of them is through visualization. In this section, we have used the Boston data set for analyzing and treating outliers. The data set has numerical values.

Basically, there are two types of outlier analysis – Uni-variate (one variable outlier analysis) and Multi-variate (two or more variable outlier analysis). We will read about both the analyses in this section.

Discover outliers with box plot: In descriptive statistics, a box plot is a method for graphically representing numerical data through their quartiles. Lines extending vertically or horizontally from the boxes indicate variability outside the upper and lower quartiles. In this diagram (Figure 10.6), outliers are plotted as individual points while other observations are grouped together and displayed as boxes.

```
from sklearn.datasets import load_boston
import pandas as pd
from matplotlib import pyplot as plt
import seaborn as sns
boston = load_boston()
x = boston.data
y = boston.target
columns = boston.feature_names#create
the dataframe
boston_df = pd.DataFrame(boston.data)
boston_df.columns = columns
print(boston_df.head())
sns.boxplot(x=boston_df['ZN'])
plt.show()
```

> An outlier is a data point in a data set that is distant from all other observations.

OUTPUT

	CRIM	ZN	INDUS	CHAS	NOX	...	RAD	TAX	PTRATIO	B	LSTAT
0	0.00632	18.0	2.31	0.0	0.538	...	1.0	296.0	15.3	396.90	4.98
1	0.02731	0.0	7.07	0.0	0.469	...	2.0	242.0	17.8	396.90	9.14
2	0.02729	0.0	7.07	0.0	0.469	...	2.0	242.0	17.8	392.83	4.03
3	0.03237	0.0	2.18	0.0	0.458	...	3.0	222.0	18.7	394.63	2.94
4	0.06905	0.0	2.18	0.0	0.458	...	3.0	222.0	18.7	396.90	5.33

[5 rows x 13 columns]

The above code performed uni-variate outlier analysis as only the ZN column was checked for the presence of any outlier. Multi-variate outlier analysis can be performed when we have to check for outliers in a categorical value. In such a case, we club the categorical value with a numerical value or continuous value.

Scatter plot can also be used to show values for two variables.

Discover outliers with mathematical function Z-Score: *Z-score* is the signed number of standard deviations by which the value of an observation or data point is above the mean value of what is being observed or measured.

Z-score is generally used to describe any data point by finding its relationship with the Standard Deviation and Mean of the group of data points. Z-score usually finds distribution of data where mean is 0 and standard deviation is 1 (i.e. normal distribution).

Z-score can be re-scaled and data can be centered so that data points which are too far from zero can be easily identified as outliers. Usually, a threshold of +3 or –3 is used. This means that Z-score value greater than +3 or less than –3 is identified as outliers.

We can also see this graphically (Figure 10.7). Z-score also called standard score is used to understand if a data value is greater than or smaller than mean and how far away it is from the mean. That is, it tells us how many standard deviations away a data point is from the mean.

Z score = (x – mean) / std deviation

A normal distribution shown below indicates that,

68% of the data points lie between +/– 1 standard deviation.
95% of the data points lie between +/– 2 standard deviation
99.7% of the data points lie between +/– 3 standard deviation

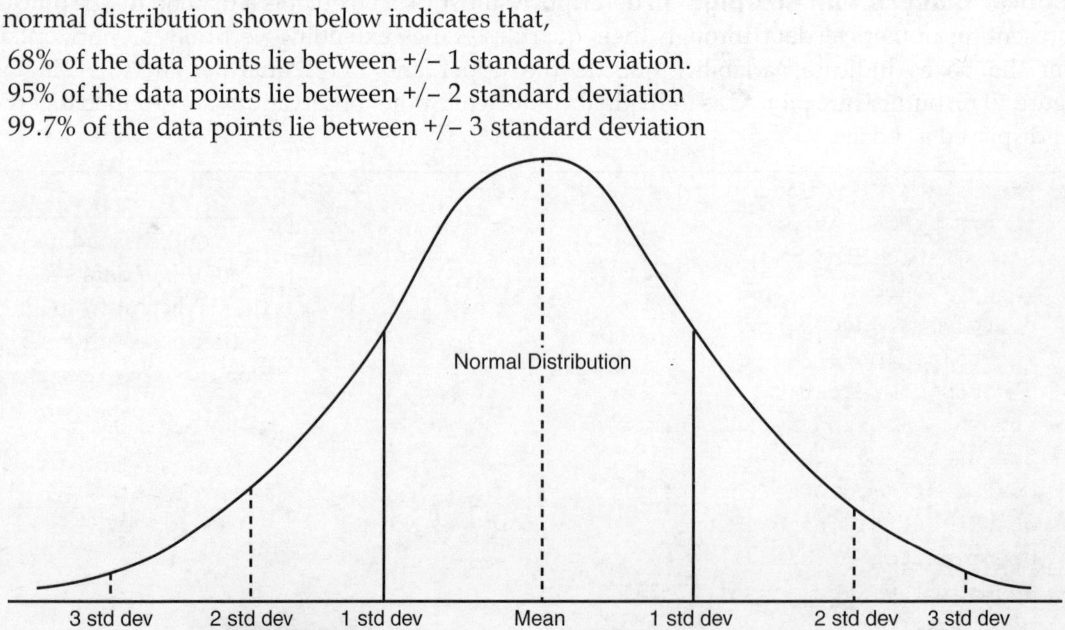

Figure 10.7 Spread of Data Points in a Normal Distribution

Example: Write a code to detect outliers in Boston data set using z-score technique.

```
from sklearn.datasets import load_boston
import pandas as pd
from matplotlib import pyplot as plt
import seaborn as sns
boston = load_boston()
print(boston)
x = boston.data
y = boston.target
columns = boston.feature_names#create the dataframe
boston_df = pd.DataFrame(boston.data)
from scipy import stats
import numpy as np
z = np.abs(stats.zscore(boston_df))
print(z)

SAMPLE OUTPUT
[[0.41978194 0.28482986 1.2879095  ... 1.45900038 0.44105193 1.0755623 ]
 [0.41733926 0.48772236 0.59338101 ... 0.30309415 0.44105193 0.49243937]
 [0.41734159 0.48772236 0.59338101 ... 0.30309415 0.39642699 1.2087274 ]
 ...
 [0.41344658 0.48772236 0.11573841 ... 1.17646583 0.44105193 0.98304761]
 [0.40776407 0.48772236 0.11573841 ... 1.17646583 0.4032249  0.86530163]
 [0.41500016 0.48772236 0.11573841 ... 1.17646583 0.44105193 0.66905833]]
```

In the above code, we have used the Z-score function defined in the SciPy library to identify the outliers. However, from the above output, it is difficult to detect outliers, so we can even use threshold values to do the same.

Example: Identifying outliers using threshold values from the Boston data set.

```
from sklearn.datasets import load_boston
import pandas as pd
from matplotlib import pyplot as plt
import seaborn as sns
import numpy as np
boston = load_boston()
print(boston)
x = boston.data
y = boston.target
columns = boston.feature_names#create the dataframe
boston_df = pd.DataFrame(boston.data)
from scipy import stats
import numpy as np
z = np.abs(stats.zscore(boston_df))
#defining threshold
threshold = 3
print(np.where(z > 3))
```

```
SAMPLE OUTPUT
(array([ 55,  56,  57, 102, 141, 142, 152, 154, 155, 160, 162, 163, 199,
       200, 201, 202, 203, 204, 208, 209, 210, 211, 212, 216, 218, 219,
       220, 221, 222, 225, 234, 236, 256, 257, 262, 269, 273, 274, 276,
       277, 282, 283, 283, 284, 347, 351, 352, 353, 353, 354, 355, 356,
       357, 358, 363, 364, 364, 365, 367, 369, 370, 372, 373, 374, 374,
       380, 398, 404, 405, 406, 410, 410, 411, 412, 412, 414, 414, 415,
       416, 418, 418, 419, 423, 424, 425, 426, 427, 427, 429, 431, 436,
       437, 438, 445, 450, 454, 455, 456, 457, 466], dtype=int32), array([
 1,  1,  1, 11, 12,  3,  3,  3,  3,  3,  3,  3,  1,  1,  1,  1,  1,
        1,  3,  3,  3,  3,  3,  3,  3,  3,  3,  3,  3,  5,  3,  3,  1,  5,
        5,  3,  3,  3,  3,  3,  3,  1,  3,  1,  1,  7,  7,  1,  7,  7,  7,
        3,  3,  3,  3,  3,  5,  5,  5,  3,  3,  3, 12,  5, 12,  0,  0,  0,
        0,  5,  0, 11, 11, 11, 12,  0, 12, 11, 11,  0, 11, 11, 11, 11, 11,
       11,  0, 11, 11, 11, 11, 11, 11, 11, 11, 11, 11, 11, 11, 11],
      dtype=int32))
```

In the above output, the first array contains the list of row numbers and the second array contains the respective column numbers, which means, z[55][1] have a Z-score higher than 3. This is to say that, the data point – 55th record on column ZN is an outlier. In the code, data points that fall outside of 3 standard deviations are treated as outliers.

Detecting Outliers using IQR score: We have seen that a Box plot uses interquartile range (IQR) to display data and outliers. Now, to get a list of identified outliers, we will use the mathematical formula of IQR.

The IQR, also called the midspread or middle 50%, is a measure of statistical dispersion. Its value is equal to the difference between the 75th and 25th percentiles. This can also be expressed as, IQR = $Q3 - Q1$, where, Q3 and Q1 are upper and lower quartiles (Figure 10.8).

Though IQR is a measure of the dispersion similar to standard deviation or variance, it is much more robust against outliers. Like Z-score, IQR also finds the distribution of data and identifies outliers by using some threshold.

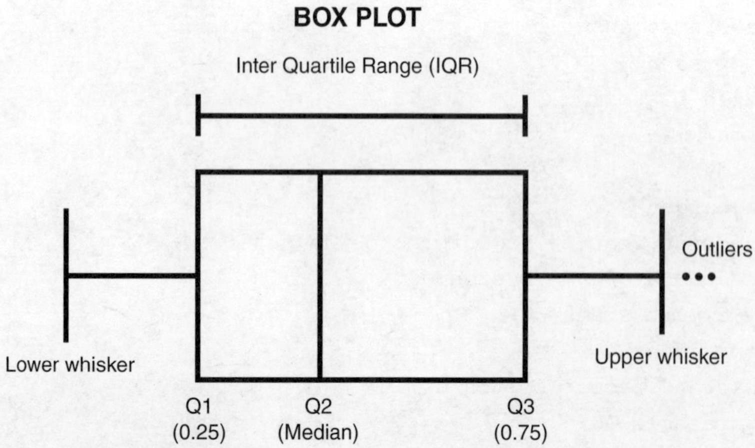

Figure 10.8 A boxplot to identify outliers accurately

Example: Detecting outliers using IQR

```
from sklearn.datasets import load_boston
import pandas as pd
from matplotlib import pyplot as plt
import seaborn as sns
boston = load_boston()
print(boston)
x = boston.data
y = boston.target
columns = boston.feature_names#create the dataframe
boston_df = pd.DataFrame(boston.data)
Q1 = boston_df.quantile(0.25)
Q3 = boston_df.quantile(0.75)
IQR = Q3 - Q1
# to print IQR of each column
print(IQR)
# to detect outliers
print(boston_df < (Q1 - 1.5 * IQR)) |(boston_df > (Q3 + 1.5 * IQR))

OUTPUT
0       3.595038
1      12.500000
2      12.910000
3       0.000000
4       0.175000
5       0.738000
6      49.050000
7       3.088250
8      20.000000
9     387.000000
10      2.800000
11     20.847500
12     10.005000
dtype: float64
         0      1      2      3      4  ...      8      9     10     11     12
0    False  False  False  False  False  ...  False  False  False  False  False
1    False  False  False  False  False  ...  False  False  False  False  False
2    False  False  False  False  False  ...  False  False  False  False  False
3    False  False  False  False  False  ...  False  False  False  False  False
4    False  False  False  False  False  ...  False  False  False  False  False
..     ...    ...    ...    ...    ...  ...    ...    ...    ...    ...    ...
501  False  False  False  False  False  ...  False  False  False  False  False
502  False  False  False  False  False  ...  False  False  False  False  False
503  False  False  False  False  False  ...  False  False  False  False  False
504  False  False  False  False  False  ...  False  False  False  False  False
505  False  False  False  False  False  ...  False  False  False  False  False
[506 rows x 13 columns]
```

In the above output, we see that the data point with a False indicates a valid value and that with a True signifies an outlier.

Identifying Outliers with Skewness: In later chapters, we will see that many ML algorithms assume that the input data follows a normal (or Gaussian) distribution. We can easily check this by carefully observing the *skewness value*. The skewness value explains the extent to which the data is normally distributed. Ideally, it should vary from –1 and +1. Any major deviation from this range indicates the presence of extreme values.

Example: Checking skewness in the third column of Boston data set.

```
from sklearn.datasets import load_boston
import pandas as pd
from matplotlib import pyplot as plt
import seaborn as sns
boston = load_boston()
print(boston)
x = boston.data
y = boston.target
columns = boston.feature_names#create the dataframe
boston_df = pd.DataFrame(boston.data)
print(boston_df.head())
print(boston_df[2].skew())

OUTPUT
         0     1     2    3      4  ...    8      9    10      11    12
0  0.00632  18.0  2.31  0.0  0.538  ...  1.0  296.0  15.3  396.90  4.98
1  0.02731   0.0  7.07  0.0  0.469  ...  2.0  242.0  17.8  396.90  9.14
2  0.02729   0.0  7.07  0.0  0.469  ...  2.0  242.0  17.8  392.83  4.03
3  0.03237   0.0  2.18  0.0  0.458  ...  3.0  222.0  18.7  394.63  2.94
4  0.06905   0.0  2.18  0.0  0.458  ...  3.0  222.0  18.7  396.90  5.33
[5 rows x 13 columns]
0.29502156787351164
```

The skewness value of 6.5 shows that the variable 'Income' has a right-skewed distribution, indicating the presence of extreme higher values. The maximum 'Income' value of USD 108,000 proves this point.

10.8.2 Correcting and removing outliers

During data analysis, if we find outliers in the data, then one of the most difficult decisions would be to remove the outlier or to correct it.

To remove an outlier, we can use the Z-score technique or the IQR technique as given below.

Using Z-score: Writing just a single line of code will remove the outliers in the Boston data set that we have been using so far.

```
boston_df_final = boston_df[(z < 3).all(axis=1)]
```

This line of code will remove around 90+ rows from the dataset to clean the data set by wiping out all outliers.

Example: Removing Outliers using Z-score

```
from sklearn.datasets import load_boston
import pandas as pd
from matplotlib import pyplot as plt
import seaborn as sns
from scipy import stats
import numpy as np
boston = load_boston()
print(boston)
boston_df = pd.DataFrame(boston.data)
x = boston.data
y = boston.target
columns = boston.feature_names#create the dataframe
z = np.abs(stats.zscore(boston_df))
boston_df_final = boston_df[(z < 3).all(axis=1)]
print(boston_df_final.head())

OUTPUT
         0     1     2    3      4  ...    8      9    10      11    12
0  0.00632  18.0  2.31  0.0  0.538  ...  1.0  296.0  15.3  396.90  4.98
1  0.02731   0.0  7.07  0.0  0.469  ...  2.0  242.0  17.8  396.90  9.14
2  0.02729   0.0  7.07  0.0  0.469  ...  2.0  242.0  17.8  392.83  4.03
3  0.03237   0.0  2.18  0.0  0.458  ...  3.0  222.0  18.7  394.63  2.94
4  0.06905   0.0  2.18  0.0  0.458  ...  3.0  222.0  18.7  396.90  5.33
[5 rows x 13 columns]
```

Using IQR Score: The IQR score can also be used to filter out the outliers by keeping only valid values. The following line of code removes outliers from the Boston data set. You can also print the shape of the boston_df_out to confirm the number of rows and columns after dropping the outliers.

```
boston_df_out = boston_df[~((boston_df < (Q1 - 1.5 * IQR)) |(boston_df >
(Q3 + 1.5 * IQR))).any(axis=1)]
```

Here, the rule of thumb is that anything not in the range of (*Q1 – 1.5* IQR) and (*Q3* + 1.5 IQR) is an outlier, and can therefore be removed from the data set.

Example: Removing Outliers using IQR technique

```
from sklearn.datasets import load_boston
import pandas as pd
from matplotlib import pyplot as plt
import seaborn as sns
from scipy import stats
import numpy as np
boston = load_boston()
print(boston)
boston_df = pd.DataFrame(boston.data)
x = boston.data
y = boston.target
```

```
columns = boston.feature_names#create the dataframe
Q1 = boston_df.quantile(0.25)
Q3 = boston_df.quantile(0.75)
IQR = Q3 - Q1
boston_df_out = boston_df[~((boston_df < (Q1 - 1.5 * IQR)) |(boston_df >
(Q3 + 1.5 * IQR))).any(axis=1)]
print(boston_df_out.head())

OUTPUT
         0     1     2    3      4  ...    8      9    10      11    12
0  0.00632  18.0  2.31  0.0  0.538  ...  1.0  296.0  15.3  396.90  4.98
1  0.02731   0.0  7.07  0.0  0.469  ...  2.0  242.0  17.8  396.90  9.14
2  0.02729   0.0  7.07  0.0  0.469  ...  2.0  242.0  17.8  392.83  4.03
3  0.03237   0.0  2.18  0.0  0.458  ...  3.0  222.0  18.7  394.63  2.94
4  0.06905   0.0  2.18  0.0  0.458  ...  3.0  222.0  18.7  396.90  5.33
[5 rows x 13 columns]
```

Quantile-based Flooring and Capping: In this technique, flooring and capping is done to overwrite the outlier values with other values like the 10th and 90th percentile for lower and higher quantiles, respectively. Flooring is done for the lower values and capping is done for the higher values.

Example: Use quantile-based flooring and capping to remove outliers.

```
from sklearn.datasets import load_boston
import pandas as pd
from matplotlib import pyplot as plt
import seaborn as sns
import numpy as np
boston = load_boston()
print(boston)
x = boston.data
y = boston.target
columns = boston.feature_names#create the dataframe
boston_df = pd.DataFrame(boston.data)
print("10th Quantile = ",boston_df[2].quantile(0.10))
print("90th Quantile = ",boston_df[2].quantile(0.90))
# Overwritting outlier values
boston_df[2] = np.where(boston_df[2] <2.91, 2.91,boston_df[2])
boston_df[2] = np.where(boston_df[2] >19.58, 19.58,boston_df[2])
# Checking skewness
print(boston_df[2].skew())

OUTPUT
10th Quantile =  2.91
90th Quantile =  19.58
0.16143812314655426
```

Trimming: In this technique, data points that are identified as outliers are removed from the dataset. For example, in the second column of the data set any value less than 1 and greater than 25 is removed. This is done by first creating an index for all such data points and then these index rows are dropped from the data. Finally, we print summary statistics for the variable. Now, the data set has only acceptable values.

```
from sklearn.datasets import load_boston
import pandas as pd
from matplotlib import pyplot as plt
import seaborn as sns
import numpy as np
boston = load_boston()
print(boston)
x = boston.data
y = boston.target
columns = boston.feature_names#create the dataframe
boston_df = pd.DataFrame(boston.data)
index = boston_df[(boston_df[2] >= 25)|(boston_df[2] <= 1)].index
boston_df.drop(index, inplace=True)
print(boston_df[2].describe())

OUTPUT
count    492.000000
mean      10.804390
std        6.483306
min        1.210000
25%        5.130000
50%        8.560000
75%       18.100000
max       21.890000
Name: 2, dtype: float64
```

Log Transformation: We can transform skewed variables to correct the distribution of variables. These could be logarithmic, square root, or square transformations. The most common is the logarithmic transformation. The code given below transforms the variable using logarithmic transformation.

Example: Improve skewness of data using log transformation

```
from sklearn.datasets import load_boston
import pandas as pd
from matplotlib import pyplot as plt
import seaborn as sns
import numpy as np
boston = load_boston()
print(boston)
x = boston.data
y = boston.target
```

```
columns = boston.feature_names#create the dataframe
boston_df = pd.DataFrame(boston.data)
boston_df["Log_2"] = boston_df[2].map(lambda i: np.log(i) if i > 0 else 0)
print(boston_df[2].skew())
print(boston_df["Log_2"].skew())

OUTPUT
0.29502156787351164
-0.6431257054895457
```

The above output shows that the skewness value has drastically reduced from 0.29 to –0.64 thereby treating the distribution for extreme values.

Replacing Outliers with Median Values: We can also replace the extreme values with median values. As a rule of thumb, never replace extreme values with mean value, as the mean values are affected by outliers. In the code given below, the median value is identified by retrieving the 50th percentile value and then replacing extreme values for those greater than 95th percentile value with the median value. Finally, summary statistics are displayed.

Example: Removing extreme value by replacing it with median value.

```
from sklearn.datasets import load_boston
import pandas as pd
from matplotlib import pyplot as plt
import seaborn as sns
import numpy as np
boston = load_boston()
print(boston)
x = boston.data
y = boston.target
columns = boston.feature_names#create the dataframe
boston_df = pd.DataFrame(boston.data)
med = boston_df[2].quantile(0.50)
extreme = boston_df[2].quantile(0.95)
boston_df[2] = np.where(boston_df[2] > extreme, med, boston_df[2])
print(med, extreme)

OUTPUT
9.69 21.89
```

> Global minimum is the least value of a function, while local minimum is the least value of a function in a certain neighbourhood.

10.9 Gradient descent

Gradient Descent is an optimization algorithm that iteratively finds the minima of a function. For this purpose, it finds parameters or coefficients of a function where the function has a minimum value. For optimal algorithms, we need to write functions having minimum cost. In such cases, computing gradient descent is very helpful. However, remember that many a times, gradient descent does not always guarantee to find a global minimum and returns only a local minimum.

To understand the difference between local and global minimum, let us consider an analogy. A person at the top of a mountain in bad weather with low visibility wants to reach the base camp at the lowest point of the mountain. He will use his feet to know where the land tends to descend. This will give him an idea in what direction the steep is low and he should keep his first step to proceed. After that, he would follow the descending path until he reaches a plain area.

In case the person finds a slight rise in the ground when going downhill, he would immediately stop assuming that he has reached the base camp (global minima). But in reality, he is actually still stuck at the mountain at a local minimum.

Technically, gradient descent finds values of parameters (coefficients) of a function (f) that minimizes a cost function (cost). This algorithm is especially used when the parameters cannot be calculated analytically (for example, using linear algebra).

10.9.1 Gradient descent procedure

Step I: Gradient descent algorithm starts with initial values for the coefficient(s) for the function. This can be either 0.0 or a small random value.

```
coefficient = 0.0
```

> Higher the gradient, steeper is the slope and the faster a model can learn. If the slope is zero, the model stops learning.

Step 2: The value of the coefficient(s) can be put in the function to calculate cost of the function.

```
cost = f(coefficient)
```

Step 3: Calculate derivative of the cost. Note that derivative is a concept from calculus and refers to slope of a function at a given point. Value of the slope (or delta) helps us to know the direction (sign) in which the coefficient values need to be updated to get a lower cost on the next iteration.

```
delta = derivative(cost)
```

Step 4: Specify a learning rate parameter (alpha) to control how much the coefficients can change on each update.

```
coefficient = coefficient - (alpha * delta)
```

This process is repeated until the cost of the coefficients (cost) is 0.0 or close enough to zero to be good enough.

10.9.2 Importance of the learning rate

Learning rate is a very important factor in determining how big steps, gradient descent takes in the direction of the local minimum. That is, it determines how fast or slow we will move towards the optimal weights.

For an optimal gradient descent algorithm, an appropriate value for learning rate (neither too high nor too low) is set to reach the local minimum (Figure 10.9). If the steps are too big, it may

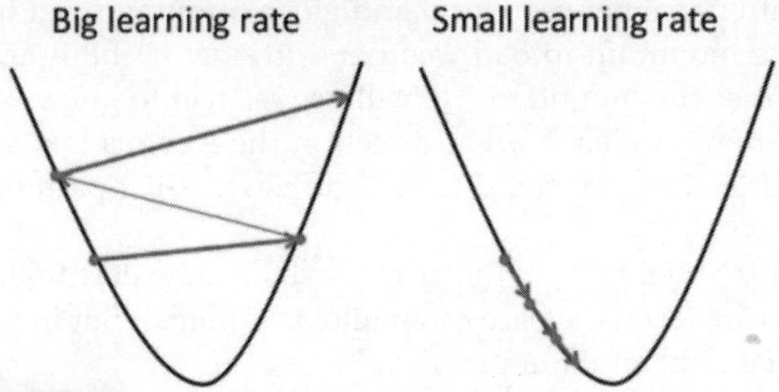

Figure 10.9 Impact of Learning Rate on Reaching Local Minimum

not reach the local minimum because it bounces back and forth between the convex function of gradient descent. In case, the learning rate is very small value, then gradient descent will eventually reach the local minimum, but that may take a while.

10.9.3 How to ensure that the algorithm works properly

To ensure optimum performance of gradient descent algorithm, we plot the cost function as the optimization runs. For this, the number of iterations is marked on the x-axis and value of the cost-function is marked on the y-axis. This helps us to better visualize how apt the learning rate is. The plot given below helps us to understand this concept (Figure 10.10).

In an optimal gradient descent algorithm, the cost function decreases after every iteration. At a point, the gradient descent will not affect the cost-function. At that time, its value is said to have converged.

Number of iterations gradient descent that needs to converge may vary from 50 to 60,000 or to even 3 million. Predicting the number of iterations to converge is a difficult task. In some algorithms, data scientist himself has to specify a threshold for the convergence beforehand, which is also not a trivial task. Therefore, we must plot these values to easily spot the effect of number of iterations on the cost-function.

Many-a-times, the cost-function increases due to high-learning rate. If the plot depicts that the learning curve is quickly going up and down, without touching a lower point, then decrease the learning rate. As a rule of thumb, when applying gradient descent on a given problem, try 0.001, 0.003, 0.01, 0.03, 0.1, 0.3, 1, etc., as the learning rates and check which value give the best performance.

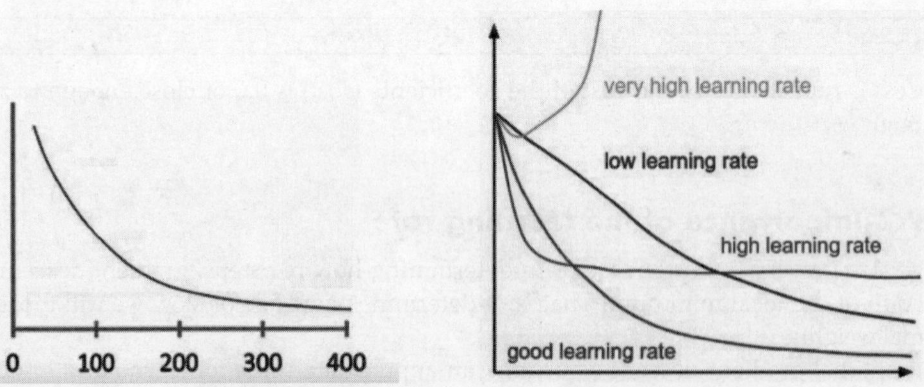

Figure 10.10 Cost Function vs Learning Rate

10.9.4 Variants of gradient descent

There are three popular types of gradient descent. These techniques usually differ in the amount of data they use. Depending on the amount of data, there is always a trade-off between the accuracy of the parameter update and the time it takes to perform an update.

10.9.4.1 Batch gradient descent

Batch or vanilla gradient descent calculates error for each example within the training dataset. Once all training examples have been evaluated, only then the ML model is updated. This entire process is like a cycle and is called a training epoch.

> For best results, gradient descent algorithm will reach the minimum cost faster if the shape of the cost function is not skewed and distorted. This can be achieved by rescaling input variables to the same range, such as [0, 1] or [−1, 1].

Advantages: Batch gradient descent is computationally efficient, produces a stable error gradient and a stable convergence.

Disadvantages: Stable error gradient may result in a state of convergence that is not the best the model can achieve. It also mandates the entire training dataset be in memory so that the algorithm can be applied on it and the final result is computed.

10.9.4.2 Stochastic gradient descent (SGD)

Stochastic Gradient Descent updates the parameters for each training example one by one. Depending on the problem, SGD usually works faster than batch gradient descent.

Advantage: Frequent updates are helpful in improving the algorithm. Moreover, it may not be always possible to keep the entire dataset in RAM. In such cases, SGD is a big relief as it supports vectorization techniques, so that each sample can be easily loaded and processed. Usually, SGD takes 1 to 10 iterations through the training dataset to converge on good or good enough coefficients.

Disadvantage: Frequent updates are more computationally expensive than batch gradient descent technique. Moreover, higher number of updates may result in noisy gradients and thus higher error rate.

10.9.4.3 Mini-batch gradient descent

Mini-batch gradient descent is a perfect combination of SGD and batch gradient descent techniques. The algorithm splits the training dataset into small batches and performs an update for each of those batches. This maintains a good balance between robustness of SGD and efficiency of the batch gradient descent.

In a mini-batch, size of the training data set may vary from 50 to 256. Mini-batch gradient descent algorithm is most commonly used even with deep learning techniques.

This type of gradient descent works faster than the above two techniques. Neither we use all the dataset all at once nor is the processing applied on a single example at a time. Rather, a batch of a fixed number of training examples is used which helps to achieve the advantages of both the former variants.

Business Scenario: Data Preprocessing in a Retail Sales Dataset

Consider a retail sales dataset. As the data engineer of the company, prepare this data for analysis. For processing the data, you are supposed to handle missing values, encode categorical variables, scale numerical features, and standardize the values. These steps are a pre-requisite for any machine learning model to give reliable and accurate results.
The retail sales dataset has the following attributes.

Date	**Product_ID**	**Product_Category**	**Quantity_Sold**	**Price_Per_Unit**
	Discount	**Store_Location**	**Customer_Age**	

```
import pandas as pd
import numpy as np
from sklearn.model_selection import train_test_split
from sklearn.preprocessing import StandardScaler, LabelEncoder
from sklearn.impute import SimpleImputer
import matplotlib.pyplot as plt
import seaborn as sns
# Load the dataset
data = pd.read_csv("retail_sales.csv")
# Display the first few rows of the dataset
print(data.head())
# Check for data types and missing values
print(data.info())
# Checking for missing values
print(data.isnull().sum())
# Encode 'Product_Category' and 'Store_Location' using Label Encoding
label_encoder = LabelEncoder()
data['Product_Category'] = label_encoder.fit_transform(data['Product_Category'])
data['Store_Location'] = label_encoder.fit_transform(data['Store_Location'])
# Create a new feature for total sale value
data['Total_Sale_Value'] = data['Quantity_Sold'] * data['Price_Per_Unit']
# Convert 'Date' to datetime format
data['Date'] = pd.to_datetime(data['Date'])

# Extract day, month, and year from the date column
data['Day_of_Week'] = data['Date'].dt.dayofweek
data['Month'] = data['Date'].dt.month
data['Year'] = data['Date'].dt.year
# Features to scale
scaler = StandardScaler()
scaled_columns = ['Quantity_Sold', 'Price_Per_Unit', 'Discount', 'Total_Sale_Value']
data[scaled_columns] = scaler.fit_transform(data[scaled_columns])
# Plot the distribution of the total sale value
sns.histplot(data['Total_Sale_Value'], bins=30, kde=True)
plt.title('Distribution of Total Sale Value')
plt.show()
```

```
# Correlation heatmap to find relationships between numerical features
corr_matrix = data.corr()
sns.heatmap(corr_matrix, annot=True, cmap='coolwarm')
plt.title('Correlation Matrix')
plt.show()
```

Key Terms

Anomaly Detection: An unsupervised learning technique that is used to find out the occurrences of rare events or observations that generally do not occur.

Association Analysis: An unsupervised learning technique that aims to discover rules that describe large portions of data.

Classification Algorithm: A supervised ML algorithm that classifies data into a particular group.

Clustering: An unsupervised learning technique that aims to discover inherent groupings in the data or discover hidden patterns.

Data Standardization: Shifting the distribution of each attribute in such a way that it has a mean value zero and a standard deviation of one (unit variance).

Dimensionality Reduction: An unsupervised learning technique that reduces the number of feature variables for the data set.

Gradient Descent: An optimization algorithm that iteratively finds the minima of a function.

Machine Learning: A branch of artificial intelligence that extracts patterns from raw data by using a well-defined algorithm.

Outlier: A data point in a data set that is distant from all other observations.

Performance (P): A measure that indicates how well a particular ML algorithm has performed the given task T using experience E. Performance is analyzed based on well-defined metrics including accuracy, F1 score, confusion matrix, precision, recall, sensitivity, etc.

Reinforcement Learning: An unsupervised ML algorithm in which an agent is trained over a period of time so that it can interact with a specific environment.

Semi-Supervised Learning Algorithms: ML algorithms that use small amount of pre-labeled data and a large number of unlabeled data for training.

Supervised ML Algorithms: Algorithms which apply learning from past data (or experiences) to new data using labeled examples.

Unsupervised Learning: An ML algorithm that trains the machine using information that is neither classified nor labeled.

Chapter Highlights

- ★ Supervised learning should be used when output of data in the training set is known.
- ★ In supervised learning, clear instructions are given specifying what needs to be learnt and how it needs to be learnt.
- ★ Normalization refers to rescaling of floating-point values into the range 0 and 1. It is also known as Min-Max scaling.
- ★ In L1 Normalization, dataset values are modified in such a way that in each row the sum of the absolute values will always be up to 1.
- ★ L2 Normalization modifies the dataset values in such a way that in each row the sum of the squares will always be up to 1.

- Data feature selection is used to select a subset of features in the data that are most relevant to the output or for predicting value(s) for another variable.
- The interquartile range (IQR), also called the midspread or middle 50%, is a measure of statistical dispersion. Its value is equal to the difference between the 75th and 25th percentiles. This can also be expressed as, IQR = $Q3 - Q1$, where, $Q3$ and $Q1$ are upper and lower quartiles.
- The skewness value explains the extent to which the data is normally distributed. Ideally, it should vary from –1 to +1.
- In Quantile-based Flooring and Capping technique, flooring and capping is done to overwrite the outlier values with other values like the 10th and 90th percentile for lower and higher quantiles, respectively. Flooring is done for the lower values and capping is done for the higher values.
- Machine learning aims at enabling the machines make decisions, based on data, with efficiency and scale particularly to automate the data-driven decision-making process.
- The most important part of an ML algorithm is the data. Success of any ML model depends on the quantity as well as quality of data.

Review Questions

1. Define machine learning.
2. What is an ML model?
3. Explain some challenges faced by ML algorithm.
4. Write a short note on the applications of ML algorithms.
5. How is ML a boon for health-care systems?
6. Differentiate between supervised and unsupervised ML techniques.
7. With the help of examples explain the types of supervised learning algorithms.
8. How does the machine perform unsupervised learning?
9. How does semi-supervised ML algorithm work?
10. Explain the basic concept of reinforcement learning.
11. It is said that data is the most important component of any ML system. What steps are performed to ensure good quality data?
12. What is normalization? How is it performed?
13. What do you understand by the term data feature selection? How is it performed?
14. Write a short note on outlier analysis.
15. With the help of an example explain how a box plot can be used to detect outliers.
16. Explain the Quantile-based Flooring and Capping technique.
17. Give the importance of gradient descent algorithm. Also write the steps involved.
18. Explain the different variants of gradient descent algorithm.

Programming Exercise

1. Read the mtcars.csv file and do the following:
   a. Print the first 10 rows.
   b. Print the shape.

   c. Check for outliers using bar plot.
   d. Print outlier data values.
   e. Remove outliers.
   f. Recheck the shape of data.
2. Read the car-mpg.csv and do the following:
   a. Check the shape of the data.
   b. Print the Z-score table.
   c. Identify the outliers.
   d. Recheck the shape.
3. Write a Python code to detect outliers using Z-score technique.
4. Download the loan_applications data set that has 600 observations and 6 variables: Income, Loan_amount, Term_months, Credit_score, Age and Approval_status. Now,
   a. Read the data set.
   b. Print a statistical summary of all the quantitative variables.
   c. Identify outliers using IQR technique.
   d. Identify outliers using skewness in the Income column.
   e. Represent distribution of data using box plot of the numeric variable 'Loan_amount'.
   f. Verify skewness of Income column by plotting a histogram.
   g. Identify outlier using a scatter plot.
   h. Remove outliers from Income column using flooring and capping technique.
   i. Trim the data set so that every row with Age <18 and Age >100 are removed from the data set.
   j. Remove outliers using IQR technique.
   k. Use log transformation to reduce skewness of data.
   l. Replace extreme values with median value.
5. Write a code that normalizes the age, height and weight values of the baseball data set.
6. Use the diabetes.csv file to rescale the data values using MinMaxScaler in the range of 0 to 1. Print the first 10 rows in the output.
7. Read the diabetes.csv and then with the help of StandardScaler class, convert the data into Gaussian Distribution with mean = 0 and SD = 1.
8. Write a code that displays outliers in the Boston data set using a scatter plot.

Fill in the Blanks

1. Machine learning automates _______ decision-making process.
2. _______ acquired through ML model or algorithm is used to solve task T.
3. In _______ learning, clear instructions are given specifying what needs to be learnt and how it needs to be learnt.
4. _______ learning trains the machine using information that is neither classified nor labeled.
5. _______ is an unsupervised learning technique that aims to discover rules that describe large portions of data.
6. A _______ algorithm predicts a real value.
7. _______ model automatically finds patterns and relationships in the dataset by creating clusters in it.

8. ____________ algorithms that use small amount of pre-labeled data and a large number of unlabeled data for training.
9. ____________ is a type of dynamic programming that trains algorithms using a system of reward and punishment.
10. __________ techniques help to remove noisy data (or outliers), normalize, aggregate and generalize data to improve its credibility.
11. ________ refers to rescaling of floating-point values into the range 0 to 1.
12. Standardization means shifting the distribution of each attribute in such a way that it has a mean value _____ and a standard deviation of _____.
13. ________ is a data point in a data set that is distant from all other observations.
14. ______ is used to convert our data into binary values.
15. ________ function defined in the SciPy library is used to identify the outliers.
16. ________ is a measure of the statistical dispersion.
17. ______ is done for the lower values (10th percentile) and _______ is done for the higher values (90th percentile).
18. ________ removes data points that are identified as outliers from the dataset.
19. In gradient descent, _______ determines how fast or slow we will move towards the optimal weights.
20. ______ algorithm uses frequent updates to improve performance.

State True or False

1. ML allows computers to learn from experience without human intervention.
2. ML model is insensitive to high-quality data.
3. Unsupervised learning algorithms learn an association between input data and the output to predict the output value for any new input.
4. Supervised learning should be used when output of data in the training set is known.
5. Spam email detection is a regression problem.
6. Classification algorithms predict continuous values.
7. Association analysis is used to reduce the number of feature variables for the data set.
8. Reinforcement learning is similar to supervised learning.
9. Data Integration involves schema integration, resolving data conflicts (if any) and handling data redundancies.
10. In L2 Normalization, dataset values are modified in such a way that in each row the sum of the absolute values will always be up to 1.
11. Scaling changes the size of data but does not affect the shape of the data.
12. Bar graphs are the best plots to detect an outlier.
13. Gradient descent requires standardized data value.
14. We should replace extreme values with mean value.
15. In gradient descent, higher the gradient, steeper is the slope and the faster a model can learn.
16. Batch gradient descent is computationally efficient.

Give the Output

```
import numpy as np
from sklearn import preprocessing
Now, we need to provide the input labels as follows -
input_labels = ['red','black','red','green','black','yellow','white']
The next line of code will create the label encoder and train it.
encoder = preprocessing.LabelEncoder()
encoder.fit(input_labels)
test_labels = ['green','red', 'black']
encoded_values = encoder.transform(test_labels)
print("\nLabels =", test_labels)
print("Encoded values =", list(encoded_values))
encoded_values = [3,0,4,1]
decoded_list = encoder.inverse_transform(encoded_values)
print("\nEncoded values =", encoded_values)
print("\nDecoded labels =", list(decoded_list))
```

CHAPTER

11 Regression Analysis in Machine Learning*

Lasso Regression: Predicting House Prices

Imagine that you are a data analyst working for a real estate company. You have to predict the prices of houses based on the number of bedrooms, square footage, number of bathrooms, location, etc. you are curious to identify the features that are most important in predicting house prices. The dataset contains several features, which may or may not be relevant. You found that a linear regression model is not performing well due to multicollinearity. So, you decided to perform feature selection before using Lasso Regression to predict house prices. Assuming that the dataset contains following attributes, write the code to accomplish the given task.

Bedrooms	SquareFootage	Bathrooms	Age	Location	Price

Regression analysis is a statistical method tool that allows users to study the relationship between a dependent (target) and one or more independent (predictor) variables. This helps the analyst to understand how the value of the dependent variable changes with respect to independent variables. The values to be predicted are usually continuous or real (like temperature, age, salary, price, etc.). For example, a company can analyze its data to find out the extent to which expenditure on advertisements increases sales of a particular product. Similarly, we can use regression analysis to predict rainfall using temperature and other factors, determine market trends, predict road accidents due to rash driving, etc.

Regression analysis is widely used for prediction, forecasting, modeling time series data, and inferring the causal-effect relationship between variables.

In regression analysis, a graph that best fits the given data points is plotted. This graph can either have a straight line or a curve that passes through all the data points on the graph that is drawn depicting the dependent and independent variable(s). The vertical distance between the data points and the regression line should be minimum as this line indicates whether the model has captured a strong relationship or not.

11.1 How regression analysis works?

Regression analysis creates a mathematical equation that defines y as a function of the x variables. This equation is then used to predict the value of y on the basis of values of the predictor variables (x).

Linear regression is the most basic, simple and widely used technique for predicting values of a continuous variable. It assumes that there exists a linear relationship between the outcome and the predictor variables.

*Note: The datasets and colored pictorial representation of graphs and charts from this chapter is available online. For more details, please refer to the back cover of the book.

The linear regression equation can be given as,

$$y = b_0 + b \times x + e,$$

where: b_0 is the intercept,
b is the coefficient of x
e is the residual error

Values of the coefficients are determined in such a way that the residual error is minimized. This method of computing the beta coefficients is known as Ordinary Least Squares (OLS) method.

In case of multiple predictor variables, say x_1 and x_2, the regression equation can be written as $\mathbf{y = b_0 + b_1 \times x_1 + b_2 \times x_2 + e}$. There may also exist an interaction effect between two or more predictor variables. For example, increasing the value of one predictor variable may in turn increase the effectiveness of the other predictor(s) in explaining the variation in the outcome variable.

When there are multiple predictors in the regression model, the best combination of predictors needs to be chosen (like best subsets regression and stepwise regression) to construct the optimal predictive model. In such cases, we use model selection technique that compares multiple models built with different sets of predictors to select the best performing model that minimizes the prediction error.

Linear regression models work well with both continuous and categorical predictor variables. However, before applying linear regression model on our data set, we must first make sure that the linear model is suitable for the underlying data. It may happen that the relationship between the outcome and the predictor variables is not linear. In such cases, a non-linear regression model (like polynomial and spline regression) is preferred over a linear model.

When there is a large multi-variate data set containing some correlated predictors, then such variables are summarized into a few new variables that are a linear combination of the original variables. These techniques based on **principal components** include principal component regression and partial least squares regression. Alternatively, we can use penalized regression to simplify a large multi-variate model. Such a regression model penalizes the model for having too many variables. Ridge regression and Lasso regression are popular examples of penalized regression model.

Thus, different regression models can be applied on the data and their performance can be compared to select the best one that explains the data. Statistical metrics are used to compare the performance of the different models in explaining the data and predicting the outcome of new test data.

11.2 Model evaluation metrics

The best regression model is one with lowest prediction error. The most widely used metrics for comparing regression models are:

Root Mean Squared Error (RMSE) measures the model prediction error. It is calculated as the average difference between the observed known values of the outcome and the predicted value by the model. Mathematically, `RMSE = srt(mean((observeds - predicteds)^2)`. Lower the RMSE, better is the model.

Adjusted R-square represents the proportion of variation in the data thereby reflecting the overall quality of the model. Higher the adjusted R^2, better is the model.

These metrics are computed on a new test data that has not been used to train or build the model. In a large data set with many records, rows can be randomly split in 80:20 ratio, where 80% of the rows are used to build the predictive model and the rest 20% are used as test set or validation set for evaluating the model performance.

One of the best techniques for estimating a model's performance is **k-fold cross-validation**. This can be applied even on a small data set. Steps followed to perform k-fold cross-validation are:

Step 1: Randomly split the data set into k-subsets (or k-fold). For example, to generate 5 subsets, value of k = 5.
Step 2: Reserve one subset and call it as test data. Use rest of the subsets to train the model.
Step 3: Test the performance of the model using the test data set and record the prediction error.
Step 4: Repeat the above steps until each of the k-subsets have been used as the test set.
Step 5: Calculate the average of the k recorded errors. This is also known as cross-validation error. Finally, the best model is the one that has the lowest cross-validation error, RMSE.

11.3 Types of regression

The type of regression analysis that can be applied on a particular data set depends on the attributes, target variables, shape and nature of the regression curve that represents the relationship between dependent and independent variables. Some important regression techniques are:

Linear regression: It is the simplest regression technique used for predicting values for a dependent variable that has linear relationship between the response and predictors (or descriptive variables). The general equation of linear regression can be given as,

$$Y = bX + C$$

Where, Y is a dependent variable
X is the independent variable
b is the slope of the regression line and
C is the intercept.

Though, linear regression suffers from overfitting issues, it is still used as it is fast and easy to model and evaluate. It is best used when the target relationship is not complex or enough data is not available. Linear regression is also very useful for detecting outliers (Figure 11.1).

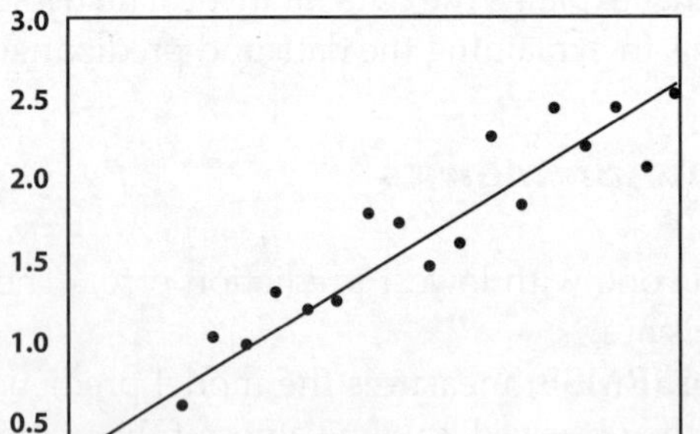

Figure 11.1 Plotting the linear regression line

Logistic Regression: It is preferred when the dependent variable is binary (dichotomous) in nature (like 0 or 1, true or false, yes or no). That is, logistic regression is preferred when there is a need to ascertain the probability of an event in terms of either success or failure. In such a case, the relationship between the dependent and independent variables is calculated by computing probabilities using the logit function. Logistic regression is mostly used to analyze categorical data (Figure 11.2).

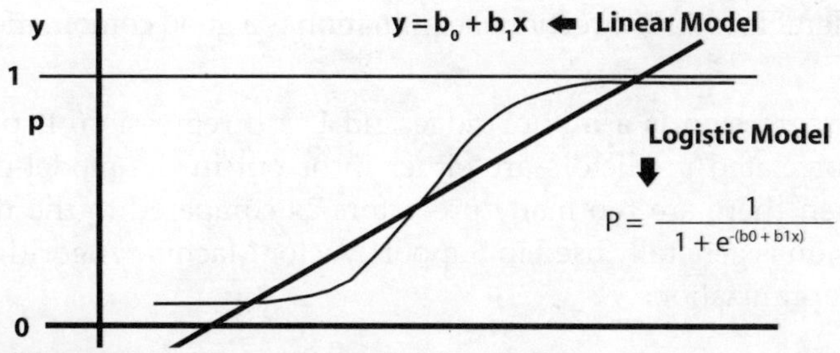

Ridge regression eases collinearity in between predictors of a model

Figure 11.2 Plotting points satisfying logistic regression equation

Ridge Regression: Ridge regression is basically used for analyzing numerous regression data. In case of multi-collinearity, least-square calculations get unbiased, so the regression model becomes too complex and approaches to overfit. In such a case, we need to minimize the variance in the model and save it from overfitting. Ridge regression helps us to do this by correcting the size of the coefficients. A bias degree is affixed to the regression calculation which in turn reduces standard errors.

Lasso (*Least Absolute Shrinkage Selector Operator*) Regression: It is a widely used regression analysis technique for variable selection and regularization. Lasso regression uses thresholds to select a subset of the covariates given for the implementation of the final model. It reduces the number of dependent variables if the penalty term is huge. This is done by reducing the coefficients to zero so that features can be selected easily. Lasso regression is also known as L1 regularization.

Polynomial Regression: Polynomial regression is used to construct a model that fits non-linearly separated data. In such a case, the best-fitted line is not a straight line, but a curve.

The equation of polynomial regression is given as, $Y = b_0 + b_1x_1 + b_2 \times {}_2{}^2 + \cdots b_n \times n^n$

Polynomial regression is widely used to analyze curvilinear form of data and best fitted for least-squares method (Figure 11.3).

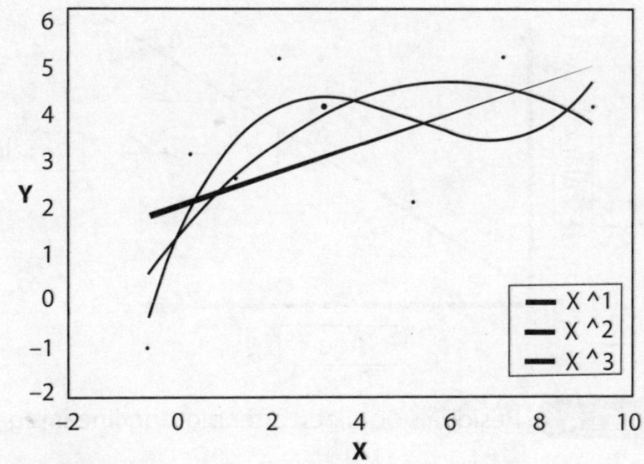

Figure 11.3 Plotting points satisfying polynomial regression

Stepwise Regression: It is used to build predictive regression models that are carried out naturally. With every forward step, a variable gets added or subtracted from a group of descriptive variables.

We can use ***forward selection, backward elimination*** or ***bidirectional elimination*** for adding/removing variables at each step. As the name suggests, forward selection continuously adds variables to the set and reviews the performance of the model. It stops when no further improvement is needed (or being achieved). Backward elimination removes variables until no extra variable is left to be deleted without considerable loss. Bidirectional elimination is a good combination of both these approaches.

ElasticNet Regression: Elastic regression is a mix of ridge and Lasso regression. It produces a grouping effect when highly correlated predictors are either in or out in the model combined. This technique is preferred when there are too many predictors as compared to the number of observations. ElasticNet regression is generally used in Support Vector Machine Algorithm (SVM), metric training, and document optimizations.

11.4 Linear regression

Linear regression is a supervised learning algorithm that is generally used for predictive analysis. The term "linearity" in algebra means a linear relationship between two or more variables. We get a straight line when we draw this relationship in a 2-D graph.

Linear regression predicts a dependent variable value (y) based on a given independent variable (x). Here, exists a linear relationship between x (input) and y (output). Therefore, linear regression is used whenever there is a linear relation between the dependent and the independent variables. This relationship can be given using the formula,

$$Y = b_0 + b_1 \times x$$

Where, b_0 is the intercept and
b_1 is the slope of the line.

Here, our goal is to understand how much the value of *y* will change, when there is a change in the value of x. Linear regression helps us to find the most optimal value for the intercept and the slope (in two dimensions). The X and Y variables cannot be changed as they represent data features. We can only control the intercept and slope (Figure 11.4).

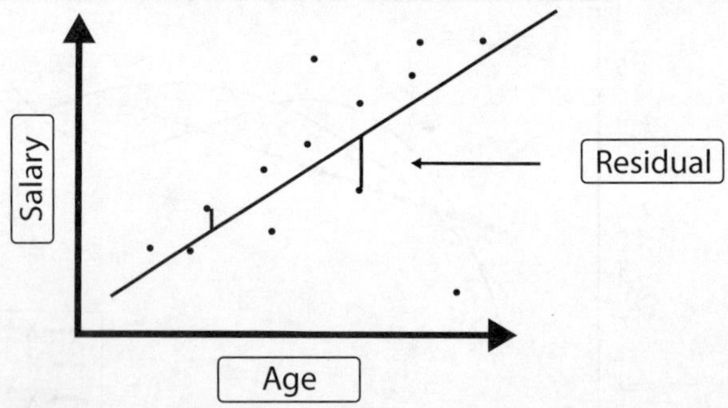

Figure 11.4 Residuals obtained after plotting linear regression line

Moreover, there can be multiple straight lines depending upon the values of intercept and slope. But linear regression algorithm fits multiple lines on the data points and returns the line that results in least error.

11.4.1 Linear regression line of best fit

The line of best fit is the line that best expresses the relationship between the data points. To find the best-fit line in linear regression, we need to understand the concept of residual values.

In the graph, red lines indicate residual values which are nothing but the difference between the actual values and the predicted values. To find the best-fit line, residual sum of squares (RSS) is calculated as the sum of squares of residuals. Mathematically, it can be written as,

$$\text{RSS} = \sum_{k=2}^{n} (Actual - Predicted)^2$$

The line with the lowest value of RSS gives the best-fit line (Figure 11.5).

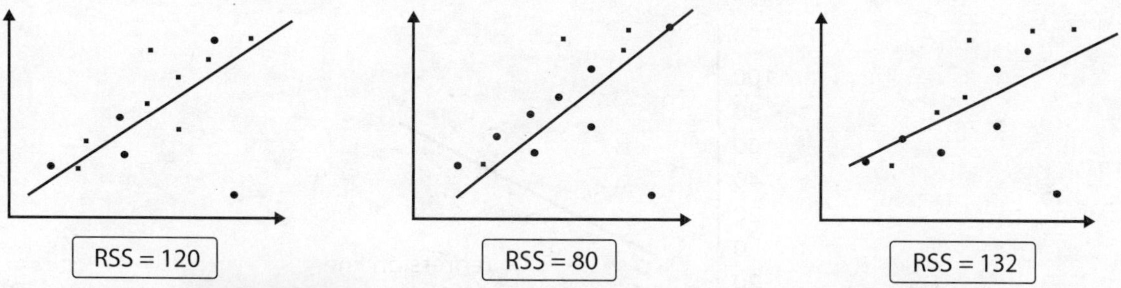

Figure 11.5 Calculating RSS for different Linear Regression Lines

11.4.2 Regression coefficient

In simple linear regression, if the coefficient of x is positive, then the relationship between the independent and the dependent variables is positive. So, if the value of x increases, the value of y also increases (Figure 11.6).

If the coefficient of x is negative, then the relationship between the independent and the dependent variables is negative. This means that if the value of x increases, the value of y decreases (Figure 11.7). We know that the equation of a straight line is basically:

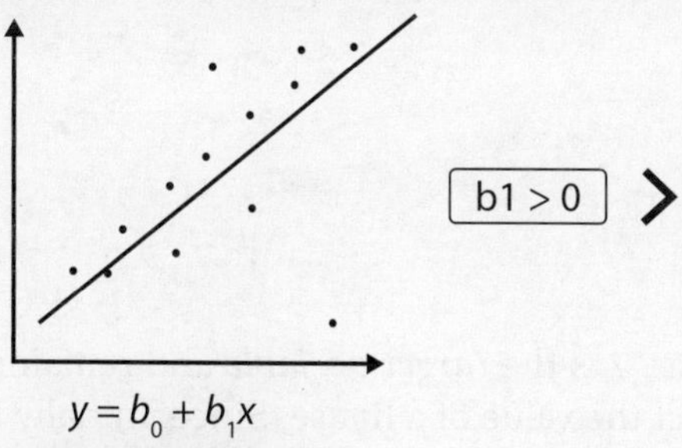

Figure 11.6 Positive relationship

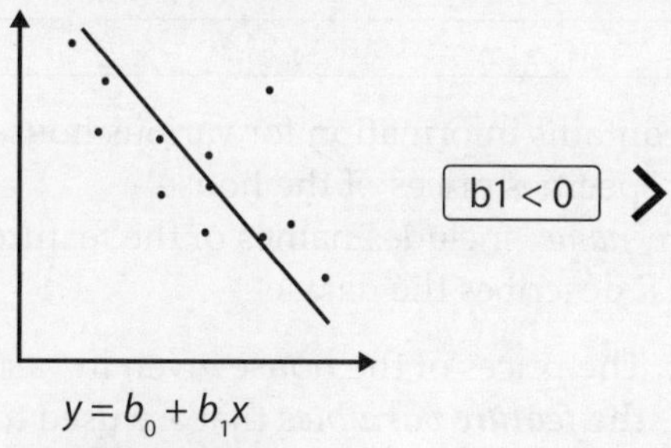

Figure 11.7 Negative relationship

11.4.3 Errors

For regression algorithms, three evaluation metrics are commonly used:

Mean Absolute Error (MAE) is the mean of the absolute values of the errors. It is calculated as:

$$\text{MAE} = \frac{1}{n}\sum_{j=1}^{n} |y_j - y_j|$$

Mean Squared Error (MSE) is the mean of the squared errors. It is calculated as:

$$\text{MSE} = \frac{1}{N}\sum_{i}^{n} (Y_i - y_i)^2$$

Root Mean Squared Error (RMSE) is the square root of the mean of the squared errors and can be mathematically given as,

$$\text{RMSE} = \frac{1}{n}\sqrt{\sum_{j=1}^{n}(y_j - y_j)^2}$$

We can also visualize errors by plotting the regression line and then comparing regression line with data line as illustrated in Figure 11.8.

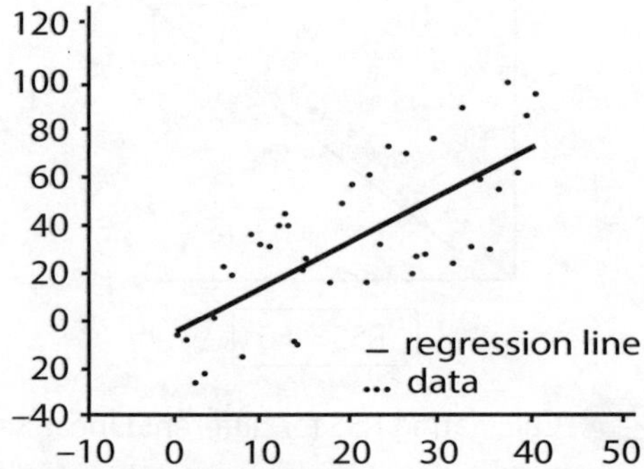

Figure 11.8 Visualizing errors by observing data line and regression line

11.4.4 Implementing linear regression

Before starting to code, let us first understand the steps involved in performing linear regression.

Step 1: Load the dataset

Step 2: Print the data set keys. These keys include: data, target, feature_names and DESCR, where

```
re_names', 'DESCR'])
```

- *data* contains information for various houses
- *target* specifies prices of the house
- *feature_names* includes names of the features
- *DESCR* describes the dataset

Step 3: The prices of the house given in variable `MEDV` is the ***target variable*** and remaining are the ***feature variables*** that are used to predict the value of a house. Since, initially MEDV is missing from the data set, we can create a new column of target values and add it to the data frame.

Step 4: Check for any null values. If present, data should be cleaned before further processing.

Step 5: Create a correlation matrix that measures the linear relationships between the variables. The correlation coefficient varies from -1 to 1. A value close to 1 indicates a strong positive correlation between the two variables. Correspondingly, a value close to -1 specifies a strong negative correlation between variables. Since, the heatmap shows a strong positive relationship between MEDV and RM, we have used these two variables for fitting a linear regression model.

Step 6: LSTAT and RM columns are concatenated using np.c_ provided by the NumPy library.

Step 7: Data is split into two sets – training and testing sets. The model is trained with 80% of the samples and tested with the remaining 20%. Testing data set helps us *to assess the model's performance on unseen data*. The train_test_split function is used to split data. This function is available in the scikit-learn library. Shapes of the training and test set are printed to verify if the splitting has been done properly.

Step 8: The LinearRegression() function is used to train the ML model on both the training and test sets.

Step 9: Evaluate the model by computing RMSE and R2 score.

Example: Implementing Linear Regression

```
from sklearn.datasets import load_boston
import pandas as pd
from matplotlib import pyplot as plt
import seaborn as sns
import numpy as np
boston_data = load_boston()
print(boston_data.keys())
boston = pd.DataFrame(boston_data.data, columns=boston_data.feature_names)
print(boston.head())

boston['MEDV'] = boston_data.target
# count the number of missing values for each feature
print(boston.isnull().sum())

correlation_matrix = boston.corr().round(2)
# annot = True to print the values inside the square
plt.show()
sns.heatmap(data=correlation_matrix, annot=True)
X=pd.DataFrame(np.c_[boston['LSTAT'],boston['RM']],columns=['LSTAT','RM'])
Y = boston['MEDV']
from sklearn.model_selection import train_test_split

X_train, X_test, Y_train, Y_test = train_test_split(X, Y, test_size = 0.2,
random_state=5)
print(X_train.shape)
print(X_test.shape)
print(Y_train.shape)
print(Y_test.shape)
from sklearn.linear_model import LinearRegression
from sklearn.metrics import mean_squared_error

lin_model = LinearRegression()
lin_model.fit(X_train, Y_train)

# model evaluation for training set
y_train_predict = lin_model.predict(X_train)
rmse = (np.sqrt(mean_squared_error(Y_train, y_train_predict)))

print("The model performance for training set")
print("--------------------------------------")
print('RMSE is {}'.format(rmse))
```

```
# model evaluation for testing set
y_test_predict = lin_model.predict(X_test)
rmse = (np.sqrt(mean_squared_error(Y_test, y_test_predict)))

print("The model performance for testing set")
print("--------------------------------------")
print('RMSE is {}'.format(rmse))
```

OUTPUT

```
dict_keys(['data', 'target', 'feature_names', 'DESCR', 'filename'])
      CRIM    ZN  INDUS  CHAS    NOX ... RAD    TAX  PTRATIO       B  LSTAT
0  0.00632  18.0   2.31   0.0  0.538 ... 1.0  296.0     15.3  396.90   4.98
1  0.02731   0.0   7.07   0.0  0.469 ... 2.0  242.0     17.8  396.90   9.14
2  0.02729   0.0   7.07   0.0  0.469 ... 2.0  242.0     17.8  392.83   4.03
3  0.03237   0.0   2.18   0.0  0.458 ... 3.0  222.0     18.7  394.63   2.94
4  0.06905   0.0   2.18   0.0  0.458 ... 3.0  222.0     18.7  396.90   5.33
[5 rows x 13 columns]
CRIM       0
ZN         0
INDUS      0
CHAS       0
NOX        0
RM         0
AGE        0
DIS        0
RAD        0
TAX        0
PTRATIO    0
B          0
LSTAT      0
MEDV       0
dtype: int64
(404, 2)
(102, 2)
(404,)
(102,)
The model performance for training set
--------------------------------------
RMSE is 5.6371293350711955
The model performance for testing set
--------------------------------------
RMSE is 5.13740078470291
```

Download weather.csv file and find relationship between Min Temp and Max Temp values using linear regression.

To predict the MaxTemp depending upon the MinTemp recorded, represent "MinTemp" column as the X variable, and the "MaxTemp" column as the Y variable.

```
import pandas as pd
import numpy as np
import matplotlib.pyplot as plt
import seaborn as seabornInstance
from sklearn.model_selection import train_test_split
from sklearn.linear_model import LinearRegression
from sklearn import metrics
dataset = pd.read_csv('weather.csv')

dataset.plot(x='MinTemp', y='MaxTemp', style='o')
plt.title('MinTemp vs MaxTemp')
plt.xlabel('MinTemp')
plt.ylabel('MaxTemp')
plt.show()
X = dataset['MinTemp'].values.reshape(-1,1)
y = dataset['MaxTemp'].values.reshape(-1,1)
# Split 80% of the data to the training set and 20% to test set
X_train, X_test, y_train, y_test = train_test_split(X, y, test_size=0.2,
random_state=0)
# fit() method is used to train data.
regressor = LinearRegression()
regressor.fit(X_train, y_train) #training the algorithm
#To retrieve the intercept:
print(regressor.intercept_)

#For retrieving the slope:
print(regressor.coef_)
# use test data to check accuracy of the model
y_pred = regressor.predict(X_test)
df = pd.DataFrame({'Actual': y_test.flatten(), 'Predicted': y_pred.flatten()})
df1 = df.head(25)
# visualize comparison result as a bar graph
df1.plot(kind='bar',figsize=(16,10))
plt.grid(which='major', linestyle='-', linewidth='0.5', color='green')
plt.grid(which='minor', linestyle=':', linewidth='0.5', color='black')
plt.show()
```

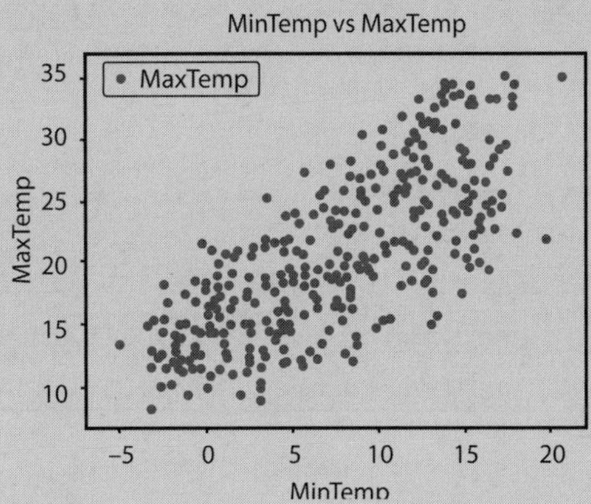

```
plt.scatter(X_test, y_test,  color='gray')
plt.plot(X_test, y_pred, color='red', linewidth=2)
plt.show()
```

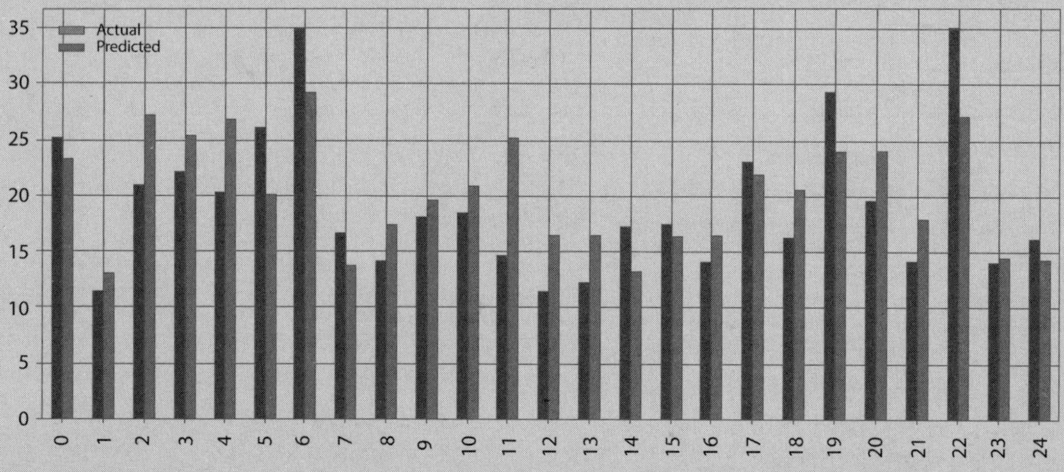


```
print('Mean Absolute Error:', metrics.
mean_absolute_error(y_test, y_pred))
print('Mean Squared Error:', metrics.
mean_squared_error(y_test, y_pred))
print('Root Mean Squared Error:',
np.sqrt(metrics.mean_squared_error
(y_test, y_pred)))
```

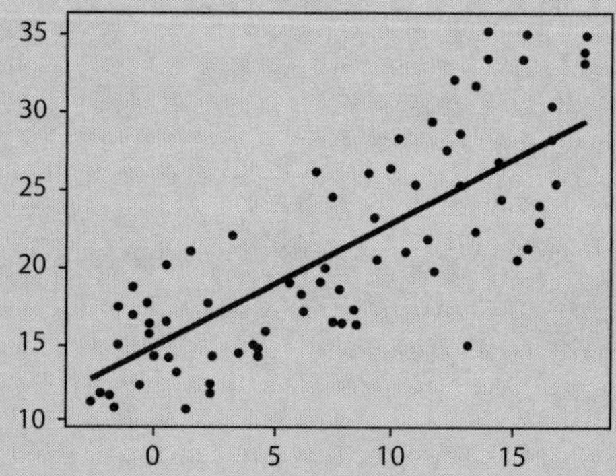

OUTPUT

```
[14.56202411]
[[0.81953755]]
Mean Absolute Error: 3.5094353112899603
Mean Squared Error: 17.011877668640626
Root Mean Squared Error: 4.124545753006096
```

Since RMSE is 4.12, which is more than 10% of the mean value of the percentages of all the temperatures, i.e. 22.41, the algorithm is not very accurate but can still make reasonably good predictions.

11.4.5 Assumptions

Given below are some assumptions that Linear Regression algorithms make about the underlying dataset.

- Linear regression model assumes that there is very little or no multi-collinearity in the data. This means that independent variables have no dependency between them.

- Linear regression model assumes that there is very little or no auto-correlation in the data. This means that there is no dependency between residual errors.
- Linear regression model assumes a linear relationship between response and feature variables.

11.4.6 Issues in regression analysis

Outliers: An outlier is an observation or a data point having either too high or too low value as compared to other observations/data points. Since outliers can affect the results, they should be avoided.

Multi-collinearity: It occurs when the independent variables are highly correlated with each other than the other variables. It is an undesirable characteristic of the data set as it creates problem while ranking the most affecting variable.

Underfitting and Overfitting: Overfitting means that the ML model works well with the training dataset but provides poor performance with the test dataset. Correspondingly, underfitting occurs when the ML model does not perform well even with training dataset.

11.5 Multiple regression

The concept of linear regression can be extended to be used in cases where there are more than two variables. This is called multiple linear regression or multi-variate linear regression. In real-world applications, we hardly use a single variable for predicting value of another variable. This is because values of a variable depend on more than one factor. For example, to predict the price of a house, we need to consider its area, number of bedrooms, average income of people in the area, age of the house, etc. In this scenario, the dependent variable (target variable – price) is dependent upon several independent variables.

Mathematically, formula for a regression model involving multiple variables can be given as:

$$y = b_0 + m_1b_1 + m_2b_2 + m_3b_3 + \ldots m_nb_n$$

To better understand the equation of multiple linear regression, see Figure 11.9. Recall that this is the equation of a hyperplane. A linear regression model in two dimensions is a straight line, in three dimensions it is a plane, and in more than three dimensions, it is a hyperplane. Multiple linear regression can be used to find out which factor has the highest impact on the predicted output and how different variables relate to each other.

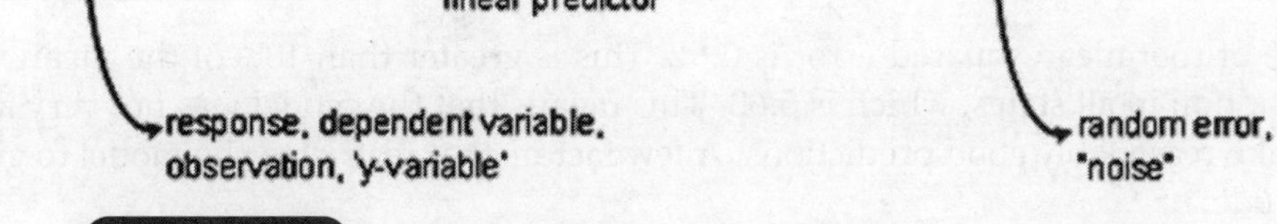

Figure 11.9 Understanding multiple linear regression equation

Example: Download the winequality-red.csv. Use multiple linear regression to use input features like fixed acidity, volatile acidity, citric acid, residual sugar, chlorides, free sulphur dioxide, total sulphur dioxide, density, pH, sulphates, alcohol to predict the quality of the wine.

```
import pandas as pd
import numpy as np
import matplotlib.pyplot as plt
import seaborn as seabornInstance
from sklearn.model_selection import train_test_split
from sklearn.linear_model import LinearRegression
from sklearn import metrics
dataset = pd.read_csv('winequality-red.csv')
dataset.isnull().any()
dataset = dataset.fillna(method='ffill')
X = dataset[['fixed acidity', 'volatile acidity', 'citric acid', 'residual
sugar', 'chlorides', 'free sulfur dioxide', 'total sulfur dioxide', 'density',
'pH', 'sulphates','alcohol']].values

y = dataset['quality'].values

X_train, X_test, y_train, y_test = train_test_split(X, y, test_size=0.2,
random_state=0)

regressor = LinearRegression()
regressor.fit(X_train, y_train)
y_pred = regressor.predict(X_test)
df = pd.DataFrame({'Actual': y_test, 'Predicted': y_pred})

df1 = df.head(25)

df1.plot(kind='bar',figsize=(10,8))
plt.grid(which='major', linestyle='-', linewidth='0.5', color='green')
plt.grid(which='minor', linestyle=':', linewidth='0.5', color='black')
plt.show()
print('Mean Absolute Error:', metrics.mean_absolute_error(y_test, y_pred))
print('Mean Squared Error:', metrics.mean_squared_error(y_test, y_pred))
print('Root Mean Squared Error:',
np.sqrt(metrics.mean_squared_error(y_test, y_pred)))
OUTPUT
Mean Absolute Error: 0.4696330928661103
Mean Squared Error: 0.3844711978201236
Root Mean Squared Error: 0.6200574149384261
```

Here, value of root mean squared error is 0.62. This is greater than 10% of the mean value of the gas consumption in all states, which is 5.63. This means that the model was not very accurate but can still make reasonably good predictions. A few factors that restricted the model to give accurate results include:

Amount of data: For best results, ML algorithms must be operated on massive amounts of data.

Assumptions: Before making the model, we assumed a linear relationship between variables. However, this assumption may not hold true always.

Correlation: Variables used for prediction may not have a high enough correlation to the variables for which values are being predicted.

11.6 Applications of linear regression

Evaluating Trends and Sales Estimates: Linear regression can be used in organizations to identify trends and make estimates or forecasts. Basically, a trend line represents variation in some quantitative data with passage of time. For example, we can analyze the GDP, oil prices, and unemployment rate using trend lines. These trends usually follow a linear relationship. Therefore, linear regression can be used to predict future values if any other potential change(s) does not affect the data.

For example, if a company's sales is increasing every month for last two years then conducting a linear analysis on the sales data depicting monthly sales on the y-axis and time on the x-axis will generate a straight line indicating an upward trend in sales. Once the trend line is drawn, slope of the line can be used to forecast sales in the coming months (Figure 11.10).

Figure 11.10 Analyzing data using linear regression

Analyzing the Impact of Price Changes: Linear regression can be used to predict the effect of pricing on consumer behavior.

For example, if a company changes the price of a product, then it can use linear regression to evaluate the quantity of items sold and its price. Here, quantity sold is used as the dependent variable and price is taken as the explanatory variable. The resultant line will help the analyst to find out the extent to which consumers reduced their consumption of the product when its price was increased. This information can be used to guide future pricing decisions.

Assessing Risk: Linear regression can be used to analyze risk. For example, a health insurance company performs linear regression to plot number of claims per customer against age to understand to what extent older customers tend to make more health insurance claims. Results of such analysis help to take better decision when the risk involved is especially moderate to high (Figure 11.11).

Figure 11.11 Analyzing the intensity of risk

Economics: Linear regression is used to predict consumption, optimal spending on fixed investments, inventory investment, purchases of a country's exports, spending on imports, the demand to hold liquid assets, forecast gaps in demand and supply of labor and other inputs.

Finance: Linear regression is used by Capital price asset model to analyze and quantify the systematic risks of an investment.

Biology: Linear regression is used in Biology to model causal relationships between parameters in biological systems.

11.7 Polynomial regression

Polynomial Regression is a form of linear regression in which the relationship between the independent variable x and dependent variable y is modeled as an *nth* degree polynomial. This means that polynomial regression fits a non-linear relationship between the value of x and the corresponding conditional mean of y, denoted by E(y | x).

> *A non-linear data set should use the Polynomial Regression model instead of Simple Linear Regression*

Polynomial regression is used when,

- The relationship has a polynomial term.
- In case of plotting scatter plot of curved data produces patches of many positive residuals in the middle.
- All the independent variables are actually not independent.
- The need of Polynomial regression can be clearly understood as,
- A linear model applied on a **linear dataset**, generates good results but the same linear model when applied on a non-linear dataset, produces erroneous results.
- When data points are arranged in a **non-linear fashion**, Polynomial regression model should be used.

The first figure depicts resultant line obtained by applying linear regression model on data points of non-linear data set (Figure 11.12). The line hardly covers any data point. On the other hand, a curve is suitable to cover most of the data points, which is of the Polynomial model.

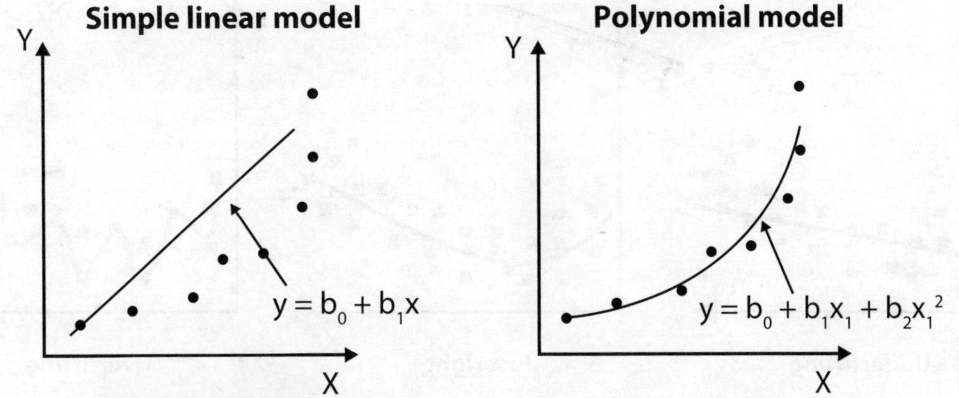

Figure 11.12 Simple linear model vs polynomial model

11.7.1 Applications of polynomial regression

Polynomial regression is used to define or describe non-linear phenomenon like, Growth rate of tissues, progression of disease epidemics, distribution of carbon isotopes in lake sediments, to name a few.

We have seen that the goal of linear regression is to predict the value of a dependent variable using the value of an independent variable, intercept and slope of the best-fit line. However, in cases where there is a polynomial relationship between variables, linear model will not work out. A polynomial relation expressed using nth power of x can be given as,

$$y = \beta_0 + \beta_1 x + \beta_2 x^2 + \beta_3 x^3 + \ldots + \beta_n x^n + \varepsilon.$$

Where y is the dependent variable and the betas are the coefficient for different nth powers of the independent variable x. Here, epsilons are errors. To understand this calculation, we can take a matrix as shown below.

$$\begin{bmatrix} y_1 \\ y_2 \\ y_3 \\ \vdots \\ y_n \end{bmatrix} = \begin{bmatrix} 1 & x_1 & x_1^2 & \ldots & x_1^m \\ 1 & x_2 & x_2^2 & \ldots & x_2^m \\ 1 & x_3 & x_3^2 & \ldots & x_3^m \\ \vdots & \vdots & \vdots & \ddots & \vdots \\ 1 & x_n & x_n^2 & \ldots & x_n^m \end{bmatrix} \begin{bmatrix} \beta_0 \\ \beta_1 \\ \beta_2 \\ \vdots \\ \beta_m \end{bmatrix} + \begin{bmatrix} \varepsilon_1 \\ \varepsilon_1 \\ \varepsilon_1 \\ \vdots \\ \varepsilon_n \end{bmatrix},$$

Size of the matrix depends on the amount of data and correlation among each data type. Though we always wish to fit the curve and decrease error, we must check whether fitting all the points makes sense logically. We must avoid overfitting as polynomial regression is just a statistical tool that requires human logic and intelligence to decide on right and wrong. You can visualize the problems related to overfitting by looking at the Figure 11.13.

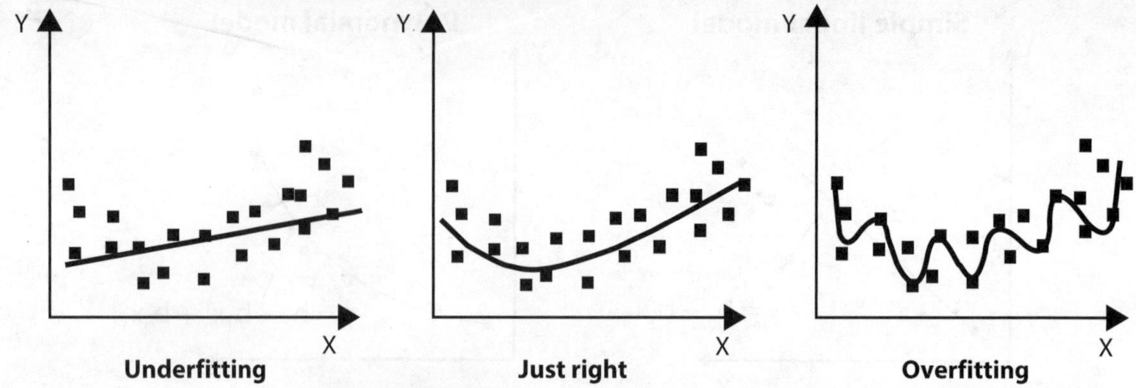

Figure 11.13 Regression lines and data fitting

We must also keep the order of the polynomial low to avoid complexities. There are two ways of doing a **Polynomial regression – forward selection** and **backward selection. In** forward selection, the degree of polynomial is continuously increased till the t-test for the highest order is insignificant. But in backward selection, the highest order polynomial is deleted till the t-test for the higher order polynomial is significant.

11.7.2 Steps for polynomial regression

The main steps involved in Polynomial regression include:

Step 1: Data Pre-processing
Step 2: Build a Linear Regression model and fit it to the dataset
Step 3: Build a Polynomial Regression model and fit it to the dataset
Step 4: Visualize the result for Linear Regression and Polynomial Regression model
Step 5: Predict the output (values of dependent variable)

In the above procedure, we have created linear regression just for reference. The Polynomial regression model will be actually used for seeing the predicted values.

Example: Download a sample data set data1.cv and compare the performance of linear and polynomial regression.

```
# Importing the libraries
import numpy as np
import matplotlib.pyplot as plt
import pandas as pd
# Importing the dataset
datas = pd.read_csv('data1.csv')
print(datas )

# Dividing the dataset into 2 components

X = datas.iloc[:, 1:2].values
y = datas.iloc[:, 2].values
```

A Polynomial Regression algorithm is also called Polynomial Linear Regression because it does not depend on the variables, instead, it depends on the coefficients, which are arranged in a linear fashion

```
# Fitting Linear Regression to the dataset
# Fitting Linear Regression to the dataset
from sklearn.linear_model import
LinearRegression
lin = LinearRegression()

lin.fit(X, y)
# Visualising the Linear Regression results
plt.scatter(X, y, color = 'blue')

plt.plot(X, lin.predict(X), color = 'red'
plt.title('Linear Regression')
plt.xlabel('Temperature')
plt.ylabel('Pressure')
plt.show()
# Fitting Polynomial Regression to the dataset
from sklearn.preprocessing import
PolynomialFeatures

poly = PolynomialFeatures(degree = 4)
X_poly= poly.fit_transform(X)
poly.fit(X_poly, y)
lin2 = LinearRegression()
lin2.fit(X_poly, y)
# Visualising the Polynomial Regression result
plt.scatter(X, y, color = 'blue')

plt.plot(X, lin2.predict(X_poly), color = 'red')
plt.title('Polynomial Regression')
plt.xlabel('Temperature')
plt.ylabel('Pressure')
  plt.show()
```

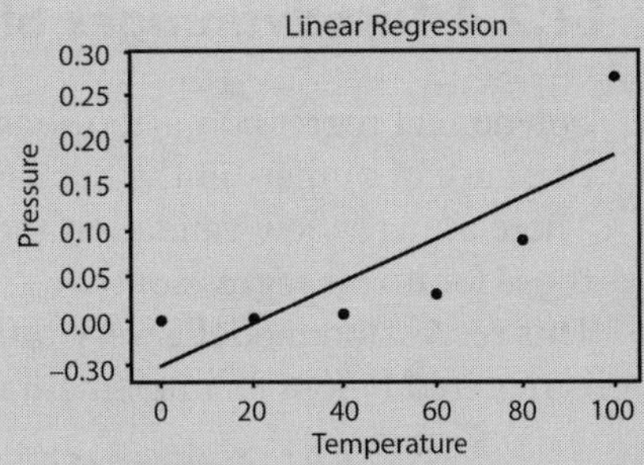

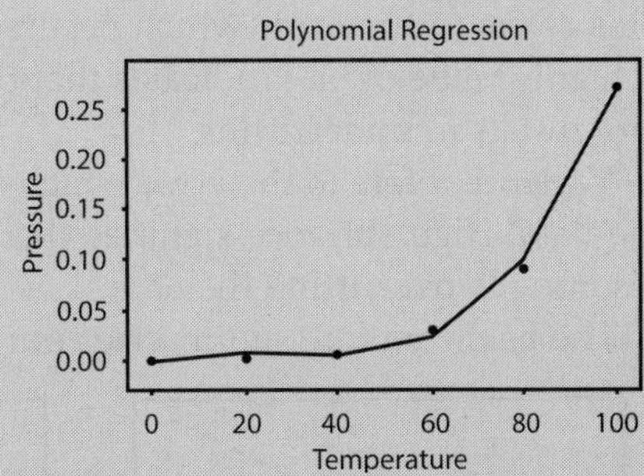

To prevent over-fitting, we can add more training samples so that the algorithm doesn't learn the noise in the system and can become more generalized

11.7.3 Advantages of using polynomial regression

- Polynomial regression supports functionality that allows a wide range of function to fit under it.
- It fits wide range of curvature.
- It also provides the best approximation of the relationship between dependent and independent variables.
- The fitted model is more reliable when it is built on large numbers of observations.
- The model does not extrapolate beyond the limits of observed values.
- Values for independent variable (x) must not be too large as they will cause overflow with higher degree polynomials (that is, scale down x if necessary).

11.7.4 Disadvantages of using polynomial regression

- Polynomial regression is too sensitive to the outliers.
- Presence of outliers in the data affects the results of a non-linear analysis.
- There are very few validation tools for the detection of outliers in non-linear regression than those for linear regression.
- This regression model is very difficult to implement and an in-depth knowledge of this model is required before its implementation.

11.7.5 The bias vs variance trade-off

Bias refers to the error which occurs due to a model's simplistic assumptions in fitting the data. A higher value of bias indicates that the model is unable to capture patterns in the data and therefore results in **underfitting**.

Variance refers to the error which arises because of a complicated model that tries its best to fit the data. High variance signifies that the model passes through most of the data points, thereby resulting in **overfitting** the data.

The below picture summarizes our learning (Figure 11.14).

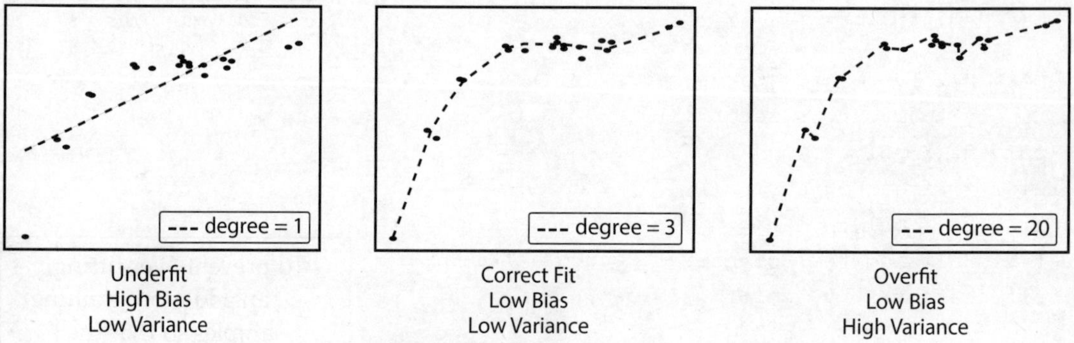

Figure 11.14 Bias vs variance

From the figure, we can conclude that as the complexity of the model increases, the value of bias decreases and variance increases and vice-versa (Figure 11.15). An ideal machine learning model should have **low variance and low bias**. However, practically, this goal is impossible to achieve. So, we usually strive hard to select a model that performs well both on the train and unseen data, a **trade-off** is made.

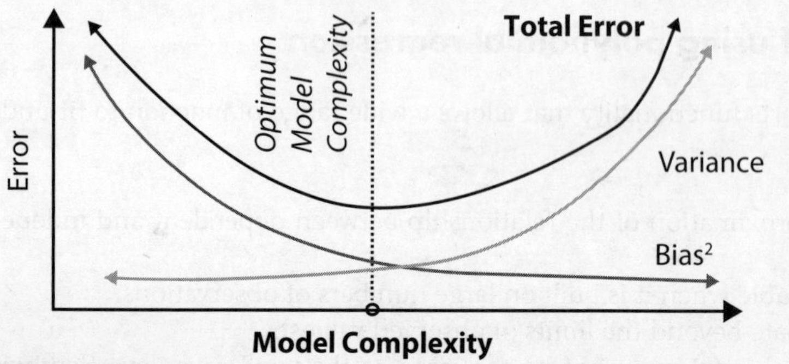

> Ridge and Lasso regression are some of the simple techniques to reduce model complexity and prevent overfitting which may result from simple linear regression

Figure 11.15 Visualizing relationship between bias, variance, model complexity and error

11.8 Regularized regression

We have studied that in linear regression algorithm, coefficients for each independent variable are selected in such a way that the loss function is minimized. Too large coefficients result in overfitting the model on the training dataset. Such a model will not generalize well on the unseen data. Therefore, to overcome this limitation, we perform regularization that penalizes large coefficients. In this section, we will read about Lasso regression and Ridge regression that implements regularization.

11.8.1 Ridge regression

Ridge regression is an extension of linear regression. In this algorithm, the loss function is modified to minimize the complexity of the model. In the loss function, a penalty parameter is added. This penalty is equivalent to the square of the magnitude of the coefficients. Mathematically, this can be expressed as,

```
Loss function = OLS + alpha * summation (squared coefficient values)
```

Here, ***OLS*** is ordinary least square, and

alpha is the parameter we need to select. A low alpha value can lead to overfitting, whereas a high alpha value can result in underfitting.

Scikit-learn helps users to create a Ridge regression model using the Ridge class. Some important parameters of the ridge function can be given as,

$$\sum_{j=1}^{m}\left(Y_i - W_0\sum_{i=1}^{n}W_iX_{ji}\right)^2 + \alpha\sum_{i=1}^{n}W_i^2 = loss\_function + \alpha\sum_{i=1}^{n}W_i^2$$

Alpha, is a floating-point value that acts like a tuning parameter and specifies how much we want to penalize the model.

fit_intercept, is a Boolean value that specifies a constant value that should be added to the decision function. No intercept will be used in calculation, if fit_intercept is set to False.

tol is a floating-point value that represents the precision of the solution.

normalize is an optional Boolean value that is set to False by default.

max_iter is an optional integer value that represents the maximum number of iterations taken for conjugate gradient solvers.

solver represents which solver to use in the computational routines – 'auto', 'svd', 'cholesky', 'lsqr', 'sparse_cg', 'sag', or 'saga'.

Attributes

Some important attributes used by Ridge module:

coef_ provides the weight vectors.

Intercept_ represents the independent term in decision function.

n_iter_ returns the actual number of iterations for each target.

> .intercept_ is a one-dimensional array with the single element b0 and .coef_ is a two-dimensional array with the single element b1

11.8.2 Implementation example

Example: Generate a random data set having 10 samples and 5 features. Use Ridge Regression with an alpha value =0.2 to create a model. Print the score of this model and also the value of attributes.

```
from sklearn.linear_model import Ridge
import numpy as np
n_samples, n_features = 10, 5
#np.random.RandomState() constructs a random number generator.
rng = np.random.RandomState(0)
y = rng.randn(n_samples)
X = rng.randn(n_samples, n_features)
rdg = Ridge(alpha = 0.2)
rdg.fit(X, y)
print(rdg.score(X,y))
print(rdg.coef_)
print(rdg.intercept_)
OUTPUT
0.8657654687023124
[ 1.1961396  -0.09574812 -0.96234511  0.06421247  1.66880754]
1.1808729929860098
```

As per the output, accuracy of the model is 86%. We can increase accuracy by increasing the number of samples and features.

Example: Download US Economics time series data set , US economics.csv and perform ridge regression.

```
import pandas as pd
import numpy as np
from sklearn import model_selection
from sklearn.linear_model import Ridge
from sklearn.metrics import r2_score
from sklearn.model_selection import train_test_split
from sklearn.metrics import mean_squared_error
from math import sqrt
df = pd.read_csv('economics.csv')
print(df.shape)
print(df.describe())
target_column = ['unemploy']
predictors = list(set(list(df.columns))-set(target_column))
print(predictors)
df[predictors] = df[predictors]/df[predictors].max()
df.describe()
X = df[predictors].values
y = df[target_column].values
X_train, X_test, y_train, y_test = train_test_split(X, y, test_size=0.30,
random_state=40)
print(X_train.shape); print(X_test.shape)
```

```
rr = Ridge(alpha=0.01)
rr.fit(X_train, y_train)
pred_train_rr= rr.predict(X_train)
print(np.sqrt(mean_squared_error(y_train,pred_train_rr)))
print(r2_score(y_train, pred_train_rr))
pred_test_rr= rr.predict(X_test)
print(np.sqrt(mean_squared_error(y_test,pred_test_
rr)))
print(r2_score(y_test, pred_test_rr))
OUTPUT
975.8314265299163
0.8672577596814723
1017.3110662731054
0.8402957317988335
```

> Ridge regression shrinks the coefficients and it helps to reduce the model complexity and multi-collinearity

The above output shows that the RMSE and R-squared values for the Ridge regression model on the training data is 975 thousand and 86.7%, respectively. For the test data, the result for these metrics is 1017 thousand and 84%, respectively.

```
import pandas as pd
import numpy as np
import matplotlib.pyplot as pl
from sklearn.preprocessing import scale
from sklearn.model_selection import train_test_split
from sklearn.linear_model import Ridge, RidgeCV, Lasso, LassoCV
from sklearn.metrics import mean_squared_error

df = pd.read_csv('Hitters.csv').dropna().drop(['Division','NewLeague','Leag
ue'], axis=1)
print(df)
X = df.drop('Salary', axis = 1)
y = df.Salary
# Split data into training and test sets
X_train, X_test , y_train, y_test = train_test_split(X, y, test_size=0.5,
random_state =1)
ridge2 = Ridge(alpha = 4, normalize = True)
ridge2.fit(X_train, y_train) # Fit a ridge regression on the training data
pred2 = ridge2.predict(X_test) # Use this model to predict the test data
print(pd.Series(ridge2.coef_, index = X.columns)) # Print coefficients
print(mean_squared_error(y_test, pred2)) # Calculate the test MSE
OUTPUT
    AtBat  Hits  HmRun  Runs  RBI  ...  CWalks  PutOuts  Assists  Errors  Salary
1     315    81      7    24   38  ...     375      632       43      10   475.0
2     479   130     18    66   72  ...     263      880       82      14   480.0
3     496   141     20    65   78  ...     354      200       11       3   500.0
..    ...   ...    ...   ...  ...  ...     ...      ...      ...     ...     ...
```

```
320   573   144      9   85   60  ...      332      1314        131       12   960.0
321   631   170      9   77   44  ...      249       408          4        3  1000.0
[263 rows x 17 columns]
AtBat        0.097932
Hits         0.444881
HmRun        1.416463
Runs         0.659390
RBI          0.852001
Walks        1.001633
Years        2.732596
CAtBat       0.008208
CHits        0.034024
CHmRun       0.267417
CRuns        0.070169
CRBI         0.069769
CWalks       0.082515
PutOuts      0.106396
Assists     -0.000890
Errors       0.338381
dtype: float64
108389.65151741082
```

Instead of arbitrarily choosing an appropriate value of alpha, we can use cross-validation to choose the tuning parameter alpha. This is done by using the cross-validated Ridge regression function, RidgeCV(). To use this function, we can first declare alphas as:

```
alphas = 10**np.linspace(10,-2,100)*0.5
```

and recording the value of coefficients by writing,

```
ridge = Ridge(normalize = True)
coefs = []

for a in alphas:
    ridge.set_params(alpha = a)
    ridge.fit(X, y)
    coefs.append(ridge.coef_)
```

We can identify the value of alpha that produces the smallest cross-validation error by writing,

```
ridgecv = RidgeCV(alphas = alphas, scoring = 'neg_mean_squared_error', nor-
malize = True)
```

```
ridgecv.fit(X_train, y_train)
ridgecv.alpha_
```

We can then use the best value for ridgecv.alpha_ to refit our Ridge regression model on the full data set

```
ridge4 = Ridge(alpha = ridgecv.alpha_, normalize = True)
ridge4.fit(X_train, y_train)
mean_squared_error(y_test, ridge4.predict(X_test))
```

The complete code for using the ridge cross validation can be given as,

```
import pandas as pd
import numpy as np
import matplotlib.pyplot as plt
from sklearn.preprocessing import scale
from sklearn.model_selection import train_test_split
from sklearn.linear_model import Ridge, RidgeCV, Lasso, LassoCV
from sklearn.metrics import mean_squared_error
df = pd.read_csv('Hitters.csv').dropna().drop(['Division','NewLeague','Leag
ue'], axis=1)
print(df)
X = df.drop('Salary', axis = 1)
y = df.Salary
# Split data into training and test sets
X_train, X_test , y_train, y_test = train_test_split(X, y, test_size=0.5,
random_state =1)

ridge = Ridge(normalize = True)
coefs = []
alphas = 10**np.linspace(10,-2,100)*0.5
for a in alphas:
    ridge.set_params(alpha = a)
    ridge.fit(X, y)
    coefs.append(ridge.coef_)
# Split data into training and test sets
X_train, X_test , y_train, y_test = train_test_split(X, y, test_size=0.5,
random_state=1)
ridgecv = RidgeCV(alphas = alphas, scoring = 'neg_mean_squared_error', nor-
malize = True)
ridgecv.fit(X_train, y_train)
print("ridgecv.alpha_ = ",ridgecv.alpha_)
ridge4 = Ridge(alpha = ridgecv.alpha_, normalize = True)
ridge4.fit(X_train, y_train)
print("MSE = ",mean_squared_error(y_test, ridge4.predict(X_test)))
```

OUTPUT

```
     AtBat  Hits  HmRun  Runs  RBI  ...  CWalks  PutOuts  Assists  Errors  Salary
1      315    81      7    24   38  ...     375      632       43      10   475.0
2      479   130     18    66   72  ...     263      880       82      14   480.0
3      496   141     20    65   78  ...     354      200       11       3   500.0
..     ...   ...    ...   ...  ...  ...     ...      ...      ...     ...     ...
320    573   144      9    85   60  ...     332     1314      131      12   960.0
321    631   170      9    77   44  ...     249      408        4       3  1000.0
[263 rows x 17 columns]
ridgecv.alpha_ =  0.5748784976988678
MSE =  104628.72833197894
```

11.9 Lasso regression

Lasso regression is a modification of linear regression algorithm. It modifies the loss function to minimize the complexity of the model by limiting the sum of the absolute values of the model coefficients.

The loss function for Lasso regression is given as,

```
Loss function = OLS + alpha * summation (absolute values of the magnitude of
the coefficients)
```

Here, alpha is the penalty parameter that should be appropriately chosen.

In scikit-learn, a Lasso regression model is constructed by using the Lasso class. Some important parameters and attributes of Lasso regression function are given below.

Parameters

alpha is an optional floating-point value with a default value 1.0. It is used as a tuning parameter that decides how much we want to penalize the model.

fit_intercept is an optional Boolean value which is set to True by default. This parameter specifies that a constant (bias or intercept) should be added to the decision function.

normalize is an optional Boolean value that is False by default. If set to True, the regressor X will be normalized before regression.

max_iter is an optional integer value that represents the maximum number of iterations taken.

precompute is a Boolean value that is set to False by default. It is used to decide whether to use a pre-computed matrix to speed up the calculation or not.

warm_start is an optional Boolean value that is set to False by default. If True, solution of the previous call is reused else previous solutions are erased.

random_state is a Boolean value that represents the seed of the pseudo-random number generated which is used while shuffling the data.

Attributes

coef_ provides the weight vectors.

Intercept_ represents the independent term in decision function.

n_iter_ gives the number of iterations run

Example: Implementing Lasso regression on cancer data

```
import math
import matplotlib.pyplot as plt
import pandas as pd
import numpy as np
# difference of lasso and ridge regression is that some of the coefficients can
be zero i.e. some of the features are
# completely neglected
```

```
from sklearn.linear_model import Lasso
from sklearn.linear_model import LinearRegression
from sklearn.datasets import load_breast_cancer
from sklearn.model_selection import train_test_split
cancer = load_breast_cancer()
#print cancer.keys()
cancer_df = pd.DataFrame(cancer.data, columns=cancer.feature_names)
#print cancer_df.head(3)
X = cancer.data
Y = cancer.target
X_train,X_test,y_train,y_test=train_test_split(X,Y, test_size=0.3, random_
state=31)
# instantiate the Lasso Regression model
lasso = Lasso()
# fits the model to the training data.
lasso.fit(X_train,y_train)
train_score=lasso.score(X_train,y_train)
test_score=lasso.score(X_test,y_test)
coeff_used = np.sum(lasso.coef_!=0)
print("training score:", train_score )
print("test score:", test_score)
print("number of features used:", coeff_used)
# instantiates the Lasso Regression model with an alpha value of 0.01
lasso1 = Lasso(alpha=0.01, max_iter=10e5)
lasso1.fit(X_train,y_train)
train_score1=lasso1.score(X_train,y_train)
test_score1=lasso1.score(X_test,y_test)
coeff_used1 = np.sum(lasso1.coef_!=0)
print("training score for alpha=0.01:", train_score1 )
print("test score for alpha =0.01:", test_score1)
print ("number of features used: for alpha =0.01:", coeff_used1)
OUTPUT
training score: 0.5600974529893081
test score: 0.5832244618818156
number of features used: 4
training score for alpha=0.01: 0.7037865778498826
test score for alpha =0.01: 0.6641831577726227
number of features used: for alpha =0.01: 10
```

Lasso regression not only helps in reducing over-fitting but it can help us in feature selection

Example: Perform Lasso regression on the Hitlers.csv file. Demonstrate the use 10-fold cross-validation to choose the best alpha, refit the model, and compute the associated test error.

```
import pandas as pd
import numpy as np
import matplotlib.pyplot as plt
from sklearn.preprocessing import scale
from sklearn.model_selection import train_test_split
```

```
from sklearn.linear_model import Ridge, RidgeCV, Lasso, LassoCV
from sklearn.metrics import mean_squared_error
df = pd.read_csv('Hitters.csv').dropna().drop(['Division','NewLeague','Leag
ue'], axis=1)
print(df)
X = df.drop('Salary', axis = 1)
y = df.Salary
# Split data into training and test sets
X_train, X_test , y_train, y_test = train_test_split(X, y, test_size=0.5,
random_state=1)
# create a lasso model
lasso = Lasso(max_iter = 10000, normalize = True)
coefs = []
alphas = 10**np.linspace(10,-2,100)*0.5
for a in alphas:
    lasso.set_params(alpha=a)
    lasso.fit(scale(X_train), y_train)
    coefs.append(lasso.coef_)
# perform 10-fold cross-validation to choose the best alpha
lassocv = LassoCV(alphas = None, cv = 10, max_iter = 100000, normalize =
True)
# fit the model
lassocv.fit(X_train, y_train)
# use the best alpha value and calculating the error
lasso.set_params(alpha=lassocv.alpha_)
lasso.fit(X_train, y_train)
print("MSE =", mean_squared_error(y_test, lasso.predict(X_test)))
```

OUTPUT

```
     AtBat  Hits  HmRun  Runs  RBI  ...  CWalks  PutOuts  Assists  Errors  Salary
1      315    81      7    24   38  ...     375      632       43      10   475.0
2      479   130     18    66   72  ...     263      880       82      14   480.0
3      496   141     20    65   78  ...     354      200       11       3   500.0
..     ...   ...    ...   ...  ...  ...     ...      ...      ...     ...     ...
320    573   144      9    85   60  ...     332     1314      131      12   960.0
321    631   170      9    77   44  ...     249      408        4       3  1000.0
[263 rows x 17 columns]
MSE =  111160.39367053012
```

After analyzing the program, we can conclude that the default value of regularization parameter, alpha is 1. Out of 30 features in the data-set, only 4 are used having non-zero value of the coefficient.

Since 4 features are very less, the model is underfitting the cancer data-set. To reduce the effect of this underfitting, we can decrease the value of alpha and increase the number of iterations. If you take $\alpha = 0.01$, number of features = 10, training and test score increases.

Further reducing α to 0.0001, and increasing features to 22, training and test scores will be similar to basic linear regression.

11.10 Elasticnet regression

ElasticNet regression is a combination of Ridge and Lasso regression. Scikit-learn provides the ElasticNet class to implement the ElasticNet regression model.

Some important parameters of the ElasticNet function can be given as,

alpha is an optional floating-point value that specifies penalty for the model. Its default value is 1.0.

fit_intercept is an optional Boolean value that specifies whether a constant (bias or intercept) should be added to the decision function or not. Its default value is True.

tol is an optional floating-point value that represents the tolerance for the optimization.

normalize is an optional Boolean value which is False by default. If set to True, the regressor X will be normalized before regression.

max_iter an optional integer value that specifies the maximum number of iterations to be taken.

warm_start is an optional Boolean parameter with default value set to False. If True, any previous solution can be reused else it will erase the previous solution.

random_state is an integer value that represents the seed of the pseudo-random number generated used for shuffling the data. By default, its value is none.

Attributes of the ElasticNet regression model are,

coef_ that provides the weight vectors.

Intercept_ represents the independent term in decision function.

n_iter_ gives the number of iterations run.

Example: Implement ElasticNet Regression on the Boston Housing Data Set.

```
# import model
from sklearn.linear_model import ElasticNet
import pandas as pd
import numpy as np
import matplotlib.pyplot as plt
from sklearn import datasets
from sklearn.model_selection import train_test_split
# Loading pre-defined Boston Dataset
boston_dataset = datasets.load_boston()
print(boston_dataset.DESCR)
# Load the dataset into Pandas Dataframe
boston_pd = pd.DataFrame(boston_dataset.data)
boston_pd.columns = boston_dataset.feature_names
boston_pd_target = np.asarray(boston_dataset.target)
boston_pd['House Price'] = pd.Series(boston_pd_target)
# input
X = boston_pd.iloc[:, :-1]
```

```
#output
Y = boston_pd.iloc[:, -1]
print(boston_pd.head())
x_train, x_test, y_train, y_test = train_test_split(
    boston_pd.iloc[:, :-1], boston_pd.iloc[:, -1],
    test_size = 0.25)
print("Train data shape of X = % s and Y = % s : "%(
    x_train.shape, y_train.shape))
print("Test data shape of X = % s and Y = % s : "%(
    x_test.shape, y_test.shape))
# Train the model
e_net = ElasticNet(alpha = 1)
e_net.fit(x_train, y_train)
# calculate the prediction and mean square error
y_pred_elastic = e_net.predict(x_test)
mean_squared_error = np.mean((y_pred_elastic - y_test)**2)
print("Mean Squared Error on test set", mean_squared_error)
e_net_coeff = pd.DataFrame()
e_net_coeff["Columns"] = x_train.columns
e_net_coeff['Coefficient Estimate'] = pd.Series(e_net.coef_)
print("COEFFICIENT = ", e_net_coeff)
```

OUTPUT

```
      CRIM    ZN  INDUS  CHAS  ...  PTRATIO       B  LSTAT  House Price
0  0.00632  18.0   2.31   0.0  ...     15.3  396.90   4.98         24.0
1  0.02731   0.0   7.07   0.0  ...     17.8  396.90   9.14         21.6
2  0.02729   0.0   7.07   0.0  ...     17.8  392.83   4.03         34.7
3  0.03237   0.0   2.18   0.0  ...     18.7  394.63   2.94         33.4
4  0.06905   0.0   2.18   0.0  ...     18.7  396.90   5.33         36.2
[5 rows x 14 columns]
Train data shape of X = (379, 13) and Y = (379,) :
Test data shape of X = (127, 13) and Y = (127,) :
Mean Squared Error on test set 23.968225718955683
COEFFICIENT =      Columns  Coefficient Estimate
0      CRIM             -0.073887
1        ZN              0.037001
2     INDUS             -0.025703
3      CHAS              0.000000
4       NOX             -0.000000
5        RM              0.855715
6       AGE              0.029336
7       DIS             -0.711843
8       RAD              0.372780
9       TAX             -0.019305
10  PTRATIO             -0.777579
11        B              0.010634
12    LSTAT             -0.794296
```

From the above analysis we can conclude the following points about different regularization methods:

- Regularization is used to reduce the dependencey on any particular independent variable. Dependency is reduced by adding a penalty to the Loss function. This penalty prevents the coefficients of the independent variables to take extreme values.
- In Ridge regression, adding penalty to the loss function reduces the coefficients but does not make them 0. This means that it does not eliminate any independent variable completely. It can however, be used to measure the impact of the different independent variables.
- In Lasso regression adding penalty to loss function not only reduces the coefficients but also makes them 0, thus effectively eliminate the corresponding independent variable completely. It can also be used for feature selection.
- ElasticNet is a combination of Lasso and Ridge regression and thus performs better than both the techniques for most of the test cases.

11.10.1 Tuning ElasticNet hyperparameters

To know the best values of parameters like alpha and l1_ratio, we can use the gird search *l1_ratio* values between 0 and 1 with a 0.1 or 0.01 separation and *alpha* values from perhaps 1e-5 to 100 on a log-10 scale and identify which value works best for a particular dataset.

The scikit-learn library provides the ElasticNetCV class that automatically finds good hyperparameters. Before making the prediction, it is first fit on the dataset and then automatically finds appropriate hyperparameters.

Example: Implement the GridSearchCV class with a grid of values for the housing data set.

> Linear regression performs prediction of continuous values

```
from numpy import arange
from pandas import read_csv
from sklearn.model_selection import GridSearchCV
from sklearn.model_selection import RepeatedKFold
from sklearn.linear_model import ElasticNet
# load the dataset
dataframe = read_csv('housing.csv', header=None)
data = dataframe.values
X, y = data[:, :-1], data[:, -1]
# define model
model = ElasticNet()
# define model evaluation method
em = RepeatedKFold(n_splits=10, n_repeats=5, random_state=1)
# define grid
grid = dict()
grid['alpha'] = [1e-5, 1e-4, 1e-3, 1e-2, 1e-1, 0.0, 1.0, 10.0, 100.0]
grid['l1_ratio'] = arange(0, 1, 0.01)
# define search
search = GridSearchCV(model, grid, scoring='neg_mean_absolute_error', cv=em,
n_jobs=-1)
```

```
# perform the search
results = search.fit(X, y)
# summarize
print('MAE: %.3f' % results.best_score_)
print('Config: %s' % results.best_params_)
OUTPUT
MAE: -3.384
Config: {'alpha': 0.01, 'l1_ratio': 0.97}
```

From the output, we can see that the MAE has improved to 3.384. Ignore the negative sign as the library just uses this for optimization purposes. The value of alpha should be 0.01.

By default, the model will test 100 alpha values and use a default ratio. However, even we can specify our own lists of values to test via the *"l1_ratio"* and *"alphas"* arguments by writing,

```
ratios = arange(0, 1, 0.01)
alphas = [1e-5, 1e-4, 1e-3, 1e-2, 1e-1, 0.0, 1.0, 10.0, 100.0]
model = ElasticNetCV(l1_ratio=ratios, alphas=alphas, cv=cv, n_jobs=-1)
```

11.11 Logistic regression

Logistic regression belongs to a group of linear classifiers that is somewhat similar to polynomial and linear regression. It is a very simple, fast and easy-to-understand regression technique that is primarily used for binary classification; though it can also be applied to multi-class problems.

> Logistic regression classifies new data point by specifying which category it most closely aligns with

To understand logistic regression, we must understand the sigmoid function and the natural logarithm function.

In Figure 11.16, graph a. shows the sigmoid function (or S-shaped curve) of some variable x and graph b. depicts the natural logarithm $\log(x)$ of some variable x, for values of x between 0 and 1.

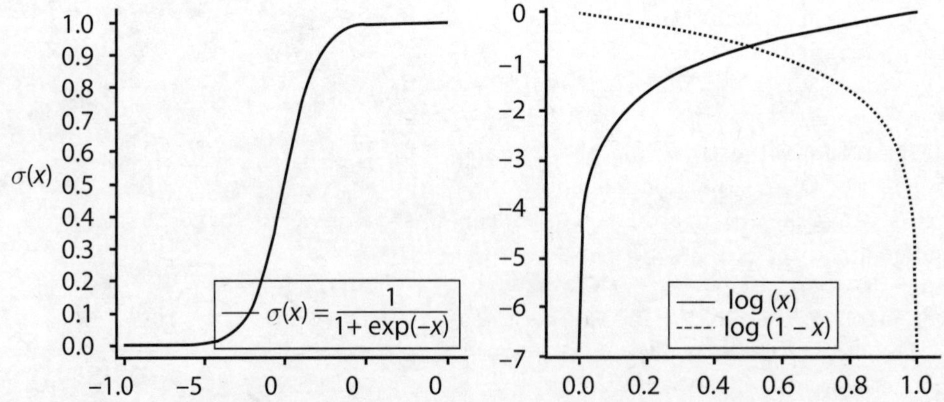

a. Sigmoid Curve

b. Logarithmic Curve

Figure 11.16 Sigmoid Curve vs Logarithmic Curve

The sigmoid function has values very close to either 0 or 1 across most of its domain. This makes it suitable for application in classification methods. In the logarithmic graph, as x approaches zero, the natural logarithm of x drops towards negative infinity. When $x = 1$, $\log(x)$ is 0. The opposite is true for $\log(1 - x)$.

The sigmoid function is an S-shaped curve that can take any floating-point number as input and map it into a value between 0 and 1. If the curve goes to positive infinity, then it means that the predicted value of y will be 1. And, if the curve goes to negative infinity, the predicted value of y will be 0. If the output of the sigmoid function is more than 0.5, then that observation is classified as 1 or YES. Similarly, if the output is less than 0.5, we can classify it as 0 or NO. If the output is 0.75, then we can say that there is a 75% chance for the target value to be 1, Yes or True.

The equation for the sigmoid function can be given as,

$$f(x) = \frac{1}{1+e^{-(x)}}$$

Logistic regression is used to classify an email as spam or not-a-spam, select or reject a loan application or to diagnose a particular disease.

11.11.1 Problem formulation

The aim of logistic regression is to find some dependent variable y on the set of independent variables $\mathbf{x} = (x_1, ..., x_r)$, where r is the number of predictors (or inputs). We start with the known values of the predictors $\mathbf{x}_i$ and the corresponding actual response (or output) y_i for each observation $i = 1, ..., n$.

The predicted responses $(\mathbf{x}_i)$ should be as close as possible to the actual response y_i for each observation $i = 1, ..., n$. In case of binary classification, the actual response can be only 0 or 1. So in such cases, using the sigmoid function is a preferred choice.

Once we have the logistic regression function ($\mathbf{x}$, it can be used to predict the outputs for new and unseen inputs.

11.11.2 Methodology

Logistic regression is a linear classifier that uses the logit function that can be mathematically expressed as, $(\mathbf{x}) = b_0 + b_1x_1 + ... + b_rx_r$. Here, the variables $b_0, b_1, ..., b_r$ are the estimators of the regression coefficients.

The logistic regression function $(\mathbf{x})$ is the sigmoid function of $(\mathbf{x})$: $p(\mathbf{x}) = 1/(1 + \exp(-f(\mathbf{x}))$. Here, $(\mathbf{x})$ is interpreted as the predicted probability such that the output for a given x is equal to 1. Therefore, $1 - (\mathbf{x})$ is the probability that the output is 0.

The aim of logistic regression function is to determine the best values of $b_0, b_1, ..., b_r$ such that $p(\mathbf{x})$ is as close as possible to all the actual responses (y). The process of calculating the best coefficients using available data is known as model training or fitting.

Moreover, $\log(p(\mathbf{x})/(1 - p(\mathbf{x}))) = f(\mathbf{x})$; hence, the name logit (of f(x)). This means that $(\mathbf{x}) = 0.5$ when $(\mathbf{x}) = 0$ and that the predicted output is 1 if $f(\mathbf{x}) > 0$, and 0 otherwise.

11.11.3 Classification performance

Binary classification results can be categorized as,

1. **True negatives:** specifies the number of correctly predicted negatives (zeros)
2. **True positives:** specifies the number of correctly predicted positives (ones)

3. **False negatives:** specifies the number of incorrectly predicted negatives (zeros)
4. **False positives:** specifies the number of incorrectly predicted positives (ones)

Performance of the classifier is calculated by comparing the actual and predicted outputs. It is also calculated by counting the number of correct and incorrect predictions. For example, classification accuracy is calculated as the ratio of number of correct predictions to the total number of predictions.

Other performance indicators of binary classifiers are:

Positive predictive value is the ratio of number of true positives to the sum of the numbers of true and false positives.

Negative predictive value is the ratio of the number of true negatives to the sum of the numbers of true and false negatives.

Sensitivity also known as recall or true positive rate is the ratio of the number of true positives to the number of actual positives.

Specificity or true negative rate is the ratio of the number of true negatives to the number of actual negatives.

11.11.4 Single-variate and multi-variate logistic regression

Single-Variate Logistic Regression: It is the most straightforward logistic regression in which there is only one independent variable, x. Figure 11.17 illustrates single-variate logistic regression:

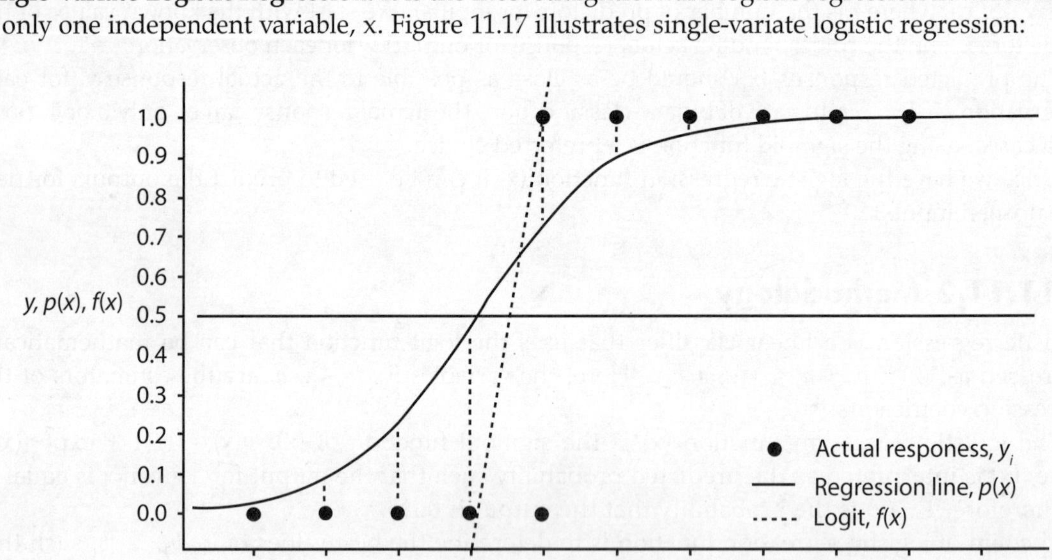

Figure 11.17 Single-Variate logistic regression

In the figure, threshold $(x) = 0.5$ and $(x) = 0$ corresponds to the value of x slightly higher than 3. The leftmost green circle has the input $x = 0$ and the actual output $y = 0$. The rightmost observation has $x = 9$ and $y = 1$. Coefficients b_0 and b_1, depicted using a dashed black line and the predicted probability $(x) = 1/(1 + \exp(-f(x)))$, is shown using a full black line.

Multi-Variate Logistic Regression: It has more than one input variable. Figure 11.18 shows the classification with two independent variables, x_1 and x_2:

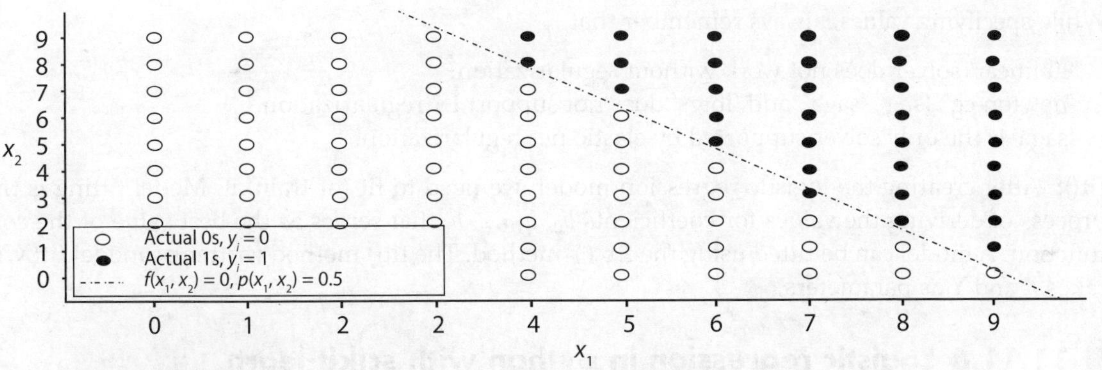

Figure 11.18 Multi-Variate regression for classifying two independent variables

Here, both the axes represent the inputs. The white circles show the data points classified as zeros and the green circles are those classified as ones. Remember that,

The logit $(x_1, x_2) = b_0 + b_1x_1 + b_2x_2$

The probabilities $(x_1, x_2) = 1 / (1 + \exp(-f(x_1, x_2)))$

The dash-dotted black line separates the two classes. This line corresponds to $(x_1, x_2) = 0.5$ and $(x_1, x_2) = 0$.

11.11.5 Functions used for logistic regression

LogisticRegression(): Some important parameters in LogisticRegression() function can be given as,

penalty is a string that decides whether regularization will be used or not and which approach will be used for it. The default value is '12' and other values are 'l1', 'ElasticNet', and 'none'.

dual is a Boolean variable with its default value as False. It decides whether to use primal (when False) or dual formulation (when True).

tol is a floating-point number having 0.0001 as the default value. It defines the tolerance for stopping the procedure.

C is a positive floating-point number with 1.0 as its default value. It defines the relative strength of regularization. Smaller the value of C, stronger is the regularization.

fit_intercept is a Boolean variable with default value set to True. It determines whether intercept b_0 (when b_0 = True) has to be calculated or taken as zero (when b_0 = False).

intercept_scaling is a floating-point number that defines the extent to which the value of b_0 has to be scaled. Its default value is 1.0.

random_state is an integer that defines the pseudo-random number generator to be used.

solver is a string that specifies the solver to be used for fitting the model. Its default value is 'liblinear'. Other values include 'newton-cg', 'lbfgs', 'sag', and 'saga'.

max_iter is an integer that specifies the maximum number of iterations taken by the solver to fit the model.

warm_start is a Boolean variable that decides whether to reuse the previously obtained solution. Its default value is False.

n_jobs is a variable having an integer value or None. It specifies the number of parallel processes to use. By default, the value of n_jobs is None.

l1_ratio is either a floating-point number between zero and one or None (default). It defines the relative importance of the L1 part in the elastic-net regularization.

While specifying values, always remember that,

'liblinear' solver does not work without regularization.
'newton-cg', 'sag', 'saga', and 'lbfgs' does not support L1 regularization.
'saga' is the only solver supported by elastic-net regularization.

fit(): After creating the logistic regression model, we need to fit (or train) it. Model fitting is the process of deriving the values for coefficients b_0, b_1, ..., b_r that serves as the best value of the cost function. A model can be fitted using the `fit ()` method. The fit() method written as model.fit(X,Y) takes X and Y as parameters.

11.11.6 Logistic regression in python with scikit-learn

The basic steps to implement logistic regression in Python include:

Step 1: Import required packages, functions, and classes. For logistic regression, we need to import LogisticRegression, classification_report(), and confusion_matrix() from scikit-learn.
Step 2: Fetch data, clean it, standardize it and transform it (if required).
Step 3: Create a classification model.
Step 4: Train (or fit) the model with the existing data.
Step 5: Evaluate the model.
Step 6: If the performance of the model is satisfactory, then use it for predicting new, unseen data.

Example: Implement binary logistic regression on random data values. Calculate the accuracy of the model and plot the confusion matrix. Set the value of C = 10 and check whether the model performs better or not.

```
from sklearn.linear_model import LogisticRegression
from sklearn.metrics import classification_report, confusion_matrix
import numpy as np
# array of consecutive, equally-spaced values within a given range
x = np.arange(10).reshape(-1, 1) # make x a 2D array
# have a value for each observation in x
y = np.array([0, 0, 0, 0, 1, 1, 1, 1, 1, 1])
model = LogisticRegression()
model.fit(x, y)
print("model.classes_ = ", model.classes_)
print("model.intercept = ", model.intercept_)
print("model.coef = ", model.coef_)
# to get matrix of probabilities that the predicted output is equal to zero: 1 - p(x) or one: p(x)
p_pred = model.predict_proba(x)
y_pred = model.predict(x) # predict y values
score_ = model.score(x, y) # accuracy of the model
conf_m = confusion_matrix(y, y_pred)
# to get a more comprehensive report on the classification
report = classification_report(y, y_pred)
print("p_pred = ", p_pred)
print("y_pred = ", y_pred)
print ("Accuracy- ratio of the number of correct predictions to the number of observations
= ", score_)
```

We must evaluate our model with the data that was not used for training

```
print("conf_m = ", conf_m)
print("report = ", report)
OUTPUT
model.classes_ =  [0 1]
model.intercept =  [-1.04608067]
model.coef =  [[0.51491375]]
p_pred =  [[0.74002157 0.25997843]
 [0.62975524 0.37024476]
 [0.5040632  0.4959368 ]
 [0.37785549 0.62214451]
 [0.26628093 0.73371907]
 [0.17821501 0.82178499]
 [0.11472079 0.88527921]
 [0.07186982 0.92813018]
 [0.04422513 0.95577487]
 [0.02690569 0.97309431]]
y_pred =  [0 0 0 1 1 1 1 1 1 1]
score_ =  0.9
conf_m =  [[3 1]
 [0 6]]
report =               precision    recall  f1-score   support
           0       1.00      0.75      0.86         4
           1       0.86      1.00      0.92         6
    accuracy                           0.90        10
   macro avg       0.93      0.88      0.89        10
weighted avg       0.91      0.90      0.90        10
```

In the output, note that the confusion matrix prints **True negatives** in the upper-left position, **False negatives** in the lower-left position, **False positives** in the upper-right position and **True positives** in the lower-right position.

Note that we can go a step ahead and visualize the confusion matrix using the `imshow()` function from Matplotlib. The function accepts the confusion matrix as an argument. The code given below plots the confusion matrix.

```
cm = confusion_matrix(y, model.predict(x))
fig, ax = plt.subplots(figsize=(8, 8))
ax.imshow(cm)
ax.grid(False)
ax.xaxis.set(ticks=(0, 1), ticklabels=('Predicted 0s',
'Predicted 1s'))
ax.yaxis.set(ticks=(0,  1),  ticklabels=('Actual  0s',
'Actual 1s'))
ax.set_ylim(1.5, -0.5)
for i in range(2):
    for j in range(2):
        ax.text(j, i, cm[i, j], ha='center', va='center', color='red')
plt.show()
```

To avoid overfitting issues, always select test data that is different from the training data

From the output, we can see that a confusion matrix is a table that is used to evaluate the performance of a classification model. It sums up the number of correct and incorrect predictions class-wise (Figure 11.19).

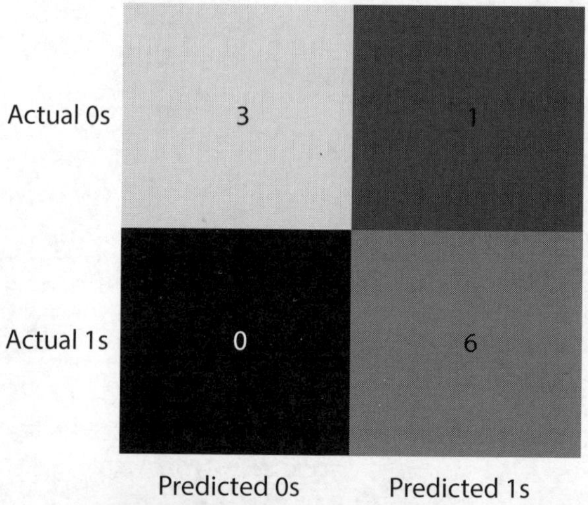

Figure 11.19 Confusion matrix

Points to remember about logistic regression

- In Binary logistic regression, the dependent variable must be binary.
- In case of binary regression, the factor level 1 of the dependent variable should represent the desired outcome.
- Only a subset of variables that are meaningful in the current context should be included.
- The independent variables should be independent of each other to avoid multi-collinearity problems.
- Logistic regression must be applied on large data sets.

11.11.7 Types of logistic regression

Different types of Logistic Regression are,

- **Binary Logistic Regression:** In this type of regression, the target variable has only two possible outcomes such as 0 or 1, True or False, Yes or No.
- **Multi-nomi**al Logistic Regression: In multi-nomial regression, the target variable has three or more nominal categories such as Students Grades.
- **Ordinal Logistic Regression:** In ordinal regression, the target variable has three or more ordinal categories. For example, we can use a rating from 1 to 5 to specify to what extent the customer is satisfied with a new product.

11.11.8 Model evaluation using confusion matrix

A confusion matrix is a table that is used to evaluate the performance of a classification model. You can also visualize the performance of an algorithm. The fundamental of a confusion matrix is that the numbers of correct and incorrect predictions are summed up class-wise.

```
# import the metrics class
from sklearn import metrics
cnf_matrix = metrics.confusion_matrix(y_test, y_pred)
cnf_matrix
```

In case of binary classification, the dimension of the confusion matrix is 2*2 as we have two classes 0 and 1. Diagonal values represent accurate predictions, while non-diagonal elements are inaccurate predictions.

Precision: Precision indicates how accurate the model is. That is, when a model makes a prediction, how often it is correct.

Receiver Operating Characteristic (ROC) Curve: A plot of the true positive rate against the false positive rate. It shows the trade-off between sensitivity and specificity. The code given below plots an ROC curve.

```
y_pred_proba = logreg.predict_proba(X_test)[::,1]
fpr, tpr, _ = metrics.roc_curve(y_test, y_pred_proba)
auc = metrics.roc_auc_score(y_test, y_pred_proba)
plt.plot(fpr,tpr,label="data 1, auc="+str(auc))
plt.legend(loc=4)
plt.show()
```

11.11.9 Advantages

- Simple and straightforward
- Efficient
- Does not require high computation power
- Easy to implement
- Easily interpretable
- Does not require scaling of features
- Calculates a probability score for observations

11.11.10 Disadvantages

- Logistic regression cannot be used to handle a large number of categorical features/variables.
- It is vulnerable to overfitting issues.
- We cannot solve non-linear problems with the logistic regression. All non-linear features must first be transformed before they can be used with logistic regression model.
- Logistic regression does not perform well with independent variables that are not correlated to the target variable and are very similar or correlated to each other.

Example: Implementing Logistic Regression on digits dataset

```
from sklearn.datasets import load_digits
from sklearn.linear_model import LogisticRegression
digits = load_digits()
from sklearn.model_selection import train_test_split
x_train, x_test, y_train, y_test = train_test_split(digits.data, digits.tar-
get, test_size=0.25, random_state=0)
```

```
# all parameters not specified are set to their defaults
logisticRegr = LogisticRegression()
logisticRegr.fit(x_train, y_train)
# Returns a NumPy Array
# Predict for One Observation (image)
logisticRegr.predict(x_test[0].reshape(1,-1))
#Predict for Multiple Observations (images) at Once
logisticRegr.predict(x_test[0:10])
#Make predictions on entire test data
predictions = logisticRegr.predict(x_test)
# Use score method to get accuracy of model
score = logisticRegr.score(x_test, y_test)
print(score)
OUTPUT
0.95
```

Example: Download the bank-full.csv and apply logistic regression on this data set.

```
import pandas as pd
import numpy as np
from sklearn import preprocessing
import matplotlib.pyplot as plt
plt.rc("font", size=14)
from sklearn.linear_model import LogisticRegression
from sklearn.model_selection import train_test_split
import seaborn as sns
# load the data from the csv file
df =pd.read_csv('bank-full.csv',sep=';',header =0)
print(df.head())
print(df.shape)
# select the data fields
print(list(df.columns))
# delete rows with NaN values
df = df.dropna()
data = pd.get_dummies(df, columns =['job', 'marital', 'default', 'housing',
'loan', 'poutcome'])
print(data.head())
print(data.columns)
#drop columns which are not needed.
data.drop(data.columns[[0,1,2,3,4,5,6,7,8,9,10,11,12,16,   18,   21,   24]],
axis=1, inplace=True)
# selecting features for X and Y
X = data.iloc[:,1:]
Y = data.iloc[:,0]
# splitting data set
```

```
X_train, X_test, Y_train, Y_test = train_test_split(X, Y, random_state=0)
# building the classifier
classifier = LogisticRegression(solver='lbfgs',random_state=0)
classifier.fit(X_train, Y_train)
predicted_y = classifier.predict(X_test)
print(predicted_y)
for x in range(len(predicted_y)):
    if (predicted_y[x] == 1):
        print(x, end="\t")
print('Accuracy: {:.2f}'.format(classifier.score(X_test, Y_test)))
OUTPUT
   age           job  marital  education  ... pdays  previous poutcome   y
0   58    management  married   tertiary  ...    -1         0  unknown  no
1   44    technician   single  secondary  ...    -1         0  unknown  no
2   33  entrepreneur  married  secondary  ...    -1         0  unknown  no
3   47   blue-collar  married    unknown  ...    -1         0  unknown  no
4   33       unknown   single    unknown  ...    -1         0  unknown  no
[5 rows x 17 columns]
(45211, 17)
['age', 'job', 'marital', 'education', 'default', 'balance', 'housing',
'loan', 'contact', 'day', 'month', 'duration', 'campaign', 'pdays',
'previous', 'poutcome', 'y']
   age  education  balance  ... poutcome_other  poutcome_success poutcome_unknown
0   58   tertiary     2143  ...              0                 0                1
1   44  secondary       29  ...              0                 0                1
2   33  secondary        2  ...              0                 0                1
3   47    unknown     1506  ...              0                 0                1
4   33    unknown        1  ...              0                 0                1
[5 rows x 36 columns]
Index(['age', 'education', 'balance', 'contact', 'day', 'month', 'duration',
       'campaign', 'pdays', 'previous', 'y', 'job_admin.', 'job_blue-collar',
       'job_entrepreneur', 'job_housemaid', 'job_management', 'job_retired',
       'job_self-employed', 'job_services', 'job_student', 'job_technician',
       'job_unemployed', 'job_unknown', 'marital_divorced', 'marital_married',
       'marital_single', 'default_no', 'default_yes', 'housing_no',
       'housing_yes', 'loan_no', 'loan_yes', 'poutcome_failure',
       'poutcome_other', 'poutcome_success', 'poutcome_unknown'],
      dtype='object')
[0 0 0 ... 0 0 0]
Accuracy: 0.97
```

Example: Download the diabetes.csv and perform logistic regression. Also plot the confusion matrix.

```
#import pandas
import pandas as pd
from sklearn.model_selection import train_test_split
```

```
from sklearn.linear_model import LogisticRegression
from sklearn import metrics
import numpy as np
import matplotlib.pyplot as plt
import seaborn as sns
col_names = ['pregnant', 'glucose', 'bp', 'skin', 'insulin', 'bmi',
'pedigree', 'age', 'label']
# load dataset
data = pd.read_csv("diabetes.csv", header=None, names=col_names, delim-
iter=",", skiprows=1)
#split dataset in features and target variable
feature_cols = ['pregnant', 'insulin', 'bmi',
'age','glucose','bp','pedigree']
X = data[feature_cols] # Features
y = data.label # Target variable
# split X and y into training and testing sets
X_train,X_test,y_train,y_test=train_test_
split(X,y,random_state=0)
# create the model
logreg = LogisticRegression()
# fit the model with data
logreg.fit(X_train,y_train)
# predict values
y_pred=logreg.predict(X_test)
cnf_matrix = metrics.confusion_matrix(y_test, y_pred)
print(cnf_matrix)
# plotting confusion matrix
class_names=[0,1] # name of classes
fig, ax = plt.subplots()
tick_marks = np.arange(len(class_names))
plt.xticks(tick_marks, class_names)
plt.yticks(tick_marks, class_names)
print("Accuracy:",metrics.accuracy_
score(y_test, y_pred))
print("Precision:",metrics.precision_
score(y_test, y_pred))
print("Recall:",metrics.recall_score(y_
test, y_pred))
# create heatmap
```

Any change in the coefficient leads to a change in both the direction and the steepness of the logistic function. It means positive slopes result in an S-shaped curve and negative slopes result in a Z-shaped curve

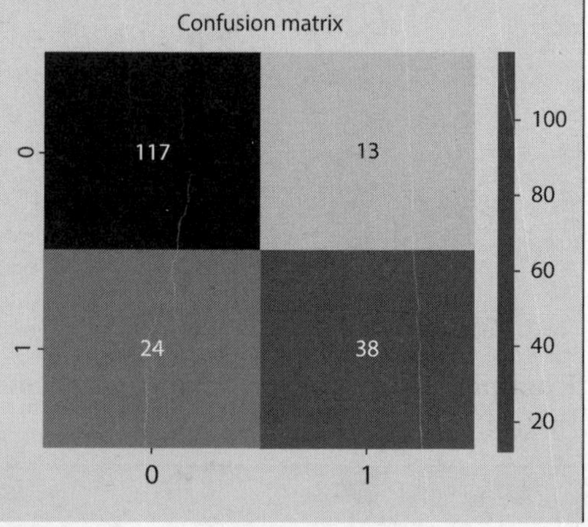

```
sns.heatmap(pd.DataFrame(cnf_matrix), annot=True, cmap="YlGnBu" ,fmt='g')
ax.xaxis.set_label_position("top")
plt.tight_layout()
plt.title('Confusion matrix', y=1.1)
plt.ylabel('Actual label')
plt.xlabel('Predicted label')
y_pred_proba = logreg.predict_proba(X_test)[::,1]
fpr, tpr, _ = metrics.roc_curve(y_test, y_pred_proba)
auc = metrics.roc_auc_score(y_test, y_pred_proba)
plt.plot(fpr,tpr,label="data 1, auc="+str(auc))
plt.legend(loc=4)
plt.show()
OUTPUT
[[117 13]
 [ 24 38]]
Accuracy: 0.8072916666666666
Precision: 0.7450980392156863
Recall: 0.6129032258064516
```

11.11.11 Differences between linear and logistic regression

Linear Regression	Logistic Regression
Linear regression is used to predict the value of continuous dependent variable using a given set of independent variables.	Logistic regression is used to predict the value of categorical dependent variable using a given set of independent variables.
Linear regression is used for solving Supervised Regression problems.	Logistic regression is used for solving Supervised Classification problems.
In linear regression, the best fit line is drawn that can be used to predict the output.	In Logistic regression, an S-curve is plotted to classify data.
To calculate accuracy, least square estimation method is used.	Maximum likelihood estimation method is used for estimating accuracy.
The output for Linear Regression is a value like, price, age, etc.	The output of Logistic regression is a class like, 0 or 1, Yes or No, etc.
Relationship between dependent variable and independent variable must be linear.	There is no such compulsion in case of logistic regression.
Collinearity between the independent variables may exist.	Collinearity between the independent variable(s) must not exist in any case.
No activation function is used.	Activation function is used to convert a linear regression equation to the logistic regression equation
No threshold value is needed.	A threshold value is added.
Linear regression assumes the normal or Gaussian distribution of the dependent variable.	Logistic regression assumes the binomial distribution of the dependent variable.

Business Scenario: Predicting Sales Based on Advertising Budget

TV	Radio	Newspaper	Sales
230.1	37.8	69.2	22.1
44.5	39.3	45.1	10.4
17.2	45.9	69.3	9.3
151.5	41.3	58.5	18.5
180.8	10.8	58.4	12.9
...	...	...	...

Assume that you are data analyst in a retail company. You are assigned the task of predicting sales based on various advertising expenditures, including TV, radio, and newspaper budgets. You have to make a report on how much impact each advertising medium has on sales. This information would help the company to optimize its advertising strategy. So, you have decided to create a model to predict future sales based on the three advertising budgets. After looking at the snapshot of the dataset given in the table, you decided to use multiple linear regression using the formula,

$$\text{Sales} = \beta_0 + \beta_1 \times \text{TV} + \beta_2 \times \text{Radio} + \beta_3 \times \text{Newspaper} + \epsilon$$

Where:

- β_0 is the intercept.
- $\beta_1, \beta_2, \beta_3$ are the coefficients of the respective variables.
- ϵ is the error term.

```
# Import necessary libraries
import pandas as pd
import numpy as np
import matplotlib.pyplot as plt
import seaborn as sns
from sklearn.model_selection import train_test_split
from sklearn.linear_model import LinearRegression
from sklearn.metrics import mean_squared_error, r2_score
# Load the dataset
data = pd.DataFrame({
    'TV': [230.1, 44.5, 17.2, 151.5, 180.8],
    'Radio': [37.8, 39.3, 45.9, 41.3, 10.8],
    'Newspaper': [69.2, 45.1, 69.3, 58.5, 58.4],
    'Sales': [22.1, 10.4, 9.3, 18.5, 12.9]
})
# Data Exploration
print(data.describe())
sns.pairplot(data)
# Split the data into features and target variable
X = data[['TV', 'Radio', 'Newspaper']]  # Features
y = data['Sales']  # Target variable
# Split into training and testing sets
X_train, X_test, y_train, y_test = train_test_split(X, y, test_size=0.2,
random_state=42)
# Initialize and train the regression model
model = LinearRegression()
model.fit(X_train, y_train)
# Predict the sales on test data
```

```
y_pred = model.predict(X_test)
# Evaluate the model
mse = mean_squared_error(y_test, y_pred)
r2 = r2_score(y_test, y_pred)
print("Mean Squared Error: ", mse)
print("R-squared: ", r2)
# Coefficients and Intercept of the model
print("Intercept: ", model.intercept_)
print("Coefficients: ", model.coef_)
# Visualize Actual vs Predicted Sales
plt.scatter(y_test, y_pred)
plt.xlabel('Actual Sales')
plt.ylabel('Predicted Sales')
plt.title('Actual vs Predicted Sales')
plt.show()
```

Key Terms

Bias: Error which occurs due to a model's simplistic assumptions in fitting the data.
Confusion matrix: A table that is used to evaluate the performance of a classification model.
False negatives: Number of incorrectly predicted negatives (zeros).
False positives: Number of incorrectly predicted positives (ones).
Model Training: The process of calculating the best coefficients using available data is known as model training or fitting.
Outlier: An outlier is an observation or a data point having either too high or too low value as compared to other observations/data points.
Polynomial Regression: A form of linear regression in which the relationship between the independent variable x and dependent variable y is modeled as an ***nth*** degree polynomial.
Receiver Operating Characteristic (ROC) Curve: A plot of the true positive rate against the false positive rate. It shows the trade-off between sensitivity and specificity.
Regression analysis: A statistical method tool that allow users to study the relationship between a dependent (target) and one or more independent (predictor) variables.
True negatives: Number of correctly predicted negatives (zeros).
True positives: Number of correctly predicted positives (ones).
Variance: Error which arises because of a complicated model that tries it's best to fit the data.

Chapter Highlights

- ✶ Regression analysis is widely used for prediction, forecasting, modeling time series data, and inferring the causal-effect relationship between variables.
- ✶ The vertical distance between the data points and the regression line should be minimum as this line indicates whether the model has captured a strong relationship or not.
- ✶ Regression analysis creates a mathematical equation that defines y as a function of x variables. This equation is then used to predict the value of y on the basis of values of the predictor variables (x).
- ✶ Linear regression assumes that there exists a linear relationship between the outcome and the predictor variables.

- ✶ If the relationship between the outcome and the predictor variables is not linear, then a non-linear regression model (like *polynomial and spline regression)* is preferred over a linear model.
- ✶ In a large multi-variate data set containing some correlated predictors, variables are summarized into a few new variables that are a linear combination of the original variables using techniques based on principal components.
- ✶ Penalized regression simplifies a large multi-variate model by penalizing the model for having too many variables.
- ✶ Ridge regression is basically used for analyzing numerous regression data.
- ✶ Lasso regression uses thresholds to select a subset of the covariates given for the implementation of the final model.
- ✶ Polynomial regression is used to construct a model that fits non-linearly separated data. In such a case, the best-fitted line is not a straight line, but a curve.
- ✶ Forward selection continuously adds variables to the set and reviews the performance of the model. It stops when no further improvement is needed (or being achieved).
- ✶ Backward elimination removes variables until no extra variable is left to be deleted without considerable loss. Bidirectional elimination is a good combination of both the approaches.
- ✶ Multiple linear regression can be used to find out which factor has the highest impact on the predicted output and how different variables relate to each other.
- ✶ Dependency is reduced by adding a penalty to the Loss function. This penalty prevents the coefficients of the independent variables to take extreme values.

Review Questions

1. Explain the importance of regression analysis.
2. Give the equation of the most basic regression analysis technique.
3. Write a short note on different metrics that are used to evaluate a regression model.
4. Explain the k-fold cross-validation technique.
5. What are different types of regression models?
6. List the errors that are calculated to identify the best-fit line in case of linear regression.
7. What assumptions do Linear regression algorithms make about the underlying dataset?
8. Linear regression faces some critical issues. Comment.
9. List some reasons for not getting effective results from multiple linear regression model.
10. Give some applications of linear regression.
11. Write a short note on polynomial regression.

Programming Exercise

1. Create a data frame with random values. Use linear regression model on this data that predicts values.
2. Consider the following data set in which salaries of the top 10 positions are mentioned with their levels. Use the polynomial regression model to prove that there exists a non-linear relationship between the Position levels and the salaries. Visualize the results using a scatter plot. Choose different value of degrees and test the accuracy. Also predict value for a given value of x.

Position	Level (X-Variable)	Level (Y-variable)
Business Analyst	1	45000
Junior Consultant	2	50000
Senoir Consultant	3	60000
Manager	4	80000
Country Manager	5	110000
Region Manager	6	150000
Partner	7	200000
Senior Partner	8	300000
C-level	9	500000
CEO	10	1000000

3. Generate some random data to compare the performance of linear and polynomial regression.
4. Perform polynomial regression on the housing data set.
5. Perform Ridge regression on the housing data set.
6. Evaluate the Lasso regression model on the housing dataset using repeated 10-fold cross-validation and report the average mean absolute error (MAE) on the dataset. Use this model to make predictions on new data.
7. Perform multiple linear regression on Boston Housing data set.
8. Perform linear regression on economics.csv and check the error rate.
9. Use the Lasso regression model on Boston housing data set to predict values for new data.
10. Use the LassoCV function to try a grid of values between 0 and 1 with a separation of 0.01 to choose the best value for alpha parameter for the housing data set.
11. Write a code using automatically configured ElasticNet algorithm. Specify the values of alpha to be tested as a list.
12. Demonstrate the application of logistic regression on MNIST dataset.
13. Download the Student-Pass-Fail-Data.csv and perform logistic regression on it. Use this model to predict values for Pass_Or_Fail variable and calculate its accuracy.
14. Download the user_behavior_dataset and predict whether a user will purchase the product or not. Also find out the relationship between Age and Estimated Salary.
    Hint: Scale the values of Age and Salary.
15. Use the cars.csv and predict the value of CO_2 based on weight and volume using linear regression.
16. Modify the code of Programming Exercise 15 by scaling the values before implementing linear regression model.
17. Create a 2D array with random values and demonstrate the application of linear regression on it.
18. Create a data set with random values and demonstrate the application of polynomial regression on it.

Fill in the Blanks

1. __________ analysis is widely used for prediction, forecasting, modeling time series data, and inferring the causal-effect relationship between variables.
2. The vertical distance between the data points and the regression line should be ________ (minimum/ maximum).

3. The best regression model is one with the ________ prediction error.
4. __________ represents the proportion of variation in the data thereby reflecting the overall quality of the model.
5. ______ regression is applied when relationship between the dependent and independent variables are calculated by computing probabilities.
6. _________ selection continuously adds variables to the set and reviews the performance of the model.
7. ________ regression is preferred when there are too many predictors as compared to the number of observations.
8. Linear regression helps us to find the most optimal value for ________ and the ______.
9. _________ regression can be used to find out which factor has the highest impact on the predicted output and how different variables relate to each other.
10. ________ refers to the error which occurs due to a model's simplistic assumptions in fitting the data.
11. High variance signifies that the model passes through most of the data points, thereby resulting in ________ the data.
12. In Ridge regression, _______ acts like a tuning parameter that specifies how much we want to penalize the model.
13. ______ to a loss function prevents the coefficients of the independent variables to take extreme values.
14. _________ regression eliminates any independent variable completely.
15. Performance of the classifier is calculated by comparing the ______ and ______ outputs.
16. ________ is calculated as the ratio of the number of correct predictions to the total number of predictions.
17. ________ is the ratio of the number of true negatives to the number of actual negatives.
18. In Binary logistic regression, the dependent variable must be ______.
19. In a confusion matrix, diagonal values represent ________ predictions, while non-diagonal elements are ______ predictions.

State True or False

1. Regression analysis is used to predict discrete values only.
2. The graph plotted after regression analysis can either have a straight line or a curve.
3. Linear regression assumes that there exists a linear relationship between the outcome and the predictor variables.
4. Linear regression simplifies a large multi-variate model by penalizing the model for having too many variables.
5. Higher the RMSE, better is the model.
6. Linear regression suffers from underfitting issues.
7. Linear regression cannot detect outliers.
8. Logistic regression is mostly used to analyze continuous data.
9. Lasso regression reduces the number of dependent variables if the penalty term is huge.

10. Polynomial regression plots a straight line that best fits the data.
11. Linear regression assumes that there is very little or no auto-correlation in the data.
12. A higher value of bias indicates that the model results in underfitting.
13. Bias is an error which arises because of a complicated model that tries its best to fit the data.
14. Cross-validation can be done to choose the tuning parameter alpha.
15. The sigmoid function has values very close to either 0 or 1 across most of its domain.
16. False negatives specify the number of correctly predicted negatives or zeros.

Give the Output

```
import numpy as np
import matplotlib.pyplot as plt
np.random.seed(0)
x = 2 - 3 * np.random.normal
(0, 1, 20)
y = x - 2 * (x ** 2) + 0.5 *
(x ** 3) + np.random.normal(-3, 3, 20)
plt.scatter(x,y, s=10)
plt.show()
```

CHAPTER 12

Classification and Clustering*

Fraud Detection Using Classification and Clustering

Assume that being the Vice President of a renowned bank, you are focused to detect fraudulent transactions to minimize financial losses. Your bank processes millions of transactions every day. In such a scenario, you need to classify transactions as fraudulent or non-fraudulent to prevent financial losses.

Every transaction has features like:

Transaction amount	**Transaction time**	**Customer location**
Merchant details	**Transaction frequency for a customer**	**Device or card used**

Fraudulent transactions are identified by finding anomalies in the transactions.

After reading about regression analysis in the last chapter, let us learn about some crucial clustering techniques in this chapter.

12.1 K-Nearest algorithm

The k-nearest neighbor (KNN) algorithm is a supervised learning algorithm in which the output value of data is known, but how to get the output is not known. For example, if we have several groups of labeled samples and all items available are homogeneous, then to find which group an item with an unknown label belongs to, we will find similarities between the item (at hand) and with items in each group. Finally, we will conclude that the item belongs to the group to which it is most similar. The KNN algorithm works in exactly the same way.

The KNN algorithm stores all available cases and classifies new cases by a majority vote of its k neighbors. The algorithm segregates unlabeled data values into well-defined groups.

Technically speaking, KNN is a non-parametric supervised learning algorithm which classifies data into a particular category with the help of training set. Here, the word non-parametric means that it makes assumptions on the underlying data distribution. Non-parametric methods do not have fixed numbers of parameters in the model. The parameters in the model grow with the training dataset.

KNN uses all of the data for training while classifying a new data point or instance

In the KNN algorithm, the value for a new instance (x) is predicted by searching the training set for the k most similar cases (neighbors) and summarizing the output values for those k cases. In other words, this is the mode (or most common) value.

*Note: The datasets and colored pictorial representation of graphs and charts from this chapter is available online. For more details, please refer to the back cover of the book.

12.1.1 Choosing an appropriate k value

The most important thing to do in the KNN algorithm is to determine an appropriate value of k, that is, the number of nearest neighbors. A large value of k reduces the noisy data. But if we have more number of data points in one group then we may ignore the smaller patterns which may have useful insights.

12.1.2 Example of KNN algorithm

If we have n number of students rated on two parameters – Academic Score and EC Score on a scale of 1 to 10, as given in Table 1.

Table 1: || Student's Record

Name	Academic Score	EC Score	Grade
Ria	8	8	Outstanding
Khushank	9	1	Academically Sound
Mehar	4	8	Sporty
Nagma	2	1	Below Average

Then, Academic Score is an indication of how well the student performs academically and EC Score is the score obtained by the student in extra-curricular activities.

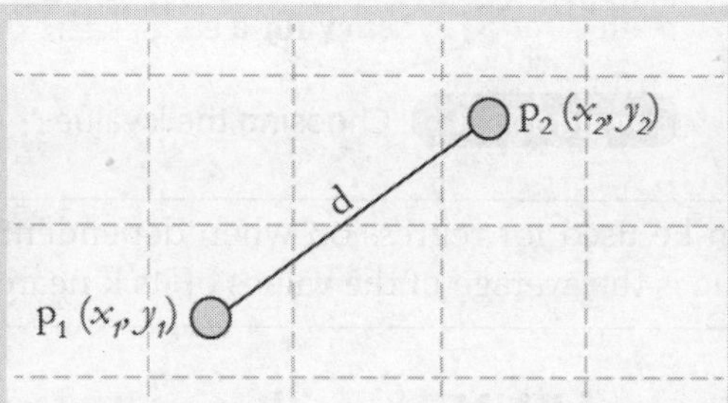

$$\text{Euclidean distance (d)} = \sqrt{(x_2 - x_1)^2 + (y_2 - y_1)^2}$$

Equation for Euclidean Distance

Now, if we have a new student to categorize then we will calculate the distance between 'New Student' and its nearest neighbors ('Outstanding', 'Sporty', 'Academically Sound' and 'Below Average') using the Euclidean distance formula.

Assuming that co-ordinates of the New Student are (8,2), we calculate the distance between Below Average (2,1) and New Student as:

dist(Below Average, New Student) = 6.08

Similarly, calculate the distance of New Student from each of its nearest neighbors as shown in Table 2.

Table 2: || Updated Student's Records

Name	Academic Score	EC Score	Grade	Distance to new Student
Ria	8	8	Outstanding	6.08
Khushank	9	1	Academically Sound	1.41
Mehar	4	8	Sporty	7.21
Nagma	2	1	Below Average	6.08

We see that the distance between New Student and Academically Sound is the least, so the New Student belongs to the group of academically sound students.

KNN algorithm can also be used for prediction. It is extensively used in pharmaceutical industry to detect the growth of oncogenic (cancer) cells or presence of a disease. We will read more about it in Chapter 12, where the implementation of the algorithm is discussed in detail.

12.1.3 Choosing the k value

Consider the given Figure 12.1. If we have two classes – class A denoted by red stars and class B indicated by blue triangles, then to classify a new green square object, the value of k plays an important role. If k = 3, then according to our figure the 3 nearest neighbors belong to class B. So the new object is placed in class B. But if we take k = 7, then the new object will be a member of class A. If we take k = 1, then the new object will belong to class B. Hence, value of k greatly influences the classification.

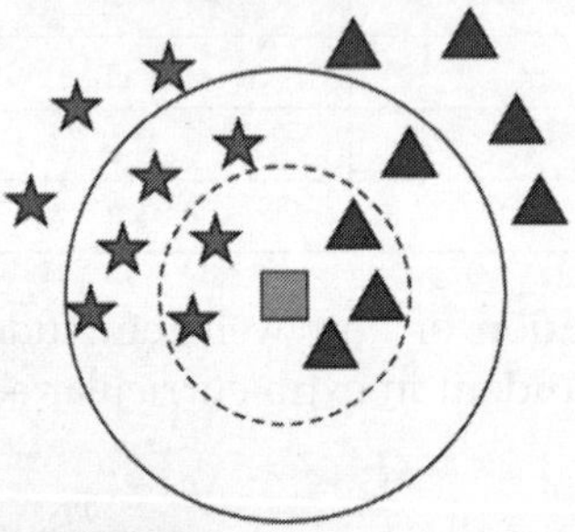

Figure 12.1 Choosing the k value

> The K-nearest neighbor can be used for regression when dependent variable is continuous. In this case, the predicted value is the average of the values of its k nearest neighbors.

12.1.4 Pros and Cons of KNN algorithm

Pros:

- The KNN algorithm is a very simple and effective algorithm.
- Users can easily implement the algorithm which has made the algorithm quiet popular with data professionals.
- The algorithm is highly unbiased in nature and does not make any prior assumption of the underlying data.
- The KNN algorithm works well with multi-class algorithms.
- The algorithm can be applied to both classification and regression.

> KNN is a non-parametric learning algorithm, which means that it doesn't assume anything about the underlying data

Cons:

- Usually, simple things are not very powerful. Same is the case with KNN algorithm.
- Although the algorithm trains the model really fast, the prediction time is high.
- Many a times useful insights may get ignored.
- The algorithm is sensitive to the scale of data, so data must first be standardized.
- The performance of the algorithm deteriorates when there are multiple independent variables.
- The algorithm requires more memory and is computationally expensive.
- It does not work well if the target variable is skewed.
- The accuracy of the algorithm depends on k value. For any given problem, a small value of k will lead to a large variance in predictions. And setting k to a large value may lead to a large model bias.

Handling categorical variables in KNN

If you have categorical variables, then create k dummy variables out of these categorical variables. For example, if a categorical variable named "Designation" has 3 unique levels/categories then create 3 dummy variables. Each dummy variable has 1 against its designation and 0 otherwise.

12.1.5 Implementing KNN on the iris dataset

The iris dataset has four attributes – sepal-width, sepal-length, petal-width and petal-length. We can use the KNN algorithm to predict the class to which a specific iris plant belongs.

It is extremely straight forward to train the KNN algorithm and make predictions with it, especially when using scikit-Learn.

To implement the KNN algorithm, we must first import the KNeighborsClassifier class from the sklearn.neighbors library. KNeighborsClassifier class is initialized with one parameter – n_neighbors, which is actually the value of k. There is no ideal value for K. Though we have set it to 7, we can always select the k value after testing and evaluating the accuracy of the algorithm as shown in Figure 12.2.

Example: Perform KNN on the iris dataset

```
import numpy as np
import matplotlib.pyplot as plt
import pandas as pd
url = "https://archive.ics.uci.edu/ml/machine-learning-databases/iris/iris.
data"
# Assign column names to the dataset
names = ['sepal-length', 'sepal-width', 'petal-length', 'petal-width',
'Class']
# Read dataset to pandas dataframe
dataset = pd.read_csv(url, names=names)
dataset.head()
# split our dataset into its attributes and labels
X = dataset.iloc[:, :-1].values  # X contains first four columns of dataset
y = dataset.iloc[:, 4].values           # y has labels
from sklearn.model_selection import train_test_split
# to avoid over-fitting, create training and test splits
X_train, X_test, y_train, y_test = train_test_split(X, y, test_size=0.20)
from sklearn.preprocessing import StandardScaler
scaler = StandardScaler()
scaler.fit(X_train)
X_train = scaler.transform(X_train)
X_test = scaler.transform(X_test)
# use k-nn algorithm
from sklearn.neighbors import KNeighborsClassifier
```

```
classifier = KNeighborsClassifier(n_neighbors=7)
classifier.fit(X_train, y_train)
y_pred = classifier.predict(X_test)
# generating the confusion matrix
from sklearn.metrics import classification_report, confusion_matrix
print(confusion_matrix(y_test, y_pred))
print(classification_report(y_test, y_pred))
error = []
# Calculating error for K values between 1 and
40
for i in range(1, 40):
    knn = KNeighborsClassifier(n_neighbors=i)
    knn.fit(X_train, y_train)
    pred_i = knn.predict(X_test)
    error.append(np.mean(pred_i != y_test))
plt.figure(figsize=(12, 6))
plt.plot(range(1, 40), error, color='red', linestyle='dashed', marker='o',
         markerfacecolor='blue', markersize=10)
plt.title('Error Rate K Value')
plt.xlabel('K Value')
plt.ylabel('Mean Error')
```

> Overfitting happens when a model learns the details and noise in the training data to the extent that it negatively impacts the performance of the model on new data. This means that the noise or random fluctuations in the training data is picked up and learned as concepts by the model

OUTPUT

```
[[11  0  0]
 [ 0 13  0]
 [ 0  0  6]]
                 precision    recall  f1-score   support
    Iris-setosa       1.00      1.00      1.00        11
Iris-versicolor       1.00      1.00      1.00        13
 Iris-virginica       1.00      1.00      1.00         6
       accuracy                           1.00        30
      macro avg       1.00      1.00      1.00        30
   weighted avg       1.00      1.00      1.00        30
```

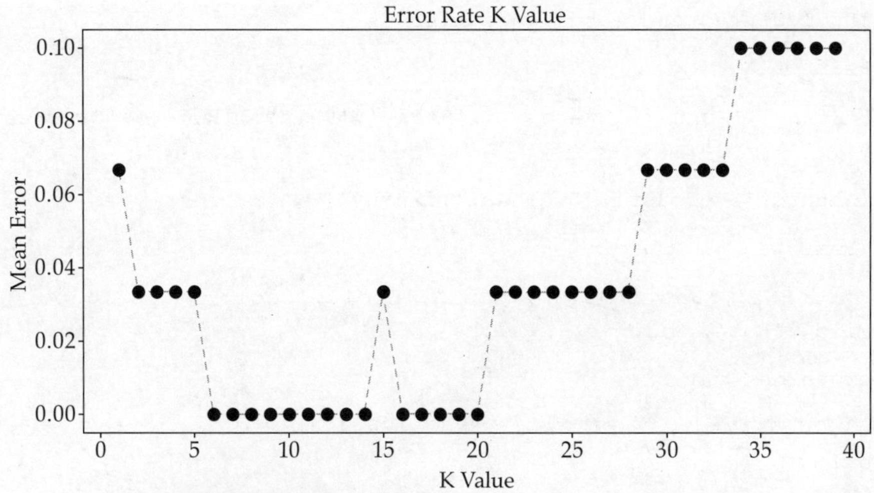

Figure 12.2 Mean error for different values of k

As per the output, the k-nn algorithm could classify all the 30 records in the test set with 100% accuracy. However, it is not necessary that the same algorithm will perform equally well with every dataset. This is because the KNN does not always perform as well with high-dimensionality or categorical features.

12.1.6 Comparing error rate with the K value

As said before, there is no ideal value of k. Randomly setting any value does not help much. So, a better way is to plot the graph of K value and the corresponding error rate for the dataset. In the above code, we have taken different values of k in the range 1 to 40. In each iteration, the mean error for predicted values of test set is calculated and the result is appended to the error list. The next step is to plot the k-values against the error rate. After plotting these values, we found that error rate is minimum, when the value of k is between 5 and 10. Hence, we had set k = 7.

Create a dataset with two features – weather (with values 'Sunny', 'Overcast','Rainy') and temperature (with values 'Hot','Mild','Cool') and one label - play (with value 'Yes','No'). Convert these categorical values into numeric.

```
import numpy as np
import pandas as pd
from matplotlib import pyplot as plt
from sklearn.datasets import load_breast_cancer
from sklearn.metrics import confusion_matrix
from sklearn.neighbors import KNeighborsClassifier
from sklearn.model_selection import train_test_split
import seaborn as sns
```

> Zip() function is used to combine multiple columns or features into a single set of data

```
# Assigning features and label variables
# First Feature
weather=['Sunny','Sunny','Overcast','Rainy','Rainy','Rainy','Overcast','Sunn
y','Sunny',
'Rainy','Sunny','Overcast','Overcast','Rainy']
# Second Feature
temp=['Hot','Hot','Hot','Mild','Cool','Cool','Cool','Mild','Cool','Mild',
'Mild','Mild','Hot','Mild']
# Label or target varible
play=['No','No','Yes','Yes','Yes','No','Yes','No','Yes','Yes','Yes','Yes',
'Yes','No']
# Import LabelEncoder
from sklearn import preprocessing
#creating labelEncoder
le = preprocessing.LabelEncoder()
# Converting string labels into numbers.
weather_encoded=le.fit_transform(weather)
print("Weather Encoded : ",weather_encoded)
# converting string labels into numbers
temp_encoded=le.fit_transform(temp)
print("Temp Encoded : ",temp_encoded)
label=le.fit_transform(play)
#combinig weather and temp into single listof tuples
features=list(zip(weather_encoded,temp_encoded))
from sklearn.model_selection import train_test_split
X_train,  X_test,  y_train,  y_test  =  train_test_split(features,  label,
random_state=1)
from sklearn.neighbors import KNeighborsClassifier
model = KNeighborsClassifier(n_neighbors=3)
# Train the model using the training sets
model.fit(X_train,y_train)
#Predict Output
y_pred= model.predict(X_test)
print(confusion_matrix(y_test, y_pred))
```

In KNeighbors Classifier, the distance metric (Euclidean, Manhattan, etc.), default is Euclidean

```
OUTPUT
Weather Encoded :  [2 2 0 1 1 1 0 2 2 1 2 0 0 1]
Temp Encoded :  [1 1 1 2 0 0 0 2 0 2 2 2 1 2]
[[1 0]
 [0 3]]
```

> Underfitting refers to a model that can neither model the training data nor generalize to new data

12.2 Decision trees

Do you remember the "Guess What" game that we used to play in our childhood? One of us will think of something, and the others had to guess what it is. For that they can ask questions, answers of which will be either "Yes" or "No" based on these clues, the answer is given. For example, consider the tree given below. (Note, it is just a sample tree, not a general tree). According to the rules specified, if you are thinking of an animal that is herbivores and does not live in forest then it is a rabbit (Figure 12.3).

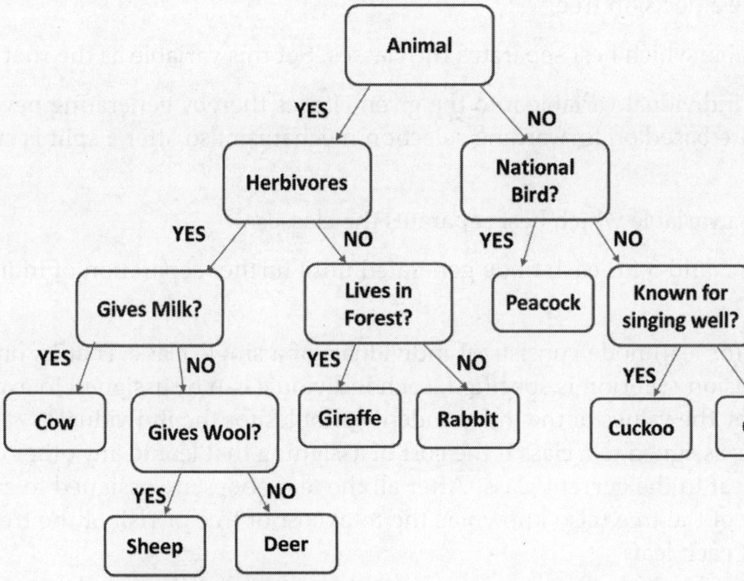

Figure 12.3 Decision Tree to identify the animal

The same concept is used to create a Decision Tree for any Data Science problem. Now let us study in detail the math behind it.

12.2.1 Basic introduction

Decision Tree is one of the most intuitive and popular techniques in data mining that provides explicit rules for classification. It works well with heterogeneous data and predicts the target value of an item by mapping observations about the item.

A decision tree represents choices and their results in the form of a tree. The nodes represent an event or choice and the edges of the graph represent the decision rules or conditions. Some common applications of decision tree include:

- predicting an email as spam or not spam
- predicting if a tumor is cancerous or not
- predicting a loan as good or bad
- predicting credit risk based on certain factors

Basically, decision trees can perform either classification or regression. For example, identifying a credit card transaction as genuine or fraudulent is an example of classification but using a decision tree to forecast prices of stock would be regression task.

Unlike linear models, decision trees map non-linear relationships quite well.

12.2.2 Principle of decision trees

Decision trees can be used to divide a set of items into n predetermined classes based on a specified criterion. They belong to a class of **recursive partitioning algorithms** that are simple to describe and implement. To create a decision tree,

Step 1: Select a variable which best separates the classes. Set this variable as the root node.

Step 2: Divide each individual variable into the given classes thereby generating new nodes. Note that decision trees are based on forwarding selection mechanism; so after a split is created, it cannot be re-visited.

Step 3: Again select a variable which best separates the classes.

Step 4: Repeat steps 2 and 3 for each node generated until further separation of individuals is not possible.

Now each terminal (or leaf) node consists of individuals of a single class. That is, once the tree is constructed and division criterion is specified, each individual can be assigned to exactly one leaf. This is determined by the values of the independent variables for the individual.

Moreover, a leaf is assigned to a class if the cost of assigning that leaf to any other class is higher than assigning the leaf to the current class. After all the leaf nodes are assigned to a class, we calculate the error rate of the tree (also known as the total cost of tree or risk of the tree) by starting with an error rate of each leaf.

Thus, we see that a Decision Tree is a supervised learning predictive model that uses rules to calculate a target value. This target value can be either:

- a continuous variable, for regression trees. Such trees are also known as Continuous Variable Decision Tree. Example, predict the price of a product or income of a customer (based on his occupation, experience, etc.).
- a categorical variable, for classification trees. Such trees are also known as Categorical Variable Decision Tree. Example, to check if the target value is "Yes" or "No"– whether a customer will buy a product or not.

Programming Tip

Decision tree works for both categorical and continuous input and output variables

Pruning the Tree: When the decision tree becomes very deep, it must be pruned as it may contain some irrelevant nodes in the leaves. Therefore, pruning avoids creating very small nodes with no real statistical significance.

An algorithm based on decision tree is said to be good if it creates a largest-sized tree and automatically prunes it after detecting the optimal pruning threshold.

The algorithm should also use Cross-validation technique and combine error rates found for all possible sub-trees to choose the best sub-tree.

For example, if Information Gain of a node is –10 (loss of 10) and then the next split on that gives us IG of 20, then a simple decision tree will stop at step 1. But in pruning, the overall gain would be taken as + 10 and both the leaves will be retained.

> A tree with each node having no more than two child nodes is called binary tree.

12.2.3 Key terminology

Some important terms that are frequently used in decision trees include (Figure 12.4):

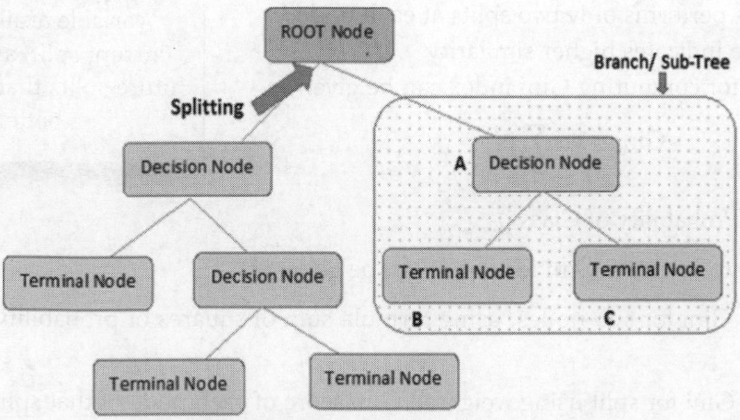

Figure 12.4 Structure of a Decision Tree

- *Root Node:* This is the node that performs the first split.
- *Terminal Nodes/Leaves:* These nodes predict the outcome.
- *Branches:* They are depicted by arrows that connect nodes and show the flow from question to answer. Technically, a branch is a sub-section of the entire tree.
- *Splitting:* The process of dividing a node into two or more sub-nodes. In a decision tree, splitting is done until a user-defined stopping-criterion is reached. For example, the programmer may specify that the algorithm should stop once the number of items per node becomes less than 30.
- *Decision Node:* A sub-node that splits into further sub-nodes.
- *Terminal or Leaf Node:* A sub-node that does not split further.
- *Parent Node:* A node which splits into sub-nodes is called a parent node of the sub-nodes (or child of the parent node).

> **Decision Tree Classifier**
> is capable of both binary (where the labels are [-1, 1]) classification and multiclass (where the labels are [0, ..., K-1]) classification

12.2.4 Measures used for split

The decision of making splits has a great impact on the accuracy of decision trees. Moreover, the decision criterion is different for classification and regression trees. Multiple algorithms can be used to decide to split a node in two or more sub-nodes. The sub-nodes should increase the homogeneity of resultant sub-nodes. For this, the decision tree splits the nodes on all available variables and then selects the split which results in the most homogeneous sub-nodes.

Some of the algorithms used for splitting the node are given below. The algorithm selection depends on the type of target variables.

Gini Index: Gini index measures inequality of distribution. It is a measurement of the purity of nodes and is used for all dependent variables. It says that if we randomly select two items from a population (with replacement) then they must be of same class. According to this measure,

- For a pure population, the probability of two items belonging to the same class is 1.
- Gini index works when the target value to be predicted is categorical.
- This measure performs only two splits at each node.
- A lower value indicates higher similarity.
- The formula for computing Gini index can be given as,

$$\text{Gini} = 1 - \sum_j p_j^2$$

> **Programming Tip**
>
> Decision trees come under greedy algorithms because, the algorithm looks for best variable available at the current split, and not about future splits that may result to a better tree

where **p(j)** is the Probability of Class j.

An alternate way to calculate Gini for a split can be given as,

Step 1: Calculate Gini for sub-nodes, using formula sum of squares of probability for success and failure ($p^2 + q^2$).

Step 2: Calculate Gini for split using weighted Gini score of each node of that split.

For example, consider Figure 12.5 given below and perform a split producing more homogeneous sub-nodes using Gini index.

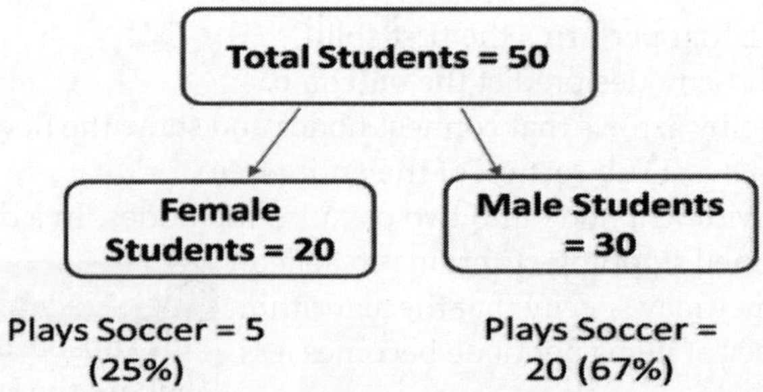

Gini for sub-node Female = (0.25)*(0.25)+(0.75)*(0.75) = 0.0625 + 0.5625 = 0.625
Gini for sub-node Male = (0.67)*(0.67)+(0.33)*(0.33) = 0.4489 + 0.1089 = 0.5578
Weighted Gini for Split = (20/50)*0.63 + (30/50)*0.56 = 0.252 + 0.336 = 0.588

Figure 12.5 Computing weighted Gini score of each node of that split.

Entropy: Entropy measures impurity. It is used for categorical target value. Higher the impurity more is the information required to describe it and vice versa. Therefore, if a population is completely homogeneous, then the entropy is zero. Correspondingly, if the value of entropy is one then it indicates that the items are equally divided in the population.

$$\text{Entropy} = -\sum_{j} p_j \log_2 pj$$

Entropy of a node can also be calculated using the formula:

$$\text{Entropy} = -\text{ p} \log_2 \text{p} - \text{q} \log_2 \text{q}$$

where, p and q is probability of success and failure, respectively in that node. A split with lowest entropy compared to parent node and other splits is chosen as lesser the entropy, the better it is.

Steps to calculate entropy for a split:

1. Calculate entropy of parent node.
2. Calculate entropy of each individual node of split.
3. Calculate weighted average of all sub-nodes available in split as illustrated in Figure 12.6.

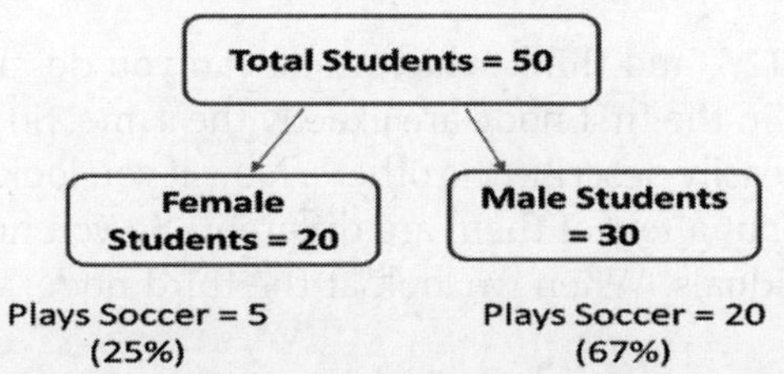

Entropy for parent node = -(25/50) log2 (25/50) – (25/30) log2 (25/30) = 1.

Entropy for Female node = -(5/20) log2 (5/20) – (15/20) log2 (15/20)

= -(0.25)(-2) – (.75)(-0.41) = 0.5 + 0.30 = 0.8

Entropy for male node = -(20/30) log2 (20/30) – (10/30) log2 (10/30)

= -(0.67)(-0.57) – (.33)(-1.59) = 0.44 + 0.52 = 0.96

Entropy for split Gender = Weighted entropy of sub-nodes = (20/50)*0.8 + (30/50)*0.96

= (0.4)(0.8) + (0.6)(0.96) = 0.32 + 0.57 = 0.89

Figure 12.6 Computing Entropy of a split

Similarly, calculate entropy for the other split at the same level and select the split with lowest entropy.

> A tree generated by using Chi Square test is known as CHAID (Chi-square Automatic Interaction Detector)

Chi-Square: The Chi-Square test is used to deduce the statistical significance of the differences between sub-nodes and parent node. It is calculated by sum of squares of standardized differences between observed and expected frequencies of target variable. The advantage of using this test is that it works well with categorical target variable. A higher value of Chi-Square indicates higher statistical significance of differences between sub-node and Parent node. It is calculated using the formula,

$$\text{Chi-square} = ((\text{Actual} - \text{Expected})^2/\text{Expected})^{1/2}$$

Steps to Calculate Chi-square for a split:

1. Calculate Chi-square for individual node by calculating the deviation for both Success and Failure.
2. Calculated Chi-square of Split using Sum of all Chi-square of Success and Failure of each node of the split.

For example, let us form a table (Table 3) containing actual and expected values for "Play Soccer" and "Not Play Soccer". We have kept expected value for "Play Soccer" and "Not Play Cricket" as 10 for Female node because parent node has probability of 50%.

Calculate Chi-square of node for "Play Soccer" and "Not Play Soccer" using the formula, = $((\text{Actual} - \text{Expected})^2/\text{Expected})^{1/2}$. Similarly, calculate Chi-square value for Male node also. Finally, add all Chi-square values to calculate Chi-square for split on Gender (Male and Female).

Table 3. || Find Chi Square

NODE	PLAY SOCCER	NOT PLAY SOCCER	TOTAL	EXPECTED PLAY SOCCER	EXPECTED NOT PLAY SOCCER	CHI-SQUARE	
						Play Soccer	Not Play Soccer
Female	5	15	20	10	10	1.58	0.7
Male	20	10	30	15	15	1.29	1.29
TOTAL CHI QUARE VALUE FOR GENDER						4.86	

Information Gain: Consider Figure 12.7 and think which node can you describe easily? The first node, right? Since all the individuals in the first node are exactly the same. So if you know the features of one individual, then you can easily describe the others. Now if you look at the second node, a majority of the elements are same but a few of them are different. So you need some additional information to describe all the individuals. When we look at the third node, we see that we need maximum information here.

Figure 12.7 Role of Information

Technically, we can say that the first node is a pure node, second node is less impure and the third is more impure. Less impure node requires less information to describe it. Correspondingly, more impure node requires more information. Information Gain is calculated as, **1- Entropy.**

Thus, Information Gain captures the amount of information one gains by selecting a particular attribute. We start at the root node of the tree and split the data on the feature that results in the largest **information gain (IG)**. Therefore, IG tells us how important a given attribute is.

12.2.5 Best split for continuous variables

Reduction in Variance is an excellent technique for continuous target variables. It uses the standard formula of variance to choose the best split. The split with lower variance is chosen as the best split to divide the individuals.

$$\text{Variance} = \frac{\sum (X - \bar{X})^2}{n}$$

where, X-bar is mean of the values and X is actual value and n is number of values.

Steps to calculate Variance:

1. Calculate variance for each node.
2. Calculate variance for each split as weighted average of each node variance.

Example: Let us use the same example and assign numerical value 1 for playing soccer and 0 for not playing soccer.

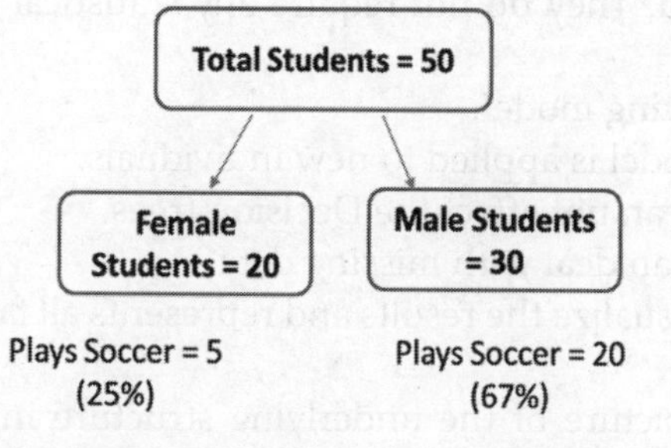

Mean of Female node = (5*1+15*0)/20=0.25 and Variance = (5*(1-0.25)^2+15*(0-0.25)^2) / 20 = ((5*0.56) + 15*(0.06))/20 = (2.8 + 8.4)/20 = 0.04

Mean of Male Node = (20*1+10*0)/30=0.67 and Variance = (20*(1-0.67)^2+10*(0-0.67)^2) / 30 = (20 * .10 + 10 * 0.44)/30 = (2 + 4.4)/30 = 0.21

Mean of Root Node = (25*1+25*0)/50=0.5 and Variance = (25*(1-0.5)^2+25*(0-0.5)^2) / 50 = 0.25

Variance for Split Gender = Weighted Variance of Sub-nodes = (20/50)*0.04 + (30/50) *0.21 = (0.4 * 0.04) + (0.6 * 0.21) = 0.016 + 0.12 = 0.136

Points to Remember

> **Programming Tip**
> As the purity of node increases, Gini index decreases

- ❑ To choose the best separation, the **X2** test is used which tests the independence of two variables X and Y.
- ❑ The number of degrees of freedom can be calculated as, `p = (number of rows - 1) X (number of columns - 1)`

Decision trees are biased toward selecting categorical variables with large numbers of levels. So, if there are categorical variables with high numbers of levels then try to remove them to have fewer levels.

- ❑ It is possible to set various options while constructing a decision tree. These options include:
  - o *Maximum Depth* which specifies the number of levels deep a tree can go. This limits the complexity of a tree.
  - o *Minimum Number of Records in Terminal Nodes.* This is important because if splitting a terminal node results in less number of records than that specified, the split is not made and the tree ceases to grow to the next level. This parameter is basically used to control overfitting problems.
  - o *Minimum Number of Records in Parent Node* to determine where a split can occur. For example, if records in a node are less than the number of records specified then it is not split further. This parameter is used to control overfitting. A higher value prevents a model from learning relations which might be important for a particular sample. Thus, a higher value may result in underfitting.
  - o *Bonferroni Correction* should be used as it adjusts for many comparisons when Chi-square statistics is used for a categorical input variable rather than categorical target variable.

12.2.6 Advantages of R decision trees

Decision trees are one of the most popular statistical techniques because they provide following advantages to the users.

- They are easy to implement.
- Results can be easily understood. They do not require any statistical knowledge to read and interpret them.
- Programmers can code the resulting model.
- They execute faster when the model is applied to new individuals.
- Outliers or extreme individuals can not affect the Decision trees.
- Some Decision tree algorithms can deal with missing data.
- A Decision tree allows users to visualize the results and represents all factors that are important in decision making.
- Decision trees provide a clear picture of the underlying structure in data and relationships between variables.
- They can also be used to identify the most significant variables in the data-set.
- Decision tree closely mirrors human decision-making compared to other regression and classification approaches.
- Decision trees require less data cleaning as compared to other techniques.
- They are not influenced by missing values to a fair degree.
- They can handle both numerical as well as categorical variables.
- Decision trees employ **non-parametric method as they** have no assumptions about the space distribution and the classifier structure.

OUTLIERS

An outlier is an individual data item or observation that lies at an abnormal distance from other data values in a random sample of a data set. It is the work of the data analyst to decide what will be considered abnormal. Outliers should be carefully investigated as they may contain valuable information about the data being processed. Data analyst must be able to answer questions like the reasons for the presence of outliers in the data set, probability that such values will continue to appear, etc. for example, if an examination was held of maximum marks 100, then one or more students getting more than 100 will be treated as an outlier.

Outlier analysis is extensively used for detecting fraudulent cases. In some cases, outliers may be contextual outliers. This means that a particular data value is an outlier only under a specific condition. For example, in hot summer season when temperature is 40°C and above, then an unexpected windstorm and rain may bring it to 32°C. Another example could be that a bank customer may not be withdrawing more than ₹50K in a month but because of a family wedding may withdraw ₹2.5 lakhs in a day.

12.2.7 Limitations of decision trees

The disadvantages of using R decision trees are as follows:

- The tree detects local, and not global, optima.
- All independent variables are evaluated sequentially, not simultaneously.

- ❑ The modification of a single variable may change the whole tree if this variable is located near the top of the tree.
- ❑ Decision trees lack robustness. Though this can be overcome by resampling, in which one can construct the trees on many successive samples and can aggregate by mean, but this will lead to a complex tree that is difficult to read and interpret.
- ❑ Since each split reduces the number of remaining records, later splits based on very few records have less statistical power.
- ❑ The property of forwarding variable selection and constant splits of nodes makes prediction by trees not as accurate as done by other algorithms.
- ❑ Overfitting is a key challenge in modeling decision trees. If there is no limit set for a decision tree, it will give 100% accuracy on training set because in the worst case, there will be a single leaf for each observation.

The problem of overfitting could be overcome by tree pruning and setting constraints.on tree size.

12.2.8 Overfitting and underfitting problems in ML algorithms

In statistics and ML algorithms, a fit refers to how well a target function is approximated. In ML algorithms, the target function is used to make predictions. Thus, it is important to know whether the target function is suffering from overfitting or underfitting problems.

Overfitting: Overfitting means that a model fits the training data too well. It occurs when a model learns the details and noise in the training data to the extent that it negatively impacts the performance of the model on new data. In such a situation, outliers in the training data are picked up and learned as concepts by the model. Thus, an overfitted model is trained with a lot of data.

Overfitting is more likely with non-parametric (like decision trees) and non-linear models that have more flexibility when learning a target function. To rectify this problem, the decision tree must be pruned after it has learned so that some of the unnecessary details that it has learnt can be easily removed.

Underfitting: Underfitting refers to a model that can neither model the training data nor generalize to new data. An underfit ML model also gives poor performance on the training data.

An ML model is said to be underfitted when it cannot capture the underlying trend of the data. Such a model does not fit the data well enough. It usually happens when we have less data to build an accurate model and also when we try to build a linear model with a non-linear data. An underfitted model can be avoided by using more data and performing dimensionality reduction.

Good Fit Model: An ML model is said to be good if it generalizes any new input data from the problem domain in a proper way. This helps us to make predictions in the future data, that the data model has never seen. Ideally, the model should be neither underfitted nor overfitted. Such a model is at the sweet spot between underfitting and overfitting. If we measure the performance of a model over time, the number of errors decreases as the training model learns. But, if we train a model for too long, the performance of the model on the training dataset may continue to decrease due to the problem of overfitting and learning the irrelevant detail and outliers in the training dataset. Simultaneously, errors in the test data start to rise as the model's ability to generalize decreases.

A good-fit model makes predictions with 0 errors. In order to get a good fit, we will stop at a point just before where the error starts increasing. At this point, the model has good skills on training dataset as well as on the testing dataset.

Limiting Overfitting Issues: While both overfitting and underfitting can result in poor performance, by far the most common problem in applied machine learning is overfitting. Overfitting can be limited by using resampling technique like the k-fold cross validation to estimate model accuracy. The k-fold cross validation allows you to train and test your model k-times on different subsets of training data and build up an estimate of the performance of an ML model on unseen data.

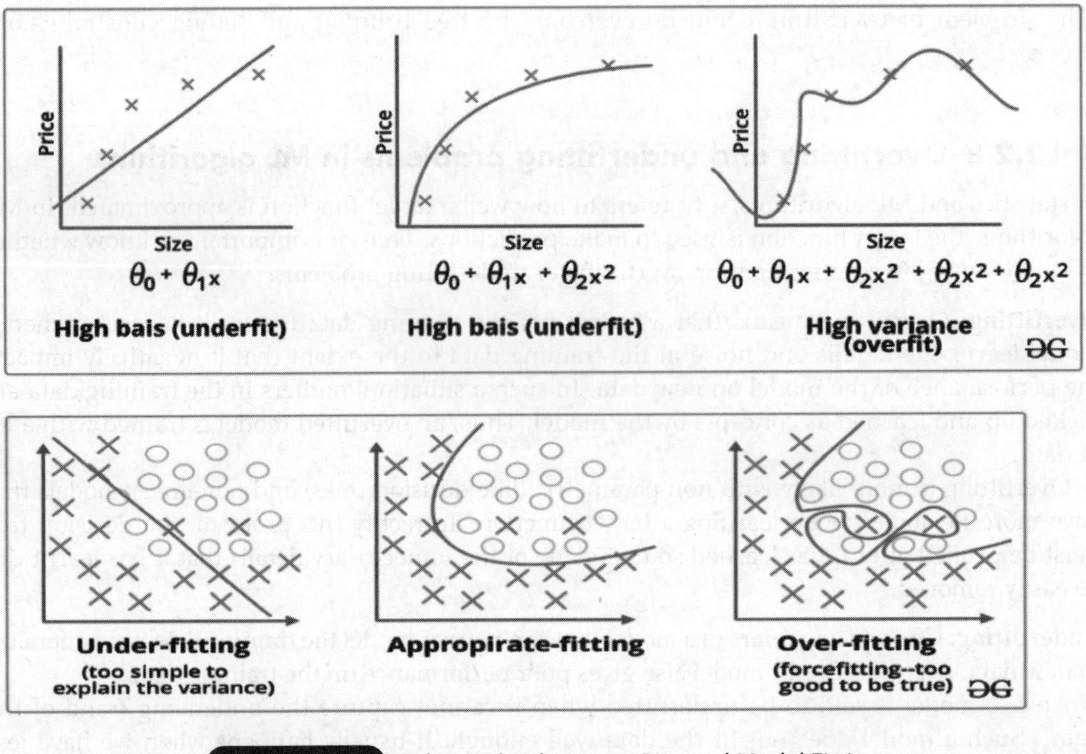

Figure 12.8 Relationship between Bias and Model Fitting

Figure 12.8 shows that an overfitted model shows low bias but high variance. Underfitted model, on the other hand, shows low variance but high bias. While overfitting results due to a complex mode, underfitting is a result of a very simple model. Both overfitting and underfitting lead to poor predictions on new datasets.

12.2.9 Improving performance of decision trees

The performance of decision trees can be enhanced by aggregating many decision trees, using methods like *bagging, random forests*, and *boosting*. In this section, we will discuss all three of them but implement random forest.

Bagging: The decision trees suffer from *high variance*. That is, if the training data is randomly divided into two parts and a decision tree is created for both the parts, then the two decision trees will be quite different. Ideally, we should get similar results when the algorithm is applied repeatedly to distinct datasets.

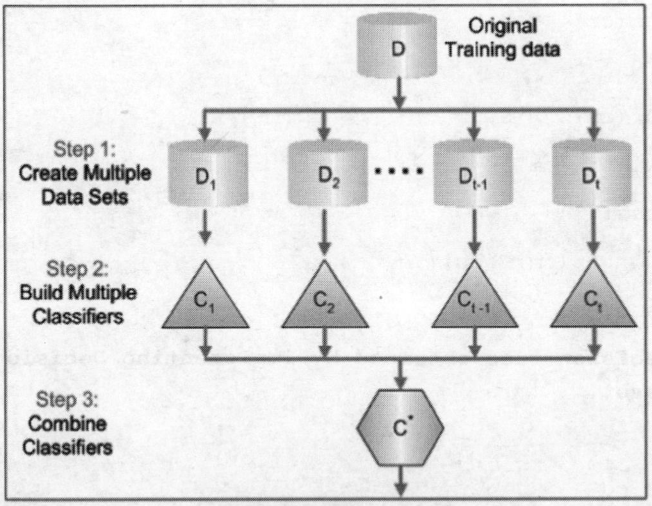

Figure 12.9 Bagging

Bagging also known as *bootstrap aggregation*, is used to reduce the variance of predictions by combining the result of multiple classifiers modeled on different sub-samples of the same dataset. This technique can be mathematically represented as,

$$\hat{f}_{bag}(x) = \frac{1}{B}\sum_{b=1}^{B}\hat{f}_b(x)$$

Look at Figure 12.9 to understand how bagging is done.

Step 1: The original dataset is divided into multiple datasets where each dataset has a fraction of the original dataset's data.

Step 2: A classifier is created on each dataset.

Step 3: Take the average of predictions made by all the classifiers.

> **Programming Tip**
> Besides decision trees, bagging can also be used to improve predictions for other many regression and classification methods

Implementing Decision Tree Algorithm

```
from sklearn.datasets import load_iris
from sklearn.tree import DecisionTreeClassifier
from sklearn.tree import export_text
iris = load_iris()
decision_tree = DecisionTreeClassifier(random_state=0, max_depth=2)
decision_tree = decision_tree.fit(iris.data, iris.target)
```

```
r = export_text(decision_tree, feature_names=iris['feature_names'])
print(r)
```

OUTPUT

```
|--- petal width (cm) <= 0.80
|   |--- class: 0
|--- petal width (cm) >  0.80
|   |--- petal width (cm) <= 1.75
|   |   |--- class: 1
|   |--- petal width (cm) >  1.75
|   |   |--- class: 2
```

Visualize the decision tree obtained by implementing DecisionTreeClassifier() on diabetes dataset.

```
# Load libraries
import pandas as pd
from sklearn.tree import DecisionTreeClassifier # Import Decision Tree Classifier
from sklearn.model_selection import train_test_split # Import train_test_split function
from sklearn import metrics #Import scikit-learn metrics module for accuracy calculation
from sklearn import tree
import pydotplus
from sklearn.tree import plot_tree
col_names = ['pregnant', 'glucose', 'bp', 'skin', 'insulin', 'bmi', 'pedigree', 'age', 'label']
# load dataset
pima = pd.read_csv("diabetes.csv", header=1, names=col_names, sep=",", skiprows=1)
print(pima.head())
#split dataset in features and target variable
feature_cols = ['pregnant', 'insulin', 'bmi', 'age','glucose','bp', 'pedigree']
X = pima[feature_cols] # Features
y = pima.label # Target variable
# Split dataset into training set and test set
```

```
X_train, X_test, y_train, y_test = train_test_split(X, y, test_size=0.3,
random_state=1) # 70% training and 30% test

# Create Decision Tree classifer object

clf = DecisionTreeClassifier()

# Train Decision Tree Classifer

clf = clf.fit(X_train,y_train)

#Predict the response for test dataset

y_pred = clf.predict(X_test)

# Model Accuracy, how often is the classifier correct?

print("Accuracy:",metrics.accuracy_score(y_test, y_pred))

# Visualising the graph without the use of graphvizplt.figure(figsize = (20,20))

tree.plot_tree(decision_tree=clf, feature_names = feature_cols, class_names
= ['0','1'],rounded = True)

plt.show()

OUTPUT

   pregnant  glucose  bp  skin  insulin   bmi  pedigree  age  label

0         8      183  64     0        0  23.3     0.672   32      1

1         1       89  66    23       94  28.1     0.167   21      0

2         0      137  40    35      168  43.1     2.288   33      1
```

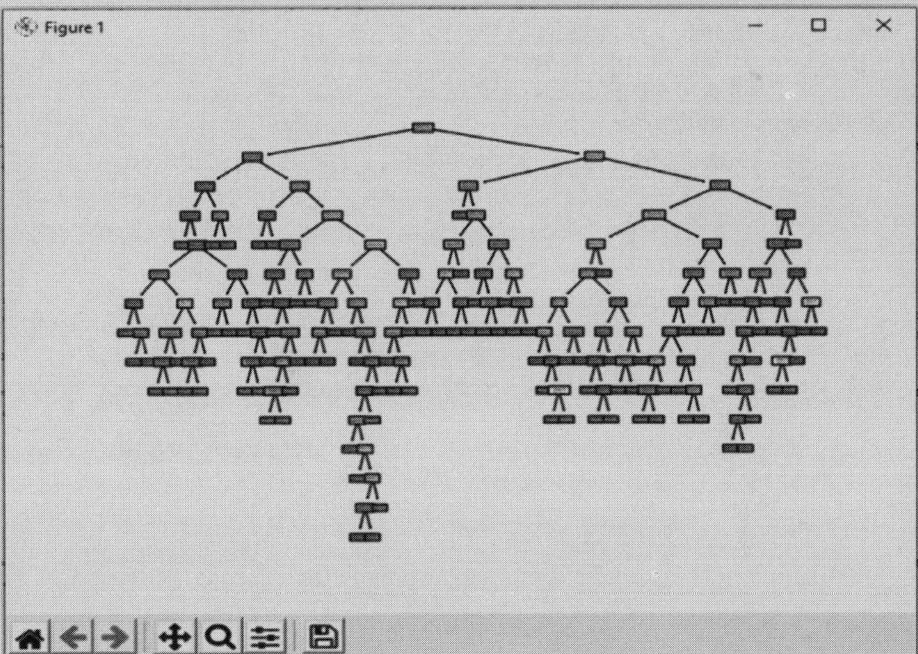

```
3         5     116  74     0          0  25.6      0.201   30      0
4         3      78  50    32         88  31.0      0.248   26       1
Accuracy: 0.7043478260869566
```

Use the petrol_consumption dataset to predict the values using decision tree algorithm.

```
import pandas as pd
import numpy as np
import matplotlib.pyplot as plt
dataset = pd.read_csv('petrol_consumption.csv')
dataset.head()
X = dataset.drop('Petrol_Consumption', axis=1)
y = dataset['Petrol_Consumption']
from sklearn.model_selection import train_test_split
X_train, X_test, y_train, y_test = train_test_split(X, y, test_size=0.2,
random_state=0)
from sklearn.tree import DecisionTreeRegressor
regressor = DecisionTreeRegressor()
regressor.fit(X_train, y_train)
y_pred = regressor.predict(X_test)
df=pd.DataFrame({'Actual':y_test, 'Predicted':y_pred})
print(df.head())
from sklearn import metrics
print('Mean Absolute Error:', metrics.mean_absolute_error(y_test, y_pred))
print('Mean Squared Error:', metrics.mean_squared_error(y_test, y_pred))
print('Root Mean Squared Error:', np.sqrt(metrics.mean_squared_error(y_test,
y_pred)))
```

OUTPUT

```
    Actual  Predicted
29     534      541.0
4      410      414.0
26     577      574.0
30     571      554.0
32     577      631.0
```

```
Mean Absolute Error: 47.1

Mean Squared Error: 3831.3

Root Mean Squared Error: 61.89749591057784
```

12.2.10 Random forests

Like decision trees, Random Forests is also a versatile ML technique that can perform both regression and classification. It gives better performance than decision trees as it does everything for reducing number of dimensions (or variables), treating missing values, outlier values and exploring data.

Random Forests performs better than bagged trees as it *de-correlates* the trees. Like in bagging, Random Forest also creates a number of decision trees on training datasets. For creating these trees, each split considers a *random sample of m predictors* as split candidates from the full set of predictors. A split uses only one of those m predictors. Therefore, the main difference between bagging and Random Forest is that while bagging chooses all predictors, Random Forest selects only one of m predictors.

To summarize, we can say that,

- If the number of cases in the training set is K, then a random sample of these K cases is taken as the training set.
- Out of p input variables, specify a number m, such that m < p. At each node, m random variables out of p predictors are chosen. The best split on these m variables is used to split the node.
- Each tree is subsequently grown to the largest extent possible.
- Take the average of all the predictions made by the target trees to finally predict new data.
- To classify a new object based on attributes, each tree gives a classification and finally the classification occurring most frequently is chosen.

In simpler terms, we can understand the working of a random forest in the following steps (Figure 12.10).

Step 1: Random samples are selected from a given dataset.

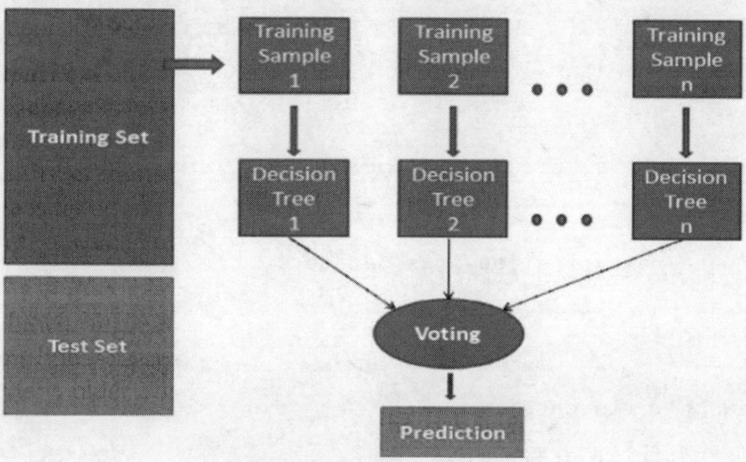

Figure 12.10 Random Forest

Step 2: A decision tree is constructed for each sample to obtain a prediction result from each decision tree.

Step 3: Voting for each predicted result is performed.

Step 4: Prediction result with the maximum votes is selected as the final prediction.

Other major advantages of using Random Forests include:

- It can be very effectively used to estimate missing data.
- It maintains accuracy when a large proportion of the data is missing.
- It can balance errors in datasets where the classes are imbalanced.
- It can handle huge datasets with large number of dimensions.

Limitations:

- Random Forests might easily overfit noisy datasets, especially when performing regression.
- Each tree is grown to the largest extent possible without pruning.
- Random Forests is slow in generating predictions as multiple decision trees are constructed and then the process of voting selects the best prediction result.
- Random Forest is difficult to interpret as and when compared to a decision tree model.

Implement Random Forest Algorithm on iris DataSet

```
# Import scikit-learn dataset library
from sklearn import datasets
# Load dataset
iris = datasets.load_iris()
# print the label species(setosa, versicolor,virginica)
print(iris.target_names)
# print the names of the four features
print(iris.feature_names)
# print the iris data (top 5 records)
print(iris.data[0:5])
# print the iris labels (0:setosa, 1:versicolor, 2:virginica)
print(iris.target)
# Creating a DataFrame of given iris dataset.
import pandas as pd
data=pd.DataFrame({
    'sepal length':iris.data[:,0],
    'sepal width':iris.data[:,1],
    'petal length':iris.data[:,2],
```

```
    'petal width':iris.data[:,3],
    'species':iris.target
})
data.head()
# Import train_test_split function
from sklearn.model_selection import train_test_split
X=data[['sepal length', 'sepal width', 'petal length', 'petal width']]  #
Features
y=data['species']  # Labels
# Split dataset into training set and test set
X_train, X_test, y_train, y_test = train_test_split(X, y, test_size=0.3) #
70% training and 30% test
# Import Random Forest Model
from sklearn.ensemble import RandomForestClassifier
# Create a Gaussian Classifier
clf=RandomForestClassifier(n_estimators=100)
# Train the model using the training sets y_pred=clf.predict(X_test)
clf.fit(X_train,y_train)
y_pred=clf.predict(X_test)
# Import scikit-learn metrics module for accuracy calculation
from sklearn import metrics
# Model Accuracy, how often is the classifier correct?
print("Accuracy:",metrics.accuracy_score(y_test, y_pred))
```

OUTPUT

```
['setosa' 'versicolor' 'virginica']
['sepal length (cm)', 'sepal width (cm)', 'petal length (cm)', 'petal width
(cm)']
[[5.1 3.5 1.4 0.2]
 [4.9 3.  1.4 0.2]
 [4.7 3.2 1.3 0.2]
 [4.6 3.1 1.5 0.2]
 [5.  3.6 1.4 0.2]]
[0 0 0 0 0 0 0…….1 1 1 1 1 1 1 1 1 1 1 1 1 1 1 1 ………. 2 2 2 2 2 2]
Accuracy: 0.9555555555555556
```

12.2.11 Boosting

Like bagging and Random Forests, boosting is a technique that can be applied to improve performance of many statistical learning methods that are used in regression or classification. The process of boosting is similar to bagging, except that the trees are grown *sequentially*. That is, each tree is grown using information obtained from previously grown trees. Therefore, each tree is fitted on a modified version of the original dataset (refer Figure 12.11).

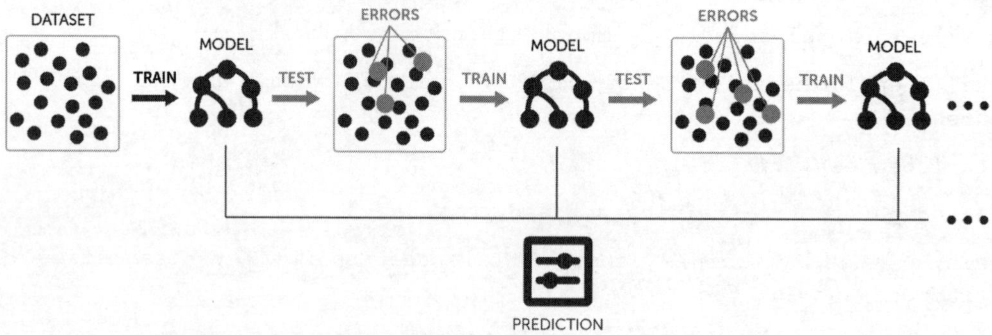

Figure 12.11 Boosting

Boosting is especially very useful when there is a lot of data and decision trees become very complex. Boosting is used to provide solution for many challenging classification and regression problems, including risk analysis, sentiment analysis, predictive advertising, price modeling, sales estimation and patient diagnosis, to name a few.

Implement the Random Forest Algorithm for regression on petrol_consumption dataset.

```
# Import scikit-learn dataset library
from sklearn import datasets
import pandas as pd
import numpy as np
# Load dataset
dataset = pd.read_csv('petrol_consumption.csv')
X = dataset.iloc[:, 0:4].values
y = dataset.iloc[:, 4].values
from sklearn.model_selection import train_test_split
X_train, X_test, y_train, y_test = train_test_split(X, y, test_size=0.2,
random_state=0)
# Feature Scaling
from sklearn.preprocessing import StandardScaler
sc = StandardScaler()
X_train = sc.fit_transform(X_train)
```

```
X_test = sc.transform(X_test)
from sklearn.ensemble import RandomForestRegressor
regressor = RandomForestRegressor(n_estimators=20, random_state=0)
regressor.fit(X_train, y_train)
y_pred = regressor.predict(X_test)
from sklearn import metrics
print('Mean Absolute Error:', metrics.mean_absolute_error(y_test, y_pred))
print('Mean Squared Error:', metrics.mean_squared_error(y_test, y_pred))
print('Root Mean Squared Error:', np.sqrt(metrics.mean_squared_error(y_test,
y_pred)))
OUTPUT
Mean Absolute Error: 51.765000000000001
Mean Squared Error: 4216.166749999999
Root Mean Squared Error: 64.93201637097064
```

12.3 Clustering

Clustering is a set of techniques used to partition data into a number of groups, also called clusters. A cluster can be considered as a group of data objects that are similar to other objects in the same cluster and dissimilar to data objects in other clusters. Clustering helps data scientists to identify two main qualities of data – meaningfulness and usefulness.

Meaningful clusters enhance domain knowledge. For example, in the healthcare industry, clustering is used to make groups of patients whose bodies responded differently to the same medical treatment.

Useful clusters serve as an intermediate step in a data pipeline. For example, businesses use this technique for making different clusters of customers depending on their purchasing patterns to create targeted advertising campaigns.

12.3.1 Overview of clustering techniques

Data objects can be clustered using a variety of techniques. Each of these techniques has its own strengths and weaknesses. Depending upon the input data, we need to select the most appropriate technique that results in more natural cluster assignment. To select the most suitable clustering algorithm for the dataset is not a trivial task. Some important factors that affect this decision include the characteristics of the clusters, the features of the dataset, the number of outliers, and the number of data objects. Based on these features, three popular categories of clustering algorithms include:

1. Partitional clustering
2. Hierarchical clustering
3. Density-based clustering

Partitional Clustering: It divides data objects into non-overlapping groups in such a way that every object belongs to one and only one cluster, and every cluster must have at least one object.

In such algorithms, users can specify the number of clusters (indicated by the variable *k*). These algorithms iteratively assign subsets of data points into *k* clusters. Two examples of partitional clustering algorithms are *k*-means and *k*-medoids. Note that, these algorithms are non-deterministic. That is, such algorithms produce different results from two separate runs even if the same data was used in every run.

Advantages

- Works well when clusters have a spherical shape.
- Scalable with respect to algorithm complexity.

Limitations

- Does not perform well with complex cluster shapes having different sizes.
- Does not work with clusters of different densities.

Hierarchical Clustering: It creates clusters in a hierarchy either by using a bottom-up or a top-down approach.

In Agglomerative clustering, bottom-up approach is used to merge two points that are most similar. This process is repeated until all points have been merged into a single cluster.

In Divisive clustering, top-down approach is used in which the algorithm starts with all points as one cluster. In each iteration, the data objects that are least similar in the cluster are split until only single data points remain.

In such an algorithm, a tree-based hierarchy of points called a dendrogram is created. Number of clusters to be created, i.e. k, is determined by the user. Clusters are created by cutting the dendrogram at a specified depth that results in *k* groups of smaller dendrograms.

Hierarchical clustering is a deterministic process. Therefore, cluster assignments do not change when the algorithm is executed two or more times using the same input data.

Advantages

- They highlight the relationships between data objects at a finer level.
- Results are easily interpretable.

Limitations

- They are computationally expensive with respect to algorithm complexity.
- They are adversely affected by noise and outliers in the dataset.

Density-Based Clustering: This technique creates clusters based on the density of data points in a region. A cluster is created where there are high densities of data points separated by low-density regions.

In contrast to other clustering categories, density-based approach does not require the user to specify the number of clusters. It uses a distance-based parameter that acts as a threshold. The threshold value helps the algorithm to determine how close points must be to be considered a cluster member.

Density-Based Spatial Clustering of Applications with Noise (or DBSCAN) and Ordering Points: To Identify the Clustering Structure (or OPTICS) are popular examples of density-based clustering algorithms.

Advantages

- Works well when clusters are of non-spherical shapes.
- Performs well even on a dataset having noise or outliers.

Limitations

- Not well suited for clustering in high-dimensional spaces.
- Difficult to identify clusters of varying densities.

12.4 k-means algorithm

We have seen that the clustering technique is used for finding sub-groups of observations within a dataset. Clusters are created in such a way that observations in the same group are similar. Correspondingly, observations in different groups are dissimilar. k-means is an unsupervised learning technique as it finds relationships between n observations without being trained by a response variable. k-means clustering is the simplest and the most commonly used clustering method for splitting a dataset into a set of k groups.

12.4.1 Properties of clusters

To understand the concept of clusters, let us take an example of a banking system that forms segments of its customers based on their income and debt. To start with, a scatter plot is used to visualize the customer data (Figure 12.12).

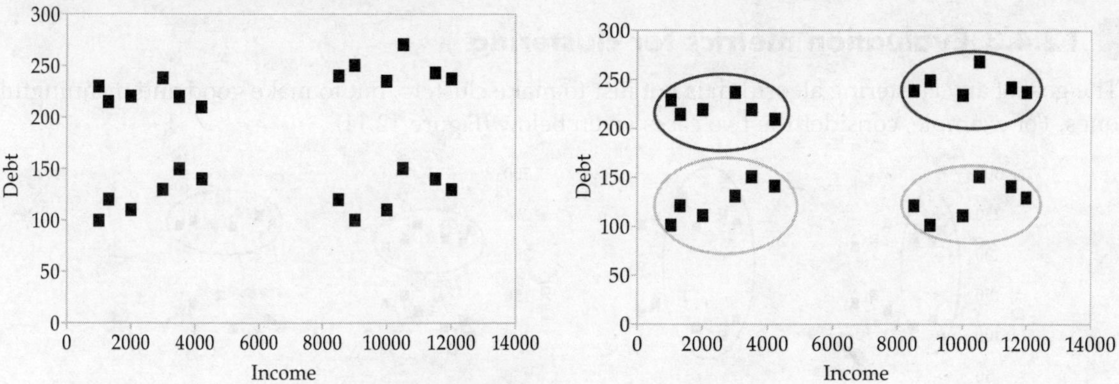

Figure 12.12 Forming Clusters

Income is plotted on the X-axis and amount of debt is plotted on the Y-axis. A very simple approach is to make four clusters as shown in the figures. Looking at the figure, we can conclude the following properties of a cluster.

All the data points in a cluster should be similar to each other. In the bank example, such a cluster allows the bank to perform targeted marketing. The data points from different clusters should be as different as possible.

12.4.2 Applications of clustering in real-world scenarios

Clustering is a widely used technique across industries in almost every domain, ranging from banking to recommendation engines, document clustering to image segmentation.

Customer Segmentation: It is to target a specific set of customers or audience in the industry (telecom, e-commerce, sports, advertising, sales, etc.).

Document Clustering: Another very common application of clustering is document clustering in which multiple similar documents are clustered similar (Figure 12.13).

Figure 12.13 Document Clustering

Image Segmentation: In image segmentation, similar pixels in the image are clubbed together in the same group.

Recommendation Engines: Clustering when used in recommendation engines can help us to recommend songs/friends/products to our friends. The algorithm makes a list of things liked by a person and then finds similar things to recommend those to that person.

There are many more applications which I am sure you have already thought of. Next, let us look at how we can evaluate our clusters.

12.4.3 Evaluation metrics for clustering

The goal of any clustering algorithm is not just to make clusters, but to make good and meaningful ones. For example, consider the two cases given below (Figure 12.14).

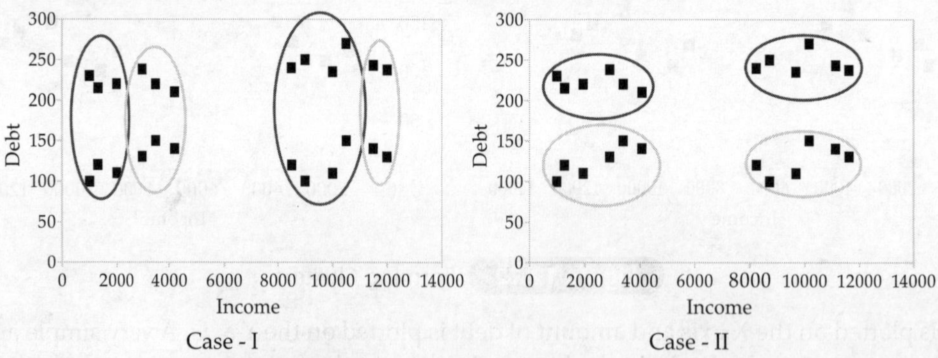

Figure 12.14 Different Clusters of Same Dataset

Since, here we have just two features; but in real-world applications, where we have too many features, visualizing all the features together and deciding which clusters are meaningful is just not possible. Therefore, in such a situation, we use evaluation metrics to evaluate the quality of the clusters.

Inertia

Inertia indicates how far the points within a cluster are. For this, sum of distances of all the points within a cluster from the centroid of that cluster is calculated. Once inertia is calculated for all the clusters, the final value of inertia is obtained by adding all these values. This final value that gives the distance within the clusters is known as intra-cluster distance. So, inertia gives us the sum of intra-cluster distances. For best results (or clusters), the inertial value should be as low as possible.

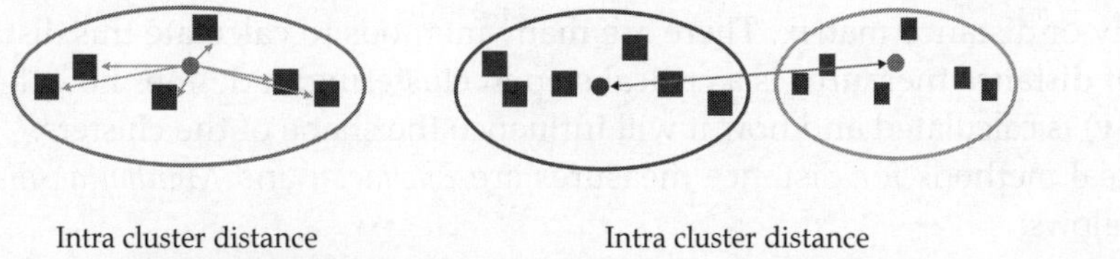

Figure 12.15 Inter and Intra Cluster Distance

Dunn Index

If the distance between the centroid of a cluster and the points in that cluster is small, it means that the points are closer to each other. So, the inertial value ensures that the first property of clusters is satisfied. However, it does not say anything about the second property – that different clusters should be as different from each other as possible. So, for this, we use the Dunn index.

Along with the distance between the centroid and points, the Dunn index also considers the distance between two clusters. Distance between the centroids of two different clusters is known as inter-cluster distance (Figure 12.15). The expression for Dunn Index can be given as,

$$\text{Dunn index} = \frac{\min(\text{inter cluster distance})}{\max(\text{intra cluster distance})}$$

That is, Dunn index is the ratio of the minimum inter-cluster distances and maximum of intra-cluster distances. Its value must be high for getting better clusters.

We must maximize the value of Dunn index. More the value of the Dunn index better will be the clusters. For a higher Dunn index, the numerator should be maximum. So, the distance between even the closest clusters should be more so that every cluster is far away from each other. Correspondingly, the denominator should be minimum. So, intra-cluster distances should be less.

12.4.4 Steps to perform k-means clustering

Step 1: Prepare data for cluster analysis.

Step 2: Understand how to measure differences in observations (also known as Clustering Distance Measures).

Step 3: Create k clusters of data.

Step 4: Identify right number of clusters to group the observations.

Programming Tip

A large k-value may improve stability of the algorithm but will result in overfitting of data thereby decreasing the performance of the model for new coming data

Step 1: Data Preparation

To perform a cluster analysis in Python, data should be clean. For this remember to put observations as rows and variables as columns. Remove any missing data. However, it is always better to estimate its value rather than completely ignoring it.

Standardize or scale the data to make variables comparable. A standardized data has mean zero and standard deviation one for all variables.

Step 2: Clustering Distance Measures

The classification of observations into groups requires some methods for computing the distance or the (dis)similarity between each pair of observations. The result of this computation is known as a dissimilarity or distance matrix. There are many methods to calculate this distance information. The choice of distance measures is a critical step in clustering. It defines how the similarity of two elements (x, y) is calculated and how it will influence the shape of the clusters.

The classical methods for distance measures are *Euclidean* and *Manhattan distances,* which are defined as follows:

Euclidean distance

$$\text{Euclidean Distance} = \sqrt{(X_1 - X_2)^2 + (Y_1 - Y_2)^2}$$

Manhattan distance

$$dman(x,y) = n\sum i = 1 \mid (x_i - y_i) \mid (2)(2) dman(x,y) = \sum i = 1n \mid (x_i - y_i) \mid$$

where, *x* and *y* are two vectors of length *n*.

Other dissimilarity measures exist such as correlation-based distances, which is widely used for gene expression data analyses. Correlation-based distance is defined by subtracting the correlation coefficient from 1. Different types of correlation methods can be used such as:

Pearson correlation distance

$$dcor(x,y) = 1 - \sum n_i = 1(x_i - \bar{x})(y_i - \bar{y})\sqrt{\sum n_i = 1(x_i - \bar{x})2\sum n_i = 1(y_i - \bar{y})2(3)(3)}$$

$$dcor(x,y) = 1 - \sum i = 1n(x_i - \bar{x})(y_i - \bar{y})\sum i = 1n(x_i - \bar{x})2\sum i = 1n(y_i - \bar{y})2$$

Spearman correlation distance

The Spearman correlation method computes the correlation between the rank of *x* and the rank of *y* variables.

$$dspear(x,y) = 1 - \sum n_i = 1(x'_i - \bar{x}')(y'_i - \bar{y})\sqrt{\sum n_i = 1(x'_i - \bar{x}')2\sum n_i = 1(y'_i - \bar{y})2(4)(4)}$$

$$dspear(x,y) = 1 - \sum i = 1n(x'_i - \bar{x}')(y'_i - \bar{y}')\sum i = 1n(x'_i - \bar{x}')2\sum i = 1n(y'_i - \bar{y}')2$$

Where $x'_i = rank(x_i)x'_i = rank(x_i)$ and $y'_i = rank(y_i)y'_i = rank(y_i)$.

Kendall correlation distance

Kendall correlation method measures the correspondence between the ranking of *x* and *y* variables. The total number of possible pairings of *x* with *y* observations is $n(n - 1)/2$, where *n* is the size of *x* and *y*. Begin by ordering the pairs by the *x* values. If *x* and *y* are correlated, then they would have the same relative rank orders. Now, for each y_{iyi}, count the number of $y_j > y_{iyj} > y_i$ (concordant pairs (c)) and the number of $y_j < y_i y_j < y_i$ (discordant pairs (d)).

Kendall correlation distance is defined as follows:

$$dkend(x,y) = 1 - nc - nd12n(n - 1)(5)(5)dkend(x,y) = 1 - nc - nd12n(n - 1)$$

The choice of distance measures is very important, as it has a strong influence on the clustering results. For most common clustering software, the default distance measure is the Euclidean distance. However, depending on the type of the data and the research questions, other dissimilarity measures might be preferred and you should be aware of the options.

Step 3: Create k Clusters of Data

In k-means clustering, each cluster is represented by its center or the centroid. As the name suggests, the center corresponds to the mean of points assigned to the cluster.

> **Programming Tip**
> The total within-cluster sum of square measures the compactness or the goodness of the clustering and we want it to be as small as possible

The basic idea is to create clusters such that the total intra-cluster variation is minimum. Many k-means algorithms are present today but the standard algorithm used is the Hartigan-Wong algorithm (1979), which defines the total intra-cluster variation as the sum of squared Euclidean distances between observations and the corresponding centroid.

$$W(C_k) = \sum_{x_i \in C_k} (x_i - \mu_k)^2$$

where:

- ❑ x_i is the individual observation belonging to the cluster *Ck*
- ❑ μ_k is the mean value of the observations assigned to the cluster *Ck*

Each observation (*xi*) is assigned to a cluster such that the sum of squares of distance of the observation to their assigned cluster center is minimum. Now, total within-cluster (or intra-cluster) variation is given as,

> **Programming Tip**
> A rule of thumb is to select clusters = sqrt(2/n) where n is the number of observations

$$\text{tot.withiness} = \sum_{k=1}^{k} W(C_k) = \sum_{k=1}^{k} \sum_{x_i \in C_k} (x_i - \mu_k)^2$$

12.4.5 How k-means algorithm works?

When implementing the k-means clustering algorithm following steps are performed.

First specify the number of clusters (k) that will be generated in the final solution. The algorithm starts by randomly selecting k observations (also known as centroids) to serve as the initial centers for the clusters.

In the next step, every remaining observation is assigned to its closest cluster, where closest is a term calculated using the Euclidean distance between the centroid of the cluster and the observation. This step is called "cluster assignment step".

The algorithm then computes the new mean value of each cluster. Therefore, this step is known as "centroid update".

Once the centers are re-calculated, every observation is checked again to determine its closeness with the same and other clusters. All the observations may have to be re-assigned a cluster based on the updated cluster means.

The cluster assignment and centroid update steps are repeatedly performed until the cluster assignments remain the same over iterations (technically, until *convergence* is achieved).

12.4.6 Pros and Cons of k-means algorithm

Pros

- ❑ k-means clustering algorithm is very simple and fast.
- ❑ The algorithm can efficiently deal with very large datasets.

Cons

- ❑ Number of clusters must be pre-specified.
- ❑ The algorithm is sensitive to outliers.

- Changing the order of data will give different results.
- Create a random dataset and then apply the k-means clustering algorithm.

12.4.7 Implementing k-means

To implement the k-means algorithm in Python, we will use the make_blobs() function that has the following parameters.

- **n_samples** gives the total number of samples to generate.
- **centers** is the number of centers to generate.
- **cluster_std** is the standard deviation.

The function returns a tuple of two values:

1. A two-dimensional NumPy array with the **x- and y-values** for each of the samples
2. A one-dimensional NumPy array containing the **cluster labels** for each sample

In addition to the make_blobs() function, we will also use the KMeans estimator class present in scikit-learn. The scikit-learn implementation is flexible and users can themselves set parameters to fine tune the algorithm. Some important parameters of this class are,

- **init** is used to control the initialization technique. It can be set to "random" or to "k-means++". Note that k-means++ employs advanced trick to speed up convergence.
- **n_clusters** sets number of clusters to be created (*k*).
- **n_init** is used to set the number of initializations to perform. Each time the k-means algorithm is executed, a different cluster assignment can be obtained. By default, ten *k*-means runs are performed and the result of the one with the lowest SSE is returned.
- **max_iter** sets the maximum number of iterations for each initialization of the *k*-means algorithm.

Implementing k-means Algorithm

```
import matplotlib.pyplot as plt
from kneed import KneeLocator
from sklearn.datasets import make_blobs
from sklearn.cluster import KMeans
from sklearn.metrics import silhouette_score
from sklearn.preprocessing import StandardScaler
features, true_labels = make_blobs(
n_samples=200, centers=3, cluster_std=2.75, random_state=42)
scaler = StandardScaler()
scaled_features = scaler.fit_transform(features)
print("FEATURES: \n",features[:5])
print("TRUE LABELS : \n ", true_labels[:5])
print("SCALED FEATURES : \n", scaled_features[:5])
kmeans = KMeans(init="random", n_clusters=3, n_init=10, max_iter=300,
random_state=42)
```

```
kmeans.fit(scaled_features)
# The lowest SSE value
print("K-means Inertia = ", kmeans.inertia_)
# Final locations of the centroid
print("CWENTERS: ",kmeans.cluster_centers_)
print("K-Means Labels : ",kmeans.labels_[:5])
OUTPUT
FEATURES:
 [[  9.77075874   3.27621022]
 [ -9.71349666  11.27451802]
 [ -6.91330582  -9.34755911]
 [-10.86185913 -10.75063497]
 [ -8.50038027  -4.54370383]]
TRUE LABELS :
  [1 0 2 2 2]
SCALED FEATURES :
 [[ 2.13082109  0.25604351]
 [-1.52698523  1.41036744]
 [-1.00130152 -1.56583175]
 [-1.74256891 -1.76832509]
 [-1.29924521 -0.87253446]]
K-means Inertia =  74.57960106819854
CWENTERS:  [[ 1.19539276  0.13158148]
 [-0.25813925  1.05589975]
 [-0.91941183 -1.18551732]]
K-Means Labels :  [0 1 2 2 2]
```

12.4.8 Choosing the appropriate number of clusters

Two commonly used methods for evaluating appropriate number of clusters are:

1. The elbow method
2. The silhouette coefficient

Basically, these two techniques are complementary to each other. To perform the **elbow method**, the *k*-means algorithm is executed several times. In each iteration, the value of k is incremented and the value of SSE is recorded.

If we plot SSE as a function of the number of clusters, then you will observe that SSE decreases as the value of k increase. More number of clusters means more centroids and the distance from each point to its closest centroid will decrease. The point at which the SSE curve starts to bend is known as the **elbow point**. The x-value of the elbow point is said to be a reasonable trade-off between error and number of clusters. In the graph given in Figure 12.16, the elbow is located at x = 3.

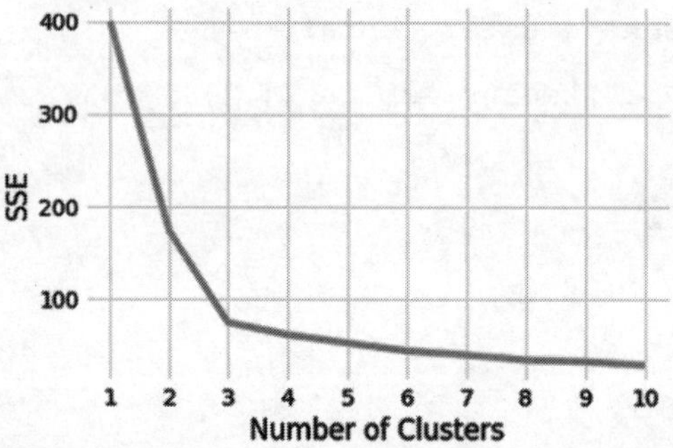

Figure 12.16 Error vs Number of Clusters

The **silhouette coefficient** is a measure of cluster cohesion and separation. It quantifies how well a data point fits into its assigned cluster. This is determined by examining two factors:

> Python package, kneed, is used to identify the elbow point programmatically

1. Proximity (or closeness) of a data point to other points in the cluster
2. Distance of a data point from other points in other clusters

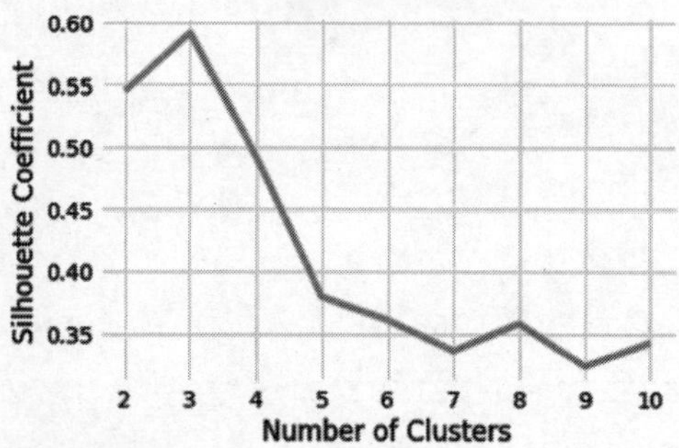

Figure 12.17 Silhouette coefficient vs Number of Clusters

The value of Silhouette coefficient varies from −1 to 1. A larger value indicates that samples are closer to their clusters than they are to other clusters. The average silhouette coefficient of all the samples is summarized into one score. The silhouette score() function needs a minimum of two clusters, or it will raise an exception. Figure 12.17 shows a sample graph that plots the average silhouette scores for different values of k. According to the plot, the best choice for k is 3 since it has the maximum score.

> Number of clusters is guided by a combination of domain knowledge and clustering evaluation metrics

```
from sklearn.cluster import DBSCAN

from sklearn.datasets import make_moons

from sklearn.metrics import adjusted_rand_score
```

```
from sklearn.preprocessing import StandardScaler
from sklearn.cluster import KMeans
from sklearn.metrics import silhouette_score
scaler = StandardScaler()
features, true_labels = make_moons(n_samples=250, noise=0.05, random_state=42)
scaled_features = scaler.fit_transform(features)
 # Instantiate k-means and dbscan algorithms
kmeans = KMeans(n_clusters=2)
dbscan = DBSCAN(eps=0.3)
# Fit the algorithms to the features
kmeans.fit(scaled_features)
dbscan.fit(scaled_features)
# Compute the silhouette scores for each algorithm
kmeans_silhouette   =   silhouette_score(scaled_features,   kmeans.labels_).
round(2)
dbscan_silhouette = silhouette_score(
scaled_features, dbscan.labels_).round (2)
print(kmeans_silhouette)
print(dbscan_silhouette)
OUTPUT
0.5
0.38
```

This time, use make_moons() to generate synthetic data in the shape of crescents. Fit both a *k*-means and a DBSCAN algorithm to the new data and visually assess the performance by plotting the cluster assignments with Matplotlib.

Print the silhouette coefficient for each of the two algorithms and compare them. A higher silhouette coefficient suggests better clusters, which is misleading in this scenario. The silhouette coefficient is higher for the *k*-means algorithm. The DBSCAN algorithm appears to find more natural clusters according to the shape of the data.

You can use the scikit-learn implementation of a common metric called the **adjusted rand index (ARI)**. Unlike the silhouette coefficient, the ARI uses true cluster assignments to measure the similarity between true and predicted labels.

Compare the clustering results of DBSCAN and *k*-means using ARI as the performance metric:

```
from sklearn.cluster import DBSCAN
from sklearn.datasets import make_moons
```

```
from sklearn.metrics import adjusted_rand_score
from sklearn.preprocessing import StandardScaler
from sklearn.cluster import KMeans
from sklearn.metrics import silhouette_score
scaler = StandardScaler()
features, true_labels = make_moons(n_samples=250, noise=0.05, random_state=42)
scaled_features = scaler.fit_transform(features)
 # Instantiate k-means and dbscan algorithms
kmeans = KMeans(n_clusters=2)
dbscan = DBSCAN(eps=0.3)
# Fit the algorithms to the features
kmeans.fit(scaled_features)
dbscan.fit(scaled_features)
# Compute the ari scores for each algorithm
ari_kmeans = adjusted_rand_score(true_labels, kmeans.labels_)
ari_dbscan = adjusted_rand_score(true_labels, dbscan.labels_)
print("ARI k_means = ",round(ari_kmeans, 2))
print("ARI DBCAN = ",round(ari_dbscan, 2))
OUTPUT
ARI k_means =  0.47
ARI DBCAN =  1.0
```

The ARI output values range between −1 and 1. A score close to 0.0 indicates random assignments, and a score close to 1 indicates perfectly labeled clusters.

Based on the above output, you can see that the silhouette coefficient was misleading. ARI shows that DBSCAN is the best choice for the synthetic crescents example as compared to *k*-means.

Use the Wholesale customers data to perform k-means++ algorithm for clustering. Use elbow method to decide the optimum number of k. Also use the inertial value to evaluate metrics.

```
# importing required libraries
import pandas as pd
import numpy as np
import matplotlib.pyplot as plt
```

```
from sklearn.cluster import KMeans
# reading the data and looking at the first five rows of the data
data=pd.read_csv("Wholesale customers data.csv")
print(data.head())
# standardizing the data
from sklearn.preprocessing import StandardScaler
scaler = StandardScaler()
data_scaled = scaler.fit_transform(data)
# statistics of scaled data
pd.DataFrame(data_scaled).describe()
# defining the kmeans function with initialization as k-means++
kmeans = KMeans(n_clusters=2, init='k-means++')
# fitting the k means algorithm on scaled data
kmeans.fit(data_scaled)
# inertia_ indicates how well the clusters are formed
print("K-means Interia = ",kmeans.inertia_)
# fitting multiple k-means algorithms and storing the values in an empty list
SSE = []
for cluster in range(1,20):
    kmeans = KMeans(n_jobs = -1, n_clusters = cluster, init='k-means++')
    kmeans.fit(data_scaled)
    SSE.append(kmeans.inertia_)
# converting the results into a dataframe and plotting them
frame = pd.DataFrame({'Cluster':range(1,20), 'SSE':SSE})
plt.figure(figsize=(12,6))
plt.plot(frame['Cluster'], frame['SSE'], marker='o')
plt.xlabel('Number of clusters')
plt.ylabel('Inertia')
plt.show()
# k means using 5 clusters and k-means++ initialization
kmeans = KMeans(n_jobs = -1, n_clusters = 5, init='k-means++')
kmeans.fit(data_scaled)
```

```
pred = kmeans.predict(data_scaled)
frame = pd.DataFrame(data_scaled)
frame['cluster'] = pred
print(frame['cluster'].value_counts())
```

OUTPUT

	Channel	Region	Fresh	Milk	Grocery	Frozen	Detergents_Paper	Delicassen
0	2	3	12669	9656	7561	214	2674	1338
1	2	3	7057	9810	9568	1762	3293	1776
2	2	3	6353	8808	7684	2405	3516	7844
3	1	3	13265	1196	4221	6404	507	1788
4	2	3	22615	5410	7198	3915	1777	5185

```
K-means Interia =  2599.384423783626
```

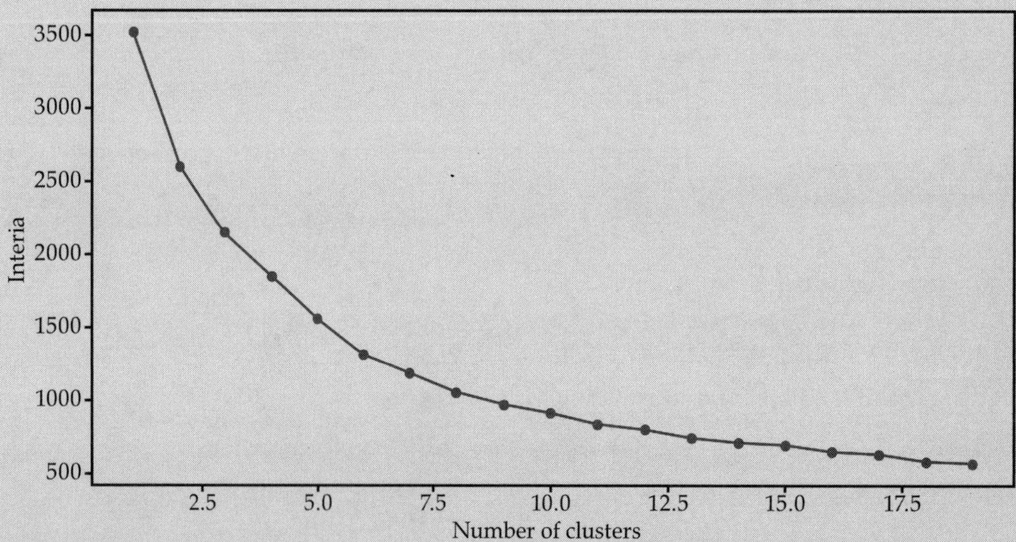


```
0    209
2    126
3     91
4     10
1      4
Name: cluster, dtype: int64
```

Apply k-means algorithm on iris dataset, where k = 5. Use the elbow method to know the optimum value of k. re-apply the k-means algorithm and show the scatter plot.

```
# importing required libraries
import pandas as pd
import numpy as np
import matplotlib.pyplot as plt
from sklearn.cluster import KMeans
# reading the data and looking at the first five rows of the data
data = pd.read_csv("iris.csv")
print(data.head())
x = data.iloc[:,[0,1,2,3]].values
kmeans5 = KMeans(n_clusters=5)
y_kmeans5 = kmeans5.fit_predict(x)
print("y with 5 clusters : ",y_kmeans5)
print("Centroids with 5 clusters : ",kmeans5.cluster_centers_)
Error =[]
for i in range(1, 11):
    kmeans = KMeans(n_clusters = i).fit(x)
    kmeans.fit(x)
    Error.append(kmeans.inertia_)
import matplotlib.pyplot as plt
plt.plot(range(1, 11), Error)
plt.title('Elbow method')
plt.xlabel('No of clusters')
plt.ylabel('Error')
plt.show()
kmeans3 = KMeans(n_clusters=3)
y_kmeans3 = kmeans3.fit_predict(x)
print("y with 3 clusters : ",y_kmeans3)
plt.scatter(x[:,0],x[:,1],c=y_kmeans3, cmap='rainbow')
plt.show()
```

```
   sepal.length  sepal.width  petal.length  petal.width variety
0           5.1          3.5           1.4          0.2  Setosa
1           4.9          3.0           1.4          0.2  Setosa
2           4.7          3.2           1.3          0.2  Setosa
3           4.6          3.1           1.5          0.2  Setosa
4           5.0          3.6           1.4          0.2  Setosa
y with 5 clusters :  [1 1 1 1 1 1 1 1 1 1 1 1 1 1 1 1 1 1 1 1 1 1 1 1 1 1 1 1 1 1 1 1 1 1 1 1
 1 1 1 1 1 1 1 1 1 1 1 1 1 0 0 0 4 0 0 0 4 0 4 4 0 4 0 4 0 0 4 0 4 0 4 0 0
 0 0 0 0 0 4 4 4 4 0 4 0 0 0 4 4 4 0 4 4 4 4 4 0 4 4 3 0 2 3 3 2 4 2 3 2 3
 3 3 0 3 3 3 2 2 0 3 0 2 0 3 2 0 0 3 2 2 2 3 0 0 2 3 3 0 3 3 3 0 3 3 3 0 3
 3 0]
Centroids with 5 clusters :  [[6.20769231 2.85384615 4.74615385 1.56410256]
 [5.006      3.428      1.462      0.246     ]
 [7.475      3.125      6.3        2.05      ]
 [6.52916667 3.05833333 5.50833333 2.1625    ]
 [5.508      2.6        3.908      1.204     ]]
y with 3 clusters :  [1 1 1 1 1 1 1 1 1 1 1 1 1 1 1 1 1 1 1 1 1 1 1 1 1 1 1 1 1 1 1 1 1 1 1 1
 1 1 1 1 1 1 1 1 1 1 1 1 1 0 0 2 0 0 0 0 0 0 0 0 0 0 0 0 0 0 0 0 0 0 0 0 0
 0 0 0 2 0 0 0 0 0 0 0 0 0 0 0 0 0 0 0 0 0 0 0 0 0 0 2 0 2 2 2 2 0 2 2 2 2
 2 2 0 0 2 2 2 2 0 2 0 2 0 2 2 0 0 2 2 2 2 2 0 2 2 2 2 0 2 2 2 0 2 2 2 0 2
 2 0]
```

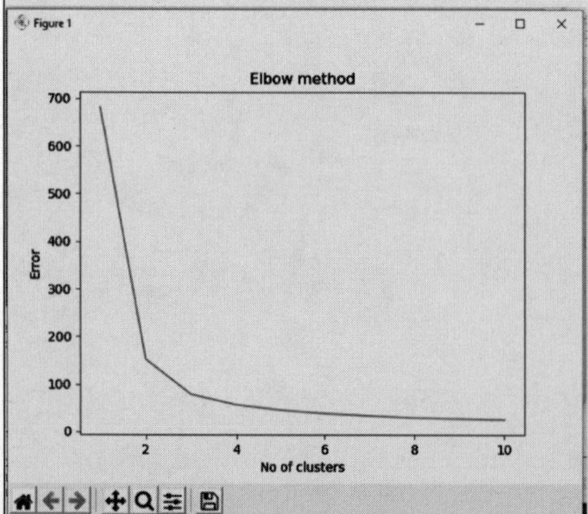

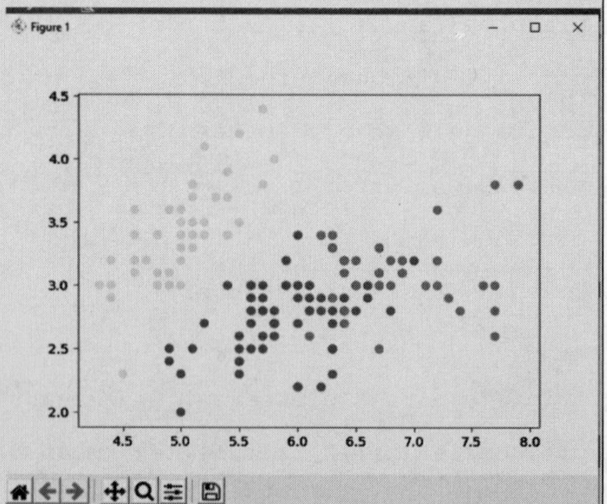

12.4.9 KNN vs. k-mean

k-mean and KNN are two different algorithms. We can realize this difference as given below.

k-mean is an unsupervised learning technique (no dependent variable) whereas KNN is a supervised learning algorithm (dependent variable are present).

K-mean is a clustering technique which tries to split data points into K-clusters such that the points in each cluster are near to each other. The KNN algorithm, however, classifies a point by combining the classification of the K nearest points.

12.5 Density-based spatial clustering of applications with noise (DBSCAN)

We have seen that clustering is an unsupervised learning technique that forms groups of the data points. All points in the same group have similar properties and those in different groups exhibit a different set of properties.

Clusters or groups in data are formed using a variety of distance measures like k-Means (distance between points), Affinity propagation (graph distance), Mean-shift (distance between points), DBSCAN (distance between nearest points), Gaussian mixtures (Mahalanobis distance to centers), Spectral clustering (graph distance), etc.

Though all clustering analysis techniques use the same approach (calculating similarities and then clustering data points into groups), here in this section, we will explore **DBSCAN** technique.

12.5.1 Why DBSCAN?

K-Means clustering, clusters loosely related observations together. Every observation or data point is eventually a part of some cluster even if the observations are scattered far away in the vector space.

The cluster to which an observation will be associated with depends on the mean value of cluster elements. Even a small change in data points *may alter* the clusters formed. However, this problem is greatly reduced in DBSCAN.

Another issue with *k*-means algorithm is that you need to specify the number of clusters (*k*) to be formed and we often err to specify the most optimal value for k. In DBSCAN, value of k need not be specified. We just need to have an idea about the distance between values and some guidance for what amount of distance is considered "close". DBSCAN produces better results than *k*-means. This is evident from the Figure 12.18 given below.

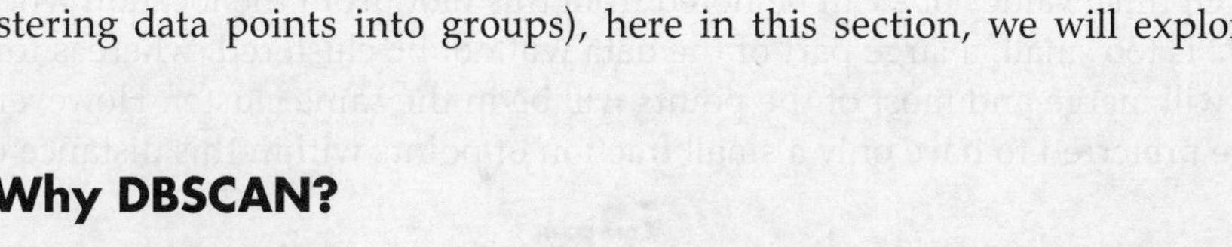

Figure 12.18 Comparison of Clusters formed by DBSCAN and k-means Algorithms

12.5.2 Understanding density-based clustering algorithms

DBSCAN is an unsupervised learning technique that identifies distinct clusters in the data. A cluster is identified as a contiguous region of high point density, separated from other such clusters by contiguous regions of low point density.

The algorithm discovers clusters of different shapes and sizes from a large amount of data that may contain several outlier values.

Two important parameters of the DBSCAN algorithm are:

minPts which indicates the minimum number of points (a threshold) clustered together for a region to be considered dense.

As a rule of thumb, value of *minPts* can be derived from the number of dimensions *D* in the dataset. Generally, ***minPts*** $\geq$ ***D* + 1**. Setting ***minPts* = 1** is of no use as then every point will form a cluster of its own. With **minPts** $\leq$ **2**, the result will be similar to hierarchical clustering. Therefore, minimum value of *minPts* should be at least 3. However, for noisy datasets we must set it to a larger value to get more significant clusters. To be more specific, we can choose ***minPts* = 2·*dim*** to choose larger values for dataset that is very large, or is noisy or contains duplicate values.

eps (ε) is the distance measure that will be used to locate the points in the neighborhood of any point.

The value for ε can be chosen by using a k-distance graph, in which the distance is plotted to the *k* nearest neighbor ordered from the largest to the smallest value. Here, the value of k can be set to ***minPts*-1.** Optimal values of ε can be noted from this plot, from the location where an "elbow" is present. If ε is too small, a large part of the data will not be clustered; whereas for a large value of ε, clusters will merge and most of the points will be in the same cluster. However, small values of ε should be preferred to have only a small fraction of points within this distance of each other.

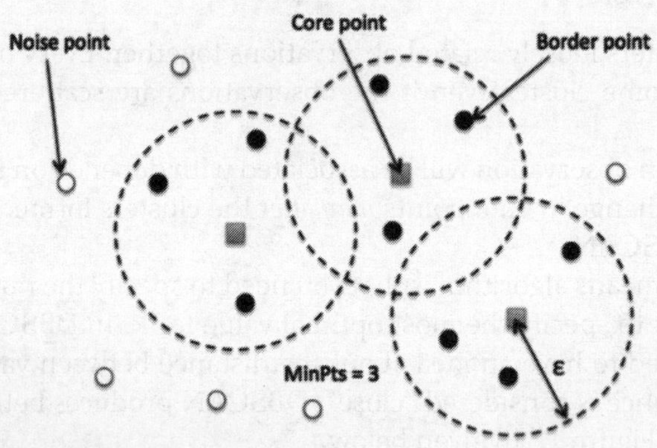

Figure 12.19 Different Categories of Points in DBSCAN

These parameters can be understood by exploring the concepts of Density Reachability and Density Connectivity.

Density Reachability establishes a point to be reachable from another if it lies within a particular distance (eps) from it.

Connectivity is a transitivity-based chaining-approach that is used to determine points that are located in a particular cluster. For example, a and e points could be connected if a->b->c->d->e, where a->b means b is in the neighborhood of a.

Once DBSCAN clustering is done, we can recognize three types of points (Figure 12.19).

Core, it is a point having at least *m* points within distance *n* from itself.

Border, is a point having at least one Core point at a distance *n*.

Noise, is a point that does not fall in the above two categories. This means that noise has less than *m* points within distance *n* from itself.

12.5.3 Algorithmic steps for DBSCAN clustering

Repeat until all points have been visited.

a. Arbitrarily pick up a point in the dataset ().
b. If there are at least 'minPoint' points within a radius of 'ε' to the point then all these points are considered to be a part of the same cluster.
c. Expand the clusters by recursively computing the neighborhood for each point.

12.5.4 Parameter estimation

Every data mining task has the problem of parameters. Every parameter influences the algorithm in specific ways. For DBSCAN, the parameters ε and **minPts** are needed.

12.5.5 DBSCAN Python implementation using sklearn

Let us first apply DBSCAN to cluster spherical data. We first generate 750 spherical training data points with corresponding labels. After that standardize the features of your training data and at last, apply DBSCAN from the scikit-learn library.

The first step to implement DBSCAN is to import all vital packages. We have included make_blobs from sklearn.datasets to generate the blob-based dataset. DBSCAN from sklearn.cluster is imported to perform clustering. NumPy is imported for number processing and Matplotlib PyPlot is imported for visualizing the generated dataset after clustering.

We have deliberately created a sample dataset, using the make_blobs function. The DBSCAN function is used to compute the clusters. For this, we have first initialized values for epsilon and min_samples and then fit the data to DBSCAN to initiate the clustering process. Once clustering is done, the generated labels, number of clusters and number of noisy samples is printed. We can play with epsilon values to make the circle bigger or minimum number of samples to generate a different set of clusters.

We have re-plotted the data by removing noise from it. Noise here is the cluster having label −1.

```
from sklearn.datasets import make_blobs

from sklearn.cluster import DBSCAN

import numpy as np

import matplotlib.pyplot as plt

# Configuration options
```

```
num_samples_total = 500
cluster_centers = [(3,3), (5,5),(7,7)]
num_classes = len(cluster_centers)
epsilon = 0.7
min_samples = 10
# Generate data
X, y = make_blobs(n_samples = num_samples_total, centers = cluster_centers,
n_features = num_classes, cluster_std = 0.4)
# Compute DBSCAN
db = DBSCAN(eps=epsilon, min_samples=min_samples).fit(X)
labels = db.labels_
print(labels)
no_clusters = len(np.unique(labels) )
no_noise = np.sum(np.array(labels) == -1, axis=0)
print('Estimated no. of clusters: %d' % no_clusters)
print('Estimated no. of noise points: %d' % no_noise)

# Generate scatter plot for training data
colors = list(map(lambda x: '#3b4cc0' if x == 1 else '#b40426', labels))
plt.scatter(X[:,0], X[:,1], c=colors, marker="o", picker=True)
plt.title('CLUSTERING WITH DBSCAN')
plt.xlabel('Axis X[0]')
plt.ylabel('Axis X[1]')
plt.show()

# Remove the noise
range_max = len(X)
X = np.array([X[i] for i in range(0, range_max) if labels[i] != -1])
labels = np.array([labels[i] for i in range(0, range_max) if labels[i] != -1])

# Generate scatter plot for training data
colors = list(map(lambda x: '#000000' if x == -1 else '#b40426', labels))
plt.scatter(X[:,0], X[:,1], c=colors, marker="o", picker=True)
```

```
plt.title(f'Noise removed')
plt.xlabel('Axis X[0]')
plt.ylabel('Axis X[1]')
plt.show()
```

OUTPUT

```
[0 1 1 2 0 2 2 0 2 0 0 2 0 2 1 1 2 1 1 2 0 1 1 1 0 0 2 1 1 0 1 1 2 1 2 2 0
 0 1 2 2 1 2 0 0 0 2 1 2 0 0 1 2 0 0 1 1 0 2 2 0 1 1 1 2 2 2 0 2 0 1 0 0 2
 1 0 1 2 0 2 1 2 0 1 0 0 0 0 2 2 0 2 2 2 2 1 1 1 0 1 1 1 0 0 2 2 0 0 1 1 2
 1 2 0 1 0 1 0 2 2 0 0 0 0 0 1 2 0 1 1 2 2 2 1 0 1 2 1 1 0 1 1 1 0 1 2 2 2
 2 2 0 0 1 0 0 2 2 0 1 2 1 2 0 0 0 0 2 2 1 1 0 1 2 2 2 2 2 0 0 2 1 1 1 0 1
 0 2 1 2 2 2 1 0 1 0 1 2 0 1 2 0 0 1 0 0 0 1 1 2 1 1 0 1 2 2 2 1 1 2 2 0 0
 2 0 2 2 0 0 0 2 0 0 0 0 0 2 1 1 2 2 2 0 2 1 1 0 0 1 1 1 2 2 1 1 1 0 1 2 1
 2 0 0 0 0 1 1 1 2 1 1 2 0 0 1 1 2 1 1 1 1 2 0 2 0 1 1 0 2 0 1 2 2 2 1 0 0
 2 2 1 2 2 2 1 2 2 1 0 1 0 0 1 1 2 1 0 0 1 1 2 1 2 2 0 2 1 0 1 2 0 1 1 1 0
 0 2 0 2 1 2 0 0 1 1 1 2 2 0 2 2 2 2 0 0 0 0 0 1 2 2 2 0 2 1 0 2 1 0 0 1 0
 1 2 0 1 1 0 0 2 1 1 1 1 2 2 0 0 2 0 0 0 2 1 2 0 2 2 0 2 0 2 0 2 1 1 2 1 0
 2 1 0 0 1 0 0 0 1 2 1 2 1 1 2 1 2 1 2 2 0 0 0 2 2 0 2 0 1 2 1 2 1 2 0 2 2
 1 0 1 0 2 0 2 0 1 2 2 2 0 0 1 2 0 2 2 0 0 1 0 0 1 1 1 0 1 1 2 0 2 1 0 0 2
 1 1 1 1 0 0 2 1 2 1 2 1 1 0 2 1 2 1 1]
Estimated no. of clusters: 3
Estimated no. of noise points: 0
```

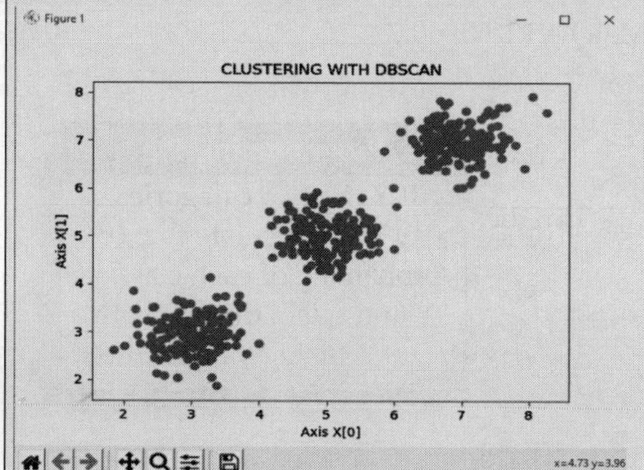

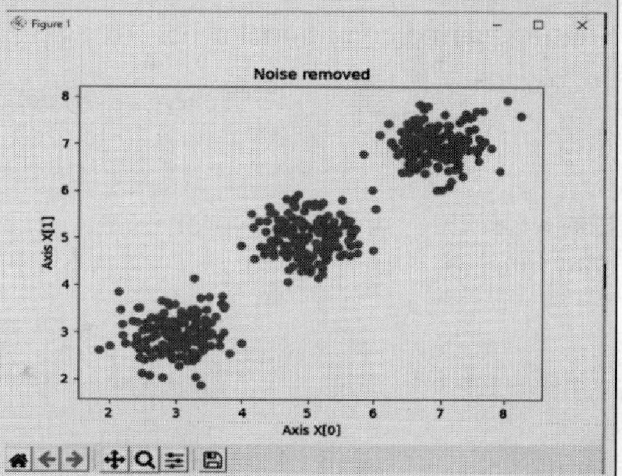

12.6 Naïve Bayes classification

Data science has progressed from simple linear regression models to complex techniques but practitioners still prefer the models that are simple and easy to interpret. In this widely used category of algorithms Naïve Bayes algorithm is one of the prominent names as it is not only simple but so powerful that it outperforms complex algorithms for very large datasets.

> **Programming Tip**
> The term naïve means that features that are used in the model are independent of each other. So when one feature changes, the other is not affected

Naïve Bayes is a probabilistic ML algorithm based on the Bayes Theorem. This algorithm is extensively used in a wide range of classification tasks varying from filtering spam, classifying documents to predicting sentiments.

12.6.1 Understanding conditional probability

To understand conditional probability, consider an example of flipping a coin. There are equal chances of getting either heads or tails. So, the probability of getting heads is 50%.

Now, in case we are supposed to find the probability of getting a queen spade from a deck of 52 cards then the denominator is 13 (the eligible population) and not 52. Since there is only one queen in 13 spades, the probability that we get a queen spade is 1/13.

Therefore, we can say that the conditional probability of A given B, denotes the probability of occurring A given that B has already occurred. Mathematically, it can be expressed as, $P(A|B) = P(A \text{ AND } B)/P(B)$.

Let's apply this concept on the dataset given below (in Table 4) and calculate the conditional probability that the teacher is a male.

Table 4: || Conditional Probability of a Teacher/Student being a Male/Female

	Female	Male	Total
Teacher	8	12	20
Student	32	48	80
Total	40	60	100

So the required conditional probability P(Teacher | Male) = 12/60 = 0.2.

$$P\,(\text{Teacher} \mid \text{Male}) = \frac{P\,(\text{Teacher} \cap \text{Male})}{P\,(\text{Male})} = 12/60 = 0.2$$

Likewise, the conditional probability of B given A can be computed as,

> **Programming Tip**
> If Y has two categories, then calculate the probability of each class of Y and select the one with higher value

$$P\,(A \mid B) = \frac{P\,(A \cap B)}{P\,(B)} \qquad (1)$$

$$P\,(B \mid A) = \frac{P\,(A \cap B)}{P\,(A)} \qquad (2)$$

12.6.2 The Bayes rule

The Bayes Rule uses P(X | Y), known from the training dataset, to find P(Y | X). For observations in test dataset, X would be known while Y is unknown. And for each row of the test dataset, we have to find the probability of Y given that X has already happened (Figure 12.20).

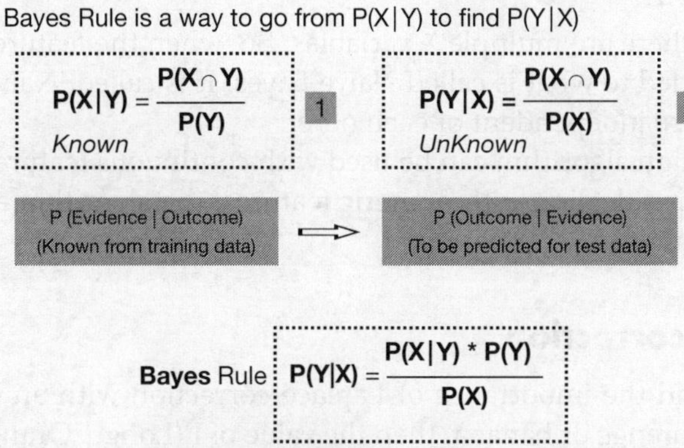

Figure 12.20 Bayes Rule

12.6.3 Types of events

If two probabilities, P(B) and P(B | A) are same, then it means that the occurrence of event A had no effect on event B. Therefore, event A and event B are *independent events*.

If the conditional probability is zero, then it means that the occurrence of event A implies that event B cannot occur. If the reverse is also true, then the events are said to be mutually exclusive events. In such a case, only one event can take place at a time.

All other cases are classified as dependent events where the conditional probability can be either lower or higher than the original.

For example, if we toss a coin twice and we want to calculate the probability of getting a head both times, then we must consider that the second event is independent of the first. The desired probability is P(Heads in first throw)*P(Heads in second throw)= ½ X ½ = ¼

Mathematically, we can say that if the events are not independent, we multiply the probability of one event with the probability of second event.

For expressing dependent events mathematically, we multiply the probability of any one event with the probability of the second event after the first has happened.

`P(A and B)=P(A)*P(B|A)` or `P(A and B)=P(B)*P(A|B)`

For example, while drawing two cards (King and Queen) without replacement, the probability of the first event is dependent on 52 cards whereas the probability of the second event is dependent on 51 cards.

This means that `P(King and Queen)=P(Queen)*P(King|Queen)`

So if P(Queen) is 4/52 then once the King is drawn, P(King | Queen) is 4/51 as now only 51 cards are left. Therefore, the desired probability = 4/52 X 4/51

The probability of two non-mutually exclusive events is given as, `P(A OR B)=P(A)+P(B)-P(A AND B)`.

For example, in a throw of dice, the probability of getting a number that is multiple of 2 or 3 is a scenario of events which are not mutually exclusive since 6 is both a multiple of 2 and 3 and is counted twice. Therefore, `P(multiple of 2 or 3) = P(Multiple of 2) + P(Multiple of 3) - P(Multiple of 2 AND 3) = P(2,4,6) + P(3,6) - P(6) = 3/6 + 2/6 -1/6 = 4/6 = 2/3.`

12.6.4 Naïve Bayes algorithm

In real-world problems, there are multiple X variables. So, when the features are independent, the Bayes Rule can be extended to what is called Naïve Bayes. It is called 'Naïve' because of the naïve assumption that the Xs are independent of each other.

Naïve Bayes classification algorithm can be used with continuous features but performs best for categorical variables. When dealing with numeric features, the algorithm assumes that numerical values are normally distributed.

12.6.5 Laplace correction

We can better understand the importance of Laplace correction with an example. If we were to classify fruits as mango, orange or banana, then the value of P(Long | Orange) will be zero as there are no 'Long' oranges.

When we use this probability in the model having multiple features, then the entire probability will become zero as anything multiplied by zero is zero. To avoid this, we need to increase the count of the variable with zero to a small value (usually 1) in the numerator, so that the overall probability does not become zero.

This correction is called 'Laplace Correction' and the function for building the Naïve Bayes model will accept this correction as a parameter.

12.6.6 Pros and Cons of Naïve Bayes algorithm

Pros

- It is a simple algorithm that is easy to build and understand.
- It predicts classes faster than many other classification algorithms.
- It can be easily trained using a small dataset.
- It can be used to predict values for even large datasets.

Cons

- If a given class and a feature have 0 frequency, then the conditional probability will become 0 resulting in the "Zero Conditional Probability Problem." This is a serious issue as it wipes out all other vital information about probabilities. However, to avoid such situations there are several sample correction techniques like the "Laplacian Correction."
- Another disadvantage is the very strong assumption of independence class features that it makes. It is near to impossible to find such datasets in real life.

12.6.7 Applications

Some of the real-world scenarios where Naïve Bayes algorithm is used includes:

Text Classification: Naïve Bayes classification algorithm is one of the most preferred algorithms to classify whether a text document belongs to one or more categories (classes).

Spam Filtration: Many popular email services use the Bayesian spam filtering to distinguish spam email from legitimate email. Many server-side email filters like DSPAM, SpamBayes, SpamAssassin, Bogofilter, and ASSP are all based on Naïve Bayes classification technique.

Sentiment Analysis: The Naïve Bayes algorithm is also used to analyze the tweets, comments, and reviews posted on social networking site to classify as being negative, positive or neutral.

Recommendation System: Companies use recommendation systems to predict whether a particular user will like their product and/or buy their product or not. For this, the Naïve Bayes algorithm is used in conjunction with collaborative filtering techniques to build hybrid recommendation systems.

Use the different values for weather and temperature to predict whether a child should go out to play out or not.

```
# Assigning features and label variables

weather=['Sunny','Sunny','Overcast','Rainy','Rainy','Rainy','Overcast'
,'Sunny','Sunny',

'Rainy','Sunny','Overcast','Overcast','Rainy']

temp=['Hot','Hot','Hot','Mild','Cool','Cool','Cool','Mild','Cool','Mild',
'Mild','Mild','Hot','Mild']

play=['No','No','Yes','Yes','Yes','No','Yes','No','Yes','Yes','Yes','Yes',
'Yes','No']

# Import LabelEncoder

from sklearn import preprocessing

# creating labelEncoder

le = preprocessing.LabelEncoder()

# Converting string labels into numbers.

weather_encoded=le.fit_transform(weather)

print(weather_encoded)

# Converting string labels into numbers

temp_encoded=le.fit_transform(temp)

label=le.fit_transform(play)

print("Temp:",temp_encoded)

print("Play:",label)

# Combinig weather and temp into single listof tuples

features=tuple(zip(weather_encoded,temp_encoded))
```

```
print(features)
import numpy as np
features = np.asarray(features)
# Import Gaussian Naive Bayes model
from sklearn.naive_bayes import GaussianNB
# Create a Gaussian Classifier
model = GaussianNB()
# Train the model using the training sets
features.reshape(-1,1)
model.fit(features,label)
# Predict Output
predicted= model.predict([[0,2]]) # 0:Overcast, 2:Mild
print("Predicted Value:", predicted)
```

OUTPUT

```
[2 2 0 1 1 1 0 2 2 1 2 0 0 1]
Temp: [1 1 1 2 0 0 0 2 0 2 2 2 1 2]
Play: [0 0 1 1 1 0 1 0 1 1 1 1 1 0]
((2, 1), (2, 1), (0, 1), (1, 2), (1, 0), (1, 0), (0, 0), (2, 2), (2, 0), (1, 2), (2, 2), (0, 2), (0, 1), (1, 2))
Predicted Value: [1]
```

Use the wine dataset and implement Naïve Bayes algorithm to predict the class label.

```
# Import scikit-learn dataset library
from sklearn import datasets
from sklearn.model_selection import train_test_split
# Load dataset
wine = datasets.load_wine()
# print the names of the 13 features
print("Features: ", wine.feature_names)
# print the label type of wine(class_0, class_1, class_2)
print( "Labels: ", wine.target_names)
# print data(feature)shape
```

```
print(wine.data.shape)

# print the wine data features (top 5 records)

print(wine.data[0:5])

# print the wine labels (0:Class_0, 1:class_2, 2:class_2)

print(wine.target)

# Import train_test_split function

# Split dataset into training set and test set

X_train, X_test, y_train, y_test = train_test_split(wine.data, wine.target,
test_size=0.3,random_state=109) # 70% training and 30% test

# Import Gaussian Naive Bayes model

from sklearn.naive_bayes import GaussianNB

# Create a Gaussian Classifier

gnb = GaussianNB()

# Train the model using the training sets

gnb.fit(X_train, y_train)

# Predict the response for test dataset

y_pred = gnb.predict(X_test)

# Import scikit-learn metrics module for accuracy calculation

from sklearn import metrics

# Model Accuracy, how often is the classifier correct?

print("Accuracy:",metrics.accuracy_score(y_test, y_pred))
```

OUTPUT

```
Features: ['alcohol', 'malic_acid', 'ash', 'alcalinity_of_ash', 'magnesium',
'total_phenols', 'flavanoids', 'nonflavanoid_phenols', 'proanthocyanins',
'color_intensity', 'hue', 'od280/od315_of_diluted_wines', 'proline']

Labels:  ['class_0' 'class_1' 'class_2']

(178, 13)

[[1.423e+01 1.710e+00 2.430e+00 1.560e+01 1.270e+02 2.800e+00 3.060e+00

  2.800e-01 2.290e+00 5.640e+00 1.040e+00 3.920e+00 1.065e+03]

 [1.320e+01 1.780e+00 2.140e+00 1.120e+01 1.000e+02 2.650e+00 2.760e+00

  2.600e-01 1.280e+00 4.380e+00 1.050e+00 3.400e+00 1.050e+03]

 [1.316e+01 2.360e+00 2.670e+00 1.860e+01 1.010e+02 2.800e+00 3.240e+00
```

```
 3.000e-01 2.810e+00 5.680e+00 1.030e+00 3.170e+00 1.185e+03]
 [1.437e+01 1.950e+00 2.500e+00 1.680e+01 1.130e+02 3.850e+00 3.490e+00
  2.400e-01 2.180e+00 7.800e+00 8.600e-01 3.450e+00 1.480e+03]
 [1.324e+01 2.590e+00 2.870e+00 2.100e+01 1.180e+02 2.800e+00 2.690e+00
  3.900e-01 1.820e+00 4.320e+00 1.040e+00 2.930e+00 7.350e+02]]
[0 0 0 0 0 0 0 0 0 0 0 0 0 0 0 0 0 0 0 0 0 0 0 0 0 0 0 0 0 0 0 0 0 0 0 0 0
 0 0 0 0 0 0 0 0 0 0 0 0 0 0 0 0 0 0 0 0 0 0 1 1 1 1 1 1 1 1 1 1 1 1 1 1 1
 1 1 1 1 1 1 1 1 1 1 1 1 1 1 1 1 1 1 1 1 1 1 1 1 1 1 1 1 1 1 1 1 1 1 1 1 1
 1 1 1 1 1 1 1 1 1 1 1 1 1 1 1 1 1 1 1 2 2 2 2 2 2 2 2 2 2 2 2 2 2 2 2 2 2
 2 2 2 2 2 2 2 2 2 2 2 2 2 2 2 2 2 2 2 2 2 2 2 2 2 2 2 2 2 2]
Accuracy: 0.9074074074074074
```

12.7 Neural network

Neural Network (NN) or Artificial Neural Network (ANN) is an ML algorithm that is inspired by the biological neuron system and learns by examples. It consists of a large number of highly interconnected processing elements called neurons to solve problems. The algorithm follows a non-linear path and information is processed in parallel throughout the nodes. The best part of neural network is that it can change its internal structure by adjusting weights of inputs.

Neural network algorithms were developed to solve problems which are easy for humans but difficult for machines. These problems include pattern recognition in which we need to identify similar pictures or patterns. Owing to its ability to do pattern recognition, neural networks application ranges from optical character recognition to object detection.

12.7.1 Working of neural networks

In a human's brain, dendrites of a neuron receive input signals from another neuron and give output based on those inputs to an axon of some other neuron. The human brain comprises billions of interconnected webs of neurons that process information and makethe brain to think and take decisions.

Similarly, the NN algorithm works using a set of connected input/output units. In this structure, each connection has a weight associated with it. In the learning phase, the network learns by adjusting the weights to predict the correct class label of the given inputs.

The learning phase is used along with back propagation error method. Therefore, when error is calculated at the output unit, it is back propagated to all the units because error at each unit contributes to total error at the output unit. The errors at each unit are then used to optimize the weight at each connection (Figure 12.21).

> The output of a neuron may vary from −infinity to +infinity. So we need a mapping function also known as the Activation function that maps inputs to the outputs.

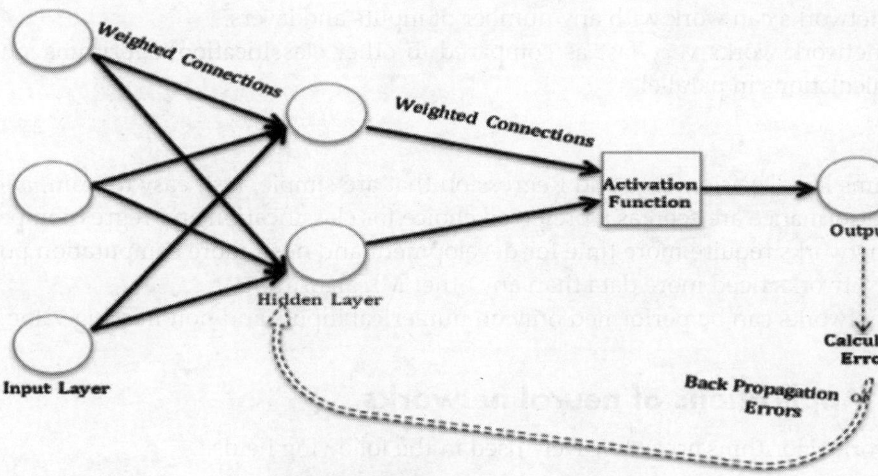

Figure 12.21 Neural Network

A simple neural network model: In Figure 12.22, we can see that it is a feedback neural network in which information is passed in both directions (forward as well as backwards). The structure of the neural network can change over time based on the inputs. Though the figure shows that there is one input layer, one hidden layer and one output layer, we can also have multiple layers of hidden layers.

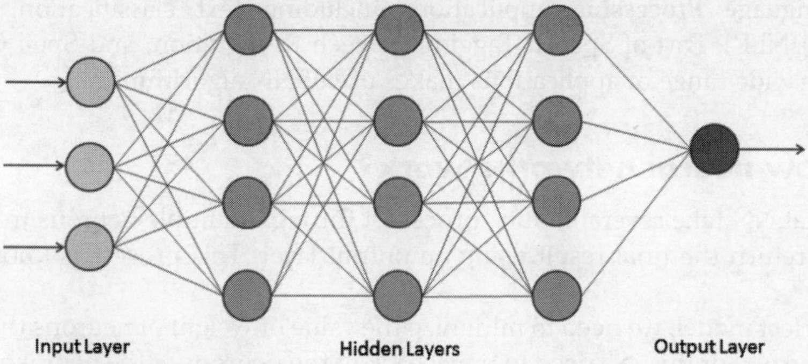

Figure 12.22 Neural Network with multiple hidden layers

Here, the input layer is the first layer of the neural network and receives the raw input. It processes the input and passes the processed information to the hidden layers. The hidden layer passes the information to the last layer, which gives the final output.

The output of a neuron can range from −infinity to +infinity. The neuron does not know the boundary. So we need a mapping mechanism between the input and output of the neuron. This mechanism of mapping inputs to output is known as Activation Function.

12.7.2 Pros and Cons

Pros

- ❑ Neural network is a flexible algorithm that can be used to solve both regression and classification problems.
- ❑ Neural networks perform well on non-linear dataset with a large number of inputs such as images.

- Neural networks can work with any number of inputs and layers.
- Neural network works very fast as compared to other classification algorithms since it performs calculations in parallel.

Cons

- Algorithms like Decision Tree and Regression that are simple, fast, easy to train, and provide better performance are seen as a preferred choice for classification and regression problems.
- Neural networks require more time for development and need more computation power.
- Neural Networks need more data than any other ML algorithm.
- Neural networks can be performed only on numerical inputs and non-missing value datasets.

12.7.3 Applications of neural networks

Neural network algorithms are extensively used in the following fields.

- **Pattern Recognition** applications like facial recognition, object detection, fingerprint recognition, etc. use NN algorithms.
- **Anomaly Detection** applications that are specifically designed to detect unusual patterns that do not fit in the general patterns use NN because of their ability to perform well in pattern recognition tasks.
- **Time Series Prediction** applications like predicting stock prices, forecasting weather prefer to use NN.
- **Natural Language Processing** applications including text classification, Named Entity Recognition (NER), Part-of-Speech Tagging, Speech Recognition, and Spell Checking which are used in a wide range of applications makes use of NN algorithms.

12.7.4 How neural networks work?

We have seen that NN take several inputs, process it through multiple neurons from multiple hidden layers, and return the final result using an output layer. This process is known as "**Forward Propagation**".

To make a perfect model, we need to minimize the value or weight of neurons that are contributing more to the error. For this, we need to travel back to the neurons of the neural network and find where the error lies. This process is known as "**Backward Propagation**". We can reduce the number of iterations to minimize the error by using the "Gradient Descent" algorithm.

A simple strategy of creating input–output relationships is discussed below.

> Neuron applies non-linear transformations (activation function) to the inputs and biases

1. **Use a subset of inputs to calculate the output.** Take only those inputs that satisfy a given threshold value. For example, if the threshold value is 0, then if x1 + x2 + x3 > 0, the output is 1 and 0 otherwise.
2. **Add weights to the inputs.** Weights give importance to an input. For example, if w1 = 4, w2 = 5, and w3 = 6 then on assigning these weights to x1, x2 and x3, we will multiply input with their weights and compare the result with threshold value. That is, w1*x1 + w2*x2 + w3*x3 > threshold. As per the details provided, more importance has been given to x3 in comparison to x1 and x2.
3. **Add bias:** Each perceptron has a bias that indicates how flexible the perceptron is. Therefore, linear representation of input will now be, w1*x1 + w2*x2 + w3*x3 + 1*bias.

Now, Back-propagation (BP) algorithms determine the loss (or error) at the output and then propagate it back into the network. The weights are updated to minimize the error resulting from each neuron. In this process, the first step is to determine the gradient (Derivatives) of each node with respect to the final output.

Note that one round of forwarding and back-propagation iteration is known as one training iteration or **Epoch**.

12.7.5 What is an activation function?

Activation Function takes the sum of weighted input (w1*x1 + w2*x2 + w3*x3 + 1*b) as an argument and returns the output of the neuron. $a = f(\sum_{i=0}^{N} w_i x_i)$

The activation function is generally used to make a non-linear transformation that allows us to fit non-linear hypotheses or to estimate the complex functions. Some commonly used activation functions include "Sigmoid", "Tanh", ReLu, etc.

Gradient Descent

There are two variants of gradient descent algorithm – Full Batch Gradient Descent and Stochastic Gradient Descent. Both these variants update the weights of the neurons. Although the underlying technique is the same, the only difference lies in the number of training samples used to update the weights and biases.

While Full Batch Gradient Descent Algorithm uses all the training data points to update each of the weights at once, the Stochastic Gradient uses 1 or more data points but never the entire training data for updating at once.

For example, if we have a dataset of 10 data points with two weights **w1** and **w2**, then in a **Full Batch** algorithm, all 10 data points are used to calculate the change in w1 (Δw1) and change in w2 (Δw2) and update w1 and w2 accordingly.

However, with **SGD algorithm, initially the first** data point is used to calculate the change in w1 (Δw1) and in w2(Δw2) and update the weights w1 and w2. Then, the second data point is used to update weights.

> An activation function is what makes a neural network capable of learning complex non-linear functions

12.7.6 Steps involved in neural network methodology

Given below are the steps involved in building a Neural Network with one hidden layer. Note that at the output layer, there is only one neuron as we are solving a binary classification problem (predict 0 or 1). In the hidden layer, we need two neurons for predicting each of both classes. So, the steps are:

Step 1: Take the input matrix X and the output matrix Y.

Step 2: Initialize weights and biases with random values. Initialization is a one-time process. In further iterations, weights and biases are updated. We say that,

`wh` is the weight matrix of the hidden layer

`bh` is the bias matrix of the hidden layer

`wout` is the weight matrix of the output layer

`bout` is bias matrix of the output layer

Step 3: Matrix dot product of input and weights assigned to edges between the input and hidden layer is calculated and biases of the hidden layer neurons are added to respective inputs. This process is known as linear transformation.

```
hidden_layer_input= matrix_dot_product(X,wh) + bh
```

Step 4: Apply non-linear transformation using an activation function (Sigmoid). This process will return the output as `1/(1 + exp(-x))`.

```
hiddenlayer_activations = sigmoid(hidden_layer_input)
```

Step 5: Perform a linear transformation on hidden layer activation. For this, compute matrix dot product with weights and add a bias of the output layer neuron. Now, apply the activation function (sigmoid or any other activation function) to predict the output.

```
output_layer_input = matrix_dot_product (hiddenlayer_activations * wout ) + bout
```

output = sigmoid(output_layer_input)

Note that steps 1 to 5 are **known as "Forward Propagation".**

> ReLU (Rectified Linear Unit) is a simple function that compares a value with zero. That is, it will return the value passed to it if it is greater than zero; otherwise, it returns zero

Step 6: Compare the predicted output with actual output. Calculate the gradient of error (Actual – Predicted).

```
E = y - output
```

Step 7: Compute the slope/gradient of hidden and output layer neurons. Slope is calculated using the derivatives of non-linear activations x at each layer for each neuron. The gradient of sigmoid can be returned as `x * (1 - x)`.

```
slope_output_layer = derivatives_sigmoid(output)
```

slope_hidden_layer = derivatives_sigmoid(hiddenlayer_activations)

Step 8: Delta, the change factor is calculated at the output layer. This is dependent on the gradient of error multiplied by the slope of output layer activation.

*d_output = E * slope_output_layer*

Step 9: Error is propagated back into the network, that is, error at the hidden layer. For this, dot product of the output layer delta with the weight parameters of edges between the hidden and output layer (wout.T) is calculated

```
Error_at_hidden_layer = matrix_dot_product(d_output, wout.Transpose)
```

Step 10: Change factor, delta at hidden layer is calculated by multiplying the error at hidden layer with slope of hidden layer activation.

*d_hiddenlayer = Error_at_hidden_layer * slope_hidden_layer*

Step 11: Weights at the output and hidden layer are updated. Weights in the network can be updated from the errors calculated for training example(s).

```
wout = wout + matrix_dot_product(hiddenlayer_activations.Transpose,
d_output)*learning_rate
```

```
wh =  wh + matrix_dot_product(X.Transpose,d_hiddenlayer)*learning_rate
```

Here, the amount by which weights are updated is controlled by a configuration parameter called the learning rate.

Step 12: Biases are updated at the output and hidden layer based on the aggregated errors at that neuron.

```
bias at output_layer = bias at output_layer + sum of delta of output_layer at row-wise * learning_rate

bias at hidden_layer = bias at hidden_layer + sum of delta of output_layer at row-wise * learning_rate
```

*bh = bh + sum(d_hiddenlayer, axis=0) * learning_rate*
*bout = bout + sum(d_output, axis=0)*learning_rate*

Note that steps from 6 to 12 are known as **"Backward Propagation"**.

Note that one forward and backward propagation iteration is known as one training cycle or EPOCH.

Write a program to implement Multi-layer Perceptron (MLP) on a simple data matrix.

```
from sklearn.neural_network import MLPClassifier
X = [[0., 0.], [1., 1.]]
y = [0, 1]
clf = MLPClassifier(solver='lbfgs', alpha=1e-5,
                    hidden_layer_sizes=(5, 2), random_state=1)

clf.fit(X, y)
print(clf.predict([[2., 2.], [-1., -2.]]))
OUTPUT
[1 0]

Write a code to implement single neuron neural network
#Python program to implement a
# single neuron neural network
  # import all necessery libraries
from numpy import exp, array, random, dot, tanh
 train_inputs = array([[0, 0, 1], [1, 1, 1], [1, 0, 1], [0, 1, 1]])
train_outputs = array([[0, 1, 1, 0]]).T
```

```
    # Using seed to make sure it'll
        # generate same weights in every run
random.seed(1)
        # 3x1 Weight matrix
weight_matrix = 2 * random.random((3, 1)) - 1
print("Weight Matrix : ",weight_matrix)
      # tanh as activation function
def tanh(x):
    return tanh(x)
      # derivative of tanh function.
    # Needed to calculate the gradients.
def tanh_derivative(x):
    return 1.0 - tanh(x) ** 2
      # forward propagation
def forward_propagation(inputs):
    return tanh(dot(inputs, weight_matrix))
          # training the neural network.
def train(train_inputs, train_outputs,num_train_iterations):
        # Number of iterations we want to
        # perform for this set of input.
    for iteration in range(num_train_iterations):
        if iteration < 400:
            output = forward_propagation(train_inputs)
        else:
            break
          # Calculate the error in the output.
        error = train_outputs - output
            # multiply the error by input and then
           # by gradient of tanh funtion to calculate
           # the adjustment needs to be made in weights
        adjustment = dot(train_inputs.T, error * tanh_derivative(output))
           # Adjust the weight matrix
```

```
        weight_matrix += adjustment
    train(train_inputs, train_outputs, 1000)
    print ('New weights after training')
    print (neural_network.weight_matrix)
        # Test the neural network with a new situation.
print ("Testing network on new examples ->")
print (forward_propagation(array([1, 0, 0])))
```

OUTPUT

```
Initial Weights :
[[-0.16595599]
 [ 0.44064899]
 [-0.99977125]]
Updated Wigths :
[[ 6.40250727]
 [-3.04600872]
 [ 3.01149641]]
Testing theneural network......
[0.99999451]
```

Write a code to implement neural network on random data.

```
# importing required libraries
import numpy as np
import matplotlib.pyplot as plt
# set random seed
np.random.seed(42)
# creating the input array
X = np.array([[0, 1, 0, 1], [0, 0, 1, 0], [1, 1, 0, 0]])
print("Input:\n", X)
# shape of input array
print("\nShape of Input:", X.shape)
# converting the input in matrix form
X = X.T
print("Input in matrix form:\n", X)
```

```
# shape of input matrix
print("\nShape of Input Matrix:", X.shape)
# creating the output array
y = np.array([[1], [1], [0]])
print("Actual Output:\n", y)
# output in matrix form
y = y.T
print("\nOutput in matrix form:\n", y)
# shape of input array
print("\nShape of Output:", y.shape)
inputLayer_neurons = X.shape[0]  # number of features in dataset
hiddenLayer_neurons = 3  # number of hidden layers neurons
outputLayer_neurons = 1  # number of neurons at output layer
# initializing weight
# Shape of weights_input_hidden should number of neurons at input layer * 
number of neurons at hidden layer
weights_input_hidden = np.random.uniform(size=(inputLayer_neurons, 
hiddenLayer_neurons))
# Shape of weights_hidden_output should number of neurons at hidden layer * 
number of neurons at output layer
weights_hidden_output = np.random.uniform(
    size=(hiddenLayer_neurons, outputLayer_neurons)
)
# shape of weight matrix
weights_input_hidden.shape, weights_hidden_output.shape# We are using sig-
moid as an activation function so defining the sigmoid function here
# We are using sigmoid as an activation function so defining the sigmoid func-
tion here
# defining the Sigmoid Function
def sigmoid(x):
    return 1 / (1 + np.exp(-x))
# hidden layer activations
hiddenLayer_linearTransform = np.dot(weights_input_hidden.T, X)
hiddenLayer_activations = sigmoid(hiddenLayer_linearTransform)
```

```
# calculating the output
outputLayer_linearTransform = np.dot(weights_hidden_output.T,
hiddenLayer_activations)
output = sigmoid(outputLayer_linearTransform)
# output
print("OUTPUT : ",output)
# calculating error
error = np.square(y - output) / 2
print("Error : ",error)
# rate of change of error w.r.t. output
error_wrt_output = -(y - output)
# rate of change of output w.r.t. Z2
output_wrt_outputLayer_LinearTransform = np.multiply(output, (1 - output))
# rate of change of Z2 w.r.t. weights between hidden and output layer
outputLayer_LinearTransform_wrt_weights_hidden_output =
hiddenLayer_activations
# rate of change of Z2 w.r.t. weights between hidden and output layer
outputLayer_LinearTransform_wrt_weights_hidden_output =
hiddenLayer_activations
# checking the shapes of partial derivatives
print("Shapes of partial derivatives : ",error_wrt_output.shape, output_wrt_
outputLayer_LinearTransform.shape,  outputLayer_LinearTransform_wrt_weights_
hidden_output.shape)
# shape of weights of output layer
print("Shape of weights of output layer : ", weights_hidden_output.shape)
# rate of change of error w.r.t weight between hidden and output layer
error_wrt_weights_hidden_output = np.dot(
    outputLayer_LinearTransform_wrt_weights_hidden_output,
    (error_wrt_output * output_wrt_outputLayer_LinearTransform).T,
)
print("Rate of change of error w.r.t weight between hidden and output layer :
",error_wrt_weights_hidden_output.shape)
# rate of change of error w.r.t. output
error_wrt_output = -(y - output)
```

```
# rate of change of output w.r.t. Z2
output_wrt_outputLayer_LinearTransform = np.multiply(output, (1 - output))
# rate of change of Z2 w.r.t. hidden layer activations
outputLayer_LinearTransform_wrt_hiddenLayer_activations =
weights_hidden_output
# rate of change of hidden layer activations w.r.t. Z1
hiddenLayer_activations_wrt_hiddenLayer_linearTransform = np.multiply(
    hiddenLayer_activations, (1 - hiddenLayer_activations)
)
# rate of change of Z1 w.r.t. weights between input and hidden layer
hiddenLayer_linearTransform_wrt_weights_input_hidden = X
# checking the shapes of partial derivatives
print("error_wrt_output.shape", error_wrt_output.shape, '\n'
"output_wrt_outputLayer_LinearTransform.shape",output_wrt_outputLayer_
LinearTransform.shape,'\n'
"outputLayer_LinearTransform_wrt_hiddenLayer_activations.shape",outputLayer_
LinearTransform_wrt_hiddenLayer_activations.shape,'\n'
"hiddenLayer_activations_wrt_hiddenLayer_linearTransform.shape",hiddenLayer_
activations_wrt_hiddenLayer_linearTransform.shape,'\n'
"hiddenLayer_linearTransform_wrt_weights_input_hidden.shape",hiddenLayer_
linearTransform_wrt_weights_input_hidden.shape
)
# shape of weights of hidden layer
print("shape of weights of hidden layer",weights_input_hidden.shape)
# rate of change of error w.r.t weights between input and hidden layer
error_wrt_weights_input_hidden = np.dot(
    hiddenLayer_linearTransform_wrt_weights_input_hidden,
    (
        hiddenLayer_activations_wrt_hiddenLayer_linearTransform
        * np.dot(
            outputLayer_LinearTransform_wrt_hiddenLayer_activations,
            (output_wrt_outputLayer_LinearTransform * error_wrt_output),
        )
    ).T,
)
```

```
print("error_wrt_weights_input_hidden.shape : ",error_wrt_weights_input_
hidden.shape)
# initial weights_hidden_output
print("initial weights_hidden_output", weights_hidden_output)
# initial weights_input_hidden
print("initial weights_input_hidden : ",weights_input_hidden)
lr = 0.1
# updating the weights of output layer
weights_hidden_output = weights_hidden_output - lr *
error_wrt_weights_hidden_output
# updating the weights of hidden layer
weights_input_hidden=weights_input_hidden-lr*error_wrt_weights_input_hidden
# updated weights_hidden_output
print("pdated weights_hidden_output : ",weights_hidden_output)
# updated weights_input_hidden
print("updated weights_input_hidden : ",weights_input_hidden)
# defining the model architecture
inputLayer_neurons = X.shape[0]  # number of features in dataset
hiddenLayer_neurons = 3  # number of hidden layers neurons
outputLayer_neurons = 1  # number of neurons at output layer
# initializing weight
weights_input_hidden = np.random.uniform(size=(inputLayer_neurons,
hiddenLayer_neurons))
weights_hidden_output = np.random.uniform(
    size=(hiddenLayer_neurons, outputLayer_neurons)
)
# defining the parameters
epochs = 1000
losses = []
for epoch in range(epochs):
    ## Forward Propogation
    # calculating hidden layer activations
    hiddenLayer_linearTransform = np.dot(weights_input_hidden.T, X)
```

```
    hiddenLayer_activations = sigmoid(hiddenLayer_linearTransform)
    # calculating the output
    outputLayer_linearTransform = np.dot(
        weights_hidden_output.T, hiddenLayer_activations
    )
    output = sigmoid(outputLayer_linearTransform)
    ## Backward Propagation
    # calculating error
    error = np.square(y - output) / 2
    # calculating rate of change of error w.r.t weight between hidden and
output layer
    error_wrt_output = -(y - output)
    output_wrt_outputLayer_LinearTransform = np.multiply(output, (1 - output))
    outputLayer_LinearTransform_wrt_weights_hidden_output =
hiddenLayer_activations
    error_wrt_weights_hidden_output = np.dot(
        outputLayer_LinearTransform_wrt_weights_hidden_output,
        (error_wrt_output * output_wrt_outputLayer_LinearTransform).T,
    )
    # calculating rate of change of error w.r.t weights between input and
hidden layer
    outputLayer_LinearTransform_wrt_hiddenLayer_activations =
weights_hidden_output
    hiddenLayer_activations_wrt_hiddenLayer_linearTransform = np.multiply(
        hiddenLayer_activations, (1 - hiddenLayer_activations)
    )
    hiddenLayer_linearTransform_wrt_weights_input_hidden = X
    error_wrt_weights_input_hidden = np.dot(
        hiddenLayer_linearTransform_wrt_weights_input_hidden,
        (
            hiddenLayer_activations_wrt_hiddenLayer_linearTransform
            * np.dot(
                outputLayer_LinearTransform_wrt_hiddenLayer_activations,
```

```
                (output_wrt_outputLayer_LinearTransform * error_wrt_output),
            )
        ).T,
    )
    # updating the weights
    weights_hidden_output = weights_hidden_output - lr *
error_wrt_weights_hidden_output
    weights_input_hidden = weights_input_hidden - lr * error_wrt_weights_input_
hidden
    # print error at every 100th epoch
    epoch_loss = np.average(error)
    if epoch % 100 == 0:
        print(f"Error at epoch {epoch} is {epoch_loss:.5f}")
    # appending the error of each epoch
    losses.append(epoch_loss)
    # updated w_ih
print("Updated w_ih : ",  weights_input_hidden)
# updated w_ho
print("Updated w_oh : ",weights_hidden_output)
# visualizing the error after each epoch
plt.plot(np.arange(1, epochs + 1), np.array(losses))
plt.show()
# final output from the model
print("final output from the model : ",output)
# actual target
print("Actual Output : ",y)
from sklearn.datasets import make_moons
X, y = make_moons(n_samples=1000, random_state=42, noise=0.1)
plt.scatter(X[:, 0], X[:, 1], s=10, c=y)
plt.show()
```

OUTPUT

```
Input:
 [[0 1 0 1]
 [0 0 1 0]
```

```
 [1 1 0 0]]
Shape of Input: (3, 4)
Input in matrix form:
 [[0 0 1]
 [1 0 1]
 [0 1 0]
 [1 0 0]]
Shape of Input Matrix: (4, 3)
Actual Output:
 [[1]
 [1]
 [0]]
Output in matrix form:
 [[1 1 0]]
Shape of Output: (1, 3)
OUTPUT :  [[0.71257368 0.66712814 0.70941533]]
Error :  [[0.04130695 0.05540184 0.25163505]]
Shapes of partial derivatives :  (1, 3) (1, 3) (3, 3)
Shape of weights of output layer :  (3, 1)
Rate of change of error w.r.t weight between hidden and output layer :  (3, 1)
error_wrt_output.shape (1, 3)
output_wrt_outputLayer_LinearTransform.shape (1, 3)
outputLayer_LinearTransform_wrt_hiddenLayer_activations.shape (3, 1)
hiddenLayer_activations_wrt_hiddenLayer_linearTransform.shape (3, 3)
hiddenLayer_linearTransform_wrt_weights_input_hidden.shape (4, 3)
shape of weights of hidden layer (4, 3)
error_wrt_weights_input_hidden.shape :  (4, 3)
initial weights_hidden_output [[0.83244264]
 [0.21233911]
 [0.18182497]]
initial weights_input_hidden :  [[0.37454012 0.95071431 0.73199394]
 [0.59865848 0.15601864 0.15599452]
```

```
 [0.05808361 0.86617615 0.60111501]
 [0.70807258 0.02058449 0.96990985]]
updated weights_hidden_output :  [[0.83026506]
 [0.20975497]
 [0.1806837 ]]
updated weights_input_hidden :  [[0.37211711 0.95013443 0.73144475]
 [0.59705704 0.15574884 0.15564327]
 [0.05962067 0.86650326 0.60142241]
 [0.70889414 0.02089457 0.9701078 ]]
Error at epoch 0 is 0.11194
Error at epoch 100 is 0.10568
Error at epoch 200 is 0.09469
Error at epoch 300 is 0.07583
Error at epoch 400 is 0.05307
Error at epoch 500 is 0.03469
Error at epoch 600 is 0.02295
Error at epoch 700 is 0.01593
Error at epoch 800 is 0.01165
Error at epoch 900 is 0.00891
Updated w_ih :  [[-1.41592119 -1.66814487  1.43325031]
 [-0.38869727 -0.61945052  0.7813556 ]
 [ 0.84853814  1.23833969 -0.24745841]
 [ 1.23475339  1.84688342 -0.53931739]]
Updated w_oh :  [[ 1.90367071]
 [ 2.84297879]
 [-2.41586348]]
final output from the model :  [[0.89808191 0.92249823 0.16167778]]
Actual Output :  [[1 1 0]]
```

12.8 Support vector machine (SVM)

Support Vector Machine is a classification algorithm that classifies data based on its features. An SVM will classify any new element into one of the two classes (Figure 12.23).

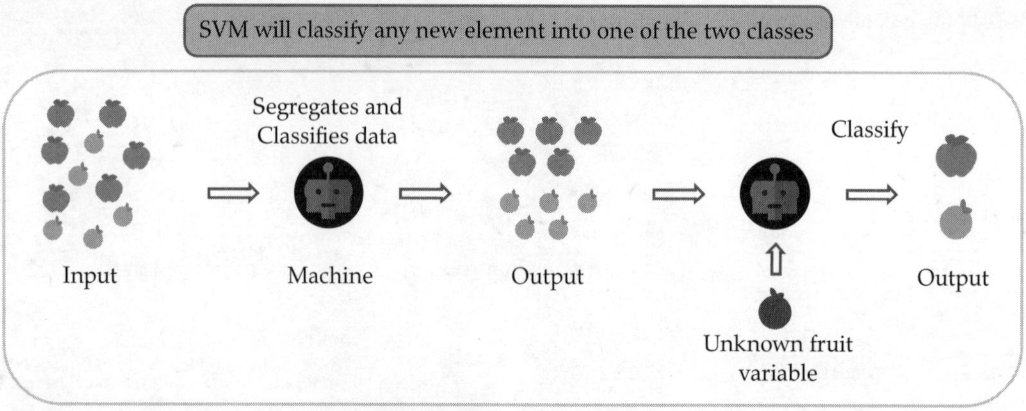

Figure 12.23 Classification by SVM

To make our ML model learn, we supply input data to it. The SVM algorithm will automatically extract features from the input data. This knowledge is used to segregate and classify the input data to generate the desired output. Once the model has learnt how to classify, any new data inputted to it can be classified (with a specific accuracy).

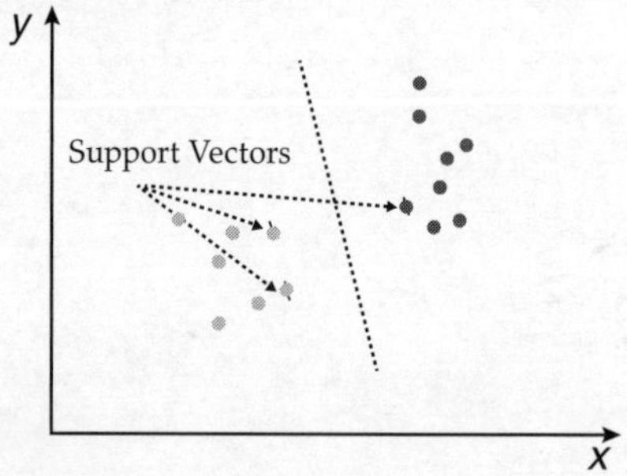

Figure 12.24 Plotting points in n-dimensional space

Support Vector Machine is therefore a supervised ML algorithm which can be used for both classification and regression challenges. However, it is mostly used to classify data. In the SVM algorithm, each data item is plotted as a point in n-dimensional space (where n is number of features refer Figure 12.24). In this plot, Support Vectors are simply the co-ordinates of individual observation. For classification, we need to identify the best hyper plane/line or class. For example, consider the scenarios given below.

Scenario 1: In Figure 12.25 given below, there are three hyper planes A, B and C. However, hyper planes B and C better segregate the two classes.

Scenario 2: When all three hyper planes (A, B and C) are segregating the classes well, we must choose one that maximizes the distances between nearest data point (either class) and hyper plane. This distance is called as **Margin**. In the figure, we see that the margin for hyper plane C is high as compared to both A and B. Hence, hyper plane C is chosen as the right decision boundary or hyper plane.

> *Note:* Hyper plane with low margin can result in mis-classification

Scenario 3: In this scenario, hyper plane A is selected as it maximizes the margin and reduces classification error.

Scenario 4: In the figure, segregation is difficult as one star lies in the territory of circle class.

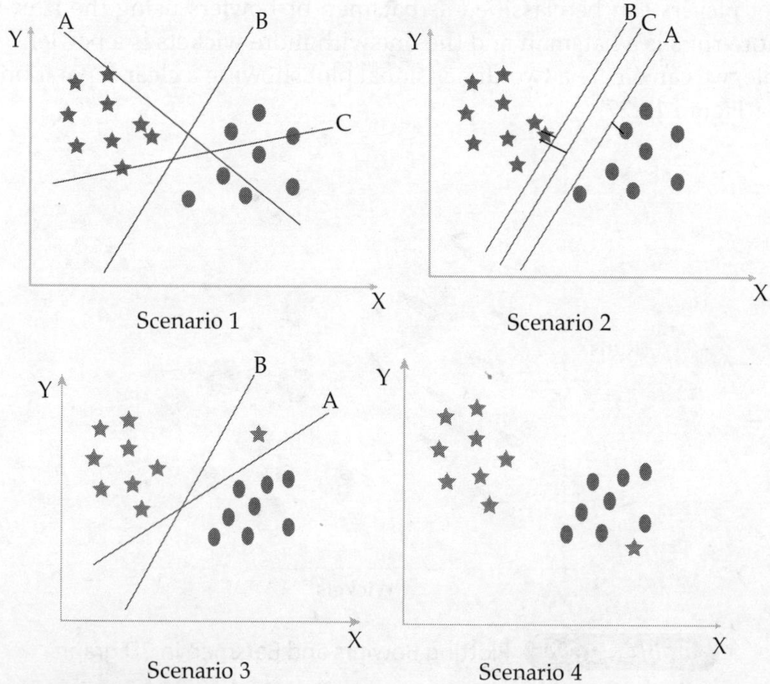

Figure 12.25 Identifying Hyperplanes in Different Scenarios

Scenario-5: In the scenario, linear hyper plane between the two classes is not possible. However, SVM can solve this solution in two ways.

Solution 1: Adding a new feature `z = x^2 + y^2` and plotting the data points on axis x and z. In the plot,

a. all values for z would be positive always because z is the sum of squares of both x and y.
b. In the original plot, red circles appear close to the origin of x and y axes because of lower value of z. Stars appear away from the origin due to higher value of z.

Solution 2: Using the kernel trick of the SVM algorithm. The SVM kernel is a function that takes low dimensional input space and transforms it to a higher dimensional space i.e. it converts not separable problem to separable problem. It is generally used in non-linear separation problem. In Figure 12.26, we see that the hyper plane in original input space looks like a circle.

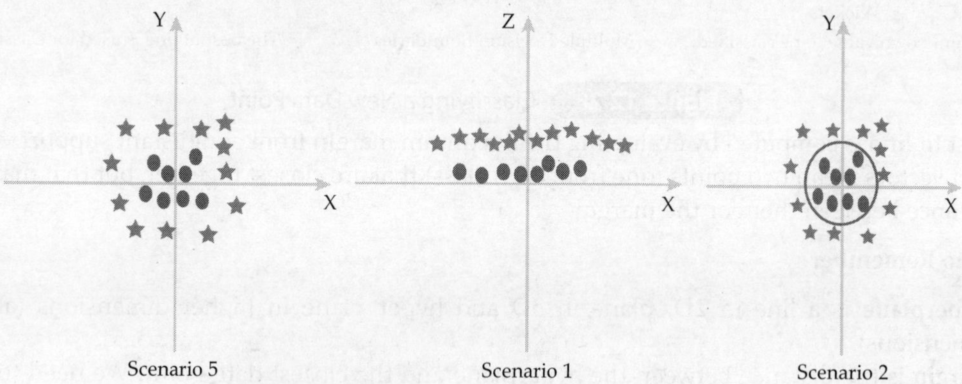

Figure 12.26 Hyperplane in Input Space

Example: Cricket players can be classified as batsmen or bowlers using the runs-to-wicket ratio. A player with more runs is a batsman and the one with more wickets is a bowler.

In this example, we can create a two-dimensional plot showing a clear separation between bowlers and batsmen (Figure 12.27).

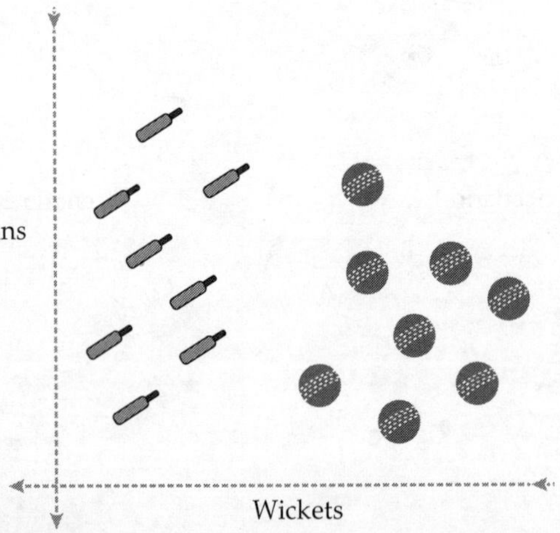

Figure 12.27 Plotting Bowlers and Batsmen in 2D graph

Whenever we get data for a new player that is not yet classified, we draw a decision boundary, or a line separating the two classes to help classify the new data points. We can draw multiple decision boundaries. Therefore, the aim is to find the line of best fit that clearly separates those two groups. The correct line will help to classify the new data point (Figure 12.28).

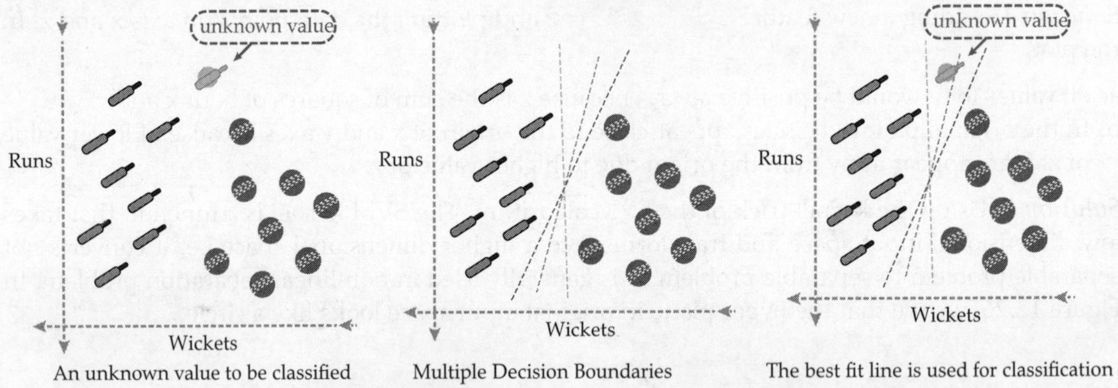

Figure 12.28 Classifying a New Data Point

The best fit line is computed by evaluating the maximum margin from equidistant support vectors. Support vectors mean two points (one from each class) that are closest together, but that maximize the distance between them or the margin.

Points to Remember

- **Hyperplane** is a line in 2D, plane in 3D and hyper plane in higher dimensions (above 3 dimensions).
- **Margin** is the distance between the hyperplane and the closest data point. We need to maximize this margin for better classification.

- The kernel function is used to handle non-linear separable data. It does this by transforming data into a higher dimensional feature space to make it possible to perform the linear separation. Different kernel functions include:
  - Gaussian RBF kernel
  - Sigmoid kernel
  - Polynomial kernel

Any of these functions can be chosen depending on the dimensions and way data has to be transformed.

- **Tuning Parameters.** For learning about tuning parameters, we can divide them in two groups – Linear Kernel SVM and Non-Linear Kernel SVM.

For ***Linear Kernel SVM***, there is only one parameter – Cost (C) which implies misclassification cost on training data.

A large C gives you low bias and high variance. Low bias as there is a penalty (cost) for misclassification. A large C means the cost of misclassification is high. This ensures that the algorithm strictly explains the input data stricter (and potentially overfits).

A small C gives higher bias and lower variance. This is because a small value of C lowers the cost of misclassification.

Ideally, a good balance must be maintained between being "not too strict" and "not too loose". For finding an optimal value of C, Cross-validation and resampling techniques along with grid search have proved to be excellent.

For ***Non-Linear Kernel (Radial)***, two parameters for fine tuning are Cost and Gamma. We have already discussed Cost (C) in case of Linear Kernel.

Gamma explains how far the influence of a single training example reaches. A small value of gamma indicates that the model is too constrained and cannot capture the complexity or "shape" of the data.

SVM algorithm is very sensitive to the choice of the kernel parameters.

12.8.1 How does SVM work?

Step 1: Select an optimal hyperplane that maximizes margin.

Step 2: Apply a penalty or cost 'c' for misclassification.

Step 3: Use kernel trick on non-linearly separable data points by transforming data to high dimensional space where it is easier to classify with linear decision surfaces.

Data Standardization

All kernel methods are based on distance. Hence, values of all variables must be scaled. If we do not standardize our variables to comparable ranges, then the variable with the largest range will completely dominate the computation of the kernel function. For example, if we have two variables – X1 and X2 where values of variable X1 lies in the range 0 to 100 while that of X2 lies in range of 100 and 10000, then values of X2 will dominate variable X1. Therefore, we must standardize each variable to the range [−1,1] or [0,1]. The Z-score and min-max are the two popular methods to standardize variables.

Moreover, standardization avoids numerical problems during computation. Since kernel values depend on the inner products of feature vectors, large attribute values often result in numerical issues.

12.8.2 Advantages of SVM

1. SVM performs well with non-linear separable data using kernel trick.
2. SVM works well in high dimensional space that is, when there are large number of predictor variables.
3. SVM can be efficiently used to classify text as well as images.
4. It is free from multi-collinearity problems
5. SVM is a memory efficient algorithm as only a subset of the training points is used to assign a class to a new member. Only these few points need to be stored in memory for making decisions.
6. It is a flexible algorithm as both linear and non-linear data can be classified using this technique.

12.8.3 Disadvantages of SVM

1. It takes more time when working with large-sized datasets.
2. SVM does not directly return probability estimates.
3. With linear separable data, linear kernel is same as logistic regression.

12.8.4 Applications of SVM in real world

In real-world, SVM is widely used for classifying data in multiple areas including:

Face detection: SVM algorithm is used to classify parts of an image as a face and non-face. You must have seen that on Facebook, whenever you post a picture, a square boundary around the face is created. This can be easily done using the SVM algorithm by detecting the face area. The algorithm creates a square boundary around faces on the basis of pixel brightness and classifies each image by using the same process.

Figure 12.29 Different Facial Expressions

We can even use SVM in various life-care systems to classify a face as being normal, happy or sad. This technique is also used in filters. For example, whenever we make certain facial expressions, specific filter is applied for that expression (Figure 12.29).

Text and hypertext categorization: SVM algorithms are used to categorize and thus differentiate between Text and hypertext. The algorithm also uses training data to classify documents into different categories including news articles, emails, and web pages. Similarly, news articles can be classified into "business" and "Movies" and web pages can be categorized as personal home pages and others.

> SVM with an RBF kernel produces a ring-shaped decision boundary instead of a line

SVMs are also used for classifying emails. An email can be classified as spam or not. Such algorithms are widely used in the email delivery systems provided by platforms like Gmail. Accuracy of such applications is as high as 97% for this application.

Classification of images: SVM algorithm provides better search accuracy for image classification. They can also be used for recognizing handwriting.

Bioinformatics: SVM algorithms are used for classifying protein, cancer, genes and other biological problems. For example, protein sequences are modeled using different kernel functions to find the similarity between different protein sequences.

Handwriting recognition: SVM algorithms are used to recognize handwritten characters so that they can be used for data entry applications and validating signatures on documents.

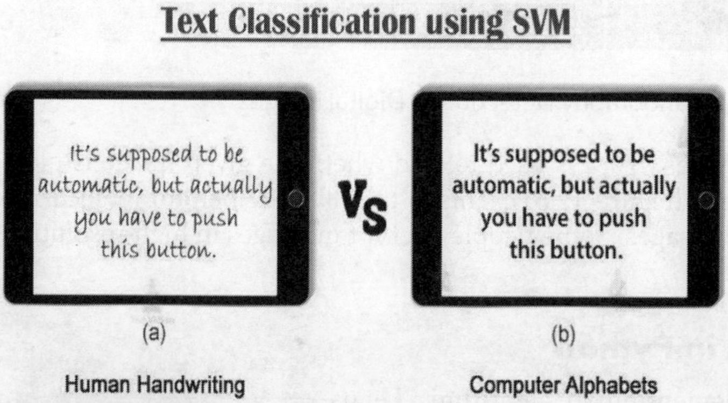

Figure 12.30 Identifying and processing Hand Written Characters

> To deal with noisy data, set C parameter to be a low value (say 1). The SVM classifier chooses a large margin decision boundary at the expense of larger number of misclassifications. When C is set to a high value (say 100), the classifier will choose a low margin decision boundary and try to minimize the misclassifications

SVM is also used to differentiate between the handwritings of two different people. The dataset contains images of various alphabets and sentences written in both handwritings. SVM is also used to differentiate between human writing and computer alphabets (Figure 12.30).

Geo and Environmental Sciences: SVMs are also used for geo (spatial) and spatiotemporal environmental data analysis. Geographical and spatial data is usually uncleaned and noisy.

Generalized Predictive Control: SVM is used to control chaotic dynamics with useful parameters. It provides excellent performance in controlling chaotic systems thereby reducing waiting time and maintaining performance of such systems.

Inverse Geo-sounding Problem: SVM algorithm is widely used to determine the layered structure of the planet. It is also used in case of electromagnetic data, where in the model is developed using linear programming techniques.

Seismic Liquefaction Potential: SVM is applied in Standard Penetration Test (SPT) and Cone Penetration Test (CPT) to check the occurrence and non-occurrence of liquefaction. Here, we use field datasets.

Mathematics: A variant of SVM – SSVM or Smooth SVM is used in mathematics for solving various math problems.

Texture Classification: SVM is also used to classify an image as smooth or rough by analyzing its texture.

Speech Recognition: SVM when applied on acoustics data can be used for speech recognition applications to design an interface for communication with deaf people.

Figure 12.31 ISteganography Detection in Digital Images

Steganography Detection in Digital Images. SVM is used to find whether a given image is plain or has some hidden message stored in it (Figure 12.31). This is usually very helpful in security-based organizations to uncover secret messages. Some people encrypt messages in high-resolution images.

12.8.5 Implementing SVM in Python

Python uses scikit-learn library for implementing ML algorithms. Let us discuss the stepwise procedure to create a binary SVM classifier.

> Higher value of gamma, will try to exact fit the as per training data set i.e. generalization error and cause over-fitting problem

Step 1: Generate a dataset. We need data that can be classified. In the example given below, we have used scikit's make_blobs function to generate a linearly separable dataset having two features.

Step 2: Build the SVM classifier using the scikit-learn library.

Step 3: Train the SVM classifier and use it to predict new data samples.

Step 4: Find support vectors of your trained SVM as they determine the decision boundary.

Step 5: Visualize the decision boundary using mesh grid or any other technique.

SVM classifier is built using scikit-learn's svm method. The syntax of this method is given as,

```
class sklearn.svm.SVC(*, C=1.0, kernel='rbf', degree=3, gamma='scale',
coef0=0.0, shrinking=True, probability=False, tol=0.001, cache_size=200, class_
weight=None, verbose=False, max_iter=-1, decision_function_shape='ovr', break_
ties=False, random_state=None)
```

Although there are many parameters in this method, we will discuss three most commonly used parameters here.

C is a *floating point parameter having default=1.0.*

kernel specifies the kernel type to be used in the algorithm. Its value can be 'linear', 'poly', 'rbf', 'sigmoid', 'precomputed' or a callable. If none is given, 'rbf' is used.

degree*int* is the degree of the polynomial kernel function ('poly'). Its default value is 3. The parameter is ignored by all other kernels.

gamma can have values ***'scale'*** or ***'auto'***. The default value is ***'scale'***. If gamma='scale', then 1/(n_features * X.var()) is used as value of gamma. However, if 'gamma' = 'auto', value of gamma is calculated as 1/n_features.

> Penalty parameter C controls the trade-off between smooth decision boundaries and classifying the training points correctly

12.8.6 Tuning hyperparameters

Kernel: The main function of the kernel is to transform the given dataset input data into the required form. There are various types of functions such as linear, polynomial, and radial basis function (RBF). Polynomial and RBF are useful for non-linear hyperplane. Polynomial and RBF kernels compute the separation line in the higher dimension. In some of the applications, it is suggested to use a more complex kernel to separate the classes that are curved or non-linear. This transformation can lead to more accurate classifiers.

Regularization: Regularization parameter in Python's scikit-learn C parameter is used to maintain regularization. Here C is the penalty parameter, which represents misclassification or error term. The misclassification or error term tells the SVM optimization how much error is bearable. This is how you can control the trade-off between decision boundary and misclassification term. A smaller value of C creates a small-margin hyperplane and a larger value of C creates a larger-margin hyperplane.

Gamma: A lower value of Gamma will loosely fit the training dataset, whereas a higher value of gamma will exactly fit the training dataset, which causes overfitting. In other words, you can say a low value of gamma considers only nearby points in calculating the separation line, while a higher value of gamma considers all the data points in the calculation of the separation line.

```
from sklearn import svm
X = [[0, 0], [1, 1]]
y = [0, 1]
clf = svm.SVC()
clf.fit(X, y)
print(clf.predict([[2., 2.]]))
```

OUTPUT

```
[1]
```

> We should always look at the cross-validation score to have effective combination of these parameters and avoid overfitting

Let us write another code to implement SVM classification algorithm on a dataset generated using make_blob() method. For this purpose, we will use a random seed for our blobs to initialize the pseudorandom numbers generator with the same start initialization.

centers represent the (X, y) positions of the centers of the blobs that are being generated.

cluster standard deviation indicates how scattered the centers are across the two-dimensional mathematical space. It can be set to any number. But lower its value, more condensed the clusters are.

fraction of the test split tells us percentage of the dataset that will be used for testing.

number of features for samples tells us the number of classes in which the data needs to be classified. In a binary classifier, data is categorized in two classes.

number of samples in total tells us the number of samples that are generated in total.

```
from sklearn.datasets import make_blobs
from sklearn.model_selection import train_test_split
import numpy as np
import matplotlib.pyplot as plt
from sklearn import svm
from sklearn.metrics import plot_confusion_matrix
# Configuration options
blobs_random_seed = 42
centers = [(0,0), (5,5)]
cluster_std = 1
frac_test_split = 0.33
num_features_for_samples = 2
num_samples_total = 1000
# Generate data
inputs, targets = make_blobs(n_samples = num_samples_total, centers = cen-
ters, n_features = num_features_for_samples, cluster_std = cluster_std)
X_train, X_test, y_train, y_test = train_test_split(inputs, targets, test_
size=frac_test_split, random_state=blobs_random_seed)
# Save and load temporarily
# np.save('./data.npy', (X_train, X_test, y_train, y_test))
X_train, X_test, y_train, y_test = np.load('./data.npy', allow_pickle=True)
# Generate scatter plot for training data
plt.scatter(X_train[:,0], X_train[:,1])
plt.title('Linearly separable data')
plt.xlabel('X1')
plt.ylabel('X2')
plt.show()
# Initialize SVM classifier
```

```
clf = svm.SVC(kernel='linear')
# Fit data
clf = clf.fit(X_train, y_train)
# Predict the test set
predictions = clf.predict(X_test)
# Generate confusion matrix
matrix = plot_confusion_matrix(clf, X_test, y_test,
                                cmap=plt.cm.Blues,
                                normalize='true')
plt.title('Confusion matrix for our classifier')
```

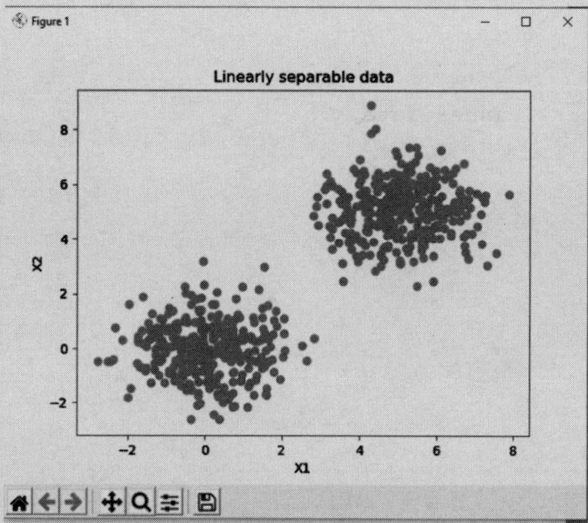


```
# plt.show(matrix)
plt.show()
# Get support vectors
support_vectors = clf.support_vectors_
# Visualize support vectors
plt.scatter(X_train[:,0], X_train[:,1])
plt.scatter(support_vectors[:,0], support_vectors[:,1], color='red')
plt.title('Linearly separable data with support vectors')
plt.xlabel('X1')
plt.ylabel('X2')
```

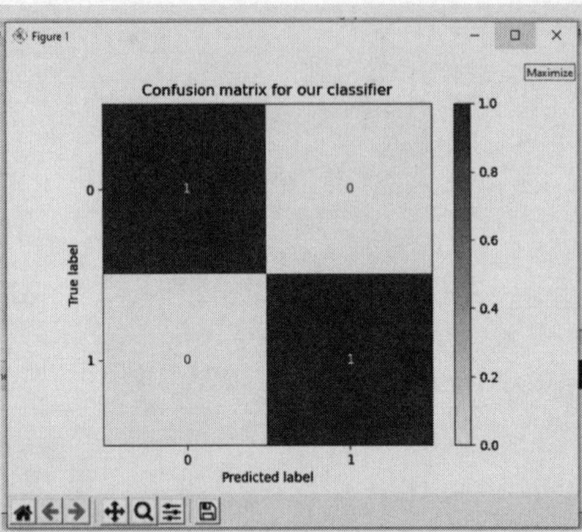

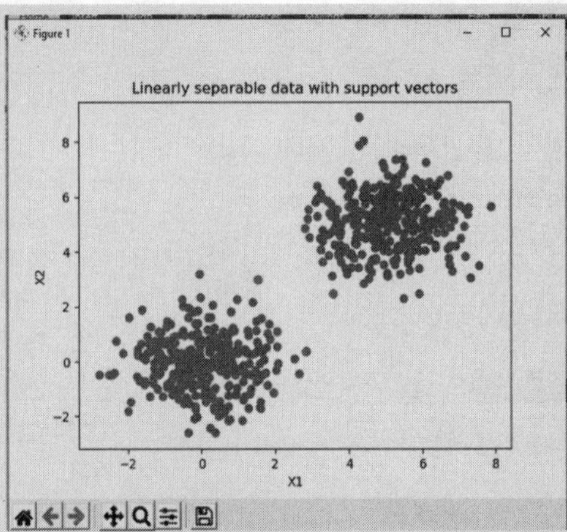


```
plt.show()
```

Perform SVM on breast cancer data.

```
# Import scikit-learn dataset library
from sklearn import datasets
# Load dataset
cancer = datasets.load_breast_cancer()
# print the names of the 13 features
print("Features: ", cancer.feature_names)
# print the label type of cancer('malignant' 'benign')
print("Labels: ", cancer.target_names)
# print data(feature)shape
print(cancer.data.shape)
# print the cancer data features (top 5 records)
# print(cancer.data[0:5])
# print the cancer labels (0:malignant, 1:benign)
# print(cancer.target)
# Import train_test_split function
from sklearn.model_selection import train_test_split
# Split dataset into training set and test set
X_train, X_test, y_train, y_test = train_test_split(cancer.data, cancer.tar-
get, test_size=0.3,random_state=109) # 70% training and 30% test
```

```
# Import svm model
from sklearn import svm
# Create a svm Classifier
clf = svm.SVC(kernel='linear') # Linear Kernel
# Train the model using the training sets
clf.fit(X_train, y_train)
# Predict the response for test dataset
y_pred = clf.predict(X_test)
# Import scikit-learn metrics module for accuracy calculation
from sklearn import metrics
# Model Accuracy: how often is the classifier correct?
print("Accuracy:",metrics.accuracy_score(y_test, y_pred))
# Model Precision: what percentage of positive tuples are labeled as such?
print("Precision:",metrics.precision_score(y_test, y_pred))
# Model Recall: what percentage of positive tuples are labelled as such?
print("Recall:",metrics.recall_score(y_test, y_pred))
```

OUTPUT

```
Features:  ['mean radius' 'mean texture' 'mean perimeter' 'mean area'
 'mean smoothness' 'mean compactness' 'mean concavity'
 'mean concave points' 'mean symmetry' 'mean fractal dimension'
 'radius error' 'texture error' 'perimeter error' 'area error'
 'smoothness error' 'compactness error' 'concavity error'
 'concave points error' 'symmetry error' 'fractal dimension error'
 'worst radius' 'worst texture' 'worst perimeter' 'worst area'
 'worst smoothness' 'worst compactness' 'worst concavity'
 'worst concave points' 'worst symmetry' 'worst fractal dimension']
Labels:  ['malignant' 'benign']
(569, 30)
Accuracy: 0.9649122807017544
Precision: 0.9811320754716981
Recall: 0.9629629629629629
```

Use the existing digit dataset and train the classifier to predict a digit and plot the image to be more distinct.

```
import matplotlib.pyplot as plt

from sklearn import datasets

from sklearn import svm

# loading the dataset

letters = datasets.load_digits()

# generating the classifier

clf = svm.SVC(gamma=0.001, C=100)

# training the classifier

X,y = letters.data[:-10], letters.target[:-10]
clf.fit(X,y)

# predicting the output

print(clf.predict(letters.data[:-10]))

plt.imshow(letters.images[6],
interpolation='nearest')

plt.show()
```

OUTPUT

```
[0 1 2 ... 5 7 9]
```

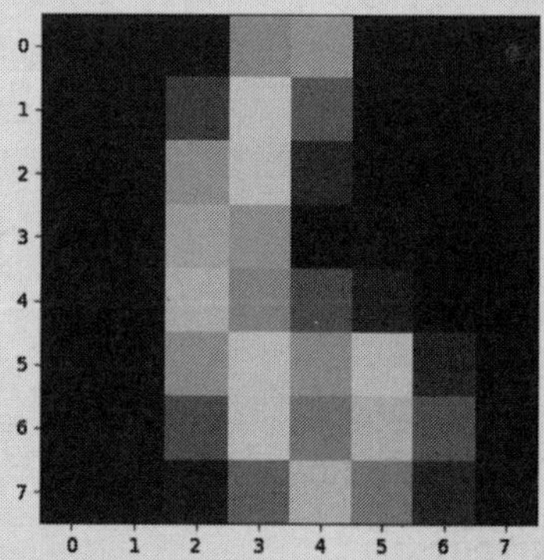

Implement SVM linear, Gaussian and Sigmoid Kernel on iris dataset and compare their performance.

```
import numpy as np

import matplotlib.pyplot as plt

import pandas as pd

url = "https://archive.ics.uci.edu/ml/machine-learning-databases/iris/iris.
data"

# Assign colum names to the dataset

colnames = ['sepal-length', 'sepal-width', 'petal-length', 'petal-width',
'Class']

# Read dataset to pandas dataframe

irisdata = pd.read_csv(url, names=colnames, header=None)

X = irisdata.drop('Class', axis=1)
```

```
y = irisdata['Class']
from sklearn.model_selection import train_test_split
X_train, X_test, y_train, y_test = train_test_split(X, y, test_size = 0.20)
from sklearn.svm import SVC
svclassifier = SVC(kernel='poly', degree=8)
svclassifier.fit(X_train, y_train)
y_pred = svclassifier.predict(X_test)
from sklearn.metrics import classification_report, confusion_matrix
print(confusion_matrix(y_test, y_pred))
print(classification_report(y_test, y_pred))
```

OUTPUT

```
[[11  0  0]
 [ 0 11  0]
 [ 0  2  6]]
                 precision    recall  f1-score   support
    Iris-setosa       1.00      1.00      1.00        11
Iris-versicolor       0.85      1.00      0.92        11
 Iris-virginica       1.00      0.75      0.86         8
       accuracy                           0.93        30
      macro avg       0.95      0.92      0.92        30
   weighted avg       0.94      0.93      0.93        30
```

```
from sklearn.svm import SVC
svclassifier = SVC(kernel='rbf')
svclassifier.fit(X_train, y_train)
```

To use Gaussian kernel, specify 'rbf' as value for the Kernel parameter of the SVC class.

```
from sklearn.svm import SVC
svclassifier = SVC(kernel='sigmoid')
svclassifier.fit(X_train, y_train)
```

To use the sigmoid kernel, you have to specify 'sigmoid' as value for the kernel parameter of the SVC class.

Comparison of Kernel Performance

When comparing the performance of different types of kernels, we see that the sigmoid kernel performs the worst. This is because the sigmoid function returns two values, 0 and 1. The sigmoid kernel works well for binary classification problems but here we have three output classes.

In our case, Gaussian kernel achieved 100% prediction rate while polynomial kernel misclassified one instance. However, there is no hard and fast rule as to which kernel performs best in every scenario. We just need to test all the kernels and select the one that gives the best results on dataset at hand.

Write a code to perform SVM on iris dataset. Plot the results of prediction using a mesh grid.

```
import numpy as np
import matplotlib.pyplot as plt
from sklearn import svm, datasets
# import some data to play with
iris = datasets.load_iris()
X = iris.data[:, :2] # we only take the first two features. We could
 # avoid this ugly slicing by using a two-dim dataset
y = iris.target
# we create an instance of SVM and fit out data. We do not scale our
# data since we want to plot the support vectors
C = 1.0 # SVM regularization parameter
svc = svm.SVC(kernel='linear', C=1).fit(X, y)
# create a mesh to plot in
x_min, x_max = X[:, 0].min() - 1, X[:, 0].max() + 1
y_min, y_max = X[:, 1].min() - 1, X[:, 1].max() + 1
h = (x_max / x_min)/100
xx, yy = np.meshgrid(np.arange(x_min, x_max, h),
np.arange(y_min, y_max, h))
plt.subplot(1, 1, 1)
Z = svc.predict(np.c_[xx.ravel(), yy.ravel()])
Z = Z.reshape(xx.shape)
```

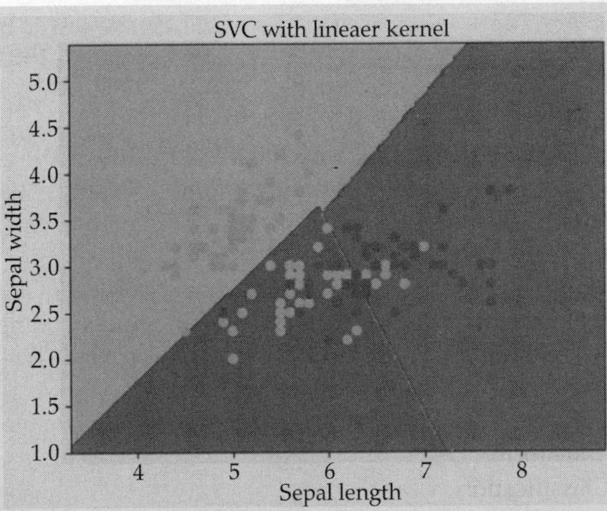


```
plt.contourf(xx, yy, Z, cmap=plt.cm.Paired, alpha=0.8)

plt.scatter(X[:, 0], X[:, 1], c=y, cmap=plt.cm.Paired)

plt.xlabel('Sepal length')

plt.ylabel('Sepal width')

plt.xlim(xx.min(), xx.max())

plt.title('SVC with linear kernel')

plt.show()
```

Business Scenario: Classification and Clustering

Assume that you are a Data Scientist in a **Retail Business. Your goal** is to improve customer segmentation and product recommendations to provide actionable insights for marketing, inventory management, and sales forecasting.

The company has a large volume of customer data that includes the purchase history, demographics, and browsing patterns. Using this data, you are supposed to **classify customers** into different segments for targeted marketing and then **cluster similar customers** based on their purchasing pattern to recommend them suitable products. Clustering customers exhibiting similar behavior may uncover groups of customers who mainly purchase during sales or discounts or customers who consistently purchase from the same brand.

```
# Importing necessary libraries
import pandas as pd
import numpy as np
from sklearn.ensemble import RandomForestClassifier
from sklearn.cluster import KMeans
from sklearn.model_selection import train_test_split
from sklearn.metrics import accuracy_score
import matplotlib.pyplot as plt
from sklearn.preprocessing import StandardScaler
```

```
# Sample customer data
data = {
    'Age': [25, 30, 35, 40, 45, 50, 55, 60, 65, 70],
    'Frequency_of_Purchase': [5, 10, 7, 3, 6, 4, 2, 5, 8, 9],
    'Average_Spending': [200, 300, 250, 150, 350, 100, 75, 125, 200, 300],
      'Preferred_Category': ['Electronics', 'Clothing', 'Home', 'Beauty', 'Electronics', 'Clothing',
'Beauty', 'Home', 'Clothing', 'Beauty']
}
df = pd.DataFrame(data)
# Convert categorical column into numeric format using one-hot encoding
df = pd.get_dummies(df, columns=['Preferred_Category'], drop_first=True)
# Feature scaling
scaler = StandardScaler()
df_scaled = scaler.fit_transform(df)
# Train-Test Split for Classification
X = df_scaled
y = ['High', 'High', 'Medium', 'Low', 'High', 'Low', 'Low', 'Medium', 'High', 'Medium']
y = pd.Categorical(y).codes  # Converting target to numeric values
X_train, X_test, y_train, y_test = train_test_split(X, y, test_size=0.2, random_state=42)
# Classification: Random Forest
clf = RandomForestClassifier(n_estimators=100, random_state=42)
clf.fit(X_train, y_train)
# Predicting the classes for test data
y_pred = clf.predict(X_test)
# Evaluate the model
classification_accuracy = accuracy_score(y_test, y_pred)
print(f"Classification Accuracy: {classification_accuracy * 100:.2f}%")
# Clustering: K-Means
kmeans = KMeans(n_clusters=3, random_state=42)
y_kmeans = kmeans.fit_predict(df_scaled)
# Plotting clusters
plt.scatter(df_scaled[:, 0], df_scaled[:, 1], c=y_kmeans, cmap='viridis')
plt.title('K-Means Clustering of Customers')
plt.show()
```

Key Terms

Bagging: Also known as bootstrap aggregation, is a technique used to reduce the variance of predictions by combining the result of multiple classifiers modeled on different sub-samples of the same dataset.

Binary Tree: A tree with each node having no more than two child nodes is called binary tree.

Clustering: A set of techniques used to partition data into a number of groups, also called clusters.

Decision tree: An ML algorithm that represents choices and their results in the form of a tree. The nodes represent an event or choice and the edges of the graph represent the decision rules or conditions.

Elbow Point: The point at which the SSE curve starts to bend is known as the elbow point. The x-value of the elbow point is said to be a reasonable trade-off between error and number of clusters.

Entropy: Entropy measures impurity. It is used for categorical target value. Higher the impurity more is the information required to describe it and vice versa. Therefore, if a population is completely homogeneous, then the entropy is zero. Correspondingly, if the value of entropy is one then it indicates that items are equally divided in the population.
Gini Index: Gini index measures inequality of distribution. It is a measurement of the purity of nodes and is used for all dependent variables. It says that if we randomly select two items from a population (with replacement) then they must be of same class.
Inter-cluster distance: Distance between the centroids of two different clusters.
k-means: An unsupervised learning technique that finds relationships between n observations without being trained by a response variable.
k-nearest neighbor algorithm: A supervised learning algorithm in which the output value of data is known but how to get the output is not known.
Margin: Distance between the hyperplane and the closest data point. We need to maximize this margin for better classification.
Maximum Depth: Number of levels deep a tree can go. This limits the complexity of a tree.
Outlier: An individual data item or observation that lies at an abnormal distance from other data values in a random sample of a dataset.
Parent Node: A node which splits into sub-nodes is called a parent node of the sub-nodes (or child of the parent node).
Pruning the Tree: The process of removing irrelevant nodes from the leaves of a decision tree when it becomes very deep.
Root Node: Node that performs the first split.
Splitting: The process of dividing a node into two or more sub-nodes. In a decision tree, splitting is done until a user-defined stopping-criterion is reached.
Terminal or Leaf Node: A sub-node that does not split further.

Chapter Highlights

* Non-parametric methods do not have fixed numbers of parameters in the model. The parameters in the model grow with the training dataset.
* The most important thing to do in the KNN algorithm is to determine an appropriate value of k, that is, the number of nearest neighbors. A large value of k reduces the noisy data.
* KNN can be used for regressionwhen dependent variable is continuous. In this case, the predicted value is the average of the values of its k nearest neighbors.
* Overfitting happens when a model learns the details and noise in the training data to the extent that it negatively impacts the performance of the model on new data.
* We need to specify minimum number of records in terminal nodes to control overfitting problems.
* Overfitting can be limited by using resampling technique like the k-fold cross validation to estimate model accuracy. The k-fold cross validation allows you to train and test your model k-times on different subsets of training data and build up an estimate of the performance of an ML model on unseen data.
* The performance of decision trees can be enhanced by aggregating many decision trees, using methods like *bagging, random forests,* and *boosting.*
* Inertia indicates how far the points within a cluster are. For this, sum of distances of all the points within a cluster from the centroid of that cluster is calculated. For best results (or clusters), the inertial value should be as low as possible.
* Naïve Bayes algorithm is a probabilistic ML algorithm based on the Bayes Theorem.

Review Exercise

1. Explain the KNN algorithm.
2. When can KNN be used for predicting values?
3. Explain the principle of decision tree algorithm.
4. Explain different measures used to split a decision tree.
5. Give some advantages and limitations of decision trees.
6. What do you understand by the term overfitting? How can it be resolved in a decision tree?
7. How can you use bagging to improve the performance of decision trees?
8. Discuss different types of clustering techniques.
9. List the evaluation metrics for clustering.
10. How k-means Algorithm Works?
11. Compare KNN and k-means algorithm.
12. Highlight the contrasting feature(s) of DBSCAN and k-means algorithm.
13. Explain the arguments in the DBSCAN function.
14. What is a neural network?
15. Differentiate between two types of kernel functions.
16. Give some applications of SVM algorithm.

Programming Exercise

1. Apply KNN on Breast Cancer dataset.
2. Apply KNN on the wine dataset. This dataset is available in the scikit-learn library, or can be downloaded from the UCI Machine Learning Library. The dataset comprises 13 features and a target (type of cultivars).
3. Download the Social Ads dataset from https://www.kaggle.com/rakeshrau/social-network-ads and apply KNN on it.
4. Implement decision tree algorithm on pima-indians-diabetes dataset.
5. Write a code to classify the balance-scale data using a decision tree with gini index. Download the dataset from https://archive.ics.uci.edu/ml/machine-learning-'+'databases/balance-scale/balance-scale.data
6. Classify breast cancer data using a decision tree classifier.
7. Download bike.csv dataset and predict the value of cnt column using decision tree algorithm.
8. Download the car_data and apply decision tree algorithm for predicting class names.
9. Apply the Random Forest for regression on bill_authentication.csv dataset.
10. Consider a dataset with random values of X and Y and form clusters using k-means algorithm.
    'x': [25,34,22,27,33,33,31,22,35,34,67,54,57,43,50,57,59,52,65,47,49,48,35,33,44,45,38,43,51,46],
    'y': [79,51,53,78,59,74,73,57,69,75,51,32,40,47,53,36,35,58,59,50,25,20,14,12,20,5,29,27,8,7]
11. Download the Naïve-Bayes-Classification-Data.csv dataset and perform Naïve Bayes classification on it.
12. Demonstrate the Implementation of Gaussian and Multimonial Naïve Bayes algorithm on the iris dataset.

13. Perform Naïve Bayes classification on Titanic Dataset.
14. Apply Naïve Bayes algorithm on breast cancer dataset and check the accuracy of the model.
15. Consider the input and outputs for the given set of data. Build a neural network model to predict the last output.
    Training Examples

Input 1	Input 2	Input 3	Output
0	1	1	1
1	0	0	0
1	0	1	1

    Now we want to predict the output the following set of inputs:
    Test Example

1	0	1	?

16. Download the heart.dat file and create a neural network that predicts if a person will have heart disease or not.
17. Download the points_class_0.txt and points_class_1.txt. Create a linear SVM Classifier. Modify this classifier so that it works well with a. noisy data b. non-linear separable data with noise. Also write a function to choose the best values for parameters C and gamma.
18. Apply SVM on bill_authentication data and print the confusion matrix.
19. Download apples_and_oranges.csv and implement SVM on it to predict the class of fruit based on its weight and size. Print the confusion matrix to calculate its accuracy.
20. Use the breast-cancer-wisconsin.data.txt dataset to predict vales for values- [[4,2,1,1,1,2,3,2,1]] using SVM classifier. https://www.geeksforgeeks.org/random-forest-regression-in-python/

Fill in the Blanks

1. _________ means that the algorithm makes assumptions on the underlying data distribution.
2. _________ happens when a model learns the details and noise in the training data to the extent that it negatively impacts the performance of the model on new data.
3. In KNN, plot the graph of K value and the corresponding ___________ for the dataset.
4. In KNeighborsClassifier, the _______ distance metric is used by default.
5. _________ refers to a model that can neither model the training data nor generalize to new data.
6. _______ of a decision tree represents a decision rule or condition.
7. The process of removing irrelevant nodes from the leaves of a decision tree when it becomes very deep is known as ________.
8. ________ specifies that when we randomly select two items from a population (with replacement) then they must be of same class.
9. Gini index works when the target value to be predicted is ________.
10. Decision trees come under _______ algorithms, because the algorithm looks for best variable available at the current split.
11. ________ is calculated as, 1- Entropy.
12. The split with _____ variance is chosen as the best split to divide the individuals.

13. As the purity of node increases, ________ decreases.
14. Minimum number of records in terminal nodes must be specified to control _______ problems.
15. ________ should be used to make adjustments when Chi-square statistics is used for a categorical input variable rather than categorical target variable.
16. Overfitting can be limited by using resampling technique like the ________ validation to estimate model accuracy.
17. _____ combines the result of multiple classifiers modeled on different sub-samples of the same dataset.
18. In ________, trees are grown sequentially.
19. _____ clustering follows a top-down approach in which the algorithm starts with all points as one cluster.
20. _______ is an unsupervised learning technique that finds relationships between n observations without being trained by a response variable.
21. _____ indicates how far the points within a cluster are.
22. _______ considers the distance between two clusters.
23. _____ is the ratio of the minimum inter-cluster distances and maximum of intra-cluster distances.
24. In k-means clustering, each cluster is represented by its ______ or ______.
25. The point at which the SSE curve starts to bend is known as the ______.
26. The ________ coefficient is a measure of cluster cohesion and separation.
27. In neural network, one round of forwarding and back-propagation iteration is known as one training iteration or ______.
28. Support Vector Machine is a ________ ML algorithm.
29. In SVM, _______ which is the distance between the hyperplane and the closest data point must be maximized for better classification.
30. _______ and ______ are the two popular methods to standardize variables.

State True or False

1. k-nearest neighbor algorithm is an unsupervised learning algorithm.
2. Items in a cluster are similar.
3. KNN uses all of the data for training while classifying a new data point or instance.
4. In KNN, large value of k increases noisy data.
5. The kNN algorithm fails with multi-class algorithms.
6. KNN is the best algorithm for data with high-dimensionality or categorical features.
7. Decision trees can perform either classification or regression.
8. Decision trees can map only linear relationships.
9. Each terminal (or leaf) node of a decision tree consists of individuals of a single class.
10. Pruning is the process of dividing a node into two or more sub-nodes.
11. A higher value of Gini index indicates higher similarity.
12. Outliers affect the results obtained from Decision trees.
13. Overfitting is more likely with non-parametric and non-linear models.

14. Underfitted model shows low bias but high variance.
15. Random Forests performs better than bagged trees.
16. In Agglomerative clustering, bottom-up approach is used to merge two points that are most similar.
17. Inertial value should be as high as possible.
18. In the Naïve Bayes model, features are independent of each other.
19. Conditional probability = zero, indicates the occurrence of event, A implies that event B cannot occur.
20. The SVM algorithm automatically extracts features from the input data.
21. In k-means, every observation is a part of some cluster even if the observations are scattered far away in the vector space.
22. DBSCAN produces better results than *k*-means.
23. For noisy datasets we must set minPts to a small value to get more significant clusters.

CHAPTER

13 Advanced Learning

Predicting Customer Churn

Imagine that you are a data engineer working to develop machine learning and deep learning models using TensorFlow and Keras that have revolutionized how models are built and deployed. You are given the task of **Predicting Customer Churn** in a telecommunications company.

For this, you need to identify which customers are likely to churn (i.e., cancel their services) based on their past behavior and service usage. This would help the company to take preventive measures like offering them discounts or additional services.

13.1 Deep learning

Deep learning (also known as deep neural learning or deep neural network) is an artificial intelligence (AI) technique that imitates working of the human brain in processing data and creating patterns for use in decision making. It is a subset of machine learning that uses unsupervised learning to learn from unstructured or unlabeled data.

In today's scenario, we generate massive amount of data (approx.2.6 quintillion bytes) every day. This huge data paves the way for application of deep learning techniques. Deep learning algorithms flourish when applied on tons of data processed using stronger computing power.

When applied on very diverse, unstructured and inter-connected data, deep learning can be used to solve complex problems. The more deep learning algorithms learn, the better they perform.

Deep learning (Figure 13.1) is generally used to detect objects, recognize speech, translate languages, recognize similar images, recommend products, make important decisions, detect fraud or money laundering, and explore the possibility of reusing drugs for new ailments among other functions. Its use became unprecedented with massive explosion of data world-wide. The big data that we collect from social media, internet search engines, e-commerce platforms, online cinemas, etc. are unstructured. Such data when analyzed using deep learning techniques, can unravel wealth of information and can be used with AI systems for automated support.

Deep learning uses a hierarchical level of ANNs to carry out the process of machine learning

Deep learning is the key technology behind driverless cars. Such cars are designed to recognize a stop sign, or distinguish a pedestrian from a lamp post. Basically, deep learning model learns to perform classification directly from images, text, or sound. For better accuracy,

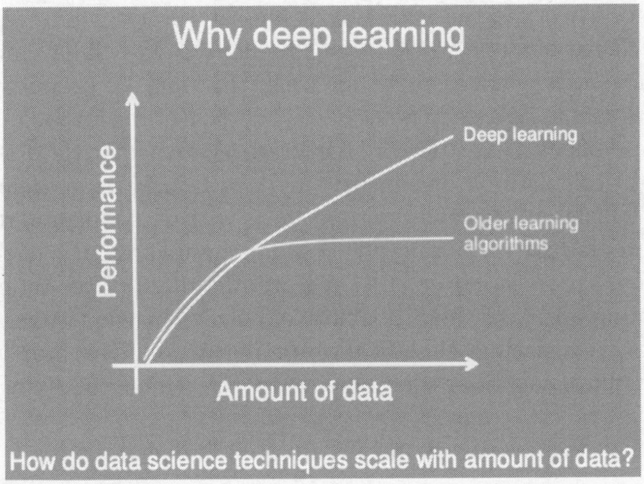

Figure 13.1 Impact of Amount of Data on the Performance of Deep Learning Algorithms

such models are trained by using a large set of labeled data and neural network architectures containing several layers. Figure 13.2 shows the relationship between AI, machine learning and deep learning.

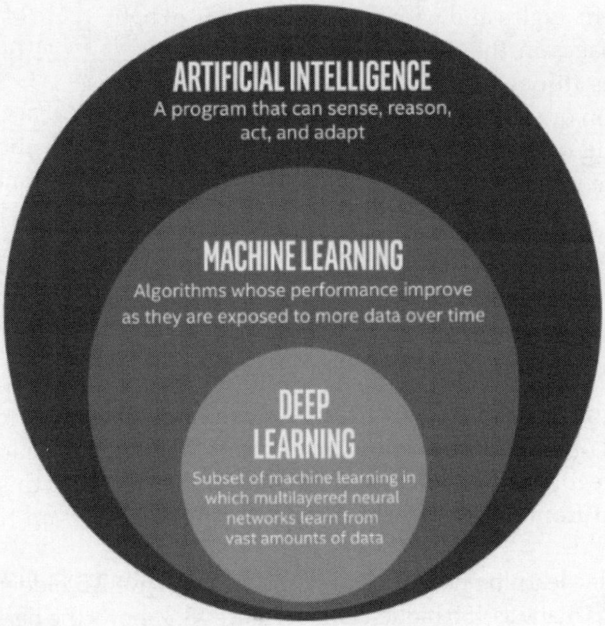

Figure 13.2 Relationship between AI, Machine Learning and Deep Learning

13.1.1 How does deep learning work?

We have studied that neural networks are layers of nodes. Deep learning is designed in the same way as the human brain is made up of neurons. Nodes within individual layers are connected to adjacent layers. While in the human brain, a single neuron receives thousands of signals from other neurons, neural networks work in the same way. A message or a signal travels between nodes and weights are assigned to every node. A node with a higher weight will have more weightage on the next layer of nodes. The final layer computes the weighted inputs to produce the final output.

A neural network is said to be a deep neural network depending on the number of layers it has. A deep learning system needs more powerful hardware as it has more layers and performs several complex mathematical calculations on a large amount of data. Large datasets ensure accurate results. For example, a facial recognition program starts with detecting and recognizing edges and lines of faces and then gradually learns to detect other significant parts of the faces. The process continues till the overall representations of faces are identified. Over time, the program trains itself with every iteration and thus the probability of correct answers increases. Neural networks can be used to perform clustering, classification or regression. The individual layers of neural networks can be thought of as a filter that increases the likelihood of giving the correct result as output.

Basically, two types of neural network models are used in deep learning,

- Convolutional Neural Network (CNN) which is used in image-related applications like autonomous driving and robot vision.
- Recurrent Neural Network (RNN) that is widely applied in most of the Natural Language Processing (NLP) based text or voice applications such as chatbots, virtual assistants, etc.

For example, when creating a neural network that identifies images having a dog, we need to train the network with pictures showing dogs at different angles and with varying amounts of light and shadow. These images in the training dataset are converted into data, which moves through different nodes in the network. Prediction, identification or classification result is finally produced by the last layer, i.e; the output layer of the neural network. The output produced by the neural network is then matched with the labels provided by any human. If the two values match, the output is confirmed otherwise the neural network notes the error and adjusts the weights provided to each node.

> Some popularly used open-source deep learning libraries include Google Tensorflow, Facebook open-source modules for Torch, Amazon DSSTNE on GitHub, and Microsoft CNTK

13.1.2 Machine learning vs deep learning

In a machine learning algorithm, relevant features are manually extracted from images and a particular classifier has to be manually implemented. The extracted features are then used to create a model that categorizes the objects in the image. In contrast to this, relevant features are automatically extracted from images by the deep learning model. Even the modeling steps are automatic.

While a typical machine learning neural network model may have 2-3 hidden layers, deep networks on the other hand have as many as 150 hidden layers. Figure 13.3 shows the performance of application of traditional machine learning, small neural network and large neural networks on the underlying data.

Moreover, deep learning performs "end-to-end learning". This means that a neural network when given raw data and a task (like classification), the model automatically learns how to do this task.

Last but not the least, deep learning algorithms scale well with data. It is free from shallow learning convergence problems that a typical machine learning model may face. Shallow learning refers to creation of plateau at a certain level of performance. Even after adding more data for training, the accuracy and performance of the model does not change.

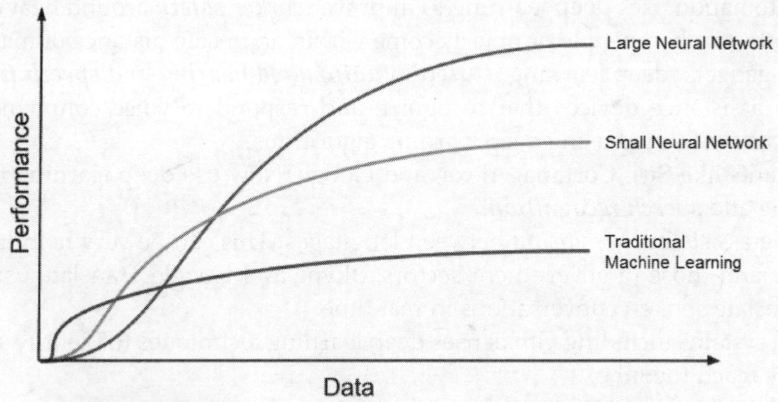

Figure 13.3 Impact of Data on Different Types of Learning

While the biggest advantage of deep learning over machine learning techniques is that it frees users from the worry about trimming down the number of features used (refer Figure 13.4), but the main drawback is that a deep learning model is very expensive to train and needs commercial-grade Graphics Processing Units (GPUs). Many data scientists treat deep learning model as a 'black box' because the model is very complex and extremely difficult to understand.

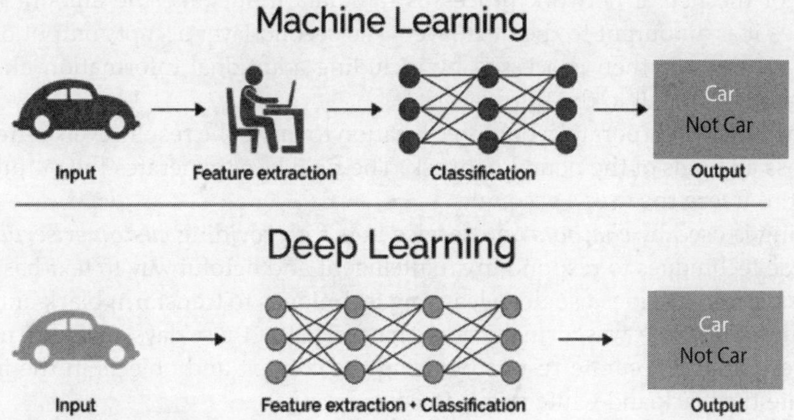

Figure 13.4 Machine Learning System vs Deep Learning System

13.1.3 Applications of deep learning

Deep learning techniques have already outperformed humans in some tasks like classifying objects in images. For example, deep learning uses millions of images and thousands of hours of video to develop driverless cars. For this, it requires substantial computing power. High-performance GPUs having a parallel architecture when combined with cloud computing allow development teams to reduce training time for a deep learning network from weeks to hours or even less. Besides driverless cars, deep learning is also used in the following areas.

In aerospace and defense sector, deep learning is used to ***identify objects from satellites*** that locate areas of interest, and safe or unsafe zones for the military troops.

In medical field, cancer researchers use deep learning to automatically ***detect cancer*** cells.

Industrial automation uses deep learning to improve ***worker safety*** around heavy machinery. It automatically detects when people or objects come within an unsafe distance of machines.

In electronic gadgets, deep learning is used in ***automated hearing and speech translation***. For example, home assistance devices that recognize and respond to voice commands and knows user's preferences are trained using deep learning algorithms.

Digital assistants like Siri, Cortana, Alexa, and Google Now use deep learning for natural language processing and ***speech recognition***.

Deep learning assists in ***translation*** between languages. This can be very helpful for travellers, business people and those in government sectors. Skype and Google Translate uses deep neural networks to translate spoken conversations in real-time.

Several email systems including Gmail uses deep learning techniques to identify ***spam messages*** even before they reach the inbox.

PayPal uses deep learning to ***prevent fraudulent*** payments.

Apps like CamFind implements deep neural networks to allow its users to take a picture of any object and ***discover details*** of that object using mobile visual search technology.

Google Deepmind's WaveNet can generate speech ***mimicking human voice*** that sounds more natural than speech systems presently on the market.

Facebook uses deep learning to identify and ***tag friends*** when a user uploads a new picture.

Example of how deep learning is used for fraud detection: To detect fraud, deep learning uses time, geographic location, IP address, type of retailer, and other features. In such a scenario, the first layer of the neural network processes raw data input (like the amount of the transaction) and passes it as an output to the next layer. The second layer accepts output of the first layer as its input. This input is then processed by including additional information like the user's IP address and passes its result to the third layer.

The third layer may incorporate geographic location to make the results even better. This process continues across all levels of the neural network. The final layer generates the output that may signal the analyst to freeze the user's account.

Deep learning is used by ***chatbots*** and service bots for providing ***customer service***. Many companies use these techniques to respond in an intelligent and helpful way to text-based questions.

Image colorization activities use deep learning techniques to transform black-and-white images into colored ones. This work was formally done manually. But these days, deep learning algorithms generate impressive and accurate results by using the context and objects in the images to color them to recreate the black-and-white image in color.

Deep learning algorithms when used in medicine and pharmaceuticals can be used to diagnose diseases and tumor in the body. They are also used to prescribe personalized medicines created specifically for an individual's genome.

Personalized shopping and entertainment can use deep learning techniques to suggest what users should buy or watch next.

13.2 Introduction to TensorFlow and Keras

TensorFlow is the most commonly used library for implementing deep learning algorithms. It is an open-sourced platform that has a very rich community support. Keras, is another high-level Application Programming Interface (API) that is built on top of TensorFlow. The main advantage of using TensorFlow is that it is extremely user-friendly and comparatively easier than TensorFlow.

TensorFlow has been developed by Google to make the power of Deep Learning accessible to all developers striving hard in the area of machine learning. TensorFlow is not only easy to use but also excels at numerical computing, which is critical for deep learning. It supports APIs for major languages (like Python, C, C++, Rust, Haskell, Go, Java, Android, IoS, Mac OS, Windows, Linux, and Raspberry Pi) and environments that are used for developing deep learning projects.

Another key advantage of TensorFlow is that it was created keeping the processing power limitations in mind. So, this library can be run on all kinds of computers (including smartphones) irrespective of their processing powers.

The current version of TensorFlow is 2.x and runs on almost all major platforms from smart phones to desktops, embedded devices and specialized workstations. It can also be used on distributed clusters of servers on the cloud or on-premise. It is because of this rich set of capabilities that TensorFlow is used to solve real-world applications ranging from analyzing images, generating data, detecting cancer, natural language processing, intelligent chatbots to robotics. TensorFlow is extensively used in voice, image and video recognition and in text-based applications like Google Translate.

> TensorFlow is much more preferred than its competitors including Caffe, Theano, Torch, and other well-known frameworks

13.2.1 Applications of TensorFlow

NASA is using TensorFlow to develop a predictive model of Near-Earth Objects (NEOs). For this, a multilayer model is developed to recognize and classify the potential of NEOs.

Companies like Airbnb, Airbus, Dropbox, Snapchat, and Uber use TensorFlow.

DeepDream, the automated image captioning software uses TensorFlow for identifying and labeling images.

Google's RankBrain uses TensorFlow to handle queries instead of the traditional static algorithm-based search.

Like Google's Inbox, the Allo application uses TensorFlow to reply to the last message from a few customized options. The application also analyses the images received in messages to suggest a relevant response.

13.2.2 What is Keras?

Keras is a high-level library built on top of TensorFlow to provide a scikit-learn type API for building neural networks without worrying about the mathematical aspects of tensor algebra, numerical techniques, and optimization methods.

Keras facilitates experimentation and aids in research by fast prototyping. It offers a very easy-to-use and intuitive APIs which help users to develop and test their deep learning model applications with least considerable efforts. Some excellent features of Keras are:

- Keras is a high-level interface that uses TensorFlow for its backend.
- It runs smoothly on both CPU and GPU.
- Keras supports almost all the models of a neural network (including fully connected, convolutional, pooling, recurrent, embedding, etc.) that can also be combined to build more complex models.
- Keras is modular, expressive, flexible, and perfect for innovative research.
- Code written using Keras is easy to debug as it is completely based on Python-based framework.
- Keras supports both convolutional and recurrent networks. While convolutional networks are used for computer vision applications, recurrent networks are used for working with sequence and time-series data.

- Keras can be used on arbitrary network architectures including multi-input or multi-output models, layer sharing, model sharing and so on. The range of architectures supported by Keras makes it best-suited for building deep learning models varying from generative adversarial networks to a neural Turing machine.
- Keras is compatible with all versions of Python from 2.7, till date.
- Keras uses various optimization techniques to make high-level neural network API easier and more efficient.
- APIs supported by Keras are consistent, simple and easily extensible.
- Keras is based on a minimal structure to get results without any frills.
- It supports multiple platforms and backends.
- Keras offers high scalability of computation.

Because of the afore-mentioned features, two main advantages of using Keras are:

- It is a highly powerful and dynamic framework that is supported by a larger community of users for basic support.
- It is easy to test.

Moreover, since Keras neural networks are written in Python, it is very simple to use.

13.2.3 Installing Keras

To install Keras on your computer, you must have first installed Python version 3.5 or higher. Once Python is installed, follow the steps given below to install Keras.

Create virtual environment (Virtualenv) to manage Python packages for different projects. This is very useful to avoid breaking the packages installed in the other environments.

As the next step, Linux or macOS users should go to project root directory and type the command given below to create virtual environment,

```
python3 -m venv kerasenv
```

After executing the above command, "kerasenv" directory is created with bin, lib and includes folders in the installation location.

Windows user should type, `py -m venv keras` to create the virtual environment.

Activate the environment to configure Python and pip executables in your shell path.

Linux/Mac OS users should move to the folder and type the command given below.

```
$ cd kerasvenv kerasvenv $ source bin/activate
```

Windows users must move inside the "kerasenv" folder and type the below command,

```
.\env\Scripts\activate
```

Finally, install Keras by writing

```
pip install keras
```

Once Keras is installed, quit virtual environment by typing

```
deactivate
```

To install TensorFlow, write the command,

```
pip install TensorFlow
```

13.3 Types of neural networks

In this section, we will learn about four types of neural networks. All these are supported by deep learning algorithms.

Artificial Neural Networks: The most popular and primary approach of deep learning is the Artificial neural network (ANN). It is based on the human brain, which is the made up of more than 90 billion tiny cells called neurons. These neurons are inter-connected through axons and dendrites (which are nothing but nerve fibers). The main work of these connections is to exchange information with connected neurons.

In ANN, nodes are tightly inter-connected and organized into different hidden layers. The input layer receives the input data. This data is processed by one or more hidden layers and the final prediction result is generated by the output layer. For example, the input may be an image of a fruit and the output may be the name of the fruit.

A single layer ANN also known as single perceptron is shown in Figure 13.5. Here, sum is calculated as value of all inputs and activation function.

Multi-Layer Perceptron (MLP): MLP consists of a single input layer, one or more hidden layer and finally an output layer in the neural network. The output layer processes the data that it receives from last hidden layer and finally outputs the result (Figure 13.6).

Convolutional Neural Network (CNN): CNN, a popular ANN, is widely used in applications involving image and video recognition. It is similar to MLP. However, the difference is that CNN contains a series of convolution layer and pooling layer before the fully connected hidden neuron layer. Layers in the CNN can be described as,

- *Convolution layer* which is the primary building block and performs computational tasks based on convolution function.
- *Pooling layer,* that is arranged next to convolution layer and is used to reduce the size of inputs by removing unnecessary information to speed up computations.

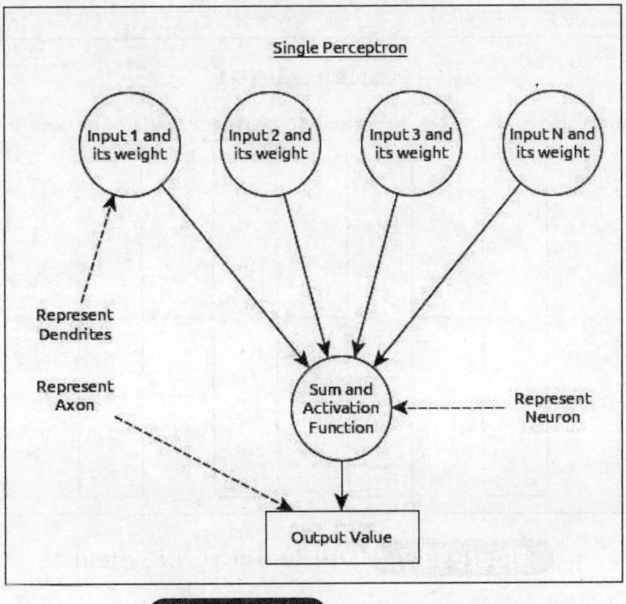

Figure 13.5 A Simple ANN

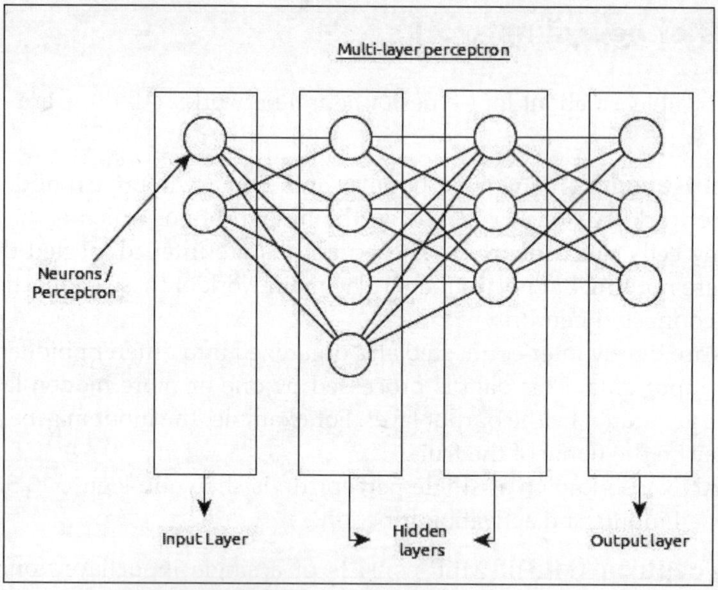

Figure 13.6 Structure of MLP System

- *Fully connected layer*, arranged next to series of convolution and pooling layer, is used to classify input into various categories.

In Figure 13.7, there are two series of Convolution and pooling layer. The convolution layer receives and processes the input to produce the output.

Recurrent Neural Network (RNN): RNN is used to address flaw(s) in other ANN models. While other ANN models do not remember the steps from previous situations and make decisions based on current context, RNN stores the past information and all its decisions are taken from what it has learnt from the past. RNNs are especially used for image classification.

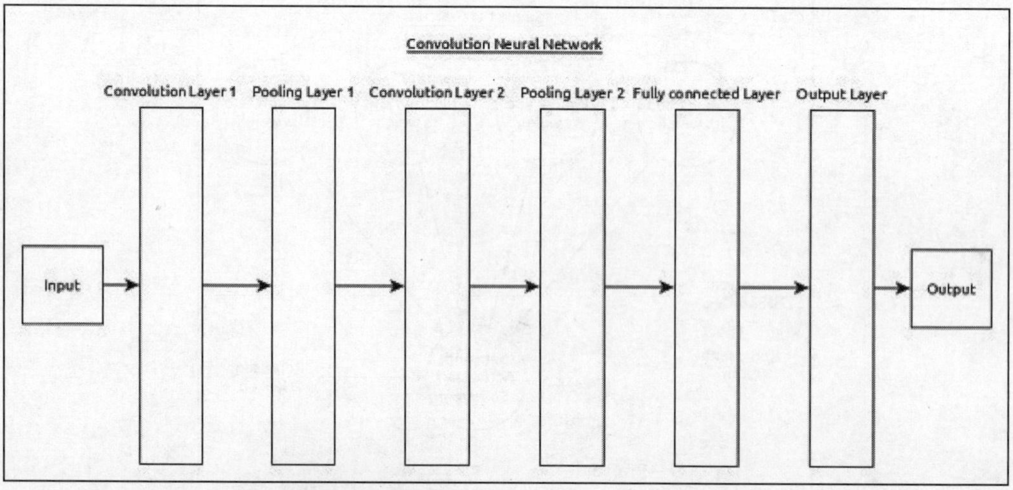

Figure 13.7 Structure of a CNN System

13.3.1 Workflow of ANN

As studied in neural networks, the workflow of ANN can be summarized in the following steps:

Collect as much data as possible, since deep learning requires lot of input data to successfully learn and predict the results.

Analyze the data to get a good understanding of the data. This understanding will help to select the correct ANN algorithm.

Choose an algorithm (or model) that best suits the learning process (like image classification, text processing, etc.) and the available input data.

Prepare data by processing it, applying filters and selecting only the required information from the data.

Split data into training and test dataset. Test data is used to evaluate the accuracy with which the model predicts results.

Compile the model so that it learns by training and predicts results. Loss function and Optimizer are used in this learning phase to find error (deviation from actual output) and optimize the model to minimize error(s).

Fit the model using the training dataset.

Predict values for unknown data. This data is separate from the training and test data.

Evaluate model by predicting the output for test data. Compare actual results with predicted ones of the test data.

If the model gives satisfactory results then freeze it for future use. Else, modify the algorithm or choose another algorithm and again train, predict and evaluate the model until an optimal algorithm (model) is found.

13.4 Architecture of Keras

Keras is a very simple module that provides a complete framework to implement any type of neural network. It supports a variety of neural networks ranging from very simple ones to extremely large and complex models. Let us understand the architecture of Keras framework and how Keras helps in deep learning in this chapter.

To understand the architecture of Keras, we can divide its API in three main categories – ***Model, Layer*** and ***Core Modules.***

In Keras, every ANN is represented by models and every model is composed of one or more layers like the input layer, hidden layer(s), output layer, convolution layer, pooling layer, etc.

Model and layers in Keras access modules for activation function, loss function, regularization function, etc. Any ANN algorithm can be easily represented in a simple and efficient manner using Keras model, layers, and modules. Figure 13.8 depicts the relationship between model, layer and core modules.

13.4.1 Model

The Sequential Model in Keras is basically a linear composition of Keras Layers which is not only easy but can represent nearly all available neural networks. The code given below creates a simple sequential model.

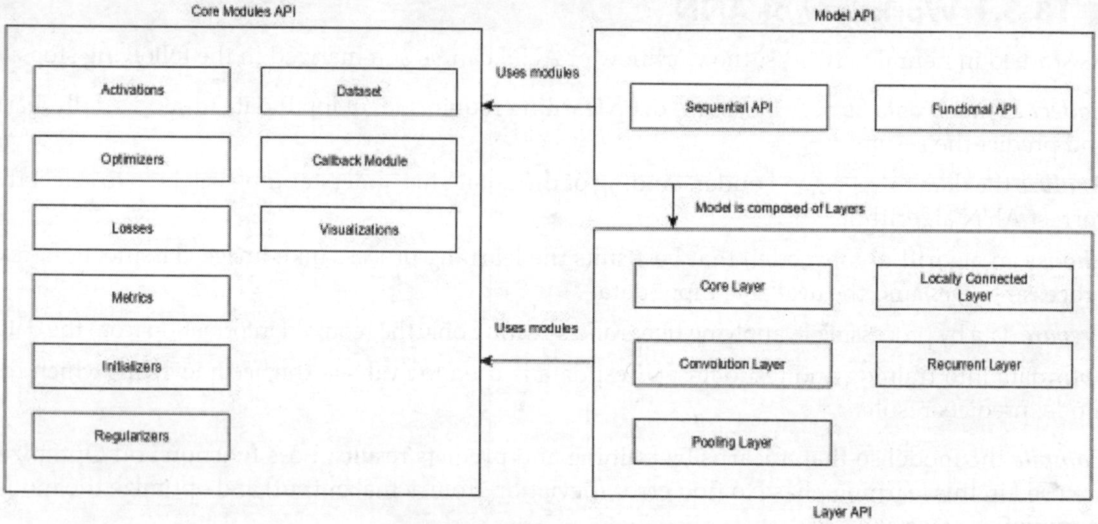

Figure 13.8 Keras Model

```
from keras.models import Sequential
from keras.layers import Dense, Activation
model = Sequential()
model.add(Dense(512, activation = 'relu', input_shape = (784,)))
```

In the code, a new sequential model using Sequential API is created. Once the model is in place, a dense layer is added with relu activation.

Sequential model exposes Model class to create customized models as well. We can use sub-classing concept to create our own complex model.

In a sequential model, all Keras layers are arranged in a sequential fashion in which data flows from one layer to another layer until the data finally reaches the output layer.

13.4.2 Layer

Keras provide a variety of pre-build layers to easily create a complex neural network. Each layer in the model represents the corresponding layer (input, hidden and output layer) in the actual proposed neural network model. The code given below represents a neural network model using sequential model.

```
from keras.models import Sequential
from keras.layers import Dense, Activation, Dropout
model = Sequential()
model.add(Dense(512, activation = 'relu', input_shape = (784,)))
model.add(Dropout(0.2))
model.add(Dense(512, activation = 'relu')) model.add(Dropout(0.2))
model.add(Dense(num_classes, activation = 'softmax'))
```

Here, we have created and added dense layers with **relu** activation function. The dropout layer is added to handle overfitting. The final dense layer uses **softmax** activation function.

Keras layers require shape of the input (input_shape) to specify the structure of the input data. It can use ***initializer*** to set the weight for each input and activators to transform the output to make it non-linear.

Moreover, constraints can be used to restrict and specify the range of weights for the input data. Regularizers are used to optimize the layer (and thus the model) by dynamically applying penalties on the weights.

Therefore, to summarize, we can say that minimum information required to create a complete Keras layer include: Shape of the input data, Number of units in the layer, Initializers, Regularizers, Constraints and Activators.

To get the model information like layers, input data and output data, we can use the ***model.layers*** that returns all the layers of the model as list. Similarly, we can use the following values.

model.inputs that returns all the input tensors of the model as list.

model.outputs that returns all the output tensors of the model as list.

model.get_weights that returns all the weights as NumPy arrays.

model.set_weights(weight_numpy_array) that is used to set the weights of the model.

Finally, the summary of the model can be printed by writing, **model.summary.**

Write a code to create one input layer, one hidden layer and one output layer.

```
from keras.models import Sequential
model = Sequential()
input_layer = Dense(32, input_shape=(8,)) model.add(input_layer)
hidden_layer = Dense(64, activation='relu'); model.add(hidden_layer)
output_layer = Dense(8)
model.add(output_layer)
```

Write a code to create a model using the input layer of a specific shape and prints its summary.

```
from keras.layers import Input
from keras.models import Model
from keras.layers import Dense
data = Input(shape=(2,3))
layer = Dense(2)(data)
model =
Model(inputs=data,outputs=layer) print(model.summary())
```

13.4.3 Loss

The loss function is used during model compilation process to find error or deviation in the machine learning process. Some loss functions included in the losses module are: mean_squared_error, mean_absolute_error, mean_absolute_percentage_error, mean_squared_logarithmic_error.

> The loss/error in turn is used to update the neural network weights and bias values

These loss functions accept two arguments: ***y_true*** *and* ***y_pred***.

13.4.4 Optimizer

Optimization is an important process in machine learning that optimizes the input weights by comparing the prediction and the loss function. In Keras some frequently used *optimizers* are: SGD – Stochastic gradient descent optimizer, RMSprop – RMSProp optimizer, Adagrad – Adagrad optimizer, Adadelta – Adadelta optimizer, Adam – Adam optimizer, Adamax – Adamax optimizer from Adam, etc.

13.4.5 Metrics

Metrics are used to evaluate the performance of the machine learning model. Some important metrics defined in the Keras module are accuracy, binary_accuracy, categorical_accuracy, sparse_categorical_accuracy, top_k_categorical_accuracy, sparse_top_k_categorical_accuracy, cosine_proximity, clone_metric. Though it is similar to loss function, it is not used in training process.

However, like the loss function, metrics also accepts two arguments: ***y_true*** and ***y_pred***.

Now, if we write

```
from keras import losses
from keras import optimizers
from keras import metrics
model.compile(loss = 'mean_squared_error',
    optimizer = 'sgd', metrics = [metrics.categorical_accuracy])
```

in the above line of code, the loss function being used is mean_squared_error, optimizer is sgd and metrics used is metrics.categorical_accuracy.

13.4.6 Training the model

Models are trained using the ***fit()* function.** This function is used to evaluate the model during the training phase. The syntax of fit() function can be given as,

```
model.fit(X, y, epochs, batch_size)
```

where,

x, y is a tuple that is used to evaluate data.

`epochs` specify number of times the model is needed to be evaluated during training.

`batch_size` indicates training instances.

Create a simple multi-perceptron artificial network by using the MNIST database of handwritten digits that has 60,000, 28x28 grayscale images. There are also 10,000 test images.

```
# import all modules
import keras
from keras.models import Sequential
from keras.layers import Dense, Dropout
from keras.optimizers import RMSprop
import numpy as np
# load the data set from keras
from keras.datasets import mnist
(x_train, y_train), (x_test, y_test) = mnist.load_
data()
# reshape the input from (28, 28) tuple to (784, )
x_train = x_train.reshape(60000, 784)
```

Other important data sources for analysis are CIFAR100 small image classification, IMDB Movie reviews sentiment classification, Reuters newswire topics classification, Fashion-MNIST database of fashion articles, Boston housing price regression dataset

```
x_test = x_test.reshape(10000, 784)
x_train = x_train.astype('float32')
x_test = x_test.astype('float32')
x_train /= 255
x_test /= 255
# to_categorical() function is used to convert vector to binary matrix
y_train = keras.utils.to_categorical(y_train, 10)
y_test = keras.utils.to_categorical(y_test, 10)
# create a sequential model
model = Sequential()
# Add a hidden layer- Dense containing 512 neurons, using 'relu' activation
function
model.add(Dense(512, activation = 'relu', input_shape = (784,)))
# Add a second hidden layer- Dropout with value 0.2
model.add(Dropout(0.2))
# Add another hidden layer- Dense with 512 neurons, using 'relu' activation
function
model.add(Dense(512, activation = 'relu'))
# Add a fourth hidden layer- Dropout with value 0.2
model.add(Dropout(0.2))
# Add the final layer containing 10 neurons and 'softmax'
activation function
model.add(Dense(10, activation = 'softmax'))
# Compile the model
model.compile(loss = 'categorical_crossentropy',
   optimizer = RMSprop(), metrics = ['accuracy'])
   # Train the model using fit() method
history = model.fit(x_train, y_train, batch_size = 128,
  pred = model.predict(x_test)
pred = np.argmax(pred, axis = 1)[:5]
label = np.argmax(y_test,axis = 1)[:5]
print(pred)
print(label) epochs = 20, verbose = 1, validation_data = (x_test, y_test))
```

The compile() function translates the Keras statements into TensorFlow instructions

Download the ionosphere.csv data and use keras to make a model for predicting values.

```
from pandas import read_csv
from sklearn.model_selection import train_test_split
from sklearn.preprocessing import LabelEncoder
from tensorflow.keras import Sequential
from tensorflow.keras.layers import Dense
# load data in a data frame
df = read_csv('ionosphere.csv', header=None)
# split into input and output columns
X, y = df.values[:, :-1], df.values[:, -1]
# ensure all data are floating point values
X = X.astype('float32')
```

```
# encode strings to integer
y = LabelEncoder().fit_transform(y)
# split into train and test datasets
X_train, X_test, y_train, y_test = train_test_split(X, y, test_size=0.33)
print(X_train.shape, X_test.shape, y_train.shape, y_test.shape)
# determine the number of input features
n_features = X_train.shape[1]
# define model
model = Sequential()
model.add(Dense(10,   activation='relu',   kernel_initializer='he_normal',
input_shape=(n_features,)))
model.add(Dense(8, activation='relu', kernel_initializer='he_normal'))
model.add(Dense(1, activation='sigmoid'))
# compile the model
model.compile(optimizer='adam',              loss='binary_crossentropy',
metrics=['accuracy'])
# fit the model
model.fit(X_train, y_train, epochs=150, batch_size=32, verbose=0)
# evaluate the model
loss, acc = model.evaluate(X_test, y_test, verbose=0)
print('Test Accuracy: %.2f' % acc)
# make a prediction
x_val  =  [1,0,0.1239,-0.0634,0.7289,0.02306,0.83398,-0.37708,  1,  0.03760,
0.85243,-0.1543,0.59755,-0.44945,0.71234,-0.2343,0.7998,-0.29867,0.58212,
-0.32192,0.56971,-0.29674,0.36946,-0.47357,0.56811,-0.51171,0.41078,
-0.46168,0.21266,-0.34090,0.42267,-0.54487,0.18641,-0.45300]
y_predict = model.predict([x_val])
print('Predicted: %.2f' % y_predict)
```

OUTPUT

```
(235, 34) (116, 34) (235,) (116,)
Test Accuracy: 0.92
Predicted: 0.78
```

13.5 Univariate and Multivariate Time Series Analysis With Python

Traditional statistical techniques like autoregressive models (AR), moving averages (MA), and their combination (ARIMA) applied on time series data are usually univariate, as they focus on a single sequence of values. But, in real-world applications, time series data has multiple variables interacting with one another. For this reason, discussion of time series data is incomplete without understanding relationships between different features. However, let us start our discussion from **Univariate Time Series.**

Univariate time series analysis considers a single variable measured over time. For example, the daily closing price of a single stock, the hourly temperature recorded in a city, and data coming from a sensor. While analyzing these values, the focus is on the historical behavior of a sequence to predict its future values. This technique is undoubtedly simple and efficient in understanding the underlying patterns but lacks the analysis of external influences or correlations between variables.

In real world applications where systems are often interconnected, ignoring these relationships may give suboptimal forecasts.

13.5.1 Multivariate Time Series

In a multivariate time series, multiple time-dependent variables are analyzed simultaneously to interpret relationships and correlations between different features, providing detailed information for predictions. For example, analyzing a single temperature sensor may not give much information about potential failures, but combining data from multiple sensors such as temperature, pressure, vibration, and energy consumption helps in in-depth analysis. For example, an increase in machine temperature is related to an increase in vibration levels. This in turn may cause a failure.

Many physical systems like machinery, climate, or energy grids, temperature cannot rise indefinitely without causing other measurable effects (like pressure changes). Thus, multiple variables incorporated in multivariate models are needed for effective analysis.

13.5.2 Univariate vs. Multivariate

Let us compare univariate and multivariate approaches by predicting machine failure.

- Univariate Approach: Assuming that a sequence of time series data, like the temperature readings, is being taken from a single sensor, the univariate model can identify trends, seasonality, or anomalies over time. This approach is simple and computationally efficient but does not consider other factors like pressure, vibration, etc. that could have added to the present context.
- Multivariate Approach: Taking readings from different types of sensors that measures temperature, vibration, and pressure will help the researcher to consider the related factors. This would in turn help to identify complex patterns that would not be apparent in a univariate analysis. For example, an increase in vibration may raise the temperature and the change in pressure. A multivariate analysis therefore helps to build better forecasts and failure detection models. Consider a scenario in which a multivariate model recognizes that a spike in vibration increases the temperature in 10 minutes. This relation can be used to issue early warnings for preventive maintenance. The points of differences are summarized in Table 1:

Table 1: || Comparing Univariate Time Series and Multivariate Time Series

Feature	Univariate Time Series	Multivariate Time Series
Definition	Time series with only one variable over time.	Time series with **multiple** variables over time.
Example	Daily temperature readings of a city.	Daily temperature, humidity, and wind speed together.
Data Structure	Single column (Timestamp + One Value).	Multiple columns (Timestamp + Multiple Values).
Complexity	Simpler to analyze and forecast.	More complex due to interdependencies between variables.
Visualization	Line plot of a single variable over time.	Multiple line plots or correlation heatmaps.
Forecasting Models	ARIMA, Exponential Smoothing, Simple RNNs.	VAR, LSTM, Transformer models.
Use Case	Stock price prediction (single stock).	Stock price prediction using multiple economic indicators.
Dependency	Assumes each value depends **only on past values** of itself.	Variables influence each other (e.g., temperature and humidity).
Best For	When a single variable is the **only** important factor.	When multiple factors influence the outcome.

13.5.3 Techniques for Multivariate Time Series Analysis

Given below are some key techniques to handle multiple variables simultaneously.

Vector Autoregressive (VAR) Models: An extension to the autoregression model, the VAR model is used for multivariate time series analysis. The VAR model identifies linear relationships between multiple variables over time.

Vector Error Correction Models (VECM): A variant of VAR, VECM is used when variables have a long-term equilibrium relationship. The model is preferred when features are cointegrated, that is, moving together over time.

Machine Learning Approaches: Recurrent Neural Networks (RNNs) and Long Short-Term Memory (LSTM) networks easily learn complex, non-linear patterns in multivariate time series data. This makes these models widely used for predictive maintenance, financial forecasting, and weather prediction.

Transformer Models: Recent advances like transformers can efficiently handle multivariate time series with long-term dependencies.

Multivariate State-Space Models: These models take into account the underlying system dynamics and constraints. This makes them best-suited for physical systems that are often governed by laws like thermodynamics or mechanics.

Bee Example: There is a correlation between bee traffic and temperature. Increase in temperature results in an increase in the bee traffic. Analyzing only bee traffic (univariate) would not consider the role of temperature and weight. So, let us perform a multivariate analysis that combines all three values for better predictions.

```
import matplotlib.pyplot as plt
from sklearn.linear_model import LinearRegression
import pandas as pd
df = pd.DataFrame({
    'temperature': [30, 32, 28, 29, 31],
    'weight': [2.1, 2.3, 1.9, 2.0, 2.2],
    'bee_traffic': [150, 180, 140, 160, 175]
})
df.index = range(1, len(df) + 1) # Creating an index for better visualization
# Defining input (X) and output (y) variables
features = df[['temperature', 'weight']]  # Predictor variables
target = df['bee_traffic']  # Target variable
# Initialize and train the regression model
traffic_predictor = LinearRegression()
traffic_predictor.fit(features, target)
# Generate predictions
df['predicted_traffic'] = traffic_predictor.predict(features)
# Visualization - Actual vs Predicted Bee Traffic
plt.figure(figsize=(10, 6))
# Line plot for actual values
plt.plot(df.index, df['bee_traffic'], label="Actual Bee Traffic", color='green',
alpha=0.6)
# Line plot for predicted values
```

```
plt.plot(df.index, df['predicted_traffic'], label="Predicted Bee Traffic",
linestyle='dashed', color='blue')
plt.title("Bee Traffic Prediction Based on Environmental Factors")
plt.xlabel("Observation Time")
plt.ylabel("Bee Traffic Count")
plt.legend()
# Save and display the plot
plt.savefig("bee_traffic_prediction.png", dpi=300)
plt.show()
```

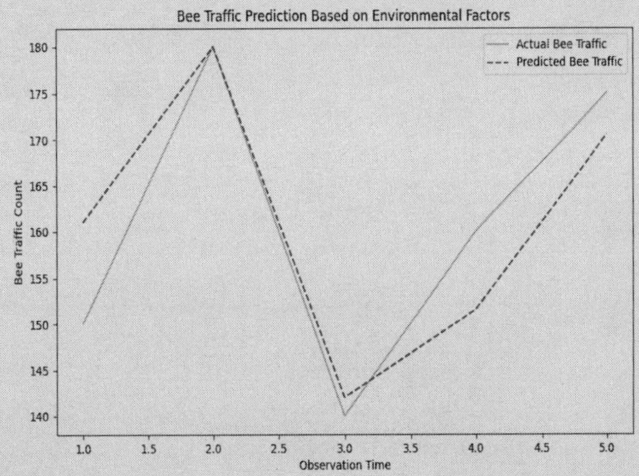

13.5.4 Multivariate Time Series Analysis using TensorFlow

We can identify the trends and relationships among multiple time series data to forecast the future values. One way to do this efficiently is using TensorFlow. We know that multivariate time series analysis is a statistical technique that analyzes multiple time series data to identify patterns and relationships between them. Such an analysis helps to forecast future values, identify causal relationships between them, and understand the interaction between them.

Multivariate time series analysis is often used in the field of finance, economics, supply chain management, business, and sales to understand how multiple variables are related to each other. For example, in finance, the analyst uses multivariate time series analysis to forecast the future price of a stock based on the past prices of other stocks, economic indicators, or news events.

The code give below uses LSTMs for multivariate time series analysis. LSTM is a major advancement of RNNs in Deep Learning. It is extensively used in sequencing data in natural language processing, speech recognition, etc. They work as intelligent information processors.

```
import numpy as np
import pandas as pd
import tensorflow as tf
from tensorflow import keras
from tensorflow.keras.models import Sequential
from tensorflow.keras.layers import LSTM, Dense
from sklearn.preprocessing import MinMaxScaler
```

```
# Generate synthetic multivariate time series data
def generate_data(n_samples=1000, n_features=3):
    np.random.seed(42)
    time = np.arange(n_samples)
    data = np.array([np.sin(time / 10) + np.random.normal(scale=0.1, 
size=n_samples),
                     np.cos(time / 20) + np.random.normal(scale=0.1, 
size=n_samples),
                     np.sin(time / 30) + np.random.normal(scale=0.1, 
size=n_samples)]).T
        return pd.DataFrame(data, columns=[f'feature_{i}' for i in 
range(n_features)])

data = generate_data()

# Normalize the data
scaler = MinMaxScaler()
data_scaled = scaler.fit_transform(data)

def create_sequences(data, seq_length):
    X, y = [], []
    for i in range(len(data) - seq_length):
        X.append(data[i:i+seq_length])
        y.append(data[i+seq_length])
    return np.array(X), np.array(y)

seq_length = 20
X, y = create_sequences(data_scaled, seq_length)

# Split into training and testing sets
split = int(len(X) * 0.8)
X_train, X_test = X[:split], X[split:]
y_train, y_test = y[:split], y[split:]

# Define LSTM model
model = Sequential([
    LSTM(50, activation=›relu', return_sequences=True, input_shape=(seq_
length, X.shape[2])),
    LSTM(50, activation=›relu'),
    Dense(X.shape[2])
])
model.compile(optimizer='adam', loss='mse')

# Train the model
history = model.fit(X_train, y_train, epochs=25, batch_size=32, validation_
data=(X_test, y_test))
```

```
# Plot validation loss
plt.figure(figsize=(8, 5))
plt.plot(history.history['loss'], label='Training Loss')
plt.plot(history.history['val_loss'], label='Validation Loss')
plt.xlabel('Epochs')
plt.ylabel('Loss')
plt.legend()
plt.title('Model Loss Over Epochs')
plt.show()

# Make predictions
y_pred = model.predict(X_test)

# Inverse transform predictions and actual values
y_test_inv = scaler.inverse_transform(y_test)
y_pred_inv = scaler.inverse_transform(y_pred)

# Display results
print("First 5 Actual values:")
print(y_test_inv[:5])
print("\nFirst 5 Predicted values:")
print(y_pred_inv[:5])
OUTPUT
First 5 Actual values:
[[-1.00186851 -0.9819888   0.98580468]
 [-0.95605903 -0.98896211  0.81396371]
 [-0.86040765 -0.8306336   0.97866395]
 [-0.87915625 -0.83112858  0.89745764]
 [-0.64606024 -1.06257044  1.06525196]]

First 5 Predicted values:
[[-0.94230384 -0.7560689   1.1070758 ]
 [-0.9171075  -0.81063396  1.1158023 ]
 [-0.87522185 -0.8674744   1.1112332 ]
 [-0.82054996 -0.9093591   1.1071955 ]
 [-0.7660463  -0.9395585   1.0932572 ]]
```

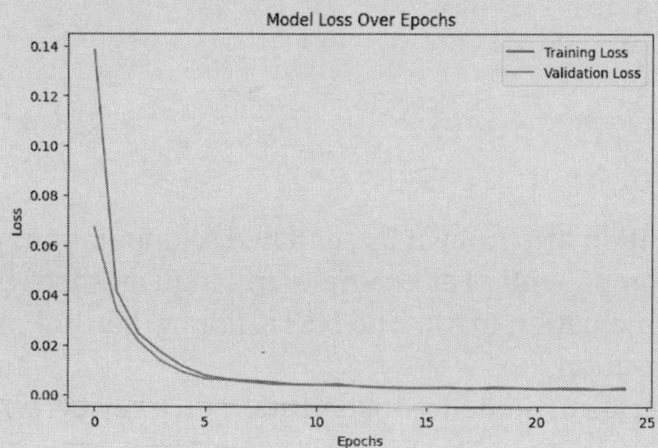

13.6 What is natural language processing?

Natural Language Processing (NLP) is the manipulation or understanding of text or speech by a computer software. As humans interact, they understand each other's views, and respond with an appropriate answer. Similarly, NLP systems also interact, understand, and respond to queries.

Natural Language Processing, a field of AI studies interactions between computers and human (natural) languages. It applies machine learning algorithms to text and speech. For example, NLP can be used to create intelligent systems for speech recognition, machine translation, question answering, spam detection, document summarization, predictive typing, named entity recognition and autocomplete, to name a few.

These days, smartphones and computers support so many applications that all modern operating systems have a built-in speech recognition module. For example,

Cortana which is the virtual assistant of Microsoft Windows recognizes human voice to set up reminders, open apps, send emails, search information, play games, get latest updates on weather, etc.

Siri, the virtual assistant of the Apple Inc.'s iOS, watchOS, macOS, HomePod, and tvOS helps users to perform their tasks with voice commands like starting a call, text someone, send an email, click a picture, set a timer, open an app, set an alarm, use navigation and so on.

Gmail, the most popular email service developed by Google uses NLP to detect and filter spam emails.

13.6.1 The NLTK library for Python

The Natural Language Toolkit (NLTK) is a free, open source, community-driven project that is widely used for building Python programs that can process human language data. For this purpose, NLTK has easy-to-use interfaces to use several resources and contains a suite of text processing libraries that has built-in functions for classification, tokenization, stemming, tagging, parsing, and semantic reasoning.

Processing natural language

The basic steps in NLP include:

1. Sentence Tokenization
2. Word Tokenization
3. Text Lemmatization and Stemming
4. Stop Words
5. Regex
6. Bag-of-Words
7. TF-IDF

Step I: Sentence Tokenization also known as sentence segmentation, divides a string written in a language into its basic components. For example, in languages like English, a sentence can be split at the position of a punctuation mark. The NLTK library has the nltk.sent_tokenize function to perform sentence tokenization.

The code given below performs sentence tokenization on a review written for the Jruma app.

```
import nltk
text = "A very great App for students! I wish to solve more and more quizzes
every day and increase my knowledge! Thank you so much for this App! This App
should be appreciated more and more! Congratulations!!:))"
sentences = nltk.sent_tokenize(text)
for sentence in sentences:
    print(sentence)
OUTPUT
A very great App for students!
I wish to solve more and more quizzes every day and increase my knowledge!
Thank you so much for this App!
This App should be appreciated more and more!
Congratulations!!
:))
```

Step 2: Word Tokenization or word segmentation divides a string of written language into its constituent words. For example, in English, two consecutive words are separated using a space. The nltk.word_tokenize() function is used **to** apply word tokenization on the given string.

```
from nltk import word_tokenize, sent_tokenize
import nltk
text = "A very great App for students! I wish to solve more and more quizzes
every day and increase my knowledge! Thank you so much for this App! This App
should be appreciated more and more! Congratulations!!:))"
words = nltk.word_tokenize(text)
for word in words:
    print(word, end = '###')

OUTPUT
A###very###great###App###for###students###!###I###wish###to###solve###more#
##and###more###quizzes###every###day###and###increase###my###knowledge###!#
##Thank###you###so###much###for###this###App###!###This###App###should###be
##Thank###you###so###much###for###this###App###!###This###App###should###be
###appreciated###more###and###more###!###Congratulations###!###!###:###)###
)###
```

Step 3: Text Lemmatization and Stemming are used for grammatical reasons to support documents that contain different forms of a word. For example, words like run, runs, running are related words having a similar meaning. In this case, stemming and lemmatization can be used to reduce all these related words to a common base.

> You can think of stemming and lemmatization as a special case of normalization

For example, am, are, is – have a common base 'be'. Similarly, run, runs, running can be reduced to the base form 'run'.

Stemming and lemmatization are special cases of normalization. However, they are different from each other.

Lemmatization performs its task with the help of a vocabulary and morphological analysis of words, to return the base or dictionary form of a word, which is often known as the lemma.

Stemmer, on the other hand, operates without knowledge of the context. It cannot understand the difference between words having a different meaning in a different context. However, stemmers are easier to implement and usually run faster.

Example: Program to demonstrate stemming text.

```
from nltk.stem import PorterStemmer
stemmer = PorterStemmer()
words = ['run', 'running', 'runs', 'runner']
stemmed = [stemmer.stem(word) for word in words]
print(stemmed)
```

OUTPUT

```
['run', 'run', 'run', 'runner']
```

Step 4: Eliminate Stop words. These words are usually filtered out before or after processing text. Since these words add a lot of noise, they are treated as irrelevant and must therefore be discarded. Some common stop words in English language are "and", "the", "a".

The NLTK library has a predefined list of common stop words. However, when using the NLTK library for the first time, you must download the stop words by writing, nltk.download("stopwords"). After downloading, the stop words can be loaded from the nltk.corpus package.

While removing stop words, we convert list into a set because search operation is performed faster on a set that on a list.

Example: Let us remove stop words from our text.

```
Note that you must first download stop words of English language by writing
nltk.download('stopwords')
from nltk import word_tokenize, sent_tokenize
from nltk.corpus import stopwords
import nltk
nltk.download('stopwords')
text = "A very great App for students! I wish to solve more and more quizzes
every day and increase my knowledge! Thank you so much for this App! This
App should be appreciated more and more! Congratulations!!:))"
stop_words = stopwords.words('english')
words = nltk.word_tokenize(text)
cleaned_text = []
for word in words:
    if word not in stop_words:
        cleaned_text.append(word)
print("Uncleaned Text : ", text)
print("Cleaned Text : ", cleaned_text)
```

OUTPUT

```
Uncleaned Text :  A very great App for students! I wish to solve more and
more quizzes every day and increase my knowledge! Thank you so much for this
App! This App should be appreciated more and more! Congratulations!!:))
```

```
Cleaned Text : ['A', 'great', 'App', 'students', '!', 'I', 'wish', 'solve',
'quizzes', 'every', 'day', 'increase', 'knowledge', '!', 'Thank', 'much',
'App', '!', 'This', 'App', 'appreciated', '!', 'Congratulations', '!', '!',
':', ')', ')']
```

POS Tagging or Parts of Speech Tagging also known as grammatical tagging, is a process that marks words in text format for a particular part of a speech depending on its definition and context. It reads text in a language and assigns some specific token (Parts of Speech) to each word. Steps involved in the POS tagging include:

Step I: Tokenize text

Step 2: Apply pos_tag using nltk.pos_tag(tokenize_text)

```
Example: To tag text using the pos_tag() method of nltk library.
Note you need to first download the averaged_perceptron_tagger' before using
the po_tag() method
from nltk import word_tokenize, sent_tokenize
from nltk.corpus import stopwords
import nltk
nltk.download('averaged_perceptron_tagger')
text = "A very great App for students! I wish to solve more and more quizzes
every day and increase my knowledge! Thank you so much for this App! This App
should be appreciated more and more! Congratulations!!:))"
stop_words = stopwords.words('english')
words = nltk.word_tokenize(text)
cleaned_text = []
for word in words:
    if word not in stop_words:
        cleaned_text.append(word)
tagged = nltk.pos_tag(cleaned_text)
print("Tagged Text is : ", tagged)

OUTPUT
Tagged Text is :  [('A', 'DT'), ('great', 'JJ'), ('App', 'JJ'), ('stu-
dents', 'NNS'), ('!', '.'), ('I', 'PRP'), ('wish', 'VBP'), ('solve', 'RB'),
('quizzes', 'JJ'), ('every', 'DT'), ('day', 'NN'), ('increase', 'VB'),
('knowledge', 'NN'), ('!', '.'), ('Thank', 'NNP'), ('much', 'JJ'), ('App',
'NNP'), ('!', '.'), ('This', 'DT'), ('App', 'NNP'), ('appreciated', 'VBD'),
('!', '.'), ('Congratulations', 'NNPS'), ('!', '.'), ('!', '.'), (':', ':'),
(')', ')'), (')', ')')]
```

In the output, VB refers to 'verb', NNS refers to 'plural nouns', DT refers to a 'determiner'.

Steps Involved in the POS tagging example:

- Tokenize text (word_tokenize)
- apply pos_tag to above step that is nltk.pos_tag(tokenize_text)

Refer to any website for a list of tags. These tags are almost always pretty accurate but we should be aware that they *can* be inaccurate at times. However, pre-trained models usually assume the English being used is written properly, following the grammatical rules.

13.6.2 Regex or regular expressions

Regular Expressions are powerful tools for various kinds of string manipulation. These are basically a special text string that is used for describing a search pattern to extract information from text such as code, files, log, spreadsheets, or even documents.

The sub() Function

The `sub()` function in the `re` module can be used to search a pattern in the string and replace it with another pattern. The syntax of `sub()` function can be given as,

```
re.sub(pattern, repl, string, max=0)
```

According to the syntax, the `sub()` function replaces all occurrences of the `pattern` in `string` with `repl`, substituting all occurrences unless `any max` value is provided. This method returns modified string.

Example: Program to demonstrate the use of sub() function.

```
import re
string = "She sells sea shells on the sea shore"
pattern = "sea"
repl = "ocean"
new_string = re.sub(pattern, repl, string, 1)
print(new_string)
OUTPUT
She sells ocean shells on the sea shore
```

In the above program, note that only one occurrence was replaced and not all because we had provided `1` as the value of `max`.

13.6.3 Meta characters in regular expression

Meta characters make regular expressions more powerful than normal string methods. They allow you to create regular expressions to represent concepts like "one or more repetitions of a vowel".

Python allows users to specify meta characters like **(+ ? . * ^ $ ( ) [ ] { } | \\)** in regular expressions. Table 2 lists some meta characters and their purpose.

Table 2: || Meta characters and their description and usage

Meta Character	Description	Example	Remarks
^	Matches at the beginning of the line	`^Hi`	Match Hi at the start of the string
$	Matches at the end of the line	`Hi$`	Match Hi at the end of the string
.	Matches any single character except newline	`Lo.`	It will match Lot, Log, etc
[...]	Matches any single character in brackets	`[Hh]ello`	Match "Hello" or "hello"
[^...]	Matches any single character not in brackets	`[^aeiou]`	Match anything other than a lowercase vowel
re*	Matches 0 or more occurrences of regular expression	`[a-z]*`	Match zero or more occurrence of lower case characters

Table 2: || *(Continued)*

<table>
<tr><th>Meta Character</th><th>Description</th><th>Example</th><th>Remarks</th></tr>
<tr><td>re+</td><td>Matches 1 or more occurrence of regular expression</td><td>[a-z]+</td><td>Match one or more occurrence of lower case characters</td></tr>
<tr><td>re?</td><td>Matches 0 or 1 occurrence of regular expression</td><td>Book?</td><td>Match "Book" or "Books"</td></tr>
<tr><td>re{ n}</td><td>Matches exactly n number of occurrences of regular expression</td><td>42{1}5</td><td>It will match 425</td></tr>
<tr><td>re{ n,}</td><td>Matches n or more occurrences of regular expression</td><td>42{1,}5</td><td>It will match 42225 or any number with more than one 2s between 4 and 5</td></tr>
<tr><td>re{ n, m}</td><td>Matches at least n and at most m occurrences of regular expression</td><td>42{1,3}5</td><td>It will match 425, 4225, 42225</td></tr>
<tr><td>a| b</td><td>Matches either a or b</td><td>"Hello" | "Hi"</td><td>Match Hello or Hi</td></tr>
<tr><td>\w</td><td>Matches word characters</td><td>re.search(r'\w', 'xx123xx')</td><td>Match will be made</td></tr>
<tr><td>\W</td><td>Matches non-word characters</td><td></td><td></td></tr>
<tr><td>\s</td><td>Matches whitespace Equivalent to [\t\n\r\f]</td><td>re.search(r'\d\s*\d\s*\d', 'xx123xx'</td><td>Match will be made</td></tr>
<tr><td>\S</td><td>Matches non-white space</td><td></td><td></td></tr>
<tr><td>\d{n}</td><td>Matches exactly n digits</td><td>\d{2}</td><td>Match exactly 2 digits</td></tr>
<tr><td>\d{n,}</td><td>Matches n or more digits</td><td>\d{3,}</td><td>Match 3 or more digits</td></tr>
<tr><td>\d{n,m}</td><td>Matches n and at most m digits</td><td>\d{2,4}</td><td>Match 2,3 or 4 digits</td></tr>
<tr><td>\D</td><td>Matches non-digits.</td><td>(\D+\d)</td><td>Match Hello 5678, or any string starting with no digit followed by digits(s)</td></tr>
<tr><td>\A</td><td>Matches beginning of string</td><td>\AHi</td><td>Match Hi at the beginning of the string</td></tr>
<tr><td>\Z</td><td>Matches end of string</td><td>Hi\Z</td><td>Match Hi at the end of the string</td></tr>
<tr><td>\G</td><td>Matches point where last match finished</td><td></td><td></td></tr>
<tr><td>\b</td><td>Matches word boundaries when outside brackets. Matches backspace when inside brackets</td><td>\bHi\b</td><td>Match Hi at the word boundary</td></tr>
<tr><td>\B</td><td>Matches non-word boundaries</td><td>\bHi\B</td><td>Hi should start at word boundary but end at a non-boundary as in High</td></tr>
<tr><td>\n, \t, etc.</td><td>Matches newlines, carriage returns, tabs, etc.</td><td>re.search(r'\t', '123 \t abc')</td><td>Match</td></tr>
</table>

Thus, we see that regex can be used for additional filtering of the text. For example, we can use regex to remove all punctuation marks, or non-alphabet characters. For best results, we can use the re.sub() function to replace a matched pattern with another string.

Bag-of-words: Machine learning algorithms cannot process text directly. We must perform feature extraction to convert text into vectors of numbers. Bag-of-words is a popular and simple feature extraction technique that describes the occurrence of each word within a document.

In the bag-of-words, a vocabulary of known words (also called tokens) is defined and a measure of the presence of known words is chosen. While designing the vocabulary, the case, punctuation, and one-character tokens are ignored. Any other information about the order or structure of words is also discarded.

> **Programming Tip**
>
> An exception re.error is raised if any error occurs while compiling or using regular expressions

The simplest scoring method is to mark the presence of words with 1 for present and 0 for absent.

The basic concept is that similar documents have similar contents. And this similar content can be used to learn something relevant about the meaning of the document.

When the vocabulary size increases, the vector representation of the documents also increases. This means that length of the document vector is equal to the number of known words.

We can use the CountVectorizer class from the scikit-learn library to do this.

Many-a-times, when there is huge amount of data, the vector that represents a document may contain thousands or millions of elements. But, each document may contain only a few of the known words in the vocabulary. In such cases, vector representation will have many zeros (thus, they form sparse vectors) and will consume more memory and computational resources.

To minimize the consumption of resources, we must therefore, decrease the number of the known words using text cleaning techniques that may involve ignoring the case, punctuation and stop words. We can even reduce the words to their base form and correct the misspelled words.

Last but not the least, grouped words can be used to change the scope of the vocabulary and get more details about the document. This approach is called n-grams. An n-gram consists of a number of items (words, letter, numbers, digits, etc.). While a unigram is made of one word, a bigram consists of two words, trigram is a sequence of three words, etc. Basically, "n" in the "n-gram" refers to the number of the grouped words. In the bag-of-words, we use only n-grams and not all possible n-grams. For example, in the sentence *I love to do work from home*, the sets n-grams are,

```
Bi-gram = [ {I love}, { to do}, {work from}, {from home}]
Tri-grams = [{I love to}, {do work from}, {work from hone}]
```

Once, the vocabulary is created, occurrence of the words in the data is scored where we mark 1 for presence and 0 for absence of a word.

Some other scoring methods are:

Counts which records the number of times each word appears in a document.

Frequencies that calculates the frequency with which each word appears in document as compared to all other words in the document.

13.6.4 Term frequency-inverse document frequency (TF-IDF)

When we score according to **word frequency**, the most frequent words in the document have the highest scores. However, these frequent words may not possess as much information as compared to some other rarer, domain-specific words. To fix this problem, we can penalize words that are frequent across all the documents. This approach is called TF-IDF. Therefore, TF-IDF is a statistical measure that evaluates the importance of a word to a document in a collection (also known as corpus).

TF-IDF increases with increase in the number of times a word appears in the document. TF-IDF for a given term **x** within a document **y** is calculated as,

$$\text{TF}(\textbf{term}) = \frac{\text{Number of times } \textbf{terms} \text{ appears in a document}}{\text{Total Number of items in the document}}$$

Similarly, **Inverse Term Frequency (ITF)** that computes how rare the word is across documents, is calculated as,

$$\text{IDF}(\textbf{term}) = \log\left(\frac{\text{Total Number of documents}}{\text{Number of documents with } \textbf{term} \text{ in it}}\right)$$

Taking both the terms together, TF-IDF score is computed as,

$$\text{TFIDF}(\textbf{term}) = \text{TF}(\textbf{term}) * \text{IDF}(\textbf{term})$$

In Python, **TfidfVectorizer** class from the scikit-learn library is used to calculate the TF-IDF scores for given documents.

Write a code to compare the working of a lemmatizer and a stemmer.

```
from nltk.stem import PorterStemmer, WordNetLemmatizer
from nltk.corpus import wordnet
import nltk
nltk.download('wordnet')
def compare_stemmer_and_lemmatizer(stemmer, lemmatizer, word, pos):
    print("Stemmer:", stemmer.stem(word))
    print("Lemmatizer:", lemmatizer.lemmatize(word, pos))
lemmatizer = WordNetLemmatizer()
stemmer = PorterStemmer()
compare_stemmer_and_lemmatizer(stemmer, lemmatizer, word = "ran", pos =
wordnet.VERB)
# compare_stemmer_and_lemmatizer(stemmer, lemmatizer, word = "drove", pos =
wordnet.VERB)
```

OUTPUT

```
Stemmer: ran
Lemmatizer: run
```

Write a code to print the two most frequently occurring words in a text.

```
message = ['She', 'sells', 'sea', 'shells', 'on', 'the',
           'sea', 'shore', 'she','said', 'on', 'the', 'sea', 'shore']
tokens = set(message)
tokens = sorted(tokens)
print(tokens[-2:])
```

OUTPUT

```
['shore', 'the']
```

Write a code to print the 10 most frequently occurring characters in a piece of text.

```
import nltk
text1 = '''
```

```
Computer Network Types
A computer network is a group of computers linked to each other that enables
the computer to communicate with another computer and share their resources,
data, and applications.
A computer network can be categorized by their size. A computer network is
mainly of four types:
Computer Network Types
LAN(Local Area Network)
PAN(Personal Area Network)
MAN(Metropolitan Area Network)
WAN(Wide Area Network)'''
fdist1 = nltk.FreqDist(text1)
print(fdist1.most_common(10))
```

OUTPUT

```
[(' ', 55), ('e', 44), ('t', 34), ('o', 33), ('r', 33), ('a', 23), ('p',
15), ('c', 14), ('n', 14), ('i', 14)]
```

Write a code to print words in a text that have more than 7 characters.

```
message = 'A computer network is a group of computers linked to each other
that enables the computer to communicate with another computer and share
their resources, data, and applications. A computer network can be catego-
rized by their size. A computer network is mainly of four types'
mes = message.split(' ')
long_words = [w for w in mes if len(w) > 7]
print(sorted(long_words))
```

OUTPUT

```
['applications.', 'categorized', 'communicate', 'computer', 'computer',
'computer', 'computer', 'computer', 'computers', 'resources,']
```

Create bigrams using a piece of quotation.

```
import nltk
text = 'All our dreams can come true, if we have the courage to pursue them.'
text = text.split(' ')
print(list(nltk.bigrams(text)))
```

OUTPUT

```
[('All', 'our'), ('our', 'dreams'), ('dreams', 'can'), ('can', 'come'),
('come', 'true,'), ('true,', 'if'), ('if', 'we'), ('we', 'have'), ('have',
'the'), ('the', 'courage'), ('courage', 'to'), ('to', 'pursue'), ('pursue',
'them.')]
```

Print collocations from the given text.

Hint: A collocation is a sequence of words that occur together unusually often.

```
import nltk
message = 'Information technology (IT) refers to everything that busi-
nesses use computers for. Information technology is building communications
networks for a company, safeguarding data and information, creating and
```

```
administering databases, helping employees troubleshoot problems with their
computers or mobile devices, or doing a range of other work to ensure the
efficiency and security of business information systems. Demand for profes-
sionals in this field is high and growing, and people entering the field have
a range of career paths to choose from.'
tokens = nltk.word_tokenize(message)
text = nltk.Text(tokens)
print(text.collocations())
```

OUTPUT

```
Information technology
```

Write a program that reads a piece of text and then returns how frequent the different lengths of words are.

```
import nltk
message = '''There are other skills and expertise that are highly desirable
as well, but these are the primary four in my opinion. These will be referred
to as the data scientist pillars for the rest of this article.
In reality, people are often strong in one or two of these pillars, but usually
not equally strong in all four. If you do happen to meet a data scientist that
is truly an expert in all, then you've essentially found yourself a unicorn.
Based on these pillars, my data scientist definition is a person who should be
able to leverage existing data sources, and create new ones as needed in order
to extract meaningful information and actionable insights. A data scientist
does this through business domain expertise, effective communication and
results interpretation, and utilization of any and all relevant statistical
techniques, programming languages, software packages and libraries, and data
infrastructure. The insights that data scientists uncover should be used to
drive business decisions and take actions intended to achieve business goals.
'''
tokens = nltk.word_tokenize(message)
text = nltk.Text(tokens)
fdist = nltk.FreqDist(len(w) for w in text)
print(fdist)
print(fdist.most_common)
```

OUTPUT

```
<FreqDist with 13 samples and 189 outcomes>
<bound method Counter.most_common of FreqDist({3: 31, 2: 31, 4: 24, 1: 23,
7: 17, 5: 13, 6: 13, 8: 13,. 9: 11, 11: 5, ...})>
```

Remarks: In the above program, the FreqDist function is used to analyze the distribution of word lengths in a text. In its output, each number is the length of the corresponding word in the text. From the above output, it is clear that majority of the words are of 3 and 2 characters long. There are 24 words of length 4 and 23 words of length 1, so on and so forth.

Some other important functions defined in the NLTK library are:

fdist.max() returns words with the greatest count.

fdist.tabulate() is used to tabulate the frequency distribution.

fdist.plot() plots a graphical chart of the frequency distribution.

fdist.plot(cumulative=True) draws a cumulative plot of the frequency distribution.

fdist1 |= fdist2 sets fdist1 with counts from fdist2.

fdist1 < fdist2 checks if words in fdist1 occur less frequently than in fdist2.

13.7 Markov decision process in reinforcement learning

Just imagine that you have to go to a nearby city. How will you go? Take a car, a bus, train, an airplane or ride a bike? To make an optimal decision, you will use **probability.** For example, if there is a 70% chance of rain that can lead to traffic jams, then you may not like to go by road. However, **deterministic costs** (like the cost of gas or an airplane ticket) as well as deterministic rewards (like time to travel) also matters. Markov Decision Process (MDP) is used to model these types of optimization problems, and can also be applied to more complex tasks in Reinforcement Learning.

Let us consider a dice game to understand the concept of MDP.

- In each round, the user can decide to **continue** with the game or **quit**.
- User gets a reward of 5$ if he quits the game. Once the user quits, the game ends.
- If the user chooses to **continue**, he receives $3 and a chance to roll a 6-sided dice. If number 1 or 2 turns up, the game ends. Else, the game continues onto the next round.

Here, the user gains if the game continues to next round but loses ($2) if the game ends.

To create an MDP to model this game, we must know the following things:

State refers to the status that the agent (decision-maker) can hold. For example, in our dice game, the state can either be *in the game* or *out of the game*.

Action is a movement that the agent can choose to make. Every action transits the agent from one state to another. Every action has a certain penalty or reward associated with it.

Transition probabilities indicates the probability of ending up in a state when an action a is taken. It is denoted as a function $P(s, a, s')$ where P is the probability of landing from the current state s and to the ending state, s' when action a is taken. For example, in our game playing scenario, if the user chooses to continue with the game (action a), then he can end up finishing the game if a 1 or 2 comes on the dice. The probability of this event is 2/6 or 1/3. So, we can write, $P(s =$ playing the game, $a =$ choose to continue playing, $s' =$ game over) is 1/3.

Rewards are given depending on the action. For example, user gets a $5 reward for quitting the game and $3 for continuing. In reinforcement algorithms we need to optimize the rewards. This can be done by formally describing an MDP as $m = (S, A, P, R,$ gamma), where:

S is the set of all states.

A is the set of possible actions.

P is transition probabilities.

R represents the rewards.

Gamma is the discount factor.

The MDP m aims to find a policy, pi, that produces an optimal long-term reward. These policies map each state s to actions a with a certain probability. These policies can also be deterministic if the agent takes action a in state s. Our MDP can be visualized as shown in Figure 13.9.

Note that the *Markov Property*, which is applicable to any MDP states that the next state can be determined solely by the current state – no 'memory' is necessary.

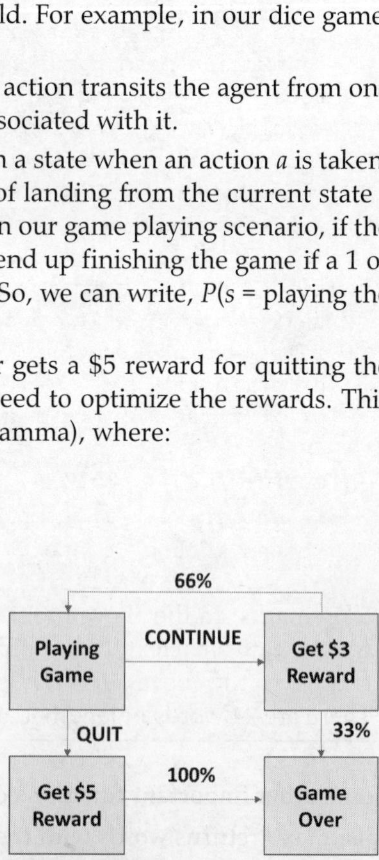

Figure 13.9 Simple MDP Model

13.7.1 The Bellman Equation and dynamic programming

The Bellman Equation is a very important concept in MDP. It outlines a framework for determining the optimal expected reward at a state s by understanding what maximum reward an agent can get on taking an optimal action now and for all future decisions. For our MDP, we can write down the Bellman Equation as,

$$V(s) = \max_a(R(s,a) + \gamma V(s'))$$

where,

V(s) is the expected return value at the current state.

R(s,a) is the expected reward for taking action at state s.

$\max_a$ is the maximum value of any possible action *a*.

γ is the discount factor. The value of γ (gamma) is between 0 or 1 (inclusive) and plays a vital role in determining the optimal reward. If its value is 0, then the model takes only the immediate reward in consideration and ignores the value of V(s'). However, if gamma is 1, the model gives equal importance to immediate as well as future rewards.

V(s') is the value at the next state

Using the Bellman equation to determine the amount of money that can be received in the dice game, we can consider two choices and then proceed with choice that gives maximum return. The equation can be, max(choice 1's reward, choice 2's reward).

Choice I: To quit the game and get a reward of $5.

Choice 2: Take a reward of $3 plus a 2/3 chance of continuing to the next stage. In the next stage, the same decision can be made again.

In this context, the equation can be given as,

$$\max\left(5, 3+\gamma\frac{2}{3}\left(\max\left(5, 3+\gamma\frac{2}{3}\left(\max\left(5, 3+\lambda\frac{2}{3}(\ldots)\right)\right)\right)\right)\right)$$

Though the equation is recursively defined, it will converge to a single value provided that the value of the next iteration will decrease by 2/3, even if $\gamma = 1$. Let's see how the game goes and computer the optimal reward in four iterations.

Thus, we see that in four iterations, we can get maximum $7.8 reward. More the number of iterations, higher is the reward (Figure 13.10).

13.7.2 Q-learning: Markov decision process + reinforcement learning

In this technique, the agent (the circle) must navigate a grid to maximize the rewards for a given number of iterations. In the example, there are 9 states,

–2 punishment –5 punishment –1 punishment +1 reward +10 reward

block that moves the agent to space A1 or B3 with equal probability

empty blocks

In the MDP, the game terminates if the agent has a punishment of –5 or less, or if the reward is 5 or more.

In Q-learning, knowledge about probabilities is not available. Instead, the model learns itself by interacting with the environment. So, this technique is preferred when a robot is being trained to navigate a complex landscape.

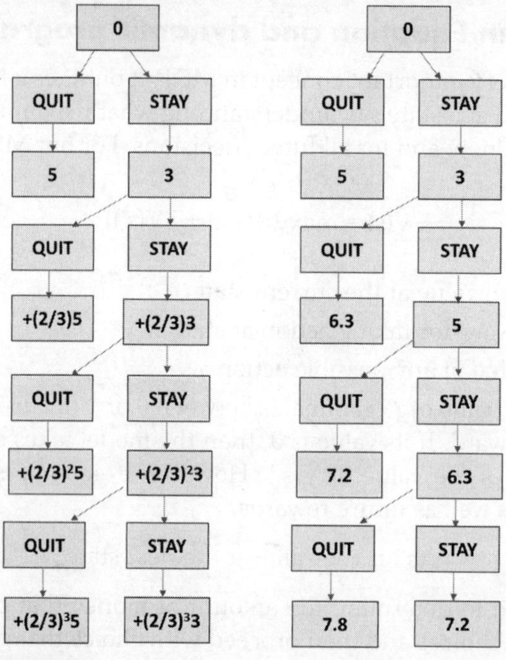

Figure 13.10 Computing Rewards Using Bellman's equation

At each step, the model updates its learnings in a Q-table (refer Figure 13.11). The Q-table stores possible state–action pairs to reflect the *current* known information about the system. This information will then be used to drive future decisions.

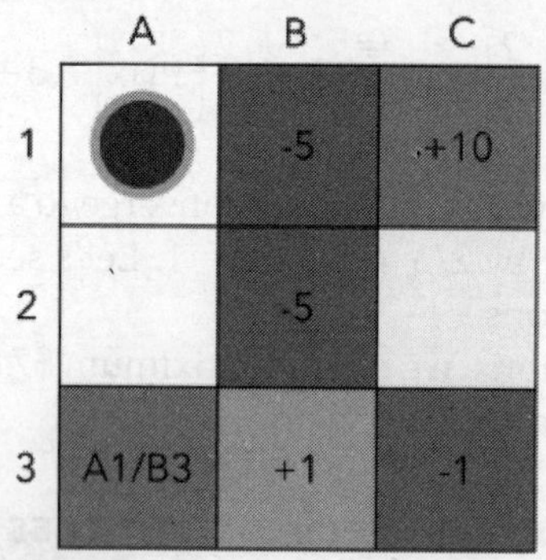

Figure 13.11 Initial Position of the Agent in the Grid

Every entry in the Q-table stores the expected value of the system when the current action is taken. Initially, all values in the table are marked as 0. This value is then updated iteratively as and when an action is taken. Did you notice that there is no state for A3? This is because the agent cannot control the movement from that point (Figure 13.12).

From the initial point, the agent cannot move up or down. It can only move in the right direction and bear a penalty of –5. However, this would terminate the game as per our rules. The updated Q-table (Figure 13.13) can be given as,

Now, next time the agent has to start from its initial position, it has learnt the consequences from right movement. So, given the current Q-table, it can choose to move down. At least, 0 is better than –5.

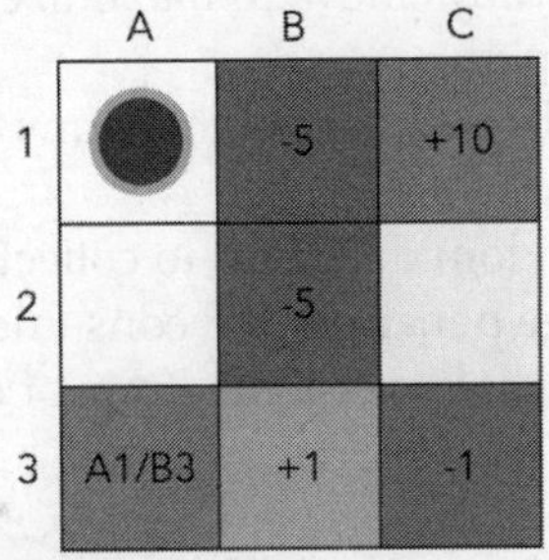

State	Left	Right	Down	Up
A1	0	0	0	0
A2	0	0	0	0
B1	0	0	0	0
B2	0	0	0	0
B3	0	0	0	0
C1	0	0	0	0
C2	0	0	0	0
C3	0	0	0	0

Figure 13.12 Initial Position of the Agent in the Grid and an Empty Q Table

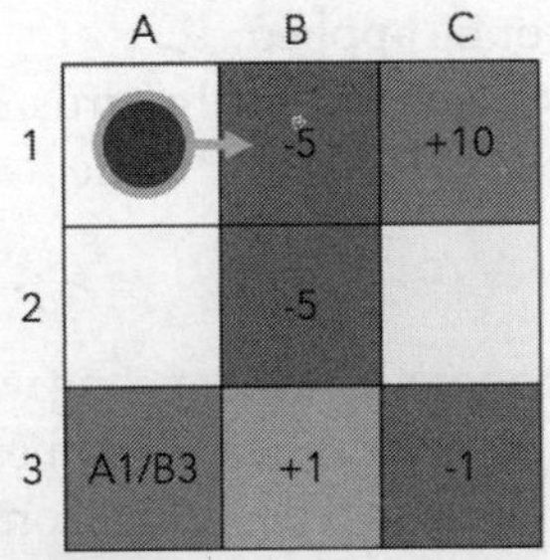

State	Left	Right	Down	Up
A1	-	-5	0	-
A2	0	0	0	0
B1	0	0	0	0
B2	0	0	0	0
B3	0	0	0	0
C1	0	0	0	0
C2	0	0	0	0
C3	0	0	0	0

Figure 13.13 Right Movement of Agent and the Corresponding Entry in the Q Table

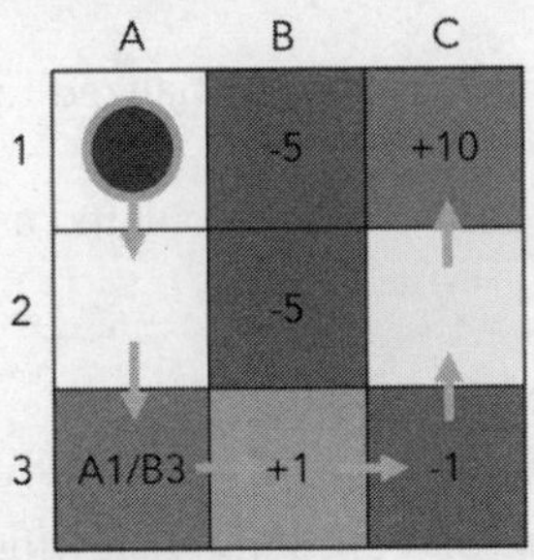

State	Left	Right	Down	Up
A1	-	-5	10	-
A2	0	0	10	0
B1	0	0	0	0
B2	0	0	0	0
B3	0	10	0	0
C1	0	0	0	0
C2	0	0	0	10
C3	0	0	0	10

Figure 13.14 Agent reaches C1, terminating the game with a reward of 10

Considering that the agent starts from A1 and finally reaches C1, terminating the game with a reward of 10, the Q-table can be updated as shown in Figure 13.14.

As of now, the Q-table is incomplete. If the agent moves down from A1 to A2, there is no guarantee that it will receive a reward of 10. Multiple iterations are required to complete the Q-table so that it tells us the best and worst decisions that must be taken at every location.

13.7.3 Exploration vs exploitation trade-off

Just image that if an agent traverses the correct path towards the goal but terminates after recording a negative value in the Q-table, every move it took will then be associated with this penalty.

An agent working in purely 'exploitative' manner will always move to maximize direct immediate gain and would not take a step in the direction of that path.

Such an agent will always follow the path to get a small reward and ignore any other path that may eventually end up earning a reward that is larger than 1.

Any agent when allowed to 'explore' more, will take random decisions to collect more information. Such an approach may be inefficient, resulting in large penalties and consume more computing time. So, we must always try to use a hybrid approach that uses a good mix of explorative and exploitative approach.

13.7.4 Monte-Carlo learning

Till now, we have seen that an entire problem can be transformed into an MDP to get an optimal strategy provided we have values of $< s, P, a, R, \gamma >$. However, in the real world, it is difficult to have all of this information at the same time. For example, the state transition probability (*P*) may not be known and in such a situation the Bellman Equation cannot be applied.

In such a scenario, the agent can run several trials, collect samples, get rewards, and evaluate the value function. The final estimated *V* value will be very close to the real *V* value.

13.7.5 Monte-Carlo evaluation

In the Monte-Carlo approach, the agent learns from the environment by interacting with it and collecting samples. Each "try" is called an episode, and all episodes must terminate. This means that the final state of the MDP should be reached. Values for each state are updated depending on the final reward G_t (and not on estimations of neighbor states as is done in case of Bellman Optimality Equation).

The Monte-Carlo technique learns from complete episodes and its updated state value can be given as, $V(s) = V(s) + \alpha[G_t - V_s)]$

where,

V(s) is the current state value that has to be estimated. Its value can be initialized randomly or with a certain strategy.

G_t is a parameter like learning rate and given terminate time t, it is calculated as,

$$G_t = R_{t+1} + \gamma R_{t+2} + \cdots + \gamma^{T-1} R_T$$

Methods to get V(s)

There are two popular approaches for calculating the value of V(s): First-visit Monte-Carlo Policy Evaluation and Every-visit Monte-Carlo Policy Evaluation. Difference between these techniques mainly exists based on two factors:

Given the state s at time $t + 1$ and time $t + 2$, both are used for calculating the state s or any of them is used.

How often the value of V(s) is updated

First-Visit Monte-Carlo Policy Evaluation: With policy for each episode, **only the first time** that the agent arrives at S counts.

Every-Visit Monte-Carlo Policy Evaluation: With policy for each episode, **every time** that the agent arrives at S counts. This can be expressed as,

First time state s appears as, N(s) = N(s) + 1

Total Reward Update = S(s) = S(s) + Gt

State's Value V(s) = S(s) /N(s)

Here, when N(s) approaches infinity, V(s) = $v_\pi(s)$. Try as many episodes as possible to get close to the real state *s* value.

Incremental Monte-Carlo Updates: It states that for each state *St* in the episode, there is a reward *Gt*, and for every time, the average value of the state, *V(St)* is calculated as,

$$N(s) = N(s) + 1$$

$$\text{State's Value } V(st) = V(st) + [Gt - V(st)] / N(st)$$

13.7.6 Temporal-difference learning

The Monte-Carlo reinforcement learning algorithm is a big leap in formulating the strategy for an unknown model. However, the only shortcoming is that the strategy can be updated after the whole episode. So, in a way, the Monte-Carlo method does not make full use of the MDP learning task structure. Therefore, we need to try a more efficient Temporal-Difference (TD) technique that overcomes this shortcoming.

The TD Learning is a good combination of Deep Programming and Monte-Carlo technique.

Instead of waiting until the end of the episode to determine V(St), the TD method, waits until the next time step. That is, at time *t + 1*, the TD method uses the observed reward Rt + 1 and immediately forms a **TD target** *R(t + 1) + V(St + 1)*, updating V(St) with **TD error**.

We can write this as,

$$R(t+1) + V(St+1) \text{ is called } \textbf{TD target value}$$

$$R(t+1) + V(St+1) - V(St) \text{ is called } \textbf{TD error}.$$

13.8 Genetic algorithms in machine learning

A genetic algorithm is a heuristic search-based algorithm that is mainly used to solve optimization problems in machine learning. These algorithms help users solve difficult problems that would otherwise take a long time to solve. Heuristic search-based algorithms are better than random search algorithms as they utilize historical data to take the search to the best performing region within the solution space.

As the name specifies, genetic algorithms are inspired by Darwin's Theory of Evolution which states that an evolution maintains a population of individuals that vary from each other (variation). Individuals that are better adapted to their environment have a better chance of survival, breeding, and passing their traits to the next generation. In other words, it works on the principle of "Survival of the fittest".

Genetic algorithms are applied in several real-life applications including data centers, electronic circuit design, code-breaking, image processing, and artificial creativity. However, before delving into this topic, let us first be familiar with key terminologies that we will be using frequently in the course of its discussion.

Population: A subset of all the probable solutions that can be used to solve the given problem. If an individual is represented as a chromosome, then population is a collection of all chromosomes (Figure 13.15).

Chromosomes: A chromosome is one of the solutions in the population (refer Figure 13.17).

Gene: An individual element in a chromosome. That is, a chromosome is a collection of genes. For example, if we consider a chromosome as a binary string then each bit is a gene (Figure 13.16).

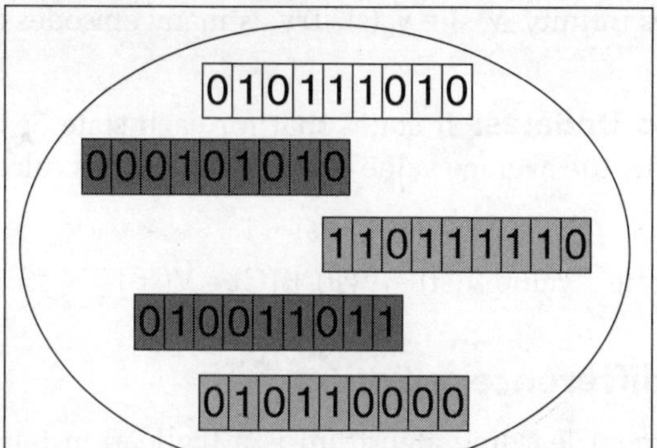

Figure 13.15 A Population of Individuals Represented by Binary-coded Chromosomes

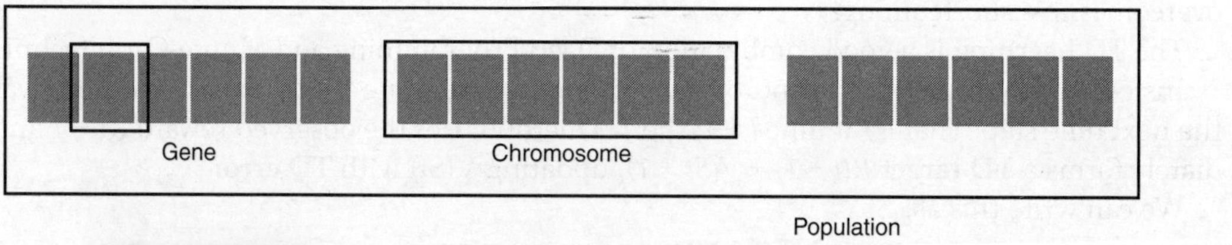

Figure 13.16 Relationship between Gene, Chromosome and Population

Figure 13.17 Simple Binary-coded Chromosome

Allele: Value of a gene in a specific chromosome.

Fitness Function: Function that uses a specific input to produce an improved output.

Genetic Operators: The main goal of genetic algorithms is to generate a better solution. For this, two best individuals mate to reproduce an offspring that is better than the parents. Technically, genetic operators are used for changing the genetic composition of the offspring to get a new and a better solution.

Like in biology, computer genetic algorithms are based on the behavior of chromosomes and their genetic structure. Every chromosome plays an important role in creating variations in the results.

13.8.1 How genetic algorithms work?

Genetic algorithms use the evolutionary generational cycle to generate high-quality solutions to solve complex optimization problems. Various steps applied in this process include:

Initialization: The first step performed by a genetic algorithm is to generate an initial population containing all probable solutions to the given problem. The most widely used technique for initialization is using random binary strings.

Fitness Assignment: In every iteration the fitness function evaluates the fitness scores of all individuals in the population. This score is used to determine the probability of being chosen for reproduction. Higher the fitness, more is the probability of being chosen for reproduction.

For example, if genetic algorithms are used for feature selection, then the accuracy of the model with those selected features would be the fitness function for evaluation.

Selection: The main goal here is to identify the region having a higher probability of producing a better solution to the problem than given by a previous generation. Therefore, in this phase, individuals are selected for producing a new offspring. The selected individuals are arranged in pairs so that they can generate a new individual by passing on their genes to the next generation (Figure 13.18).

Reproduction: In this phase, genetic operators are applied to the parent population to produce a child. The two widely used operators are:

Crossover: In the selection phase, we had chosen pairs of individuals who would be parents to a new set of solution. The crossover operator swaps the genetic information of two parents to reproduce an offspring (Figure 13.19).

Mutation: The mutation operator adds new genetic information to the new child population by flipping some bits in the chromosome. This not only overcomes the problem of getting a local minimum but also enhances diversification. For example, the following image (Figure 13.20) demonstrates how mutation is done.

Replacement: In this phase, generational replacement takes place to replace the old population with the new child population. Obviously, the new population has a higher fitness score than the old population and is thus the best solution generated so far.

Termination: Once replacement has been done, a stopping criterion is used which when specified terminates the algorithm. The stopping criterion is attained when the threshold value of the fitness is achieved. When the genetic algorithm terminates, the solution obtained is considered to be the best solution in the population.

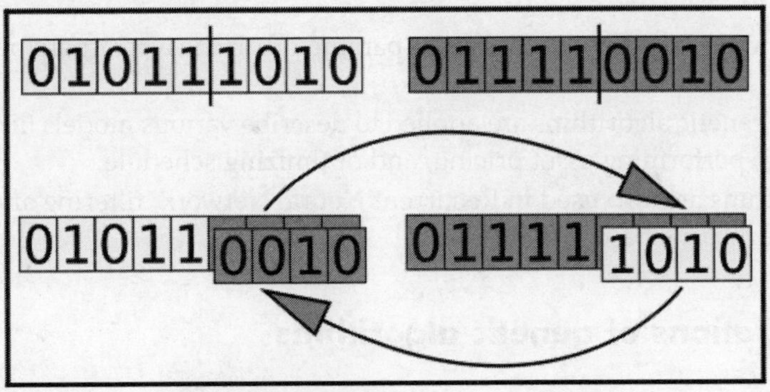

Figure 13.18 Selection Process

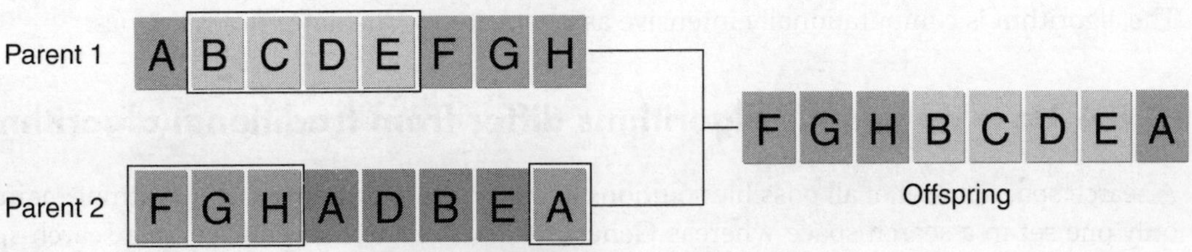

Figure 13.19 Crossover Process

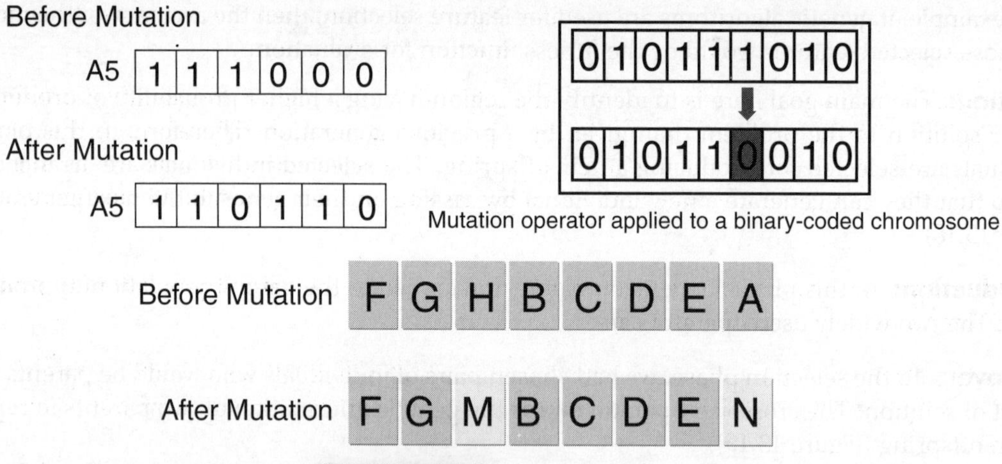

Figure 13.20 Mutation Process

13.8.2 Application areas

Genetic algorithms are applied in the following fields:

- Genetic algorithms are used to solve a very popular problem in computer science – traveling salesman problem which aims to plan a transport route of a salesman that reduces the time and cost of travel. Likewise, the algorithm is used to develop an efficient way of delivering products.
- Genetic algorithms are used to analyze DNA to identify the DNA structure using spectrometric information.
- Genetic algorithms are applied to derive optimum solutions to solve multi-modal optimization problems.
- They are used to design aircrafts. Different parameters of the aircraft are modified to generate better designs.
- In Economics, genetic algorithms are applied to describe various models (like the game theory, cobweb model), performing asset pricing, and optimizing schedule.
- Genetic algorithms are also used in Recurrent Neural Network, filtering and signal processing and learning fuzzy rule base.

13.8.3 Limitations of genetic algorithms

- They may not be very effective and efficient in solving simple problems.
- The algorithm may not generate the best result if not implemented properly.
- There is no guarantee about the quality of the final solution.
- The algorithm is computationally intensive as it repeatedly calculates fitness values.

13.8.4 How do genetic algorithms differ from traditional algorithms?

- A search space is a set of all possible solutions to the problem. Traditional Algorithms maintain only one set in a search space whereas Genetic Algorithms use several sets in a search space (Feature selection using R.F.E vs Genetic Algorithms).

- Traditional Algorithms require more information to perform a search whereas Genetic Algorithms just require one objective function to calculate the fitness of an individual.
- Traditional Algorithms cannot work in parallel whereas Genetic Algorithms can work in parallel (calculating the fitness of the individuals that are independent).
- One big difference in Genetic Algorithms is that instead of operating directly on candidate solutions, genetic algorithms operate on their representations (or coding), often referred to as chromosomes.
- Traditional Algorithms can only produce one solution in the end whereas in Genetic Algorithms multiple optimal solutions can be obtained from different generations.
- Traditional Algorithms are not more likely to produce global optimal solutions. Genetic Algorithms are not guaranteed to produce global optimal solutions as well but are more likely to produce global optimal solutions because of the genetic operators like crossover and mutation.
- Traditional algorithms are deterministic in nature whereas genetic algorithms are probabilistic and stochastic in nature.
- Real-world problems are multi-modal (contains multiple locally optimal solutions). The traditional algorithms do not handle these problems well; whereas Genetic Algorithms, with the right parameter setting, can handle these problems very well because of the large solution space.

13.8.5 Advantages of genetic algorithms

- Parallelism
- Global optimization
- A larger set of solution space
- Requires less information
- Provides multiple optimal solutions
- Probabilistic in nature
- Genetic representations using chromosomes
- Robust
- Less affected by noise

13.8.6 Disadvantages of genetic algorithms

- The need for special definitions
- Hyper-parameter tuning
- Computational complexity

Algorithm

Given below are the steps performed in a genetic algorithm (Figure 13.21)

Step I: Calculate the fitness of the individuals in a population.

Step 2: Repeat steps 3-6 until the desired number of generations or the stopping criterion is reached

Step 3: Select the fittest individual.

Step 4: Cross-over the individuals.

Step 5: Mutate the individuals.

Step 6: Calculate the fitness of the individuals again.

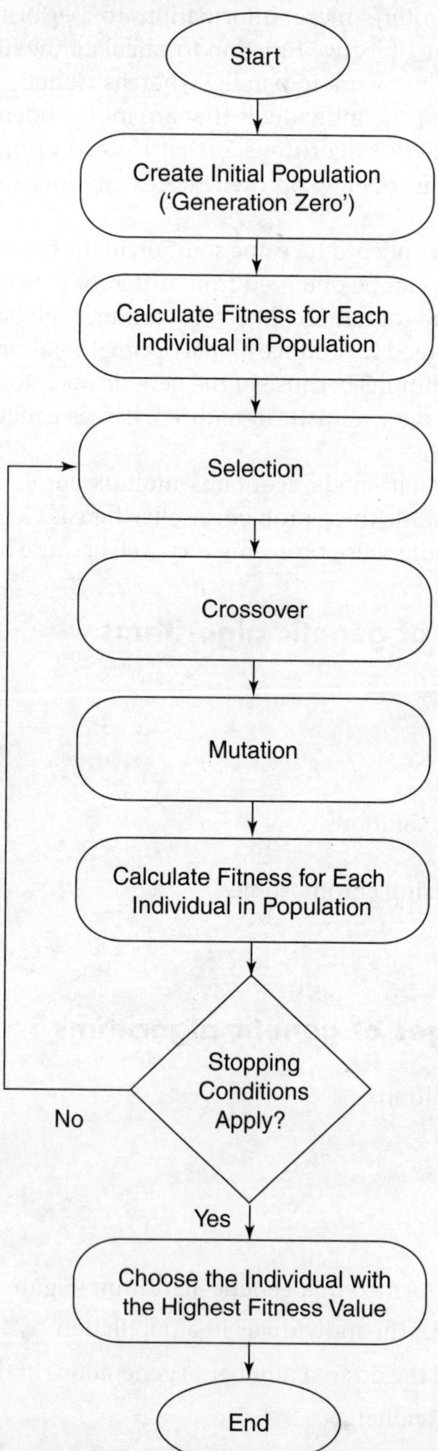

Figure 13.21 Basic Flow of a Genetic Algorithm

Example: Implementing Genetic Algorithm

```
import numpy
data_inputs = numpy.array([[1, 1],
                           [1, 0],
                           [0, 1],
                           [0, 0]])
daat_outputs = numpy.array([0,
                            1,
                            1,
                            0])
num_neurons_input = 2
num_neurons_output = 2
num_neurons_hidden_layers = [2]
hidden_activations=["relu"]
output_activation = "softmax"
num_solutions = 5
import pygad.gann
GANN_instance = pygad.gann.GANN(num_solutions=5,
                                num_neurons_input=2,
                                num_neurons_hidden_layers=[2],
                                num_neurons_output=1,
                                hidden_activations=["relu"],
                                output_activation="softmax")
#print(GANN_instance.population_networks)
population_vectors = pygad.gann.population_as_vectors(population_
networks=GANN_instance.population_networks)
print(population_vectors)
```

OUTPUT

```
[array([-0.08967126, -0.04649616,  0.08264154,  0.00373608, -0.04776243,
        0.00836679]), array([ 0.07586315, -0.00324067,  0.04323463,
0.07810089, -0.07372201,
        0.05216289]), array([-0.09859114, -0.07508463, -0.03051525,
0.00402294, -0.03516184,
        0.06906154]), array([ 0.08227591,  0.04856971, -0.0100997 ,
-0.02059963, -0.04185758,
       -0.01908773]), array([ 0.00494026, -0.05366674,  0.05792332,
-0.06749663,  0.03835708,
       -0.06406028])]
```

Example: Download ENJOYSPORT dataset and apply genetic algorithm on it.

```
import numpy as np
import pandas as pd
data = pd.read_csv('ENJOYSPORT.csv')
print(data)
concepts = np.array(data.iloc[:,0:-1])
print("\n Instances are:\n",concepts)
target = np.array(data.iloc[:,-1])
print("\nTarget Values are: ",target)
```

```
def learn(concepts, target):
    specific_h = concepts[0].copy()
    print("\nSpecific Boundary: ", specific_h)
    general_h = [["?" for i in range(len(specific_h))] for i in
range(len(specific_h))]
    print("\nGeneric Boundary: ",general_h)

    for i, h in enumerate(concepts):
        print("\nInstance", i+1 , "is ", h)
        if target[i] == 1:
            print("Instance is Positive ")
            for x in range(len(specific_h)):
                if h[x]!= specific_h[x]:
                    specific_h[x] ='?'
                    general_h[x][x] ='?'

        if target[i] == 0:
            print("Instance is Negative ")
            for x in range(len(specific_h)):
                if h[x]!= specific_h[x]:
                    general_h[x][x] = specific_h[x]
                else:
                    general_h[x][x] = '?'

        print("Specific Bundary after ", i+1, "Instance is ", specific_h)
        print("Generic Boundary after ", i+1, "Instance is ", general_h)
        print("\n")

    indices = [i for i, val in enumerate(general_h) if val == ['?', '?', '?',
'?', '?', '?']]
    for i in indices:
        general_h.remove(['?', '?', '?', '?', '?', '?'])
    return specific_h, general_h

s_final, g_final = learn(concepts, target)
print("Final Specific_h: ", s_final, sep="\n")
print("Final General_h: ", g_final, sep="\n")
```

OUTPUT

```
     Sky AirTemp Humidity    Wind Water Forecast  EnjoySport
0  Sunny    Warm   Normal  Strong  Warm     Same           1
1  Sunny    Warm     High  Strong  Warm     Same           1
2  Rainy    Cold     High  Strong  Warm   Change           0
3  Sunny    Warm     High  Strong  Cool   Change           1
 Instances are:
 [['Sunny' 'Warm' 'Normal' 'Strong' 'Warm' 'Same']
 ['Sunny' 'Warm' 'High' 'Strong' 'Warm' 'Same']
 ['Rainy' 'Cold' 'High' 'Strong' 'Warm' 'Change']
 ['Sunny' 'Warm' 'High' 'Strong' 'Cool' 'Change']]
Target Values are:  [1 1 0 1]
Specific Boundary:  ['Sunny' 'Warm' 'Normal' 'Strong' 'Warm' 'Same']
Generic Boundary:  [['?', '?', '?', '?', '?', '?'], ['?', '?', '?', '?', '?',
'?'], ['?', '?', '?', '?', '?', '?'], ['?', '?', '?', '?', '?', '?'], ['?',
'?', '?', '?', '?', '?'], ['?', '?', '?', '?', '?', '?']]
```

```
Instance 1 is  ['Sunny' 'Warm' 'Normal' 'Strong' 'Warm' 'Same']
Instance is Positive
Specific Bundary after  1 Instance is  ['Sunny' 'Warm' 'Normal' 'Strong'
'Warm' 'Same']
Generic Boundary after  1 Instance is  [['?', '?', '?', '?', '?', '?'], ['?',
'?', '?', '?', '?', '?'], ['?', '?', '?', '?', '?', '?'], ['?', '?', '?', '?',
'?', '?'], ['?', '?', '?', '?', '?', '?'], ['?', '?', '?', '?', '?', '?']]
Instance 2 is  ['Sunny' 'Warm' 'High' 'Strong' 'Warm' 'Same']
Instance is Positive
Specific Bundary after  2 Instance is  ['Sunny' 'Warm' '?' 'Strong' 'Warm'
'Same']
Generic Boundary after  2 Instance is  [['?', '?', '?', '?', '?', '?'], ['?',
'?', '?', '?', '?', '?'], ['?', '?', '?', '?', '?', '?'], ['?', '?', '?', '?',
'?', '?'], ['?', '?', '?', '?', '?', '?'], ['?', '?', '?', '?', '?', '?']]
Instance 3 is  ['Rainy' 'Cold' 'High' 'Strong' 'Warm' 'Change']
Instance is Negative
Specific Bundary after  3 Instance is  ['Sunny' 'Warm' '?' 'Strong' 'Warm'
'Same']
Generic Boundary after  3 Instance is  [['Sunny', '?', '?', '?', '?', '?'],
['?', 'Warm', '?', '?', '?', '?'], ['?', '?', '?', '?', '?', '?'], ['?', '?',
'?', '?', '?', '?'], ['?', '?', '?', '?', '?', '?'], ['?', '?', '?', '?', '?',
'Same']]
Instance 4 is  ['Sunny' 'Warm' 'High' 'Strong' 'Cool' 'Change']
Instance is Positive
Specific Bundary after  4 Instance is  ['Sunny' 'Warm' '?' 'Strong' '?' '?']
Generic Boundary after  4 Instance is  [['Sunny', '?', '?', '?', '?', '?'],
['?', 'Warm', '?', '?', '?', '?'], ['?', '?', '?', '?', '?', '?'], ['?', '?',
'?', '?', '?', '?'], ['?', '?', '?', '?', '?', '?'], ['?', '?', '?', '?', '?',
'?']]
Final Specific_h:
['Sunny' 'Warm' '?' 'Strong' '?' '?']
Final General_h:
[['Sunny', '?', '?', '?', '?', '?'], ['?', 'Warm', '?', '?', '?', '?']]
```

13.9 AutoML using TPOT

Automated Machine Learning (AutoML) refers to the techniques for automatically discovering well-performing models to complete predictive modeling tasks with very little user intervention. For this, we will use Tree-based Pipeline Optimization Tool (TPOT), an open-source library containing functions for performing AutoML in Python. This library uses scikit-learn machine learning library for transforming data and applying machine learning algorithms. It also makes extensive use of Genetic Programming stochastic global search procedure to efficiently discover a top-performing model pipeline for a given dataset.

13.9.1 TPOT for AutoML

TPOT uses a tree-based structure to represent a model pipeline for a predictive modeling problem. It automatically *designs* and *optimizes* the chosen pipeline (for data preparation and modeling algorithms and model hyperparameters). The optimization procedure generates a tree structure that maximizes the classification accuracy for a given supervised learning data set.

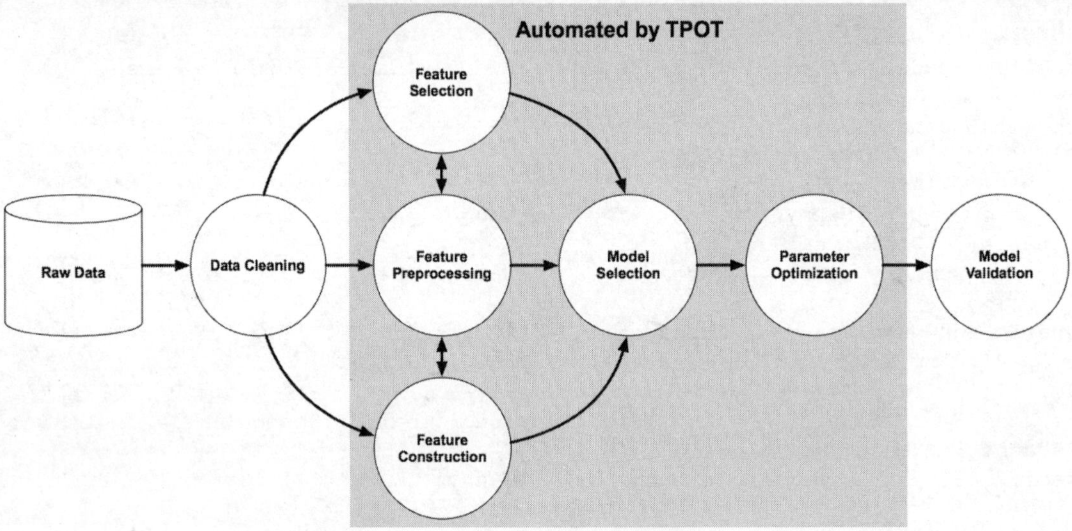

Figure 13.22 Elements of Pipeline for Implementing AutoML

Figure 13.22 shows the elements involved in the pipeline search. These elements include data cleaning, feature selection, feature processing, feature construction, model selection, and hyperparameter optimization.

13.9.2 Overview of the TPOT pipeline search

I have executed these programs on Google Collab. To use this library, we must first install it. This is done by writing *pip install tpot*.

Let us look at two program codes that use TPOT for classification and regression. As an evolutionary algorithm, we need to specify configuration parameters like size of the population, number of generations to run, and the crossover and mutation rates to control the extent of the search. As a beginner, you can set a modest population size of 100 and 5 or 10 generations. The output of the program is a pipeline that gives the best performance. We can export this model into a Python file that can be incorporated later for use in project.

13.9.3 TPOT for classification

In this section, we have used the sonar dataset containing 208 rows of data with 60 numerical variables and a target variable for binary classification.

We have printed the shape of this data and divided the dataset into input and output elements. To evaluate the model, we have used repeated stratified 10-fold cross-validation with three repeats that gives an accuracy of about 53%. A top-performing model can achieve about 88%. This provides the bounds of expected performance on this data set.

A population size of 50 for five generations for the search is used. *"n_jobs"* is set to –1 to use all cores on the system. Once this is done, the search to identify the best-performing model is performed. Note that running this program may take a few minutes. Let us quickly recapitulate vital parameters.

Generations is an integer that is optional. By default, its value is 100. It specifies the number of iterations used to the run pipeline optimization process. More the number of generations, more will be the time taken for execution to optimize the pipeline.

population_size is an optional argument that has an integer value. By default, its value is 100. This parameter specifies the number of individuals to be retained in the genetic programming population every generation. More the number of individuals more will be the time taken for execution to optimize the pipeline.

offspring_size is an optional parameter that can have an integer value to specify the number of offspring to produce in each genetic programming generation. It is usually equal to population_size.

mutation_rate value varies in the range [0.0, 1.0] and specifies the number of pipelines to apply random changes to every generation. Its default value is 0.9.

crossover_rate value varies in the range [0.0, 1.0] and specifies the number of pipelines to "breed" every generation.

> **Tip**
>
> mutation_rate + crossover_rate cannot exceed 1.0

scoring is a function that evaluates the quality of a given pipeline for classification problem. Quality can be analyzed using factors like accuracy, average_precision, roc_auc, recall, etc. The default factor is accuracy.

cv or cross-validation strategy is used to evaluate pipelines. Its default value is 5.

random_state is used to specify the seed of the pseudo-random number generator so that every time the program is executed, same results are obtained.

Then you will call the fit() method with the training set (without the target column) and the target column as the arguments.

Executing a code using TPOT may take a long time to finish execution. However, we can specify certain parameters to control the execution time of but definitely with a trade-off. In such a case, limiting the time of TPOT execution may not give sufficient time to explore all models. Hence, the best model recommended by TPOT will be the one discovered in that duration and it may not be the best model possible for that dataset otherwise. Some parameters to restrict time are:

max_time_mins to specify number of minutes to optimize the pipeline. If its value is not None then the algorithm will allow TPOT to run until max_time_mins minutes elapse.

> **Tip**
>
> The fit() method is used with the training set (without the target column)

max_eval_time_mins specifies the number of minutes TPOT is allowed to evaluate a single pipeline. With a higher value, TPOT will take more time but can evaluate more complex pipelines. The default value is 5.

early_stop specifies the number of generations checked by TPOT to ensure whether there is or there is no improvement in the optimization process. If there is no improvement in the given number of generations, the optimization process ends.

n_jobs specifies the number of procedures to be used in parallel for evaluating pipelines during the TPOT optimization process. Setting its value to –1 will use as many cores as available on the computer. The default value is 1.

subsample species fraction of training samples that are used during the optimization process. Its default value is 1. This value can vary in the range (0.0, 1.0].

You can observe the changes by setting max_time_mins = 2, max_eval_time_mins = 0.04 and population_size = 15.

Limitations: Programs using TPOT take a long time to finish its search process for the best model. This is because TPOT not just fits one model on the dataset. Rather, it considers multiple machine learning algorithms including random forests, linear models, SVMs, etc. In a pipeline with numerous preprocessing steps, like filling missing values, scaling, PCA, feature selection, etc. TPOT can recommend different solutions for the same dataset.

Example: Implementing TPOT for the sonar classification dataset.

```
from pandas import read_csv
from sklearn.preprocessing import LabelEncoder
from sklearn.model_selection import RepeatedStratifiedKFold
from tpot import TPOTClassifier
# load dataset
url = 'https://raw.githubusercontent.com/jbrownlee/Datasets/master/sonar.csv'
dataframe = read_csv(url, header=None)
# split into input and output elements
data = dataframe.values
X, y = data[:, :-1], data[:, -1]
# minimally prepare dataset
X = X.astype('float32')
y = LabelEncoder().fit_transform(y.astype('str'))
# define model evaluation
cv = RepeatedStratifiedKFold(n_splits=10, n_repeats=3, random_state=1)
# define search
model = TPOTClassifier(generations=5, population_size=50, cv=cv, scoring=
'accuracy', verbosity=2, random_state=1, n_jobs=-1)
# perform the search
model.fit(X, y)
# export the best model
model.export('tpot_sonar_best_model.py')
```

OUTPUT

```
Generation 1 - Current best internal CV score: 0.8634126984126984
Generation 2 - Current best internal CV score: 0.8777777777777778
Generation 3 - Current best internal CV score: 0.8857142857142858
Generation 4 - Current best internal CV score: 0.8857142857142858
Generation 5 - Current best internal CV score: 0.8857142857142858
Best pipeline: ExtraTreesClassifier(input_matrix, bootstrap=False,
criterion=entropy, max_features=0.4, min_samples_leaf=1, min_samples_split=8,
n_estimators=100)
```

13.9.4 TPOT for regression

In this section, we have used the auto insurance dataset for applying TPOT library for regression. This dataset contains 63 rows of data with one numerical input variable and a numerical target variable. It predicts the total amount in claims given the number of claims for different geographical regions.

We have used repeated stratified 10-fold cross-validation with three repeats. While a naive model can achieve a mean absolute error (MAE) of about 66, the best performing model can bring this value down to about 28. This provides the bounds of expected performance on this dataset.

To begin with, we have printed the shape of the dataset, divided it into input and output elements. TPOT is applied to find the best performing model for the auto insurance dataset. To evaluate the models, repeated k-fold cross-validation with three repeats and 10 folds is used. A population size of 50 for 5 generations for the search and n_jobs to 1 is set to use all cores on the system. Note that the program may take several minutes to complete its execution.

Example: Implementing TPOT for Regression

```
from pandas import read_csv
from sklearn.model_selection import RepeatedKFold
from tpot import TPOTRegressor
# load dataset
url = 'https://raw.githubusercontent.com/jbrownlee/Datasets/master/auto-insur-
ance.csv'
dataframe = read_csv(url, header=None)
# split into input and output elements
data = dataframe.values
data = data.astype('float32')
X, y = data[:, :-1], data[:, -1]
# define evaluation procedure
cv = RepeatedKFold(n_splits=10, n_repeats=3, random_state=1)
# define search
model = TPOTRegressor(generations=5, population_size=50, scoring='neg_mean_
absolute_error', cv=cv, verbosity=2, random_state=1, n_jobs=-1)
# perform the search
model.fit(X, y)
```

OUTPUT

```
Generation 1 - Current best internal CV score: -29.147625969129034
Generation 2 - Current best internal CV score: -29.139635546185936
Generation 3 - Current best internal CV score: -29.139635546185936
Generation 4 - Current best internal CV score: -29.09969585902434
Generation 5 - Current best internal CV score: -29.09969585902434
Best pipeline: RidgeCV(PolynomialFeatures(input_matrix, degree=2, include_
bias=False, interaction_only=False))
TPOTRegressor(config_dict=None, crossover_rate=0.1,
              cv=RepeatedKFold(n_repeats=3, n_splits=10, random_state=1),
              disable_update_check=False, early_stop=None, generations=5,
              log_file=None, max_eval_time_mins=5, max_time_mins=None,
              memory=None, mutation_rate=0.9, n_jobs=-1,
offspring_size=None,
              periodic_checkpoint_folder=None, population_size=50,
              random_state=1, scoring='neg_mean_absolute_error',
subsample=1.0,
              template=None, use_dask=False, verbosity=2, warm_start=False)
```

Business Scenario: TF-IDF with Implementation in Python

Imagine that you are working as a data analyst and have a good experience in text mining, natural language processing (NLP), and Term Frequency-Inverse Document Frequency (TF-IDF) techniques for analyzing text. Your company receives numerous customer reviews for its products across different platforms. Now, that the company knows that you are good at evaluating the importance of a word in a document relative to a given corpus, you have been asked to perform document classification, information retrieval, and search engines. The company expects you to classify customer reviews as **positive**, **negative**, or **neutral. Write the code** to identify key terms in reviews and feed them into a machine learning classifier for classification.

```
#pip install pandas scikit-learn nltk
import pandas as pd
import numpy as np
from sklearn.feature_extraction.text import TfidfVectorizer
from sklearn.model_selection import train_test_split
from sklearn.linear_model import LogisticRegression
from sklearn.metrics import accuracy_score, classification_report
import nltk
from nltk.corpus import stopwords
from nltk.stem import WordNetLemmatizer
# Download NLTK resources
nltk.download('stopwords')
nltk.download('wordnet')
# Sample dataset of product reviews (you can use a larger dataset)
data = {
    'Review': [
        "This product is amazing! I love it.",
        "Worst purchase ever. Totally disappointed.",
        "It works fine, but the design is a bit off.",
        "Not worth the money. Terrible quality.",
        "Absolutely fantastic! I would recommend it to everyone.",
        "Okay product, nothing special but decent.",
        "I'm happy with the purchase, but the shipping was slow.",
        "I regret buying this. Very poor quality.",
        "Great value for the price.",
        "Very bad experience, I will never buy again."
    ],
    'Sentiment': [
        'positive', 'negative', 'neutral', 'negative', 'positive', 'neutral',
        'neutral', 'negative', 'positive', 'negative'
    ]
}
# Convert the data into a DataFrame
df = pd.DataFrame(data)
# Preprocessing: Clean text (remove stopwords, lemmatize)
lemmatizer = WordNetLemmatizer()
stop_words = set(stopwords.words('english'))
```

```
def preprocess_text(text):
  # Tokenize and clean text
  words = text.lower().split()
  words = [lemmatizer.lemmatize(word) for word in words if word not in stop_words]
  return ' '.join(words)
# Apply preprocessing to the reviews
df['Cleaned_Review'] = df['Review'].apply(preprocess_text)
# Feature Extraction using TF-IDF
vectorizer = TfidfVectorizer(max_features=10)  # Limit to top 10 features for simplicity
X = vectorizer.fit_transform(df['Cleaned_Review']).toarray()
# Prepare target labels
y = df['Sentiment']
# Train-Test Split
X_train, X_test, y_train, y_test = train_test_split(X, y, test_size=0.3, random_state=42)
# Train a Logistic Regression Model
model = LogisticRegression()
model.fit(X_train, y_train)
# Make Predictions
y_pred = model.predict(X_test)
# Evaluate the Model
accuracy = accuracy_score(y_test, y_pred)
print(f"Accuracy: {accuracy:.2f}")
print("\nClassification Report:\n", classification_report(y_test, y_pred))
```

Key Terms

Allele: Value of a gene in a specific chromosome.
Bag-of-words: Feature extraction technique that describes the occurrence of each word within a document.
Chromosomes: A chromosome is one of the solutions in the population.
Convolution layer: Layer that performs computational tasks based on convolution function in MLP.
Deep learning: An artificial intelligence (AI) technique that imitates working of the human brain in processing data and creating patterns for use in decision making. It is a subset of machine learning that uses unsupervised learning to learn from unstructured or unlabeled data.
Fully connected layer: Layer arranged next to series of convolution and pooling layer that is used to classify input into various categories.
Gene: An individual element in a chromosome.
Genetic algorithm: A heuristic search-based algorithm that is mainly used to solve optimization problems in machine learning.
Natural Language Processing (NLP): Manipulation or understanding of text or speech by a computer software.
Optimization: A process in machine learning that optimizes the input weights by comparing the prediction and the loss function.
Parts of Speech Tagging: A process that mark words in text format for a particular part of a speech depending on its definition and context.
Pooling layer: Layer arranged next to convolution layer, which is used to reduce the size of inputs by removing unnecessary information to speed up computations.

Population: A subset of all the probable solutions that can be used to solve the given problem.
Regular expression: A sequence of characters that define a search pattern.
Sentence Tokenization: The process of dividing a string written in a natural language into its basic components.
Stop words: Words that are filtered out before or after processing of text.
TF-IDF: A statistical measure used to evaluate the importance of a word to a document in a collection of documents or the corpus.
Word Tokenization: The process of dividing a string of written language into its constituent words.

Chapter Highlights

- ✶ Deep learning is generally used to detect objects, recognize speech, translate languages, recognize similar images, recommend products, make important decisions, detect fraud or money laundering, and explore the possibility of reusing drugs for new ailments among other functions.
- ✶ A neural network is said to be a deep neural network depending on the number of layers it has.
- ✶ Keras is a high-level library built on top of TensorFlow to provide a scikit-learn type API for building neural networks without worrying about the mathematical aspects of tensor algebra, numerical techniques, and optimization methods.
- ✶ In Keras, every ANN is represented by models and every model is composed of one or more layers like the input layer, hidden layer(s), output layer, convolution layer, pooling layer, etc.
- ✶ Keras layers require shape of the input (input_shape) to specify the structure of the input data. It can use initializer to set the weight for each input and activators to transform the output to make it non-linear.
- ✶ NLTK or the Natural Language Toolkit is a free, open source, community-driven project that is widely used for building Python programs that can process human language data.
- ✶ Markov Decision Processes (MDP) are used to model optimization problems, and can also be applied to more complex tasks in Reinforcement Learning.
- ✶ The Bellman Equation outlines a framework for determining the optimal expected reward at a state *s* by understanding what maximum reward an agent can get on taking an optimal action now and for all future decisions.
- ✶ In the Monte-Carlo approach, the agent learns from the environment by interacting with it and collecting samples. Each "try" is called an episode, and all episodes must terminate.
- ✶ The main goal of genetic algorithms is to generate a better solution. For this, two best individuals mate to reproduce an offspring that is better than the parents.
- ✶ Automated Machine Learning (AutoML) refers to techniques for automatically discovering well-performing models to complete predictive modeling tasks with very little user intervention.

Review Questions

1. Define deep learning.
2. Give some applications of deep learning.
3. How does deep learning work?
4. Differentiate between machine learning and deep learning.
5. Explain the layers in a Multi-Later Perceptron.
6. Explain the workflow of ANN.

7. Write a short note on the architecture of Keras.
8. Explain the utility of loss function and optimization function.
9. What do you understand by the term natural language processing?
10. Explain the basic steps involved in processing natural languages.
11. What is POS Tagging?
12. Explain the Markov Decision Process with the help of an example.
13. What is Exploration vs Exploitation trade-off?
14. Differentiate between First-visit Monte-Carlo Policy Evaluation and Every-visit Monte-Carlo Policy Evaluation.
15. What is the limitation of the Monte-Carlo method?
16. Why are heuristic search-based algorithms better than random search algorithms?
17. Define the terms gene, chromosome, population in context of genetic algorithms in machine learning.
18. What are genetic operators?
19. List the steps involved in performing genetic algorithms.

Programming Exercise

1. Create a sequential model with a dense layer containing 32 neurons. The first layer will have shape (16,). Use *he_uniform* as *kernel_initializer*, regularizer as *kernel_regularizer, MaxNorm* as *kernel_constraint* and relu as the activation function.
2. Create a Keras Sequential() model in which the first layer is the hidden layer having input_ dim = 4 and 7 nodes. The number of hidden processing nodes should be determined by trial and error and may use tanh, sigmoid or ReLU as the activation function. The second layer or the output layer is chained to the hidden layer and has three nodes.
3. Download the insurance.csv data set and create a sequential model to detect fraud.
4. Write a code to create a Keras initializer for the following to:
   a. generate 0 for all input data.
   b. generate 1 for all input data.
   c. generate a constant value specified by the user for all input data.
   d. generate value using normal distribution of input data.
   e. generate value using uniform distribution of input data.
   f. generate value using truncated normal distribution of input data.
   g. generate value based on the input shape and output shape of the layer along with the specified scale.
   h. generate a random orthogonal matrix.
   i. generate identity matrix.
   j. constrain weights to be non-negative.
   k. constrain weights to be unit norm.
   l. constrain weight to norm less than or equals to the given value.
   m. constrain weights to be norm between specified minimum and maximum values.
   n. provide L1 based regularization
   o. provide L2 based regularization.
   p. apply linear activation function.

q. apply Exponential linear unit.
r. apply Scaled exponential linear unit.
s. apply Softplus function.
t. apply Softsign function.

5. Download the zoo.csv and create a TensorFlow model, train the model, evaluate it and demonstrate how it can be used for prediction.
6. Create a deep neural network model on the iris data set. Train the model and evaluate it.

Fill in the Blanks

1. Deep learning uses ________ learning techniques.
2. The big data that we collect from social media and internet search engines are ________.
3. ______ learning is the key technology behind driverless cars.
4. A neural network is said to be a deep neural network depending on the number of ______ it has.
5. ________ is used in image-related applications like autonomous driving and robot vision.
6. ________ learning refers to creation of plateau at a certain level of performance.
7. ________ use deep learning techniques to transform black-and-white images into colored ones.
8. ________ is the most commonly used library for implementing deep learning algorithms.
9. A single layer ANN also known as single ________.
10. ________ is a high-level interface that uses TensorFlow for its backend.
11. ________ layer is used to classify input into various categories.
12. In ________ phase, actual results are compared with predicted ones of the test data.
13. Ever ANN model is composed of one or more ________.
14. In Keras, dense layers are created and added using ______ activation function.
15. The ______ function is used during model compilation process to find error or deviation in the machine learning process.
16. __________ is the manipulation or understanding of text or speech by a computer software.
17. Natural Language Processing studies interactions between ________ and ________.
18. In English, a sentence can be split at the position of a __________.
19. Stemming and lemmatization are special cases of ________.
20. __________ is a special text string that is used for describing a search pattern to extract information from text.
21. The _____ function in the re module can be used to search a pattern in the string and replace it with another pattern.
22. ________ is an extraction technique that describes the occurrence of each word within a document.
23. ________ is a statistical measure that evaluates the importance of a word to a document in a collection.
24. Markov Decision Processes are used to model __________ problems.
25. In MDP, ________ is the discount factor.
26. In MDP, the next state can be determined solely by the __________ – no ________ is necessary.

27. The Bellman Equation outlines a framework for determining the __________ at a state *s* by understanding what maximum reward an agent can get on taking an optimal action now and for all future decisions.
28. _________ stores possible state-action pairs to reflect the *current* known information about the system.
29. In the Monte-Carlo approach, each "try" is called an _________.
30. __________ is a good combination of Deep Programming and Monte-Carlo technique.
31. Genetic algorithms work on the principle of survival of the _________.
32. A subset of all the probable solutions that can be used to solve the given problem is known as __________.
33. ______ is the value of a gene in a specific chromosome.

State True or False

1. Deep learning flourishes on limited data.
2. Deep learning techniques consume massive computing power.
3. Convolutional Neural Network (CNN) is applied in NLP based text or voice applications such as chatbots, virtual assistants.
4. In a deep learning algorithm, relevant features are manually extracted from images.
5. Deep networks can have as many as 150 hidden layers.
6. Keras supports both convolutional and recurrent networks.
7. Polling layer performs computational tasks based on convolution function in MLP.
8. RNN stores the past information and all its decisions are taken from what it has learnt from the past.
9. The dropout layer is added to handle overfitting.
10. epochs specify number of times the model is needed to be evaluated during training.
11. Stemming performs its task with the help of a vocabulary and morphological analysis of words, to return the base or dictionary form of a word.
12. While designing the vocabulary, the case, punctuation, and one-character tokens are ignored.
13. TF-IDF computes how rare the word is across documents.
14. In MDP Process, state refers to the status that the agent.
15. Q-learning uses knowledge about probabilities.
16. Bellman Equation cannot be applied if the state transition probability *(P)* is not known.
17. In the Monte-Carlo approach, the agent learns from the environment by interacting with it and collecting samples.
18. In Monte-Carlo approach, episodes may or may not terminate.
19. Heuristic search-based algorithms are not as good as random search algorithms.
20. A gene is a collection of chromosomes.
21. Higher the fitness, more is the probability of being chosen for reproduction.
22. Genetic Algorithms can work in parallel.
23. TPOT library is used for both classification as well as regression analysis.
24. mutation_rate specifies number of individuals to be retained in the genetic programming population every generation.

Give the Output

1. ```
   import nltk
   word_data = " Natural Language Processing (NLP) is a process of manipulating
   or understanding the text or speech by any software or machine. An analogy
   is that humans interact and understand each other's views and respond
   with the appropriate answer. In NLP, this interaction, understanding, and
   response are made by a computer instead of a human."
   nltk_tokens = nltk.word_tokenize(word_data)
   print (nltk_tokens)
   ```
2. ```
   import nltk
   sentence_data = "Natural Language Processing (NLP) is a process of
   manipulating or understanding the text or speech by any software or
   machine. An analogy is that humans interact and understand each other's
   views and respond with the appropriate answer. In NLP, this interaction,
   understanding, and response are made by a computer instead of a human."
   nltk_tokens = nltk.sent_tokenize(sentence_data)
   print (nltk_tokens)
   ```
3. ```
   import nltk
   from nltk.stem.porter import PorterStemmer
   porter_stemmer = PorterStemmer()
   word_data = "Natural Language Processing (NLP) is a process of manipulating
   or understanding the text or speech by any software or machine. An analogy
   is that humans interact and understand each other's views and respond
   with the appropriate answer. In NLP, this interaction, understanding, and
   response are made by a computer instead of a human."
   # First Word tokenization
   nltk_tokens = nltk.word_tokenize(word_data)
   #Next find the roots of the word
   for w in nltk_tokens:
       print "Actual: %s  Stem: %s"  % (w,porter_stemmer.stem(w))
   ```
4. ```
   import nltk
   from nltk.stem import WordNetLemmatizer
   wordnet_lemmatizer = WordNetLemmatizer()
   word_data = " Natural Language Processing (NLP) is a process of manipulating
   or understanding the text or speech by any software or machine. An analogy
   is that humans interact and understand each other's views and respond
   with the appropriate answer. In NLP, this interaction, understanding, and
   response are made by a computer instead of a human."
   nltk_tokens = nltk.word_tokenize(word_data)
   for w in nltk_tokens:
       print "Actual: %s  Lemma: %s"  % (w,wordnet_lemmatizer.lemmatize(w))
   ```